ELEMENTARY CALCULUS

ELEMENTARY
CALCULUS

G. Hadley

University of Hawaii

HOLDEN-DAY

San Francisco, Cambridge, London, Amsterdam

Preface

In recent years there has been a growing tendency in universities to offer a diversity of elementary calculus courses rather than the one standard course for mathematicians, scientists and engineers offered just a few years ago. The main impetus for this has been the increasing need for training in this subject by students in the social sciences, biology and other fields. This work is intended as a text for one-semester, one-quarter or two-quarter introductory calculus courses for those who do not wish to take the longer course typically offered for engineers and scientists. It avoids the emphasis on applications to physics and engineering which are typically presented in most texts and is thus especially suitable for business students, economists and other social scientists who do not have the background needed to understand such material. In fact, an attempt has been made to avoid discussions of applications that require a detailed knowledge of any particular field which beginning students would not possess, even if they intend later to major in this area.

Many beginning students, especially in the social sciences, are somewhat weak in the background needed about numbers and algebra. For this reason, an introductory chapter has been provided which covers this material. An attempt has been made to write the chapter in such a way that it will be interesting and informative even to better prepared students. Depending on the background of the students, it may be desirable to cover this chapter (Chapter 1) or to omit it from detailed coverage, allowing the students to read on their own those portions which they need to review. Chapters 2 through 5 contain the main development of analytic geometry and the calculus of one variable. The emphasis in analytic geometry is on graphing functions and relations, including inequalities, rather than on a detailed study of conics and similar material which is of little interest or value to

most students. In a similar vein, the discussion of techniques of integration
has been severely limited to those which are of greatest generality. Almost
no attention is given to the many substitutions typically studied in some
detail. Also, relatively little emphasis is placed on the trigonometric functions and, if desired, the study of these functions may be omitted completely. Chapter 6, which is devoted to numerical analysis, emphasizes the
solution of problems numerically on digital computers and contains quite a
bit of material not normally found in a text at this level. Chapter 7 gives a
brief introduction to functions of several variables that emphasizes applications to optimization problems.

The original version of this manuscript was written while the author was
a visiting professor at the University of New South Wales in Sydney, Australia. He is indebted to the School of Economics for assistance in repro-
ducing the manuscript, and especially to Miss Barbara Payne, who typed a
large portion of the manuscript. The author also appreciates the assistance
of the publisher in preparing the text for publication.

Contents

Chapter 3.   Limits and Differentiation

Chapter 4.   Sequences and Integration

ELEMENTARY CALCULUS

CHAPTER 1

Numbers, Arithmetic and Algebra

1–1 THE NATURAL NUMBERS

The art of counting is older than recorded history. Indeed, by as early as 3000 B.C., the Egyptians and the Sumerians in Persia had developed rather sophisticated methods of counting. All cultures seem to have developed at least a rudimentary ability to count. In some cases, the development has been exceedingly meager; the forest tribes in Brazil and the primitive native cultures of Australia do not seem to have developed the ability to count much above two or three. It would appear, though, that some primitive notion of counting is a characteristic of human thought.

The mere fact that a certain ability to count appeared in a society does not necessarily imply that the society evolved some type of number system to be used in counting. One of the first great developments in the history of mathematics came when the idea of a *number* was divorced from the objects being counted. The abstract concept of the number of objects in any collection expressing a property of the collection which does not depend on the nature of the objects is a rather profound and abstract concept which required centuries of human progress for its development. Although today it seems perfectly natural to anyone with a grade-school education, this abstraction has occurred only in relatively advanced societies. In many primitive cultures numbers are (or were) associated with the objects being counted, so that there is no symbolism for numbers themselves. Instead, separate words are used to indicate, for example, three cows and three bananas. It is also typical for children to associate numbers with concrete objects, often their fingers.

To count the number of objects in a collection it is only necessary to use

1

what are called the *natural numbers* or *positive integers* or *whole numbers*. We write these*

$$1, 2, 3, 4, 5, 6, 7, 8, 9, 10, 11, \ldots, 100, \ldots, 1000, 1001, \ldots. \quad (1\text{--}1)$$

Of course, the symbols used to represent the natural numbers have differed at different times and in different societies. Some other symbols which have been used are shown in Table 1–1. The reader will observe that several of

TABLE 1–1

Symbols Used for Natural Numbers

Number	1	2	3	4	5	6	7	8	9	10	20	90
Egyptian	I	II	III	III I	III II	III III	III III I	III III II	III III III	∩	∩∩	∩∩∩ ∩∩∩ ∩∩∩
Old Chinese	I	II	III	IIII	IIIII	T	TT	TTT	TTTT	—	=	≣
Mayan	°	°°	°°°	°°°°	▬	▬̇	▬̈	▬⃛	▬⃜	▬▬	👁	▬▬
Greek	A′	B′	Γ′	Δ′	E′	F′	Z′	H′	Θ′	I′	K′	Q′
Roman	I	II	III	IV	V	VI	VII	VIII	IX	X	XX	LXXXX

these appear to have developed naturally from procedures where marks were made on some material or where sticks were placed side by side. Note also that the Roman numerals are now part of our alphabet. The properties of the natural numbers are, of course, independent of the particular symbols used to denote them. As we shall see, however, the symbolism used to represent numbers is very important, because it greatly influences the ease with which computations can be made. Many of the notations illustrated in Table 1–1 are not at all suited to doing anything more complicated than the simplest counting operations.

---

* We have used in (1–1) a notation which will appear frequently. Often it is inconvenient to write out explicitly all the elements in a sequence. To avoid this we use three dots, called ellipses, to represent the omitted elements. These dots then mean "and so forth."

1–2 ADDITION AND MULTIPLICATION OF NATURAL NUMBERS

Originally, numbers were used only for direct counting. However, the need for record keeping and the requirements of commercial trade gradually led to the development of the four basic arithmetic operations which today are referred to as addition, subtraction, multiplication and division. In this section we shall discuss the development and certain properties of addition and multiplication.

The problem of adding numbers arises so naturally that addition is almost a part of the basic counting process itself. Suppose, for example, that an ancient ruler had many herds of cattle located throughout his kingdom and wanted to know how many head of cattle he had in total. If only the operation of counting were known, he would have to send out a single servant to visit all the herds and perform a sequential count. However, if addition could be performed, then the ruler could send out a number of servants—perhaps one to count each herd. After each brought in his tally, the total number of cattle could be found by adding together all these tallies.

The manner in which addition should be carried out can easily be seen by use of a pictorial device. Let us represent one of whatever we are counting by a box, as shown in Figure 1–1. Imagine now that we wish to add 3 and 5.

Figure 1–1

The numbers 3 and 5 are represented by three and five boxes, as indicated in Figure 1–1. To add these two numbers, we simply place the two collections of boxes side by side and count the number of boxes in the resulting array. This yields the natural number which we denote by 8; in other words, the sum is eight. In this manner the ancients could construct addition tables similar to those learned in elementary arithmetic. The procedure for carrying out addition just described would be incredibly clumsy if large numbers were to be added, since one would have to count huge numbers of boxes. We shall see later how to derive the simple rules learned in arithmetic which make it possible to add conveniently many large numbers.

The special symbol used to represent addition is the plus sign $+$, so to indicate that the sum of 3 and 5 is 8 we write $3 + 5 = 8$ or $5 + 3 = 8$. The equals sign $=$ is used to indicate that $3 + 5$ and 8 are the same number, and the resulting expression $3 + 5 = 8$ is called an equation. The sum is independent of the order in which we add the numbers. This is true when any two natural numbers are added. It is convenient to have a way to indicate symbolically the statement that the sum of two natural numbers does not depend on the order of addition. To do this we introduce symbols which denote arbitrary natural numbers rather than specific numbers. Thus, let m and n be any two natural numbers. Then the equation

$$m + n = n + m \tag{1-2}$$

expresses the fact that the sum of m and n is independent of the order of addition regardless of what natural numbers m and n happen to represent. Equation (1–2) expresses what is referred to in mathematics as the *commutativity of addition* for natural numbers.

Frequently we are interested in adding together three or more numbers. The reader will be well aware that the sum does not depend on how the numbers are grouped in carrying out the addition. Thus, to compute the sum of 3 and 5 and 7, we could merely place side by side three collections of boxes, as in Figure 1–1, and count the total. This would yield 15. Alternatively, we could first add 3 and 5 to o tain 8 and then add 7 to this to obtain 15, or we could add 5 and 7 to obtain 12 and add this to 3 to obtain 15. Regardless of which of these methods we use, the result is always 15. Symbolically, we can indicate this as follows:*

$$3 + 5 + 7 = (3 + 5) + 7 = 3 + (5 + 7). \tag{1-3}$$

More generally, for any three natural numbers m, n and q

$$m + n + q = (m + n) + q = m + (n + q). \tag{1-4}$$

Equation (1–4) expresses what is referred to in mathematics as the *associativity of addition* for natural numbers. The associativity property also holds if we are adding together four or five or more natural numbers. The sum in no way depends on how the numbers are grouped in carrying out the addition. Moreover, the order in which the numbers are added is irrelevant, so that commutativity also holds in general. Thus, if we are asked to determine the sum of some given set of natural numbers, we know that the sum obtained will be independent of the order in which the numbers are summed or the way in which they are grouped. This is referred to as the generalized associativity and commutativity property for the addition of natural numbers.

The reader may feel that it is silly to devote any time to discussing the commutativity and associativity of addition, since everyone knows that these properties are obviously true and could not be any other way. While it is a fact that essentially everyone realizes these properties are true, it is not at all obvious that they are true or that they must be true. Indeed, there exist many mathematical systems which do not have such properties. The reader no doubt feels them to be obvious only because he has been

---

* Here we have used parentheses () to indicate the manner in which operations are to be performed. Thus $(3 + 5) + 7$ means that we compute $3 + 5$ and then add 7 to the resulting number.

using them for many years. In actuality, the associativity and commutativity of addition are two very basic and important characteristics of the natural numbers, and this is the reason that we have discussed them.

The sum of any two natural numbers is another natural number. Thus, by adding natural numbers we can never obtain anything but a natural number. In mathematics, this property is expressed by saying that the natural numbers are *closed under addition*. If m is any natural number then $m + 1$ is also a natural number, which is called the *successor* of m. The successor of m is simply the next natural number after m. Thus, for example, 3 is the successor of 2 and 11 is the successor of 10. It follows, therefore, that the sequence of natural numbers indicated in (1–1) has no end. There is no last or largest natural number, since every natural number has a successor. The collection of all natural numbers then forms what is perhaps the simplest and most natural example in mathematics of a collection which does not contain a finite number of elements. It is not possible to count the number of natural numbers; this is indicated by saying that there are an *infinite* number of natural numbers.

Multiplication evolved initially as a simplified method for carrying out repeated addition. Suppose, for example, that a merchant bought 152 measures of wheat from a farmer at a given price per measure. To determine the total cost of the wheat, the merchant could add together 152 numbers, each of which was equal to the price per measure. This would be a clumsy way to determine the cost. Today, any schoolboy would do it by multiplying the number of measures by the price per measure. Let m and n be the arbitrary natural numbers. Suppose that we wish to compute the sum

$$\underbrace{n + n + n + \cdots + n}_{n \text{ appears } m \text{ times}}.$$

This sum is called the product of m and n and the notation we shall use for it will be mn, $m(n)$ or $m \times n$. We shall later see how to obtain the rule for multiplication which normally makes it much easier to carry out multiplication than repeated addition.

We can represent pictorially the operation of multiplication in a manner similar to addition. Suppose that we wish to compute $3(5)$. Let us now represent each 5 as a vertical column of five boxes as shown in Figure 1–2. To determine $3(5)$, we count the number of boxes in the rectangle shown in Figure 1–2 to obtain the result 15. Thus, multiplication has been reduced to counting, and in this way we can construct multiplication tables like those learned in elementary arithmetic.

The product of any two natural numbers is a natural number and, therefore, the natural numbers are closed under multiplication. The operation of multiplication obeys the same commutativity and associativity laws as

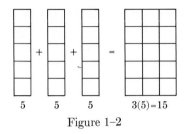

Figure 1–2

addition. Commutativity is expressed by the equation

$$mn = nm \tag{1–5}$$

and associativity by the equation

$$(mn)q = m(nq) . \tag{1–6}$$

Equation (1–6) says that to multiply together m, n and q we can first multiply m by n and then multiply the resulting number by q, or we can mul-multiply n by q and then multiply m by this number. It is easy to see pictorially that (1–5) and (1–6) are true in any particular case. For example, to verify that $3(5) = 5(3)$, we note from Figure 1–2 that $3(5) = 15$. From Figure 1–3 we see that $5(3) = 15$ also, thus confirming that $3(5) = 5(3)$.

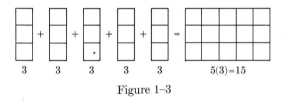

Figure 1–3

To show pictorially that (1–6) holds when $m = 4$, $n = 5$ and $q = 6$, it is now convenient to represent one unit by a cube rather than a square. Then, either expression in (1–6) is the number of cubes in the parallelepiped shown in Figure 1–4. The value mn is the number of cubes in any vertical

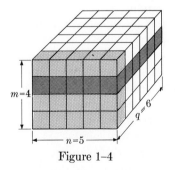

Figure 1–4

slab such as the shaded face. To obtain $(mn)q$ we place side by side q such slabs to yield the figure shown. Similarly, nq is the number of cubes in any horizontal slab such as the shaded one. To obtain $(mn)q$ we place m such slabs one on top of the other. This yields the same solid figure as $m(nq)$, which is what we wished to show. Frequently we must deal with situations where more than two or three numbers are to be multiplied together. The commutative and associative laws generalize to such cases, saying that the product of the given collection of numbers is independent of the order in which they are multiplied or the manner in which they are grouped.

There is one final important property of the combined operations of multiplication and addition which is referred to as the *distributive law*. This law says that if m, n and q are any three natural numbers then

$$q(m + n) = qm + qn . \tag{1–7}$$

In words, (1–7) says that, if we add n to m and multiply the resulting number by q, we obtain the same result as we do when multiplying q by m then multiplying q by n and adding together the two natural numbers so

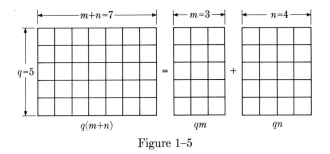

Figure 1–5

obtained. Again, pictorial diagrams can be used to verify (1–7) in any particular case. For example, Figure 1–5 illustrates the situation for $m = 3$, $n = 4$ and $q = 5$. We see that (1–7) holds, because all we are doing is splitting the rectangle representing $q(m + n)$ into two parts. This does not change the number of squares. As we shall see, the distributive law will be needed to derive the familiar rules of arithmetic.

The natural numbers which we have been discussing in these first two sections form the cornerstone for a large part of mathematics, and for this reason they are very important. We have not considered the question of where the natural numbers come from. Were they invented by man, or do they have an independent existence and did man merely discover them? This question has been of considerable interest to philosophers and mathematicians, but it lies outside the realm of mathematics proper, and hence we shall not attempt to consider it. We shall simply take the natural numbers and their properties as something obtained from experience with the real world. However, an interesting question arises as to what properties of the natural numbers must be taken as given and what ones can be proved. For example, can the associative and commutative laws be proved mathematically? The reader may feel that the pictorial devices we used actually prove these laws. This is not true, for pictorial methods only serve to verify the laws for particular values of the symbols appearing in the relevant equation. For the pictorial method to constitute a valid proof, it would be necessary to construct the appropriate picture for every possible set of values which the symbols could take on, since a valid mathematical proof requires that the result be shown to be correct in every possible case. Since there are an infinite number of natural numbers, it would be impossible to construct a picture for each possible set of values for the symbols. Therefore, the method cannot be used as a basis for a mathematical proof, in spite of the fact that we could verify in this way the truth of, say, the commutativity of multiplication for thousands or even millions of particular values for m and n. Such a procedure might serve to convince us beyond question that multiplication was commutative, but it would not suffice for a mathematical proof that $mn = nm$ for *every* pair of natural numbers m and n.

We still have not answered the question of whether or not commutativity and associativity can be proved. The answer is that this depends. It depends on which properties of the natural numbers are taken as given. The important thing to realize is that it is impossible to prove anything without beginning with *something* which is accepted without proof. The necessity of introducing *axioms* or *postulates* which are accepted without proof was apparently first realized by the Greeks several centuries before Christ. This insight was overlooked by many of the greatest mathematicians in the seventeenth and eighteenth centuries, and it was not until the nineteenth century that mathematicians once again began to recognize the importance of axioms in placing mathematical developments on a firmer foundation. In reality, it is fortunate that earlier mathematicians were not so concerned with the problems of providing rigorous proofs at every step, because otherwise they would have been unable to make the progress they did.

We shall not attempt to introduce a set of axioms from which the properties of the natural numbers and everything else we shall study can be rigorously and logically derived. This would be a long and complicated undertaking. We shall follow a more informal approach and accept as given essentially all the basic properties of the natural numbers as well as those of the other types of numbers we shall study. It is interesting to note, however, that we could begin from a few axioms and develop in a logical and rigorous manner everything that will be treated in this text. In particular, we could prove the commutativity and associativity properties referred to above.

1–3 THE RATIONAL NUMBERS

Problems associated with the physical process of making *measurements* have had an impact on the development of mathematics at least as great as those problems concerned with counting. The concept of measuring predates recorded history, just as does that of counting. The procedures for using a ruler to make measurements are now familiar to every school child. To the ancients, however, measuring introduced new problems. Initially, the only measurements made were of length or, equivalently, distance. To make such a measurement, it was first necessary to choose the fundamental unit of length (such as the foot), which might be the length of rope between two successive knots. To measure a given distance, the number of fundamental units of length in this distance would be counted. It was quickly observed, though, that regardless of how the unit of length was chosen, it seldom turned out that the distance measured was a natural number. There would be, for example, five units of length plus something left over which was not a full unit of length. For this reason it became necessary to introduce what we now call fractions. The fundamental unit of length is imagined to be subdivided into smaller parts which today we symbolize as $\frac{1}{2}$, $\frac{1}{3}$ or $\frac{1}{4}$, for example.* When the fundamental unit of length is divided into two parts, that is, into halves, the length of each half unit is written as $\frac{1}{2}$. Similarly, if it is divided into three equal parts, that is, into thirds, the length of any such part would be written $\frac{1}{3}$. The number of parts into which the fundamental unit is divided is indicated by lower number in the fraction. Thus the length of something might be $4\frac{2}{3}$, which means four units plus two of the one-third parts of a unit. Now it is natural to think of any length or distance as being represented by a number. Thus we want to think of $4\frac{2}{3}$ as a number. It is not a natural number, however; $4\frac{2}{3}$ is an example of what we call a *rational number*.

Since in measuring, some device such as a stick or a rope was used originally, it was natural to make marks on the edge of the stick or on the rope as an aid in making measurements. This gave rise to devices such as rulers, and it also gave rise to a new mathematical idea—that of representing numbers geometrically. To do this, a straight line is drawn and on it are placed two marks to indicate the length of the fundamental unit, as shown in Figure 1–6. Then, if some point from which measurements are to be made is selected (this is called the origin and would be the left edge of a ruler, for example), any length can be represented, and so can the new numbers which have fractional parts, as shown in Figure 1–6. The geometric interpretation of numbers as points on a line is a very important concept, and it is used frequently in mathematics and in everyday life.

There is another useful way of writing numbers such as $4\frac{2}{3}$. Note that each fundamental unit is made up of 3 of the $\frac{1}{3}$ parts, or subunits, of the

---

* Fractions are printed using a bar — or a solidus /, whichever is more convenient.

fundamental unit of length

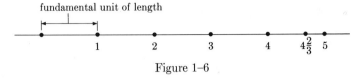

Figure 1–6

unit. Thus 4 fundamental units contain 4(3) = 12 of the $\frac{1}{3}$ parts of a unit. Hence we can write $4\frac{2}{3} = 14\frac{1}{3}$, since the measurement yields 14 of the $\frac{1}{3}$ parts of the fundamental unit. We can think of the process of changing from $4\frac{2}{3}$ to $14\frac{1}{3}$ as one in which a new unit of length is chosen that is one-third the original unit. In terms of the new unit the length is 14. However, to indicate that three of these new units make one original unit a 3 is written after the 14 in the format $14\frac{1}{3}$. We can now think of any expression m/n, where m and n are natural numbers, as a number resulting from a measurement in which n subunits are needed to make one fundamental unit. Thus any symbol m/n can be thought of as a number, and in accordance with our previous terminology it is called a rational number. Note that when $n = 1$, m/n becomes $m/1$. But $m/1$ is simply another notation for m, since in this case the subunit is the fundamental unit itself. Consequently, the natural numbers are part of the rational numbers and every natural number can also be looked upon as a rational number. Of course, not every rational number is a natural number. In general, any number of the form m/n can be referred to as a *fraction* regardless of whether or not m is less than n; m is called the *numerator* and n the *denominator* of the fraction. If m is less than n, the fraction is called *proper*.

We have just seen that to make measurements it was necessary to extend the natural numbers to include the rational numbers, which we can also call fractions. Merchants, too, used a type of computation, which we now refer to as division, that necessitated the introduction of new numbers. It turns out, as we shall see, that these new numbers are nothing but the rational numbers introduced above. Suppose, for example, that a merchant was offered four bolts of cloth for twelve dollars and that he wished to determine the price per bolt. Today, any school child could determine the price per bolt by dividing 12 by 4. Division, however, is a much more complicated operation than addition or multiplication, and it developed much later, since it presented considerable difficulties to the ancients. How do we divide 12 by 4? Clearly what we want to do is find a number which when multiplied by 4 gives 12. This gives the key to the way division was carried out initially, and indeed to the process used in arithmetic today. From a multiplication table the merchant would have noted that 3(4) = 12, thus obtaining the price of three dollars per bolt.

Now imagine that the total cost was fourteen dollars rather than twelve. In this case the merchant would have encountered difficulty. On consulting his multiplication table he would have noted that 3(4) = 12 and 4(4) = 16, but that there is no natural number which when multiplied by 4 gives 14. If the merchant were clever he might have done the following. Instead of using the dollar for the monetary unit he would have used a half-dollar, making the price of the four bolts 28 half-dollars. Now he would have seen on his multiplication table that $7(4) = 28$, so that the price per bolt would be 7 half-dollars. The trick used here is the same one used in measuring, and if we now use the rational numbers introduced for measuring, it is seen that the price per bolt in dollars is $3\frac{1}{2}$ or $\frac{7}{2}$.

The above example illustrates how the rational numbers can arise naturally in dividing natural numbers. Given two natural numbers m and n, the number* α having the property that $n\alpha = m$ is called the quotient of m by n. The number α will not, in general, be a natural number (thus implying that the natural numbers are not closed under division). It will be a rational number, however, and is in fact simply the rational number m/n, since this number is m subunits of size $1/n$; nm of these subunits just yield m fundamental units, which is precisely what is desired. This interpretation of rational numbers explains why we automatically think of a number such as $14\frac{}{6}$ as the number obtained by dividing 14 by 6 rather than merely as a rational number. In the event that α is a natural number (for example, if $m = 20$ and $n = 4$ so that $\alpha = {}^{20}\!/_4 = 5$), then we say that n *divides* m. If n does not divide m, then m/n is not a natural number. Thus 2 does not divide 1 and $\frac{1}{2}$ is not a natural number. When m is larger than n, and n does not divide m, then from our discussion of measurements we know that m/n can also be written as a natural number plus a proper fraction. Thus we can write

$$\frac{m}{n} = q + \frac{p}{n} \qquad\qquad (1\text{–}8)$$

where p is a natural number less than n. Thus $13\frac{}{3}$ can be written $4 + \frac{1}{3}$. It is conventional to use the simpler notation $4\frac{1}{3}$ which we introduced earlier. Thus any rational number m/n with m larger than n is either a natural number or can be written as the sum of a natural number and a proper fraction as in (1–8).

Obviously, there are many different ways that a given rational number can be written in the form m/n. Thus $\frac{3}{2}$, $\frac{6}{4}$, $\frac{9}{6}$ and ${}^{60}\!/_{40}$ all represent the same rational number which can be thought of as one and one half fundamental units. Similarly, $\frac{1}{1}$, $\frac{3}{3}$ and ${}^{18}\!/_{18}$ are simply different ways to write the natural number 1. In other words, if k is a natural number, then km/kn is the same rational number as m/n. This suggests that there is a simplest way to write any rational number in the form m/n. If there does not exist any natural number k greater than 1 such that $m = kq$ and $n = kp$ where

---

* In this chapter, and only in this chapter, it will be convenient to use different types of symbols to represent different types of numbers. Lower-case Greek letters will be used to represent rational numbers.

q and p are natural numbers, then m/n is the simplest way to write the rational number and we say that the rational number has been written in *least terms*. To write a number m/n in least terms we "cancel out" any common factors in m and n, to use a term from arithmetic. For example, $\frac{3}{2}$ is written in least terms while $\frac{30}{18}$ is not, because 30 and 18 have the common factor 6, so that $\frac{30}{18} = \frac{5}{3}$; $\frac{5}{3}$ is written in least terms.

In this section we have seen how it became necessary to extend the natural numbers, which had met ancient man's needs for centuries, to include what we have called rational numbers, in order to handle problems involving measurements and division of natural numbers. Although the use of rational numbers predates recorded history, it seems that they were just beginning to be used at the dawn of history. The first satisfactory written treatment of fractions appears in the Egyptian work referred to as the *Ahmes Papyrus* (c. 1550 B.C.), although they had been in use long before this in both Babylonia and Egypt. Fractions with the numerator greater than the denominator were probably first used by the Babylonians. Our present notation for writing fractions is derived from the Hindus.

1–4 OPERATIONS WITH RATIONAL NUMBERS

Just as practical problems arose which led to generalizing the operation of counting to include addition, multiplication and division of natural numbers, problems arose which led to generalizing the operations of addition, multiplication and division to apply to rational numbers as well as natural numbers. We shall now see how such generalizations should be made.

Consider addition first. Suppose that a merchant needs $5\frac{1}{2}$ yards of cloth for one customer and $2\frac{1}{3}$ yards for another. How many yards does he need for both customers combined? Clearly he needs $7 + \frac{1}{2} + \frac{1}{3}$ yards. But how much is $\frac{1}{2} + \frac{1}{3}$, or one-half of a yard plus one-third of a yard? The trick here is to choose a new, smaller subunit having the property that $\frac{1}{2}$ and $\frac{1}{3}$ are both multiples of this subunit. Suppose that we subdivide the fundamental unit into six parts. Then $\frac{1}{2}$ is 3 of the $\frac{1}{6}$ parts of the fundamental unit, that is, $\frac{1}{2} = \frac{3}{6}$, and $\frac{1}{3}$ is 2 of the $\frac{1}{6}$ parts, that is, $\frac{1}{3} = \frac{2}{6}$. Then $\frac{1}{2} + \frac{1}{3}$ must be 5 of the $\frac{1}{6}$ parts so that $\frac{1}{2} + \frac{1}{3}$ is $\frac{5}{6}$, and the total number of yards needed for the two customers is $7\frac{5}{6}$ yards. We can now see how to add any two rational numbers m/n and p/q. Imagine that the fundamental unit is divided into nq parts. Then $1/n$ is q of these nq subunits, so that $1/n = q/nq$, and $1/q$ is n of these subunits, so that $1/q = n/nq$. But then m/n is mq of the subunits and p/q is np of the subunits, so that $m/n + p/q$ is $mq + np$ of the subunits. Thus we conclude that

$$\frac{m}{n} + \frac{p}{q} = \frac{mq + np}{nq}. \tag{1–9}$$

Equation (1–9) tells us how to add the two rational numbers, thus reducing addition of rational numbers to operations with natural numbers which we already know how to perform. The sum of two rational numbers is again a rational number. The sum as computed from (1–9) may not be in least terms, but it can be converted to this form if desired. The addition of rational numbers satisfies the commutative and associative properties just as does the addition of natural numbers. Let us illustrate the addition of rational numbers with some simple numerical examples.

EXAMPLES. 1. $\dfrac{1}{6} + \dfrac{3}{7} = \dfrac{7 + 6(3)}{42} = \dfrac{25}{42}$.

2. $\dfrac{1}{2} + \dfrac{1}{2} = \dfrac{2 + 2}{4} = \dfrac{4}{4} = 1$.

3. The addition of a natural number and a rational number is a special case of the addition of rational numbers, since a natural number q is also a rational number which can be written qp/p, where p is any natural number. Thus

$$3 + \frac{16}{7} = \frac{21}{7} + \frac{16}{7} = \frac{37}{7}.$$

4. To add together three or more rational numbers one can first compute the sum of any two of these, then add another one to this sum, etc. By the commutativity and associativity of addition, the sum will be independent of the order in which the numbers are added. Thus, to add $\frac{4}{3}$, $\frac{7}{5}$ and $1\frac{1}{4}$, we can first add $\frac{4}{3}$ and $1\frac{1}{4}$ to obtain

$$\frac{4}{3} + \frac{11}{4} = \frac{4(4) + 3(11)}{12} = \frac{49}{12}.$$

Then

$$\frac{49}{12} + \frac{7}{5} = \frac{49(5) + 12(7)}{60} = \frac{329}{60},$$

so that the sum is $\frac{329}{60}$. The reader should carry out the addition in two other ways and verify that the same result is obtained.

Let us next study the multiplication of rational numbers. The product of two rational numbers m/n and p/q is the rational number whose numerator is mp and whose denominator is nq, so that

$$\left(\frac{m}{n}\right)\left(\frac{p}{q}\right) = \frac{mp}{nq} \tag{1–10}$$

and the multiplication of rational numbers is expressed in terms of multiplication of natural numbers. Multiplication of rational numbers obeys the same associative and commutative laws as for natural numbers, and the distributive law also holds. Let us now examine the reasoning behind

(1–10). Suppose that a merchant purchased $8\frac{1}{2}$ measures of wheat at a price of $1\frac{1}{4}$ dollars per measure. What is the total cost of the purchase? The total cost should be the product of the number of measures times the price per measure, that is, $(\frac{17}{2})(\frac{5}{4})$, since $8\frac{1}{2} = \frac{17}{2}$ and $1\frac{1}{4} = \frac{5}{4}$. The problem can be reduced to one of multiplying natural numbers. Note that the merchant purchased 17 half-measures of wheat. Let us now choose a monetary unit such that the price of a half-measure becomes a natural number. Suppose we use $\frac{1}{8}$ of a dollar as the monetary unit. Then the price per measure in $\frac{1}{8}$ dollars is 10 and the price of a half-measure in $\frac{1}{8}$ dollars is 5. Thus the cost in $\frac{1}{8}$ dollars is $17(5) = 85$, or the cost in dollars is $\frac{85}{8}$. This is precisely what would be obtained from (1–10) since

$$\left(\frac{17}{2}\right)\left(\frac{5}{4}\right) = \frac{(17)(5)}{(2)(4)} = \frac{85}{8}.$$

The way in which division of rational numbers should be carried out can easily be deduced from the law for multiplication. The number β which is the quotient of m/n by p/q should have the property that

$$\beta\left(\frac{p}{q}\right) = \frac{m}{n}.$$

Note from (1–10) that if $\beta = mq/np$ then

$$\beta\left(\frac{p}{q}\right) = \frac{mqp}{npq} = \frac{m}{n}$$

as desired. Thus the quotient of m/n by p/q is the rational number mq/np or

$$\frac{m/n}{p/q} = \frac{mq}{np}. \tag{1–11}$$

To divide two rational numbers, it is only necessary to know how to multiply natural numbers. Given any rational number m/n, the quotient of 1 by the number, which is from (1–11), n/m is called the *reciprocal* of m/n.

EXAMPLES. 1. The product of $\frac{6}{11}$ and $\frac{8}{3}$ is

$$\frac{6}{11}\left(\frac{8}{3}\right) = \frac{6(8)}{11(3)} = \frac{48}{33} = \frac{16}{11}.$$

2. The product of 7 and $\frac{4}{5}$ is

$$\frac{7}{1}\left(\frac{4}{5}\right) = \frac{28}{5}.$$

3. Let us check the correctness of the distributive law in the following case

$$\frac{4}{7}\left(\frac{2}{3} + \frac{9}{5}\right) = \frac{4}{7}\left(\frac{2}{3}\right) + \frac{4}{7}\left(\frac{9}{5}\right). \tag{1–12}$$

Note that

$$\frac{2}{3} + \frac{9}{5} = \frac{5(2) + 3(9)}{15} = \frac{37}{15}$$

and

$$\frac{4}{7}\left(\frac{37}{15}\right) = \frac{148}{105},$$

which is the value of the right-hand side of (1–12). Consider next the left-hand side

$$\frac{4}{7}\left(\frac{2}{3}\right) = \frac{8}{21}; \qquad \frac{4}{7}\left(\frac{9}{5}\right) = \frac{36}{35}$$

and

$$\frac{8}{21} + \frac{36}{35} = \frac{35(8) + 21(36)}{21(35)} = \frac{1036}{735}.$$

Now

$$\frac{1036}{735} = \frac{7(148)}{7(105)} = \frac{148}{105},$$

so that both sides of (1–12) are the same rational number, as the distributive law indicates should be the case.

4. The quotient of $5/3$ by $7/4$ is

$$\frac{5/3}{7/4} = \frac{5(4)}{3(7)} = \frac{20}{21}.$$

5. The reciprocal of $5/9$ is $9/5$.

1–5 SUBTRACTION AND THE NEGATIVE NUMBERS

As the mathematical computations which were needed became increasingly complex, it was found desirable to extend the rational numbers introduced in Section 1–3 to include what we call negative numbers and zero. Corresponding to every rational number m/n, there is another expression, written $-m/n$, which it is also convenient to call a number. We call $-m/n$ a negative number, or more precisely a *negative rational number*. Thus the symbols $-7/8$ or -3 we call negative numbers. In the future we shall call numbers m/n such as $7/8$ or 3 positive numbers to distinguish them from negative numbers. We shall also introduce a symbol 0, which we call the number zero. The number 0 has a clear intuitive meaning. We use 1 to indicate that we have one unit of something, perhaps one dollar, and 2 to indicate that we have two units. Zero is used to indicate that we do not have any units, perhaps to indicate that we have no money in our wallet. Thus if our bank balance is 0, this means that we have nothing in our account.

The physical interpretation of negative numbers is a little more subtle than for the other numbers we have studied because they do not arise in such natural ways. However, a good example of the usefulness of negative numbers is provided by the stock-market report printed in the newspaper each weekday. This report gives the price of each stock (high, low and last) and the change from yesterday's last price. In conversation, it is easy to say that the price was up 1 or down $\frac{1}{2}$. In printing the changes, however, it is clumsy to use the words up or down to indicate the direction of the change. A convenient way to indicate the direction of change is with the help of negative numbers. Positive numbers are used to indicate an increase in the price while negative numbers indicate a decrease. If in the change column we read $-\frac{5}{8}$, this means that the price of the stock decreased by $\frac{5}{8}$ of a dollar per share. If the price of the stock is unchanged, a 0 is used. One important use for negative numbers, then, is to represent changes in some numerical quantity. As another example, suppose that a merchant operates a grain storage bin and always wants to know how much grain he has. Whenever a customer buys grain, this decreases his stock. When a farmer sends him a resupply, this increases his stock.

The geometric representation of rational numbers as points on a line which was introduced in Figure 1–6 can be extended to provide a geometric representation of the negative rational numbers and 0 as well. This is shown in Figure 1–7. Zero is taken to be the point from which measurements

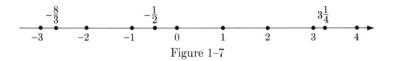

Figure 1–7

are made, since it has the connotation of no distance. As before, the positive rational numbers are located by measuring off the appropriate distance to the right of 0, so that to locate the point corresponding to m/n we measure off m/n units to the right of 0. Negative rational numbers are located to the left of 0, so that the point corresponding to $-m/n$ is m/n units to the left of 0. The points corresponding to m/n and $-m/n$ are thus the same distance from 0, but the one for m/n lies to the right of 0 while that for $-m/n$ lies to the left of 0. To make perfectly clear which side of 0 is being used for the positive numbers, we often place an arrowhead on that end of the line. There is no reason, except for the convention normally adopted in mathematics, that we could not have taken the points to the left of 0 as representing positive numbers.

The collection of all positive and negative rational numbers and zero is referred to as the *rational number system*. This is the number system that the reader will be familiar with from arithmetic. If m/n is a natural number q, then we can write $-m/n$ as $-q$ and call $-q$ a *negative integer*. This explains why the natural numbers are called the positive integers. The set of all positive and negative integers and zero is called the *set of all integers*. The integers, of course, are also rational numbers.

Let us now consider how the arithmetic operations can be generalized to include negative rational numbers and zero. Let us first obtain the rule for adding two negative numbers, say $-m/n$ and $-p/q$. If a stock dropped $\frac{1}{2}$ point yesterday and $\frac{1}{4}$ today, then it dropped $\frac{1}{2} + \frac{1}{4} = \frac{3}{4}$ of a point in the past two days. This suggests that to add $-m/n$ and $-p/q$ we merely add m/n and p/q and place a $-$ sign (minus sign) in front of the resulting number. Indeed, this is the way addition of two negative numbers is defined in mathematics. Thus from (1–9)

$$\left(-\frac{m}{n}\right) + \left(-\frac{p}{q}\right) = -\left(\frac{mq + np}{nq}\right). \tag{1–13}$$

Equation (1–13) shows that the sum of two negative rational numbers is a negative rational number.

The case where one of the numbers is positive and the other is negative is more complicated, and will require a little time to explain. Suppose that we wish to add m/n and $-p/q$. Let us take care of the easiest case first. Suppose that $m/n = p/q$, so that what we really wish to do is add m/n and $-m/n$. If the price of a stock went up $\frac{1}{2}$ yesterday and down $\frac{1}{2}$ today, there has been no net change over the past two days, that is, the net change is 0. Thus the sum in this case is

$$\frac{m}{n} + \left(-\frac{m}{n}\right) = 0 . \tag{1–14}$$

Consider now the more complicated case where m/n is not the same number as p/q. To proceed, let us first express both numbers in terms of a common subunit. The results from addition of positive numbers suggest we use $1/nq$ as the subunit. Thus $m/n = mq/nq$ and $-p/q = -np/nq$. Before proceeding we can see intuitively that the sum in this case can be either a positive or a negative number. This follows, because if a stock went up $\frac{2}{4}$ yesterday and goes down $\frac{1}{4}$ today, then the net change is positive because $\frac{2}{4}$ is larger than $\frac{1}{4}$. Conversely, if the stock went down $\frac{2}{4}$ yesterday and up $\frac{1}{4}$ today, then the net change will be negative. In general, we expect the sum to be positive if mq is larger than np and negative if np is larger than mq. Suppose that mq is larger than np. We wish to deduct from the mq subunits np subunits. How do we do this? We must introduce a new operation for natural numbers called *subtraction*.

Let u be a natural number which is larger than the natural number v. To subtract v units from u units we simply represent u by u boxes and then remove v boxes. We count the number of boxes remaining and denote this natural number by $u - v$. It is the number that results on subtracting v from u. The procedure is illustrated in Figure 1–8 for the case where $u = 8$

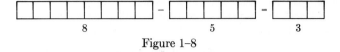

8   5   3

Figure 1–8

and $v = 5$. By counting, $u - v = 3$. With the aid of this pictorial method the ancients could carry out subtraction of natural numbers. We have just seen that we must know how to subtract a smaller natural number from a larger one to add positive and negative rational numbers. This is all we need, as we shall now see. (In passing, however, note that we have now used a minus sign in two different ways. First we used it as part of the symbol for a number to indicate a negative number. Now we are using it in a different way to indicate subtraction. We shall see below that this is a logical thing to do.)

It is now clear that the sum of m/n and $-p/q$, in the case where mq is larger than np, should just be $mq - np$ of the subunits $1/nq$. In other words,

$$\frac{m}{n} + \left(-\frac{p}{q}\right) = \frac{mq - np}{nq} \tag{1–15}$$

in this case, and this is the rule learned in arithmetic or algebra. Note that the sum is a positive rational number as desired. For example,

$$\frac{3}{2} + \left(-\frac{2}{11}\right) = \frac{3(11) - 2(2)}{22} = \frac{29}{22}.$$

The remaining case is that where np is larger than mq and we expect the sum to be a negative number. If a stock goes up mq of the subunits of $1/nq$ and down np the next, then the net change for the two days should be a decrease of $np - mq$ of the subunits when np is greater than mq. In other words, it should be true that

$$\frac{m}{n} + \left(-\frac{p}{q}\right) = -\left(\frac{np - mq}{nq}\right) \tag{1–16}$$

when np is greater than mq. This is, of course, the definition used in mathematics. For example,

$$\frac{2}{3} + \left(-\frac{8}{11}\right) = -\left(\frac{24 - 22}{33}\right) = -\frac{2}{33}.$$

It is quite obvious that if α is any rational number, then

$$\alpha + 0 = \alpha, \tag{1–17}$$

so that adding zero to a number does not change the number. On combining the results of (1–9), (1–13), (1–14), (1–15), (1–16) and (1–17) we see that when two rational numbers are added, another rational number is always obtained. Thus the rational numbers are closed under addition. The associative and commutative laws always hold for addition of rational numbers. The reader will note that addition of rational numbers is in a sense rather complicated because there are so many cases to consider. In arithmetic it takes some time to learn how to handle all these cases.

We shall now turn to multiplication of rational numbers when at least one of the numbers is negative. The product of a positive number m/n and a negative one $-p/q$ is defined to be a negative rational number which is

$$\left(\frac{m}{n}\right)\left(-\frac{p}{q}\right) = -\frac{mp}{nq}. \tag{1-18}$$

Thus, for example,

$$\left(\frac{3}{7}\right)\left(-\frac{11}{4}\right) = -\frac{33}{28}; \qquad (-1)\left(\frac{m}{n}\right) = -\frac{m}{n}.$$

We ask the reader in the problems to provide a practical example which suggests that (1-18) is the appropriate definition in this case.

The product of two negative numbers $-m/n$ and $-p/q$ is defined to be the positive rational number mp/nq, so that

$$\left(-\frac{m}{n}\right)\left(-\frac{p}{q}\right) = \frac{mp}{nq}. \tag{1-19}$$

As examples

$$\left(-\frac{9}{8}\right)\left(-\frac{1}{6}\right) = \frac{9}{48}; \qquad (-1)(-1) = 1.$$

If the reader attempts to find an intuitive justification for (1-19) similar to those we have given above in other situations, he will be unable to find one. The operation of multiplying together two negative numbers does not arise naturally in accounting operations or in measuring. What, then, is the justification for (1-19)? The first important thing to observe is that (1-19) is simply a definition, and the definition could have been made in any manner we desired. Indeed, all the rules for operating with rational numbers are definitions. The reader may feel that the practical examples we gave to motivate the definitions proved that operations with rational numbers must be carried out in a certain way. These practical problems did indeed *lead* to the development of operations with rational numbers in the way we have indicated; from a mathematical point of view, however, the operations could have been defined arbitrarily. To be useful in practice, of course, they had to be defined essentially as we have indicated. The situation is different with (1-19), however, since this operation does not occur directly in practice. The reason for the definition (1-19) lies in an entirely different consideration. In order to have the distributive law of multiplication hold, multiplication of negative rational numbers must be defined as in (1-19). Since it is very useful to have the distributive law hold, it is appropriate to make the definition (1–19) and this is the justification. To see why (1–19) is needed to make the distributive law hold consider

$$\left(-\frac{1}{2}\right)(6 + (-3)) = \left(-\frac{1}{2}\right)(3) = -\frac{3}{2}. \tag{1–20}$$

If the distributive law can be applied to the left-hand side of (1–20) then

$$\left(-\frac{1}{2}\right)(6 + (-3)) = \left(-\frac{1}{2}\right)(6) + \left(-\frac{1}{2}\right)(-3) = -\frac{6}{2} + \left(-\frac{1}{2}\right)(-3).$$

We want the result to be $-\frac{3}{2}$. This will be true only if we have $(-\frac{1}{2})(-3) = \frac{3}{2}$, in other words, if (1–19) holds.

If α is any rational number, then zero times this number is simply zero, so that

$$0(\alpha) = 0. \tag{1–21}$$

This now takes care of all cases. From (1–10), (1–18), (1–19) and (1–21) we see that the product of two rational numbers is a rational number, so that the rational numbers are closed under multiplication. The commutative, associative and distributive laws all hold for multiplication.

The rules for division of rational numbers when at least one of the numbers is a negative number or zero follow at once from the laws for multiplication, because the quotient of α divided by β is a number γ such that $\alpha = \gamma\beta$. Thus we can see immediately that

$$\frac{-m/n}{p/q} = -\frac{mq}{np} = \frac{m/n}{-p/q}; \qquad \frac{-m/n}{-p/q} = \frac{mq}{np}. \tag{1–22}$$

For example,

$$\frac{-3/7}{4/5} = -\frac{3(5)}{7(4)} = -\frac{15}{28}; \qquad \frac{-6/11}{-1/2} = \frac{6(2)}{11(1)} = \frac{12}{11}.$$

Furthermore, 0 divided by any positive or negative number is 0, thus

$$\frac{0}{m/n} = 0; \qquad \frac{0}{-p/q} = 0. \tag{1–23}$$

We encounter a new problem if we attempt to divide by 0. Let α be a positive or negative rational number. Then if there were a number β such that $\beta = \alpha/0$, it would have to be true that $0(\beta) = \alpha$. But by (1–21), $0(\beta) = 0$ for any rational number β, and this is not α. Thus there is no rational number $\alpha/0$, and therefore it follows that we cannot divide by zero when α is different from 0. We get into trouble even if $\alpha = 0$, because if $\beta = 0/0$, then $0(\beta) = 0$. Since this holds for every rational number β, division of 0 by 0 does not determine a unique rational number. *We conclude, then, that we must rule out division by zero.* Division is always defined except when the denominator is 0, and the quotient of two rational numbers is a rational number. Hence the rational numbers are closed under division when division by 0 is excluded.

We have introduced the notion of subtracting a natural number from a larger one. The general definition of subtraction can now be given in terms of operations already defined. To indicate that β is to be subtracted from α, we use the familiar notation $\alpha - \beta$; $\alpha - \beta$ is then defined to be the rational number

$$\alpha - \beta = \alpha + (-1)\beta . \tag{1-24}$$

To subtract β from α we multiply β by -1 and add. Thus

$$\frac{2}{3} - \frac{4}{7} = \frac{2}{3} + (-1)\left(\frac{4}{7}\right) = \frac{2}{3} + \left(-\frac{4}{7}\right) = \frac{2(7) - 3(4)}{21} = \frac{2}{21} .$$

In this section we introduced the negative rational numbers and zero, and we showed how to carry out arithmetic operations when negative numbers are involved. The introduction of the symbol 0 was a very important one for the development of mathematics, as we shall see in more detail later. Zero was probably first introduced by the Sumerians, although there is some indication that the Mayan Indians of Yucatan used it earlier (their mathematics, of course, had no influence on the major developments which took place in Europe). Interestingly, the Greeks made no use of 0. The introduction of negative numbers is a relatively recent development, although the Chinese made some use of them in subtraction as early as 200 B.C. They also appear in Hindu works as early as 650, but the earliest work which is modern in character seems to be that of Cardan in 1545.

1–6 COMBINED OPERATIONS

Since the rational numbers are closed under addition, subtraction, multiplication and division (excluding division by 0), it is possible to generate only rational numbers by performing these operations on rational numbers. By combining the four arithmetic operations, we can build up very complicated looking expressions such as

$$\frac{\{\rho[(\alpha\beta/\gamma) - \delta]\}}{\left\{\left(\theta + \left[\dfrac{\theta\alpha}{1 + \dfrac{\rho\epsilon}{\mu}}\right]\right)\right\}} . \tag{1-25}$$

However, if α, β, γ, δ, ϵ, μ, θ and ρ are rational numbers, then (1–25) is a rational number if division by 0 never occurs. Furthermore, we could determine the rational number in a straightforward fashion using the rules introduced in the previous sections.

In (1–25) various *enclosures*—such as parentheses ( ), brackets [ ] and braces { }—are used to remove ambiguities by indicating, where necessary, the sequence in which the operations are to be performed. The general rule followed in any nested expression involving several sets of enclosures is that operations are performed from the innermost set outwards. When writing expressions such as (1–25) care must be taken to use a sufficient number of enclosures to define uniquely the expression. For example, if an expression is printed in the form $a + b/c$ it is not clear whether

$$a + \frac{b}{c} \quad \text{or} \quad \frac{a + b}{c}$$

is implied. If it is the former, this could be indicated by writing $a + (b/c)$, and if the latter $(a + b)/c$. On the other hand, it is undesirable and clumsy to use more enclosures than necessary. In (1–25) more enclosures are used than are really needed, for the expression is uniquely defined when written as

$$\frac{\rho\left(\dfrac{\alpha\beta}{\gamma} - \delta\right)}{\theta + \dfrac{\mu}{1 + \dfrac{\rho\epsilon}{\mu}}} \, .$$

Note that the number of enclosures needed can vary depending on whether a solidus / or a bar — is used in writing fractions.

EXAMPLE. Reduce the following rational number α to the form m/n, 0 or $-m/n$.

$$\alpha = \frac{\dfrac{4}{3} - \dfrac{2}{1 - (6/7)}}{3\left[\dfrac{2}{3}(4) + \dfrac{1}{1 + (7/8)}\right] + \dfrac{1}{6}} \, .$$

By (1–9), (1–10) and (1–11)

$$1 + \frac{7}{8} = \frac{15}{8} \, ; \qquad \frac{1}{15/8} = \frac{8}{15} \, ; \qquad \frac{2}{3}(4) + \frac{8}{15} = \frac{120 + 24}{45} = \frac{144}{45} = \frac{16}{5} \, .$$

Then

$$3\left(\frac{16}{5}\right) = \frac{48}{5} \, ; \qquad \frac{48}{5} + \frac{1}{6} = \frac{288 + 5}{30} = \frac{293}{30} \, .$$

Next from (1–24), (1–15) and (1–16)

$$1 - \frac{6}{7} = 1 + (-1)\frac{6}{7} = \frac{1}{1} + \left(-\frac{6}{7}\right) = \frac{1}{7} ; \qquad \frac{2}{1/7} = 14 .$$

Thus

$$\frac{4}{3} - 14 = -\frac{42 - 4}{3} = -\frac{38}{3} ,$$

so

$$\alpha = \frac{-38/3}{293/30} = -\frac{1140}{879} = -\frac{380}{293} .$$

In the past several sections we have defined the rational numbers and have shown how to operate with them. We have not attempted to develop all the rules learned in arithmetic for working with fractions, although they could easily be obtained from what we have given. Instead, we have concentrated on showing how the need for rational numbers arose naturally in seeking solutions to practical problems, as did the rules for operating with them. We have assumed that the reader was more or less familiar with the rules from his previous study of arithmetic.

1–7 POWERS

Problems are frequently encountered in which it is necessary to multiply some given number α by itself several times. For example, we might need the quantity $\alpha\alpha\alpha\alpha$. From the generalized associative and commutative laws we know that this product is uniquely defined and is independent of the way in which the numbers are grouped and of the sequence in which the multiplication is carried out. Thus, the product is determined when we specify α and the number of times α is to be multiplied by itself. It is therefore convenient to introduce a simplified notation for such products rather than writing out something like $\alpha\alpha\alpha\alpha\alpha$. A convenient notation is α^5. The superscript 5 on α is called an *exponent* and indicates the number of α's which are to be multiplied together to form the product. The exponent is often referred to as *the power* to which α is raised, so that when we refer to the fifth power of α, we mean α^5. Sometimes α is referred to as *the base* which is raised to the given power.

In general, if n is a natural number, we write the product $\alpha \cdots \alpha$, where α appears n times, as α^n,

$$\underbrace{\alpha\alpha \cdots \alpha}_{\substack{\alpha \text{ appears} \\ n \text{ times}}} = \alpha^n . \qquad (1\text{–}26)$$

Here the ellipses $\cdots$ mean repeated multiplication. In particular then,

$$\alpha^1 = \alpha \,. \tag{1-27}$$

Let us now obtain some useful properties of the exponent notation (1–26). Consider α^p. Next let m and n be any two natural numbers such that $m + n = p$. Thus $\alpha^p = \alpha^{m+n}$. Since the product is independent of the grouping, we can split up the product into two groups, one containing m of the α's and the other n of the α's as follows

$$\underbrace{\alpha\alpha \cdots \alpha}_{m+n} = \underbrace{(\alpha\alpha \cdots \alpha)}_{m}\underbrace{(\alpha\alpha \cdots \alpha)}_{n} = \underbrace{(\alpha\alpha \cdots \alpha)}_{n}\underbrace{(\alpha\alpha \cdots \alpha)}_{m} \,. \tag{1-28}$$

When (1–28) is expressed using the notation (1–26) we have

$$\alpha^{m+n} = \alpha^m \alpha^n = \alpha^n \alpha^m \tag{1-29}$$

for any rational number α. Thus in a product exponents add. For example, (1–29) requires that

$$5^6 = 5^4 5^2 = 5^3 5^3 = 5^5 5^1 \,,$$

which the reader can readily verify is correct. Next consider a situation in which α is multiplied by itself mn times. This product can be partitioned as

$$\overset{m \text{ groups}}{\underbrace{(\alpha\alpha \cdots \alpha)}_{n}\underbrace{(\alpha\alpha \cdots \alpha)}_{n} \cdots \underbrace{(\alpha\alpha \cdots \alpha)}_{n}}$$

or

$$\overset{n \text{ groups}}{\underbrace{(\alpha\alpha \cdots \alpha)}_{m}\underbrace{(\alpha\alpha \cdots \alpha)}_{m} \cdots \underbrace{(\alpha\alpha \cdots \alpha)}_{m}} \,.$$

Therefore

$$\alpha^{mn} = \underbrace{\alpha^n \alpha^n \cdots \alpha^n}_{m \text{ groups}} = \underbrace{\alpha^m \alpha^m \cdots \alpha^m}_{n \text{ groups}} \tag{1-30}$$

We can now use the notation (1–26) again to simplify the writing of the right-hand side of (1–30) to obtain

$$\alpha^{mn} = (\alpha^n)^m = (\alpha^m)^n \,. \tag{1-31}$$

For example, (1–31) implies that

$$3^6 = (3^3)^2 = (3^2)^3 \,,$$

and the reader can easily check the correctness of this.

Consider next two rational numbers α and β. By the generalized associative and commutative laws it follows that

$$\underbrace{(\alpha\alpha\cdots\alpha)}_{n}\underbrace{(\beta\beta\cdots\beta)}_{n} = \underbrace{(\alpha\beta)(\alpha\beta)\cdots(\alpha\beta)}_{n\ \text{groups}}\ , \tag{1–32}$$

so

$$\alpha^n\beta^n = (\alpha\beta)^n\ . \tag{1–33}$$

Equation (1–33) requires, for example, that $3^2(4)^2 = 12^2$, which is correct, since $3^2 = 9$, $4^2 = 16$ and $9(16) = 144 = 12^2$.

In the above we gave a meaning to α^n where n is a natural number. This simply means $\alpha\cdots\alpha$, where α appears n times. It is convenient to extend the exponent notation to make possible additional notational simplifications. Let α be a rational number different from zero and consider the number $1/\alpha^n$. As we shall see, a convenient notation for $1/\alpha^n$ is α^{-n}, so that by definition

$$\alpha^{-n} = \frac{1}{\alpha^n}\ . \tag{1–34}$$

We then think of α^{-n} as α raised to the power $-n$. This does not mean α multiplied by itself $-n$ times, since this latter statement has no meaning; α^{-n} is simply a notation for $1/\alpha^n$. Thus

$$2^{-3} = \frac{1}{2^3} = \frac{1}{8}\ .$$

The arguments given above immediately show that

$$\alpha^{-(m+n)} = \alpha^{-m-n} = \alpha^{-m}\alpha^{-n} \tag{1–35}$$

and

$$\alpha^{-mn} = (\alpha^{-m})^n = (\alpha^m)^{-n} = (\alpha^{-n})^m = (\alpha^n)^{-m}\ . \tag{1–36}$$

Furthermore, if α and β are different from 0

$$(\alpha\beta)^{-n} = \alpha^{-n}\beta^{-n}\ . \tag{1–37}$$

We ask the reader to derive (1–35) through (1–37) in detail in the problems.

Let us now see why the α^{-n} notation is so appropriate. Consider α^n/α^m where n is larger than m. This is

$$\frac{\overbrace{\alpha\alpha\cdots\alpha}^{n}}{\underbrace{\alpha\alpha\cdots\alpha}_{m}} = \underbrace{\alpha\alpha\cdots\alpha}_{n-m} \quad \text{or} \quad \frac{\alpha^n}{\alpha^m} = \alpha^{n-m}\ .$$

On writing $1/\alpha^m = \alpha^{-m}$ we have

$$\alpha^n \alpha^{-m} = \alpha^{n-m} . \tag{1-38}$$

Therefore on using the α^{-m} notation the exponents again add in (1–38). If m is greater than n, α^n/α^m becomes

$$\frac{\overbrace{\alpha\alpha\cdots\alpha}^{n}}{\underbrace{\alpha\alpha\cdots\alpha}_{m}} = \frac{1}{\underbrace{\alpha\alpha\cdots\alpha}_{m-n}}$$

or

$$\alpha^n \alpha^{-m} = \alpha^{-(m-n)} = \alpha^{n-m} \tag{1-39}$$

since $-(m - n) = n - m$. Thus (1–38) holds in either case. When $m = n$, $\alpha^n/\alpha^n = 1$. If we desire that (1–38) hold here, it must be true that

$$\alpha^n \alpha^{-n} = \alpha^{n-n} = \alpha^0 = 1 . \tag{1-40}$$

In other words, α^0 should be defined to be 1 when α is not 0. We shall make this definition, since it is a convenient one, and we shall set $\alpha^0 = 1$ even if $\alpha = 0$. Thus by definition

$$\alpha^0 = 1 . \tag{1-41}$$

We can now make an additional generalization of the exponent notation. If α is different from 0, and k is any integer (positive, negative, or 0), we can give a meaning to α^k from our definitions above. If k is positive, say $k = n$, then $\alpha^k = \alpha^n$. If k is negative, say $k = -n$, then $\alpha^k = \alpha^{-n}$. Finally, if $k = 0$, $\alpha^k = \alpha^0 = 1$. Furthermore, the laws for exponents (1–29), (1–31) and (1–33) hold for this more general case, so that if h and k are any integers and α and β are any rational numbers different from 0, then

$$\alpha^{h+k} = \alpha^h \alpha^k ; \qquad \alpha^{hk} = (\alpha^h)^k = (\alpha^k)^h \tag{1-42}$$

and

$$(\alpha\beta)^k = \alpha^k \beta^k . \tag{1-43}$$

To verify the equations in (1–42) and (1–43), we must for each equation show that the equation is valid for every one of the nine possible cases corresponding to h and k being either positive, negative or zero. We have verified most but not all of the cases above. The remaining ones are left for the reader to verify in the problems. The exponent notation is very important and will be used repeatedly in what follows. Let us then conclude the section with some additional examples.

EXAMPLES. 1. If $\alpha = p/q$, then $\alpha^n = p^n/q^n = p^n q^{-n}$.

2. If $\beta = 1/\alpha$, then $\beta^n = 1/\alpha^n = \alpha^{-n}$.

3. When no confusion will result we can write something like $(10)^n$ as 10^n. Note that

$$10^3 = 1000, \ 10^2 = 100, \ 10^1 = 10, \ 10^0 = 1, \ 10^{-1} = 1/10, \ 10^{-2} = 1/100 \,.$$

4. On applying (1–42) twice we see that

$$(\alpha\beta\gamma)^k = (\alpha\beta)^k\gamma^k = \alpha^k\beta^k\gamma^k \,.$$

5. Since $2 = (-1)(-2)$, the second equation of (1–42) implies that

$$3^2 = (3^{-1})^{-2}$$

which is correct, since $3^{-1} = \frac{1}{3}$ and $(\frac{1}{3})^{-2} = 1/(3^{-2}) = 3^2 = 9$.

6. $10^3 + 10^2 = 10(10)^2 + 10^2 = 11(10)^2$.

1–8 POSITIONAL NOTATION AND THE DECIMAL SYSTEM

For most of the number systems presented in Table 1–1 it is continually necessary to introduce new symbols to represent larger and larger numbers. With such systems it is extremely cumbersome to carry out the four arithmetic operations, especially multiplication and division. Furthermore, the representation of large numbers and rational numbers is complicated in such systems. One of the greatest advances in the development of mathematics was the invention of the positional representation of numbers in common use today. It was apparently invented by the Hindus, and was introduced into Europe in about the tenth century by Italian merchants who learned it from the Moslems. The system was known in trading centers such as Alexandria considerably earlier, however, probably as early as the fifth century. Interestingly enough, the system used by the Mayan Indians is positional and they may have developed it even earlier than the Hindus. The Mayans' work, of course, had no influence on the later development of mathematics.

With what we call the decimal system only ten symbols, called digits, 0, 1, 2, 3, 4, 5, 6, 7, 8 and 9 (zero and the first nine natural numbers), are needed to represent any number, however large or small. This is accomplished by using what is called a positional rather than a strictly additive principle. What do we mean by 321? We mean $300 + 20 + 1$. This can also be written

$$3(10)^2 + 2(10)^1 + 1(10)^0 \,.$$

In other words, the position of any one of the ten symbols used when writing a number tells what power of 10 it is supposed to multiply. We say that $10 = 9 + 1$ is the *base* for our number system. Note how important the concept of zero is for developing the positional notation. Without this concept we could not, for example, conveniently represent numbers such as 1001 in a positional notation.

Any natural number m can be written

$$m = a_r(10)^r + a_{r-1}(10)^{r-1} + \cdots + a_0(10)^0 , \qquad (1\text{--}44)$$

where each number $a_r, a_{r-1}, \ldots, a_0$ is one of the ten digits 0, 1, 2, ... , 9. In (1–44) we have introduced a new notation that will be used frequently in the future. To indicate different numbers, we have not used different symbols such as α, β and γ, but have instead used a single letter (a in this case) with different subscripts on it. This notation is convenient because it eliminates the need for introducing a large number of different symbols, and it simultaneously serves to indicate the power of 10 with which any given number is to be associated. For example, a_1 is associated with 10 and a_4 with 10^4. We call a_u the *coefficient* of 10^u in (1–44); each power of 10 has a coefficient associated with it. The numbers $a_r, a_{r-1}, \ldots, a_0$ in (1–44) are unique, that is, there is only one set of these numbers having the characteristic that each is one of the ten digits 0, 1, ... , 9, and when a_r is multiplied by 10^r and added to a_{r-1} times 10^{r-1}, etc., the natural number m is obtained.

How can we prove that every natural number m can be written in the form (1–44)? The proof follows from (1–8). Recall that every positive rational number m/n with m larger than n can be written as

$$\frac{m}{n} = q \quad \text{or} \quad \frac{m}{n} = q + \frac{p}{n} , \qquad (1\text{--}45)$$

where q is a natural number and p is a natural number less than n. If n divides m then $m/n = q$. Otherwise there is a remainder p. We can combine both of the equations (1–45) into a single equation by writing

$$\frac{m}{n} = q + \frac{k}{n} , \qquad (1\text{--}46)$$

where k is 0 or a natural number less than n. Suppose that we now take $n = 10$. Then

$$\frac{m}{10} = q + \frac{k}{10} , \qquad (1\text{--}47)$$

or on multiplying by 10,

$$m = q(10) + k . \qquad (1\text{--}48)$$

If q is less than 10 we have expressed m in the form (1–44), where $a_0 = k$ and $a_1 = q$. If q is greater than or equal to 10, then applying (1–47) again, we can write

$$q = p(10) + a_1 , \qquad (1\text{--}49)$$

or on substituting this into (1–48) with $k = a_0$, we have

$$m = p(10)^2 + a_1(10)^1 + a_0 . \qquad (1\text{–}50)$$

If p is less than 10 we have expressed m in the form (1–44). Otherwise we repeat the procedure again. The method terminates when the coefficient of the highest power of 10 is less than 10. Thus we see that the coefficients a_u in (1–44) are nothing but the remainders obtained on successive division by 10. More precisely, if we divide (1–44) by 10 we obtain

$$\frac{m}{10} = a_r(10)^{r-1} + a_{r-1}(10)^{r-2} + \cdots + a_1(10)^0 + \frac{a_0}{10}, \qquad (1\text{–}51)$$

so that a_0 is the remainder on dividing m by 10. Let

$$q = a_r(10)^{r-1} + a_{r-1}(10)^{r-2} + \cdots + a_1(10)^0 . \qquad (1\text{–}52)$$

Then on dividing q by 10

$$\frac{q}{10} = a_r(10)^{r-2} + a_{r-1}(10)^{r-3} + \cdots + a_2(10)^0 + \frac{a_1}{10}, \qquad (1\text{–}53)$$

so that a_1 is the remainder on dividing q by 10. The other a_u follow in the same way. One case we have not accounted for is that where m is less than 10. In this case m must be one of the first nine natural numbers, and to when m in the form (1–44) all we need to do is write $m(10)^0$.

Let us illustrate the procedure which we have just gone through using 321 as an example. First,

$$\frac{321}{10} = 32 + \frac{1}{10} \quad \text{or} \quad 321 = 32(10) + 1 .$$

Then

$$\frac{32}{10} = 3 + \frac{2}{10} \quad \text{or} \quad 32 = 3(10) + 2 ,$$

so

$$321 = [3(10) + 2](10) + 1 = 3(10)^2 + 2(10)^1 + 1(10)^0 .$$

Note that 3 is less than 10 and hence we are finished.

We have shown that it is always possible to write any natural number in the form (1–44). We can now make an interesting observation. The number m is completely characterized by the numbers $a_r, a_{r-1}, \ldots, a_0$, so that if these numbers are specified m can be determined. This suggests a notational simplification. It is possible to eliminate writing the powers of 10 completely, since all we really need to know are the coefficients. We must know the order in which the coefficients appear, however, so that we know which power of 10 any given one is to multiply. A convenient way to represent m is then merely to write $a_r a_{r-1} \cdots a_1 a_0$. We write the coefficients side by side, the one multiplying the highest power of 10 coming first and that multiplying 10^0 coming last. This is then what we call the decimal positional representation of m and we can write

$$m = a_r a_{r-1} \cdots a_1 a_0 . \tag{1-54}$$

In (1–54), no multiplication is implied on the right-hand side. The numbers are merely written side by side and the position of any number indicates the power of 10 it multiplies. The decimal positional notation for numbers is the one we commonly use in everyday life.

Most number systems developed by cultures everywhere used a base of 10 even though they did not use a positional notation. This means that new symbols were introduced on the basis of multiples of 10, and perhaps also 50, 100 and 200, rather than for multiples of some other number, such as 17. There is no compelling reason, however, that 10 must be used as a base. Any natural number greater than 1 can be used and we shall later see how to obtain the representations of numbers in systems which use a base different from 10.

1–9 POSITIONAL REPRESENTATION OF PROPER FRACTIONS

In the past we have written rational numbers as fractions such as $\frac{5}{4}$ or, in the mixed form, $1\frac{1}{4}$. The reader probably feels more at home with the decimal representation of rational numbers than he does with fractions. The decimal representation of $\frac{5}{4}$ is, of course, 1.25. We shall now explain what this decimal representation means and show how to obtain it from the representation of the number as a fraction. Consider any fraction m/n. If n divides m then m/n is a natural number q and we already know how to write this number in positional form. If n does not divide m then we can write m/n as $q + (p/n)$ where p is a natural number less than n. Since we know how to write q in positional notation, all we need to do to write m/n in positional notation is to express p/n in this way. Let us then concentrate our attention on determining the positional representation of a given proper fraction p/n, with p/n being the least terms representation of the fraction. Since we are assuming the fraction to be proper, this implies that p is less than n.

Consider first the case where the denominator n divides some power of 10. This means that there exist natural numbers s and k such that $s = 10^k/n$. Then we can write

$$\frac{p}{n} = \frac{sp}{10^k} = \frac{t}{10^k} , \tag{1-55}$$

where $t = sp$ and t is a natural number. Since p is less than n it follows that t is less than 10^k. We shall now see that it is easy to obtain the positional representation of $t/10^k$. From what we learned in the previous section t can be written

$$t = a_r(10)^r + a_{r-1}(10)^{r-1} + \cdots + a_0(10)^0 \qquad (1\text{–}56)$$

and 10^r is less than 10^k or r is less than k, since t is less than 10^k (why?). Thus

$$\frac{p}{n} = \frac{t}{10^k} = t(10)^{-k} = 10^{-k}[a_r(10)^r + \cdots + a_0(10)^0]$$

$$= a_r(10)^{-(k-r)} + a_{r-1}(10)^{-(k-r)-1} + \cdots + a_0(10)^{-k} . \qquad (1\text{–}57)$$

We have here the basis for the positional representation of p/n. Before going on, however, note that the following represent particular examples of (1–57):

$$\frac{7}{25} = \frac{28}{100} = 2(10)^{-1} + 8(10)^{-2}; \qquad \frac{1}{25} = \frac{4}{100} = 4(10)^{-2} .$$

In general, as we can see from the second example just given, it need not be true that $k - r = 1$; $k - r$ can be any natural number. However, we can always write $t/10^k$ uniquely in the form

$$\frac{t}{10^k} = b_1(10)^{-1} + b_2(10)^{-2} + \cdots + b_k(10)^{-k} , \qquad (1\text{–}58)$$

where some of the initial b's may be zero. Thus

$$\frac{1}{25} = \frac{4}{100} = 0(10)^{-1} + 4(10)^{-2}$$

and $b_1 = 0$. Equation (1–58) provides the basis for a positional decimal representation of the proper fraction $t/10^k$. The fraction is completely described by the values of $b_1, \ldots, b_k$. Thus we shall represent $t/10^k$ simply by writing $b_1 b_2 \cdots b_k$. The convention is followed that the first number is the coefficient of 10^{-1}, the second of 10^{-2}, and so forth. We now encounter a problem. If we are given an expression such as 113, we must determine whether it represents the natural number

$$4(10)^2 + 1(10)^1 + 3(10)^0 \qquad (1\text{–}59)$$

or the proper fraction

$$4(10)^{-1} + 1(10)^{-2} + 3(10)^{-3} . \qquad (1\text{–}60)$$

To make clear the distinction we introduce a mark, usually represented by a period in the U.S. and by a comma in a number of other countries, which is called a *decimal point*. If the given set of digits is to represent a fraction, we place a period before the digits to indicate this. Thus to represent (1–60) we write .413, whereas to represent (1–59) we write 413. Hence $t/10^k$ of (1–58) would be written $.b_1 b_2 \cdots b_k$, and $4/100$ becomes .04.

We have noted previously that any rational number m/n can be written

$q + (p/n)$. If the decimal representation of q is $a_r a_{r-1} \cdots a_0$, and if n divides some power of 10 so that the decimal representation of p/n is $.b_1 b_2 \cdots b_k$, then for the decimal representation of m/n we use

$$\frac{m}{n} = a_r a_{r-1} \cdots a_0 . b_1 b_2 \cdots b_k . \qquad (1\text{-}61)$$

Thus

$$25\frac{2}{5} = \frac{127}{5} = 25.4 = 2(10)^1 + 5(10)^0 + 4(10)^{-1} .$$

Note that in (1-61) the decimal point functions very conveniently to indicate which powers of 10 the numbers are to multiply. The number immediately preceding the decimal point multiplies 10^0. It is often typical when printing decimal numbers which are proper fractions, say .04 to use 0.04. The 0 before the decimal point is used to show clearly that the number is indeed a proper fraction and that some digits to the left of the decimal point were not accidentally omitted. We shall follow this convention, except in tables such as those at the end of the text where the 0 is not needed. When referring to a particular digit in the decimal representation of a number, it is convenient to characterize its location by saying that it lies so many *places* to the left or to the right of the decimal point.

We have shown that any rational number m/n for which n divides some power of 10 has a decimal representation of the form (1-61). It is easy to go in the reverse direction and show that any such number

$$a_r a_{r-1} \cdots a_0 . b_1 \cdots b_k = a_r(10)^r + \cdots + a_0(10)^0 + b_1(10)^{-1} + \cdots$$
$$+ b_k(10)^{-k} \quad (1\text{-}62)$$

is a rational number of the form $t/10^k$, where t is some natural number (not necessarily less than 10^k). To do this multiply (1-62) by 10^k. This yields

$$(a_r \cdots a_0 . b_1 \cdots b_k)(10)^k = a_r(10)^{r+k} + \cdots + a_0(10)^k + b_1(10)^{k-1} + \cdots$$
$$+ b_k(10)^0 \quad (1\text{-}63)$$

which is the natural number $a_r \cdots a_0 b_1 \cdots b_k$. Thus

$$a_r \cdots a_0 . b_1 \cdots b_k = \frac{a_r \cdots a_0 b_1 \cdots b_k}{10^k} , \qquad (1\text{-}64)$$

and we have shown that the given number is a rational number of the type specified. For example, $13.221 = 13221/1000$.

From what we have done above, it follows that any number $a_r a_{r-1} \cdots a_0 . b_1 \cdots b_k$ can be written in the alternative form

$$a_r . a_{r-1} \cdots a_0 b_1 \cdots b_k (10)^r . \qquad (1\text{-}65)$$

This notation, often used in scientific work, provides a convenient way to write large or small numbers because it eliminates the need to write in a lot of initial or ending zeros. The decimal point need not be placed between the first and second places as in (1–65); it could be placed anywhere. The following provide numerical examples illustrating (1–65):

$$25 = 2.5 \times 10^1; \quad 0.025 = 2.5 \times 10^{-2}; \quad 25{,}000 = 2.5 \times 10^4;$$
$$0.0000025 = 2.5 \times 10^{-6}; \quad 25{,}000{,}000 = 2.5 \times 10^7 .$$

When writing a specific number, we often write it as 2.5×10^1 rather than $2.5(10)^1$ so that the parentheses are replaced by a multiplication sign $\times$. When writing numbers as large or larger than 10,000, the practice in the U.S. is to insert a comma after every three digits to make the numbers easier to read. This is frequently done also for numbers which range from 1000 to 9999, so that these are written 1,000 and 9,999. In many countries the comma is omitted and a space is inserted instead, so that 10,000 would be written 10 000.

It is not true that every natural number n divides some power of 10. For example, 3 does not divide any power of 10. When n is a natural number which does not divide a power of 10 then it is not possible to convert the rational number p/n to the form $t/10^k$, since if $p/n = t/10^k$, then there exists a natural number r such that $rp = t$ and $rn = 10^k$. How, then, is p/n written in positional form? We shall now study this case.

Since $10p$ is a natural number, using (1–46) we can write

$$\frac{10p}{n} = b_1 + \frac{p_1}{n} . \tag{1–66}$$

Inasmuch as p is less than n, $10p/n$ cannot be as large as 10. Hence b_1 can only have the values $1, \ldots, 9$ if $10p$ is larger than n. Let us agree to set $b_1 = 0$ and $p_1 = 10p$ if $10p$ is less than n. Thus the possible values which b_1 can have are $0, 1, \ldots, 9$, that is, one of the ten digits. On dividing (1–66) by 10 we obtain

$$\frac{p}{n} = b_1(10)^{-1} + \frac{p_1}{n}(10)^{-1} . \tag{1–67}$$

We cannot have $p_1 = 0$ for then $p/n = b_1/10$ which implies that n divides 10. Let us now repeat the above operations replacing p/n by p_1/n. We can write

$$\frac{p_1}{n} = b_2(10)^{-1} + \frac{p_2}{n}(10)^{-1} , \tag{1–68}$$

and b_2 must be one of the ten digits. It cannot be true that $p_2 = 0$, for then $p/n = t/10^2$ and n divides some power of 10. If (1–68) is substituted into (1–67) we obtain

$$\frac{p}{n} = b_1(10)^{-1} + b_2(10)^{-2} + \frac{p_2}{n}(10)^{-2} . \tag{1–69}$$

The procedure can be repeated again with p_2/n yielding a new remainder p_3 which cannot be zero. Indeed, since the remainders are never 0 this procedure can be repeated unendingly and we obtain

$$\frac{p}{n} = b_1(10)^{-1} + b_2(10)^{-2} + b_3(10)^{-3} + \cdots. \tag{1-70}$$

Here we have obtained something interesting. The expression in (1–70) does not terminate. Once again the b's can be used to provide a decimal representation of the rational number p/n, but in this case an infinite number of the b's is needed. We can write the decimal representation of p/n as

$$\frac{p}{n} = 0.b_1b_2b_3\cdots, \tag{1-71}$$

and this is called a *nonterminating decimal*. Let us now illustrate the above procedure with two concrete examples.

EXAMPLE. 1. First we shall determine the decimal representation of $\frac{1}{3}$. Here $p = 1$ and $n = 3$. Now (1–66) becomes

$$\frac{10}{3} = 3 + \frac{1}{3},$$

and on dividing by 10 we see that (1–67) becomes

$$\frac{1}{3} = 3(10)^{-1} + \frac{1}{3}(10)^{-1}. \tag{1-72}$$

Here $p_1 = 1$ also, so that (1–72) also represents (1–68). Thus (1–69) becomes

$$\frac{1}{3} = 3(10)^{-1} + 3(10)^{-2} + \frac{1}{3}(10)^{-2},$$

and $p_2 = 1$ also. Hence we see that the decimal representation of $\frac{1}{3}$ is $0.333\cdots$, an infinite sequence of 3's.

2. Let us next consider the decimal representation of $\frac{1}{11}$. In this case $p = 1$ and $10p = 10$ which is less than 11. Thus we set $b_1 = 0$ and write

$$\frac{1}{11} = 0(10)^{-1} + \frac{10}{11}(10)^{-1}. \tag{1-73}$$

Here $p_1 = 10$. Now $10p_1 = 100$ and

$$\frac{100}{11} = 9 + \frac{1}{11} \quad \text{or} \quad \frac{p_1}{11} = \frac{10}{11} = 9(10)^{-1} + \frac{1}{11}(10)^{-1}. \tag{1-74}$$

If (1–74) is substituted into (1–73) we obtain

$$\frac{1}{11} = 0(10)^{-1} + 9(10)^{-2} + \frac{1}{11}(10)^{-2}. \tag{1-75}$$

But then $p_2 = 1$ and $\frac{1}{11}$ is given by (1–73). However, it thus follows that $p_3 = 10$ and $\frac{10}{11}$ is given by (1–74), etc. Hence

$$\frac{1}{11} = 0(10)^{-1} + 9(10)^{-2} + 0(10)^{-3} + 9(10)^{-4} + 0(10)^{-5} + 9(10)^{-6} + \cdots$$

$$(1\text{–}76)$$

and the decimal representation of $\frac{1}{11}$ is $0.090909090\cdots$, an unending sequence which continually repeats the digits 09.

It is a little disconcerting to find that some rational numbers require an unending sequence of digits for their decimal representation. Let us investigate the nature of these nonterminating decimals in a little more detail. When a rational number is represented by a nonterminating decimal, the sequence of digits in the decimal representation has a very special property known as *periodicity* and the decimal is called *periodic*. We have already noted that $\frac{1}{3} = 0.333\cdots$ and $\frac{1}{11} = 0.0909\cdots$. Similarly, we can readily verify that

$$\frac{1}{6} = 0.1666\cdots; \quad \frac{1}{7} = 0.142857142857\cdots; \quad \frac{1}{13} = 0.076923076923\cdots.$$

The characteristic of each of these decimals is that, after a certain point, a given group of digits is repeated unendingly in a fixed order. For $\frac{1}{7}$ this group is 142857. This is what we mean by saying that the decimal representation is periodic. The expansion need not be strictly periodic, however, for there may first be one or more digits which are not repeated, as in the expansion of $\frac{1}{6}$. For rational numbers, however, there will only be a finite number of digits in the nonperiodic part of the decimal representation.

Let us now prove that if the decimal representation of a rational number is nonterminating then it must be periodic. To see this observe first that $p_1, p_2, \ldots$ are never zero (as we have already noted), and therefore are natural numbers which are less than n. Thus the remainders $p_1, p_2, \ldots$ cannot all be different since there are only $n - 1$ different values which a remainder can have. Consequently, there will be some natural number v which is less than n that appears as a remainder, say $p_s = v$, and after no more than $n - 2$ successive remainders which are different from v, v will again appear as a remainder, $p_{s+u} = v$, where u is not greater than $n - 2$. Thus $p_s = p_{s+u}$ and hence we will obtain the same sequence of b's on expanding p_{s+u}/n as we did on expanding p_s/n, and this set of b's will continually repeat itself. The reader might note that we have also shown that the nonperiodic part of the decimal cannot contain more than $n - 1$ digits, since if it did at least one remainder would have to be repeated and this would then yield part of the periodic sequence. We have therefore shown that any rational number which has a nonterminating decimal representation must have a decimal representation which is periodic. It can also be shown that *any* periodic decimal represents a rational number. We shall prove this later.

It might be noted that we can easily and artificially convert any terminating decimal into a periodic nonterminating decimal simply by annexing a never-ending string of zeros after the final digit. Thus, for example, $0.25 = 0.250000 \cdots$. In this way we can, if we desire, think of all proper fractions as having nonterminating decimal representations. We indicated previously that when a rational number is represented by a terminating decimal then the decimal representation is unique. One would intuitively expect this to be the case for nonterminating decimals as well, and with one exception these decimals are unique also. The exception occurs when we want to write a terminating decimal as a nonterminating one. We have already seen one way to do this, but it is not the only way. There are always precisely two ways in which this can be done. For example, both $0.25000 \cdots$ and $0.24999 \cdots$ represent $1/4$ and $1.000 \cdots$ and $0.9999 \cdots$ both represent the natural number 1. Later we shall prove that these two ways of extending a terminating decimal to a nonterminating one both represent the same number.

There is no problem in giving the decimal representation of a negative number $-m/n$ if we have the decimal representation of m/n. We merely place a minus sign in front. Since the decimal representation of $1/4$ is 0.25, the decimal representation of $-1/4$ is -0.25. The decimal representation of 0 is simply 0. Thus we have seen how it is possible to obtain a decimal representation of any rational number.

1-10 ARITHMETIC OPERATIONS USING DECIMALS

The reader is probably much more familiar with the rules for carrying out addition, subtraction, multiplication and division using the decimal representation of numbers than he is using fractions. Where do the rules learned in arithmetic come from? We shall now see that they follow directly from the meaning of positional notation.

Addition is the easiest case to consider and we shall examine it first. Suppose we wish to add two rational numbers, say 25.46 and 6.185. We know that the sum of two rational numbers is another rational number. What we wish to do is determine the positional representation for this number. By definition

$$25.46 = 2(10)^1 + 5(10)^0 + 4(10)^{-1} + 6(10)^{-2} \qquad (1\text{-}77)$$

and

$$6.185 = 6(10)^0 + 1(10)^{-1} + 8(10)^{-2} + 5(10)^{-3}. \qquad (1\text{-}78)$$

Let us now simply add the right-hand sides of (1–77) and (1–78). According to the associative law we can group the numbers in any way we desire to carry out the addition. Let us do the addition, then, by grouping together the same powers of 10. Using the distributive law (where?) as well, we obtain

$$25.46 + 6.185 = 2(10)^1 + 11(10)^0 + 5(10)^{-1} + 14(10)^{-2} + 5(10)^{-3}.$$
$$(1–79)$$

The coefficients of the right-hand side of (1–79) do not yield the decimal representation of the sum because two powers of 10 have coefficients greater than 9. Now

$$11(10)^0 = 11 = 1(10)^1 + 1(10)^0; \quad 14(10)^{-2} = 1(10)^{-1} + 4(10)^{-2}. \quad (1–80)$$

If we use (1–80) in (1–79) we obtain

$$25.46 + 6.185 = 3(10)^1 + 1(10)^0 + 6(10)^{-1} + 4(10)^{-2} + 5(10)^{-3}.$$
$$(1–81)$$

Because of the uniqueness of the representation of a number in positional form, we see that the coefficients of the powers of 10 in (1–81) provide the decimal representation of the sum of the two given numbers. The sum is 31.645. We can now note that it is unnecessary to introduce explicitly the powers of 10 in order to carry out addition, since all we really did above was to add the corresponding coefficients.

A convenient procedure is to write the two numbers one below the other (by the commutative law it makes no difference which one is on the bottom), aligning the decimal points as shown below. We now merely add the numbers in each column. If the sum in any column is 10 or greater (it cannot be greater than 18) we carry over a 1 to the column corresponding to the next higher power of 10. It is thus convenient to begin with the column at the right and move successively toward the left. In this manner we take account of the carry-overs as we go and automatically generate the decimal representation of the sum. However, this procedure

$$
\begin{array}{r}
25.46 \\
6.185 \\
\text{(carry-overs)} \quad 1\ 1 \\
\hline
31.645
\end{array}
$$

is nothing but an application of the rules learned in elementary arithmetic, and thus we have shown how these rules follow in a natural way from the positional representation. It is easy, of course, to derive in precisely the same way the rules for subtraction, but we shall not consider them in detail here.

Let us next examine multiplication, beginning with the multiplication of natural numbers. Suppose, for example, we wish to multiply 25 by 19. Now

$$25 = 2(10)^1 + 5(10)^0; \qquad 19 = 1(10)^1 + 9(10)^0 .$$

Thus

$$19(25) = [1(10)^1 + 9(10)^0][2(10)^1 + 5(10)^0] . \tag{1-82}$$

We can now apply the distributive and associative laws to write (1-82) as

$$19(25) = 10^1\{1[2(10)^1 + 5(10)^0]\} + 10^0\{9[2(10)^1 + 5(10)^0]\} . \tag{1-83}$$

There are a variety of ways we could proceed from here. One convenient way is to first determine the positional representation for each of the numbers in braces. Thus, using the same procedure introduced in (1-80), we see that

$$
\begin{aligned}
9[2(10)^1 + 5(10)^0] &= 18(10)^1 + 45(10)^0 \\
&= [1(10)^1 + 8(10)^0](10)^1 + [4(10)^1 + 5(10)^0](10)^0 \\
&= 1(10)^2 + 12(10)^1 + 5(10)^0 \\
&= 2(10)^2 + 2(10)^1 + 5(10)^0 \\
&= 225 . \tag{1-84}
\end{aligned}
$$

Similarly

$$1[2(10)^1 + 5(10)^0] = 2(10)^1 + 5(10)^0 = 25 . \tag{1-85}$$

To determine 19(25) we then, according to (1-83), add (1-84) to 10 times (1-85). It is easy to multiply a number in decimal form by a power of 10. As we have noted earlier, to multiply a number by 10^r, we merely move the decimal point r places to the right. Thus $25(10) = 250$ and

$$19(25) = 225 + 250 = 475 .$$

Just as with addition, we can now note that multiplication may be carried out without specifically including the powers of 10. For example, to multiply a_2a_1 by d_2d_1 (these being the decimal representations of the numbers) one first finds the decimal representation of $d_1(a_2a_1)$ and then adds to this 10 times the decimal representation $d_2(a_2a_1)$. To carry out multiplication we must first know how to add decimals. A convenient way to carry out multiplication is to use the format

$$
\begin{array}{r}
25 \\
19 \\
\hline
225 \\
25 \\
\hline
475 .
\end{array}
$$

First the decimal representation of 9(25) is obtained by multiplying 9(5) = 45 and then carrying over the 4 and adding it to 2(9) = 18. Next the decimal representation of 1(25) is obtained and written below 225 but shifted one place to the left to yield 10(25). (The 0 in 250 is not usually written in.) Finally, these two numbers are added to obtain the decimal representation of the product. What we have just described is nothing but an application of the familiar rules learned in arithmetic for multiplication, and we have thus shown that the rules learned in arithmetic follow directly from the positional representation.

Suppose that we next wish to multiply two rational numbers such as 2.5 and 0.19. The trick here is to write $2.5 = 25 \times 10^{-1}$ and $0.19 = 19 \times 10^{-2}$. Then

$$(0.19)(2.5) = 19(25) \times 10^{-3}.$$

We have already seen how to obtain 19(25), which is 475. To obtain the desired product we multiply 475 by 10^{-3}. This is equivalent to moving the decimal point three places to the left and therefore the answer is 0.475. This, of course, is precisely what is done in arithmetic. The method for doing multiplication learned in arithmetic is not the only convenient way to do it. There are a number of other ways that we could have grouped the powers of 10 in (1–83), for the situation here is different than in addition, where there is basically only one convenient format. The reader will recall that three or more numbers can be added directly, that is, without adding two of these and then adding the third number to this sum, etc. However, we never learn in arithmetic how to multiply three or more numbers simultaneously. We always multiply two of them and then multiply this product by the third, and so forth. In actuality, rules for multiplying three or more numbers simultaneously could be derived, but they are so complicated that no one ever bothers.

The last remaining operation is division. The problem of dividing the natural number m by n is precisely the problem of finding the decimal representation of the rational number m/n, and we have already considered this. To divide two rational numbers such as 2.5 by 0.19, we write $2.5 = 25 \times 10^{-1}$ and $0.19 = 19 \times 10^{-2}$. Thus the quotient is $(25/19) \times 10^1$, and we already know how to determine $25/19$. The reader should go back over the rules for finding the decimal representation of m/n to see how the rules for division learned in arithmetic follow from this.

1–11 **APPROXIMATION**

In the previous section we said nothing about carrying out arithmetic operations with numbers which are represented as nonterminating decimals. The reader will recall that this was never discussed in arithmetic. Clearly, one way to proceed would be to operate with the numbers as fractions rather than as decimals, for then the rules developed in Section 1–4 and 1–5 would apply. If the decimal representation of the resulting fraction were desired, it could then be obtained in the manner we have discussed previously. This, though, is not the procedure normally used, because it is more convenient to carry out operations using the decimal representation of numbers. However, it is not possible to work directly with nonterminating decimals in a simple way. In order to proceed, we must introduce the important notion of *approximation*. Nonterminating decimals are approximated by terminating ones, and the computations are then carried out in the manner described in the previous section. The answer obtained in this way will only be an approximation to the correct answer, but the approximation will be sufficient for the intended use. Let us now investigate this process of approximation in a little more detail.

If several people are asked to measure the distance between two points, the answers will all differ to a certain extent, and no one will determine the exact distance. Each measurement is what we refer to as an *approximation* to the actual distance, and each measurement involves some sort of *error*, the error being defined as the difference between the actual distance and value obtained from the measurement process. Qualitatively speaking, the measurement is said to be made accurately if the error (which can also be thought of as a distance) is small compared with the distance being measured. In the real world we must always be willing to accept approximations involving some degree of error, and the main question which arises is how large an error can be tolerated. This, of course, depends on the nature of the application, and we shall not be concerned with this problem here. However, the important thing to observe is that all the numbers which will be used in any problem are in some sense only approximations. Thus, no harm should be done if we introduce some additional approximations in actually carrying out the mathematical operations, provided the errors introduced are small enough that the error in the final answer is within allowable bounds. This, then, is a procedure often followed in mathematics when making numerical computations. In particular, nonterminating decimals are approximated by terminating decimals, and this is the way that nonterminating decimals are handled in making computations. We shall now study how this can be done.

Consider the numbers 0.1, −0.1, 0.01, −0.01, 0.001, −0.001, 0.0001 and −0.0001. Some of these numbers are represented as points on a line in Figure 1–9. Any pair of numbers such as 0.01 and −0.01 are the same distance from the origin. Furthermore, 0.01 is much closer to the origin than 0.1 (it is one-tenth the distance). Thus, if we think of these numbers as representing the error made in approximating some number by another, we

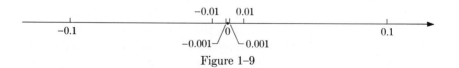

Figure 1–9

see that the approximation gets better and better as the number of zeros following the decimal point increases. Normally, if we locate the point representing the error as shown in Figure 1–9, only the distance of this point from the point representing 0 is important. It does not matter what the sign of the error is, that is, whether the approximate value is too large or too small. The distance from 0 of a point representing some given number is called the *magnitude* of the number. The magnitude of m/n is m/n and the magnitude of $-m/n$ is m/n.

We can now see how to approximate any nonterminating decimal by a terminating one. This can always be done in such a way that the magnitude of the error made in the approximation is as small as desired. As an example, suppose that we wish to approximate $\frac{1}{3}$ and have the magnitude of the error made in the approximation not be greater than 0.001. Recall that $\frac{1}{3} = 0.3333 \cdots$. Now imagine that we approximate $\frac{1}{3}$ by 0.333. Then the error is

$$0.3333 \cdots - 0.333 = 0.000333 \cdots,$$

which is smaller than 0.001. The error would be still smaller if we approximate $\frac{1}{3}$ by 0.3333. However, if we approximate $\frac{1}{3}$ by 0.33, the error is $0.0033 \cdots$, which is larger than 0.001. Thus we could approximate $\frac{1}{3}$ by any one of the terminating decimals 0.333, 0.3333 or 0.33333, and the error would be within the tolerance specified. Note that the approximations are made simply by omitting all digits in the nonterminating decimal expansion which come after a certain number of digits. When we approximate $\frac{1}{3}$ by 0.3333 we say that $\frac{1}{3}$ is being approximated by retaining four places in the decimal expansion of $\frac{1}{3}$. We must retain at least three places to prevent the error from being larger than desired and the minimum number of places required in this case is then three.

It will be observed that less error is made in approximating $\frac{1}{3}$ if we use 0.333 rather than 0.334. This is not always the case, however. If the digit following the last one to be included is greater than 5, then the approximation is improved by adding 1 to the last digit to be retained in the decimal representation of the number. This is often referred to as *rounding up*. Recall that $\frac{1}{7} = 0.1428 \cdots$. Thus if we are to approximate $\frac{1}{7}$ by retaining only three places the magnitude of the error is less if one rounds up and uses 0.143 than if one uses 0.142 (determine the error in each case). When the digit after the last one to be retained is less than 5, then the last digit kept is retained unchanged. This is often referred to as *rounding down*.

1–12 POSITIONAL REPRESENTATION USING BASES DIFFERENT FROM TEN

In the past several sections we have been considering the decimal representation of numbers. The decimal representation uses a base of 10. There is no reason why 10 must be used for a base; indeed, any natural number greater than 1 could be used. Let us now see how to represent natural numbers in terms of any base. Suppose, for example, we use the base 8. When a natural number is divided by 8 the remainder can only have one of the values 0, 1, 2, . . . , 7. These eight symbols are then the only ones needed to represent any natural number. When 8 is the base, the symbols 8 and 9 are not needed. Any natural number m can be written uniquely as

$$m = d_k 8^k + d_{k-1} 8^{k-1} + \cdots + d_0 8^0 \qquad (1\text{--}86)$$

when each of the d's takes on one of the values 0, 1, . . . , 7. The numbers d_0, . . . , d_k are nothing but the remainders on successive divisions by 8, so that d_0 is the remainder on dividing m by 8 and d_1 is the remainder on dividing $(m/8) - d_0$ by 8. Using positional notation we can then omit the powers of 8 and merely write m as $d_k d_{k-1} \cdots d_0$ when it is understood that now the base being used is 8. We then call $d_k d_{k-1} \cdots d_0$ the *octal* representation of m instead of the decimal representation. When using different bases, one must be careful in any particular case to know what base is being used. To avoid confusion we shall place parentheses around nondecimal representations and indicate the base with a subscript. Thus we shall write the octal representation of m as $(d_k d_{k-1} \cdots d_0)_8$.

Given any number in decimal form, say 523, it is easy to obtain its octal representation by successive division by 8. The process terminates when the quotient is less than 8. Thus

$$\frac{523}{8} = 65 + \frac{3}{8} \, ; \qquad \frac{65}{8} = 8 + \frac{1}{8} \, ; \qquad \frac{8}{8} = 1 + \frac{0}{8} \, .$$

Hence $d_0 = 3$, $d_1 = 1$, $d_2 = 0$ and $d_3 = 1$ so $523 = (1013)_8$. Similarly, it is easy to convert any number from its octal representation to decimal form. All we need to do is use (1–86). For example,

$$(1013)_8 = 1(8)^3 + 0(8)^2 + 1(8)^1 + 3(8)^0 = 512 + 0 + 8 + 3 = 523 \, .$$

In the same way it is easy to convert a number from its decimal representation to any other base and vice versa. It is more complicated to convert between two bases both different from 10, for then we must learn the multiplication tables for one of the bases unless we always want to make an intermediate conversion to the decimal representation.

By use of (1–86) we can easily write down the first sixteen numbers in the octal system. They are

$$1, 2, 3, 4, 5, 6, 7, 10, 11, 12, 13, 14, 15, 16, 17, 20 \, .$$

Here we have not bothered with the parentheses and subscript 8 to indicate specifically that the octal representation is implied. By referring to a decimal multiplication table we can easily develop an octal multiplication table. For example, $6(7) = (52)_8$.

When the base 2 is used we refer to the positional representation of a number as the *binary* representation. For this system only the symbols 0 and 1 are needed to represent any number. These are called *bits*. To express 54 in binary form, note that

$$\frac{54}{2} = 27 + \frac{0}{2} \; ; \qquad \frac{27}{2} = 13 + \frac{1}{2} \; ; \qquad \frac{13}{2} = 6 + \frac{1}{2} \; ;$$

$$\frac{6}{2} = 3 + \frac{0}{2} \; ; \qquad \frac{3}{2} = 1 + \frac{1}{2} \; .$$

Thus

$$54 = (110, 110)_2 \; ,$$

and six bits are required to represent this number, whereas only two digits are needed. The binary representation of numbers has become important with the advent of large-scale digital computers, since inside the computer numbers are represented in their binary form.

We can represent proper fractions to any base in precisely the same way as was done for the base 10. Thus, for example, to obtain the octal representation of $\frac{1}{3}$ we note that

$$\frac{8}{3} = 2 + \frac{2}{3} \quad \text{or} \quad \frac{1}{3} = 2(8)^{-1} + \frac{2}{3}(8)^{-1} \; ;$$

$$\frac{2(8)}{3} = 5 + \frac{1}{3} \quad \text{or} \quad \frac{2}{3} = 5(8)^{-1} + \frac{1}{3}(8)^{-1} \; .$$

So

$$\frac{1}{3} = 2(8)^{-1} + 5(8)^{-2} + \frac{1}{3}(8)^{-2} \; ,$$

and the remainder is 1, which takes us back to the beginning. Therefore

$$\frac{1}{3} = (0.252525 \cdots)_8 \; .$$

It is quite possible that a proper fraction will have a nonterminating expansion for one base and a terminating one for another. For example, $\frac{1}{3} = (0.1)_3$.

Once one learns the addition and multiplication tables it is just as easy to carry out the four arithmetic operations using the positional representation of numbers to any base as it is decimal numbers. Let us illustrate using the binary system. Addition and multiplication are extremely easy to carry out in binary since all one needs to remember is $1 + 0 = 1$, $1 + 1 = 10$, $1(1) = 1$, $1(0) = 0$. Consider the addition of 9 and 7 in the binary system. We have

$$
\begin{array}{r}
9: \quad 1001 \\
7: \quad 111 \\
\hline
16 \quad 10000 \,.
\end{array}
$$

Next consider the multiplication of 9 by 7. It becomes

$$
\begin{array}{r}
1001 \\
111 \\
\hline
1001 \\
1001 \\
1001 \\
\hline
111111
\end{array}
$$

and $(111111)_2 = 63$ as desired. To carry out multiplication, only shifting and addition are needed. This is very convenient for a digital computer (which, of course, does not use digits) to carry out multiplication because adding and shifting can easily be done electronically. Division is also relatively easy to carry out in binary but we shall leave this for the reader to study in the problems.

1–13 IRRATIONAL NUMBERS

It will be recalled that any rational number can be represented geometrically as a point on a line in the manner illustrated in Figure 1–7. Suppose now we select, in any way desired, two different points on the line shown in Figure 1–7. Consider that part of the line lying between these two points. We shall call this part of the line an interval and denote it symbolically by L. The interval L may look like that shown in Figure 1–10. Since we

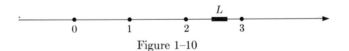

Figure 1–10

began with two different points, we can intuitively think of L as having a length. We shall now prove that, no matter how small the length of L happens to be, the interval L will always contain points corresponding to rational numbers and, in fact, will contain an infinite number of such points.

To show this let us imagine that we have a very accurately calibrated ruler, one fundamental unit in length, which has marked on it the points 10^{-n}, that is, $1, \frac{1}{10}, \frac{1}{100}, \ldots$. Let us now place the end of the ruler at the left-hand end of L and then determine a natural number k (any k) such that the mark on the ruler corresponding to 10^{-k} lies in the interval L. Intuitively, we see that there must exist such a k, although it is not easy to provide a rigorous proof from what we now know. This means that the length of L is greater than 10^{-k} and is therefore greater than 10 times 10^{-k-1}. To be specific, assume that L lies to the right of 0 as shown in Figure 1–10. Consider then the rational numbers of the form $n/10^{k+1}$. There must then be an n such that the points corresponding to $n/10^{k+1}$ and $(n + 1)/10^{k+1}$ lie in L, since the distance between these two points is 10^{-k-1}, which is less than one-tenth the length of L. This shows that there are two points in L which represent rational numbers.

Consider now the interval L_1 which consists of that part of the line lying between the points corresponding to $n/10^{k+1}$ and $(n + 1)/10^{k+1}$. Note that L_1 is contained in L. We shall show that there are an infinite number of points in L_1, and hence in L, which correspond to rational numbers. First, on multiplying and dividing by 10^p where p is any natural number we have

$$\frac{n}{10^{k+1}} = \frac{n(10)^p}{10^{p+k+1}} \; ; \qquad \frac{n + 1}{10^{k+1}} = \frac{n(10)^p + 10^p}{10^{p+k+1}} \; ; \qquad p = 1, 2, 3, \ldots . \quad (1\text{–}87)$$

However, $n(10)^p + 1$ is larger than $n(10)^p$ and smaller than $n(10)^p + 10^p$. Consequently, the point corresponding to the rational number

$$\frac{n(10)^p + 1}{10^{p+k+1}} \tag{1–88}$$

lies between $n/10^{k+1}$ and $(n + 1)/10^{k+1}$ by (1–87) and hence lies in L_1. This is true for every value of p. Furthermore, the numbers (1–88) corresponding to different values of p are different numbers and are thus represented by different points. In fact, the numbers (1–88) get smaller as p gets larger. To see this consider the case where, in (1–88), $p = q$ and where $p = q + r$, r being a natural number. Thus we are considering the numbers

$$\frac{n(10)^q + 1}{10^{q+k+1}} \quad \text{and} \quad \frac{n(10)^{q+r} + 1}{10^{q+r+k+1}} . \tag{1–89}$$

Multiply the numerator and denominator of the first of the numbers in (1–89) by 10^r to yield

$$\frac{n(10)^{q+r} + 10^r}{10^{q+r+k+1}} .$$

Now the denominator is the same as the second number in (1–89) but the numerator is larger. Therefore the first number in (1–89) is larger than the second, and it follows that we obtain a different number (1–88) for each value of p. All of these numbers lie in L_1, and hence in L, so there are an infinite number of different points in L which represent rational numbers. This is true no matter how small the length of L is. To express this property of the rational numbers, mathematicians say that the rational numbers are *everywhere dense*.

The above discussion may quite possibly have led the reader to believe that every point on the line in Figure 1–7 represents a rational number, or equivalently that every length can be represented by a rational number. If this were the case it would be always possible to subdivide an arbitrarily chosen unit of length in such a manner that any given length would be some multiple of a subunit. When thought of in these terms, it does not seem at all obvious that this is possible. The question remains: Are there lengths which are not rational numbers when the fundamental unit is specified? Interestingly enough, there are lengths which cannot be represented by rational numbers. We would still like to think of these lengths as being numbers, and to do so we must introduce some new numbers, which are called *irrational numbers*. The Greeks discovered at a fairly early date (c. 540 B.C.) that not all lengths are rational numbers, and they were astonished and somewhat dismayed by this fact. They discovered it in the following way. Suppose that we have a square field, each side of which is one fundamental unit in length, as shown in Figure 1–11. Now imagine that we wish to meas-

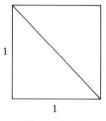

Figure 1–11

ure exactly the length of one of the diagonals of the square. Can we subdivide the fundamental unit into subunits in such a way that the length of the diagonal is an integral number of subunits? The answer is no. The Pythagoreans who made the discovery knew that the square of the length of the diagonal was 2. This was obtained using the so-called Pythagorean theorem, which we shall consider later. If the length of the diagonal is a rational number, say m/n, then the square of this number must be 2. It can be proved that this is impossible.

We shall give the proof contained in Euclid's Elements (c. 300 B.C.). It is a model of mathematical reasoning and introduces a method of proof, called a proof by contradiction, that we have not used previously. The most familiar type of proof is the direct proof. To use a direct proof we begin with what is already known and apply valid mathematical operations and the laws of logic to obtain the desired result. Note that we begin from what is known and proceed to the desired result. We do not begin with the desired result and apply valid operations until some result known to be correct is obtained. This latter procedure does not prove anything, since we could begin with a false result, apply valid operations and obtain a true result. For example, if we begin with $3 = 4$ and multiply both sides of this equation by

0 we obtain $0 = 0$ which is correct. This does not prove, however, that $3 = 4$. A proof by contradiction, which is sometimes also called an indirect proof, proceeds in a different manner from a direct proof. Any mathematical statement, call it A, is either true or false.* To prove that A is true, a proof by contradiction starts off with the statement that A is false. Then valid operations are performed to obtain a result which is known to be false. We then conclude that A cannot be false because that would imply something which is not true. Since A cannot be false, it must be true, and this is what we wanted to show.

Let us now give the proof that the length of the diagonal of the square referred to above is not a rational number. The proof by contradiction starts off by assuming that the length is a rational number. Suppose that this number when written in *least terms* is m/n. We have noted above that the square of the length of the diagonal is 2. Thus if the length of the diagonal is m/n, it must be true that $(m/n)^2 = 2$ or $m^2 = 2n^2$. Since m^2 and n^2 are natural numbers, this equation says that m^2 is divisible by 2. Any natural number which is divisible by 2 is called an *even* number. A natural number having the property that on dividing by 2 there is a remainder of 1 is called an *odd* number. Every natural number is either even or odd since the remainder on dividing by 2 is either 0 or 1. Thus m^2 is even. However, this also implies that m is even, since the square of an odd number is odd (we ask the reader to prove this in the problems). If m is even, there exists a natural number p such that $m = 2p$ or $m^2 = 4p^2$. Hence $4p^2 = 2n^2$ so $n^2 = 2p^2$, and the same reasoning as above shows that n must also be even and thus there exists a natural number q such that $n = 2q$. Therefore m and n have a common factor 2 and m/n is not in least terms. But this contradicts the fact that m/n is in least terms. Since a rational number can always be written in least terms, it cannot be true that the length of the diagonal is a rational number. The proof here is rather subtle, and is quite remarkable when we consider how early it was developed.

The above analysis has led us to the conclusion that we must introduce new numbers which are not rational numbers if all lengths are to be represented by numbers, or equivalently, if every point on the line in Figure 1–7 is to correspond to a number. How do we represent these irrational numbers? We cannot write them in the form m/n since any such number is a rational number; neither can we write them as the quotient of two rational numbers, that is, α/β, because this is a rational number. In fact, all the arithmetic operations applied to rational numbers only give back rational numbers. Next we might ask whether we can obtain a positional decimal representation of irrational numbers just as we did with rational numbers. The answer is yes, but the decimal representation is a complex one. Recall

---

* In actuality, there exist mathematical statements which are neither true nor false, but these are quite unusual and we need not be concerned about them here.

that all terminating and periodic nonterminating decimals correspond to rational numbers. What, then, is left? The only remaining forms are nonterminating, nonperiodic decimals. We know that these do not represent rational numbers, since every rational number has a terminating or a nonterminating periodic representation. Thus the irrational numbers simply correspond to all the nonterminating, nonperiodic decimals. Indeed, the fact that there could exist nonterminating, nonperiodic decimals might have suggested to us that there exist numbers which are not rational. Every irrational number is represented by a nonperiodic, nonterminating decimal and every nonperiodic, nonterminating decimal represents some irrational number.

The collection of all rational and irrational numbers is referred to as the *real number system*. It is the real number system that we shall be using throughout the remainder of this text. The real numbers are closed under the four arithmetic operations (division by 0 being excluded), so that the sum of two real numbers is always a real number, as is the product, quotient or difference. Furthermore, the commutative and associative laws hold for addition, and the commutative, associative and distributive laws hold for multiplication. We have already noted that these properties hold for the rational numbers. They also hold when the irrational numbers are included. We could actually prove these facts, although we shall not attempt to do so. The proofs of the various properties of the real number system are somewhat more complicated than the proofs that we have given up to this point, since the irrational numbers must be included in carrying out these proofs. None of these proofs will be given in this text, since they require a much more detailed development of the irrational numbers.

In the future we shall merely think of any real number as a number, and we shall not need to be concerned with whether the number is rational or irrational. This is possible since the basic laws of operation are the same regardless of whether the numbers are rational or irrational. In making numerical computations, however, we always use rational numbers, for it is not possible to perform the ordinary arithmetic operations with nonperiodic, nonterminating decimals. We use precisely the same sort of approximation procedure as for rational numbers with nonterminating decimal expansions, retaining only a finite number of places in the nonperiodic, nonterminating decimal expansion and thus approximating the irrational number by a rational one.

Since every point on the line in Figure 1–7 corresponds to a real number and vice versa, this is equivalent to saying that every point on the line represents some decimal and that every decimal number is represented by some point on the line. This can be illustrated rather clearly as follows. Suppose we are given a specific point on the line in Figure 1–7. To specify the point we might simply cut the line by drawing a vertical line at the point under consideration, as shown in Figure 1–12a. Let us now see how we could, in

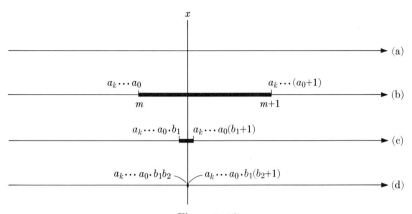

Figure 1–12

principle, directly determine the decimal representation of the number, call it x, represented by the point. To be specific, assume that the point lies to the right of 0. We first determine the natural number m such that the point lies in the interval whose end points correspond to m and $m + 1$, as shown in Figure 1–12b. The decimal representation of m then gives the decimal representation for that part of the number x lying to the left of the decimal point. Suppose that it is $a_k \cdots a_0$. Next let us divide the interval contained between the points representing m and $m + 1$ into ten equal parts or subintervals and determine which of these parts contains x. Suppose that x lies in the subinterval numbered b_1, where b_1 can only assume one of the values $0, 1, \ldots, 9$. This is shown in Figure 1–12c. Then b_1 is the first digit after the decimal point in the decimal representation of x.

Next we divide the interval contained between the points representing $a_k \cdots a_0.b_1$ and $a_k \cdots a_0.(b_1 + 1)$ into ten parts and determine which one contains x. (When we write $b_1 + 1$ we automatically assume that if this is 10 the 1 is carried over.) Suppose that it is the subinterval numbered b_2. Then the value of the second digit after the decimal point for x must be b_2. This is shown in Figure 1–12d. We can imagine that this process is continued indefinitely. At each step the length of the interval containing x is reduced by a factor of 10, and simultaneously one more place in the decimal representation of x is determined. If at any step the point representing x lies precisely at the end point of an interval, then we know that x is a rational number, since we can arrange things so that all remaining digits will be zeros. We can also arrange things so that the remaining digits will always be nines. This leads to a geometric interpretation for the nonuniqueness of the nonterminating decimal representation of rational numbers having terminating decimal representations, which we mentioned earlier. We ask the reader to show in the problems how this is done. If the point representing x never lies at the end of an interval, then we go on forever determining additional places in the decimal representation of x. This shows us that we should be able to obtain a decimal corresponding to any point on the line in Figure 1–7. By simply reversing the process we see that, given any decimal number, there is a unique point on the line in Figure 1–7 determined by this number once the origin and the unit of length are specified.

We have shown previously that the rational numbers are everywhere dense, that is, in any interval no matter how small its length there are an infinite number of points corresponding to rational numbers. Nonetheless, these points do not fill out the line; there are gaps or holes. The points in these gaps or holes represent irrational numbers. We would now like to prove the surprising fact that between any two points representing rational numbers, no matter how close together they are, there are an infinite number of points corresponding to irrational numbers. To see this consider any two rational numbers α and β such that α is smaller than β. Then the proof used at the beginning of the section to show that there were two rational numbers in the interval L also shows there are two rational numbers

$$\alpha_1 = a_r \cdots a_0.b_1 \cdots b_k; \qquad \beta_1 = a_r \cdots a_0.b_1 \cdots (b_k + 1)$$

such that the points representing these numbers lie in the interval whose end points correspond to α and β.

We shall now show that there is an infinite number of points which represent irrational numbers in the interval with end points determined by α_1 and β_1. We can see from the geometrical arguments given earlier in the section that the point corresponding to any number $x = a_r \cdots a_0.b_1 \cdots b_k b_{k+1} \cdots$ lies in the interval whose end points are determined by α_1 and β_1. Now consider the real numbers

$$a_r \cdots a_0.b_1 \cdots b_k 101001000100001 \cdots$$
$$a_r \cdots a_0.b_1 \cdots b_k 1001000100001 \cdots$$
$$a_r \cdots a_0.b_1 \cdots b_k 1000100001000001 \cdots$$
$$\cdot$$
$$\cdot$$
$$\cdot$$

which are irrational since they are nonterminating, nonperiodic decimals. There are an infinite number of these, and the points representing them all lie in the interval whose end points are determined by the numbers α_1 and β_1, and hence in the interval whose end points are determined by the numbers α and β. Thus there are an infinite number of irrational numbers between any two rationals. This is something which is not too easy to grasp intuitively. However, given that it is true, we can then say that most real numbers are irrational.

In this section we have seen that the rational numbers must be extended to include irrational numbers if all lengths are to be treated as numbers. Irrational numbers behave when performing arithmetic operations in the same way as rational numbers. Unfortunately, however, the decimal representation of irrational numbers is a complicated one, because they correspond to nonterminating, nonperiodic decimals. Hence no one has ever seen an irrational number written in detail, since an infinite number of places would be required. After the above analysis, the reader may still be concerned as to whether irrational numbers actually exist in the physical world. This depends, of course, on what we think the physical world is like. Current thinking among physicists is that neither matter nor time can be subdivided into arbitrarily small units; instead there are certain indivisible building blocks and the best that can be done is to count these. Thus it may not be true that irrational numbers actually exist in nature, and in a sense the German mathematician Kronecker may have been correct when he said, "The dear Lord made the whole numbers; everything else is man-made." Nonetheless, it is very convenient to make use of the irrational numbers even if they are merely the creation of mathematicians.

1–14 INEQUALITIES

Recall that a rational number of the form m/n is called positive while one of the form $-m/n$ is called negative. In Figure 1–7, the points corresponding to positive rational numbers lie to the right of 0 while those corresponding to the negative rational numbers lie to the left of 0. Similarly, we call an irrational number positive if the point corresponding to it lies to the right of 0, and negative if the point lies to the left of 0. The decimal representation of a negative irrational number will have a minus sign in front of it. The same laws of signs which apply for operating with rational numbers also apply for any real numbers, so that, for example, the product of two negative irrational numbers is positive. This, of course, could be proved but we shall not attempt to do so.

   In the past we have frequently used the notion of one number being greater than another without explicitly defining what this meant. We relied on the reader's intuitive understanding of this concept. What do we mean when we say that the real number x is greater than the real number y? We mean that there exists a positive real number, call it h, such that $x = y + h$. Thus 6 is greater than 4 since $6 = 4 + 2$, and $h = 2$ in this case. Also 6 is greater than -6 since $6 = -6 + 12$, and $h = 12$ here. In mathematics a special symbol $>$ called an *inequality sign* is used to indicate greater than. The symbol $>$ is sometimes referred to as a greater than sign. If x is greater than y we then write $x > y$. Another way of saying that x is greater than y is to say that y is less than x. A special symbol $<$, also called an inequality sign, is used to indicate less than. The symbol $<$ is sometimes referred to as a less than sign. Thus if x is greater than y or equivalently y is less than x we can write $y < x$. Note that $x > y$ and $y < x$ mean precisely the same thing. The real numbers have the property of being *ordered*. By this we mean that, given any two real numbers x and y, one and only one of the following relations holds: $x = y$, $x > y$, or $x < y$. Hence the numbers are equal or one of them is greater than the other. This characteristic of the real numbers will no doubt seem intuitively obvious to the reader. It can, of course, be proved, but we shall not attempt to do so. We can now use $>$ and $<$ signs to provide a convenient notational characterization of positive and negative numbers. If a number x is positive, this is equivalent to saying $x > 0$, that is, x is greater than 0. If x is positive, then $x = 0 + x$ and we can use x for h, thus implying that $x > 0$. On the other hand, if $x > 0$, then $x = 0 + h = h$ where h is positive, and thus x is positive. Similarly, saying x is negative is equivalent to writing $x < 0$.

Expressions such as $x > y$ or $x < y$ are called *inequalities*. Inequalities will appear frequently in our later work and we would now like to obtain some simple properties of the $>$ operation. To do so, however, we must first make explicit some of the properties of the equality sign $=$. We have used the $=$ sign frequently in the past without giving any detailed discussion of it. What do we mean when we write something like $x = y$? What we mean is that x and y are the same number, even though they may be written in different ways. Thus we can write $\frac{3}{2} = 1.5$, since $\frac{3}{2}$ and 1.5 are merely different ways of writing the same rational number. It therefore follows that if $x = y$, then in any expression where x appears it can be replaced by y without changing the value of the expression. This is a very useful rule to remember. Some frequently used properties of the $=$ sign which follow immediately by applying this replacement rule are:

(1) If $x = y$ and $y = z$ then $x = z$.   (1–90)
(2) If $x = y$ then $x + c = y + c$ for any number c.   (1–91)
(3) If $x = y$ then $xc = yc$ and $cx = cy$ for any number c.   (1–92)

The first of these (1–90) is usually referred to as the *transitive* property of equality. The second says that we can add an arbitrary number c to both sides of an equality without changing the equality, and the third says that we can multiply both sides of an equality by an arbitrary number c and still have an equality. Two properties of equality which we did not mention above, and which the reader will no doubt feel are completely obvious are: $x = x$ for any number x, and if $x = y$ then $y = x$. The first of these is sometimes referred to as the *reflexive* property of equality and second as the *symmetric* property. When x and y are not the same number, this can be indicated by writing $x \neq y$; the sign $\neq$ is called the not-equal sign. We shall occasionally use it in the future. If $x \neq y$, then $x > y$ or $x < y$.

We would now like to write down and prove the properties for inequalities corresponding to (1–90), (1–91) and (1–92) for equality. These are:

(1) If $x > y$ and $y > z$ then $x > z$.   (1–93)
(2) If $x > y$ then $x + c > y + c$ for any number c.   (1–94)
(3) If $x > y$ and $c > 0$ then $xc > yc$.   (1–95)
(4) If $x > y$ and $c < 0$ then $xc < yc$.   (1–96)

There is an exact correspondence between equations (1–90), (1–91) and (1–92) and equations (1–93), (1–94) and (1–95). Equation (1–96) is a little different. It says that if an inequality is multiplied by a negative number, the "direction" of the inequality is changed. However, from (1–95) it is seen that if an inequality is multiplied by a positive number the direction of the inequality is unchanged.

Let us now see how to prove the above. Consider (1–93) first. Since $x > y$ there exists an $h > 0$ such that $x = y + h$, and since $y > z$ there exists a $g > 0$ such that $y = z + g$. On substituting $z + g$ for y in $x = y + h$ we obtain $x = z + g + h$. The sum of two positive numbers is positive, and hence $g + h > 0$, so that $x > z$, which is what we desired to show. Consider next (1–94). Inasmuch as $x > y$ there exists an $h > 0$ such that $x = y + h$. Then by (1–91) $x + c = y + h + c$, and by the commutative law $x + c = y + c + h$. Therefore, $x + c > y + c$, since $h > 0$, which is what we wished to show. Now consider (1–95) and (1–96). Once again $x > y$ implies there is an $h > 0$ such that $x = y + h$. By (1–92) it follows that for any c, $xc = (y + h)c$, or by the distributive law $xc = yc + hc$. If $c > 0$, then $hc > 0$, since the product of two positive numbers is positive. In this case $xc > yc$ which is (1–95). If $c < 0$ then $hc < 0$, since the product of a positive and negative number is negative. Then we can write $xc = yc + hc$ as $yc = xc - hc$ or $yc = xc + (-1)hc$ and $(-1)hc > 0$. Hence $yc > xc$ or $xc < yc$, which is (1–96).

The definition of $x > y$ can be used to answer many questions concerning inequalities. For example, if $x > y$ and neither x nor y is 0, what can be said about the relation between $1/x$ and $1/y$? Let us show how this can be answered. By assumption, $x = y + h$, $h > 0$. On dividing by xy we obtain

$$\frac{1}{y} = \frac{1}{x} + \frac{h}{xy}. \tag{1–97}$$

If x and y have the same sign, $xy > 0$ and $h/xy > 0$ so $1/y > 1/x$. If x and y have opposite signs $h/xy < 0$ and $1/x > 1/y$. Thus the relation between $1/x$ and $1/y$ depends on the signs of x and y. As numerical examples, $-5 > -6$ and $-1/6 > -1/5$; $6 > 5$ and $1/5 > 1/6$; $5 > -1$ and $1/5 > -1$.

In the future we shall frequently find it convenient to use the notation $x \geq y$. This is read x is greater than or equal to y, and it implies that $x > y$ or $x = y$ (note that both of these cannot hold). Thus $x \geq 0$ means that x is greater than or equal to 0, and when $x \geq 0$ we say that x is non-negative. The notation $x \leq y$, which is also useful, means that x is less than or equal to y.

In the past we have often written a chain of equalities such as $x = y = z$. This means $x = y$, $y = z$ and by the transitivity property $x = z$. One can similarly employ chains of inequalities such as $x < y < z$. This is equivalent to writing $x < y$, $y < z$ and $x < z$. Very often when we write $x < y < z$ we shall interpret this as meaning that the number y lies between x and z, if we think of the numbers as being represented by points on a line. We can also write expressions such as $x < y \leq z$ or $x \leq y \leq z$. The first of these means $x < y$, $y \leq z$ and $x < z$. The second is equivalent to $x \leq y$, $y \leq z$ and $x \leq z$.

1–15 ROOTS AND RATIONAL EXPONENTS

In Section 1–7 we introduced the notion of powers of rational numbers and extended the idea to the point where α^k was given a meaning for any integer k when α was different from 0. We can, of course, make the same definitions for all the real numbers rather than merely the rational numbers, so that if x is a real number, x^k has precisely the same meaning as α^k when x is different from 0. The laws for exponents derived in Section 1–7 hold for any real numbers, not merely rational numbers, and the identical proofs used for rational numbers serve for any real numbers as well. In this section we would like to generalize the notion of exponents to the point where we can give meaning to an exponent which is an arbitrary rational number. To do this we must begin by considering a new type of operation, which we shall refer to as the operation of *taking roots*.

We introduced irrational numbers by asking whether there exists a rational number whose square is 2. This suggests a general type of operation that it may be of interest to study. Suppose that we have a positive real number x and we would like to find a number y whose square is x, that is, $y^2 = x$. Does there exist such a real number y? The answer is always yes when $x > 0$. How can we prove this? We shall prove it by showing how y can be determined numerically. The procedure is as follows. First find the unique non-negative integer k (k is 0 or a natural number) such that $k^2 \leq x$ and $(k + 1)^2 > x$. Let the decimal representation of k be $a_r \cdots a_0$. Then $a_r \cdots a_0$ is that part of the decimal representation of y to the left of the decimal point. Next determine the unique digit, call it b_1, such that $(a_r \cdots a_0.b_1)^2 \leq x$ and $(a_r \cdots a_0.(b_1 + 1))^2 > x$. Then b_1 is the digit in the first place after the decimal point in the decimal representation of y. Now determine the unique digit, call it b_2, such that $(a_r \cdots a_0.b_1b_2)^2 \leq x$ and $(a_r \cdots a_0.b_1(b_2 + 1))^2 > x$. It is then true that b_2 is the digit in the second place after the decimal point in the decimal representation of y. This process is continued, and at each step one more place in the decimal representation of y is determined. If at any stage we have $(a_r \cdots a_0.b_1 \cdots b_u)^2 = x$, we have determined a rational number whose square is x. Otherwise, the process never terminates and we progressively determine either an irrational number or a rational number with a nonterminating decimal expansion whose square is x.

If we follow the procedure just outlined to determine a number whose square is 2, we find that $1^2 = 1$ and $2^2 = 4$ so $k = 1$. Then $(1.4)^2 = 1.96$ and $(1.5)^2 = 2.25$ so $b_1 = 4$. Next $(1.41)^2 = 1.9881$ and $(1.42)^2 = 2.0164$ so $b_2 = 1$. Then $(1.414)^2 = 1.999396$ and $(1.415)^2 = 2.002225$ and thus $b_3 = 4$. We know that the process will never terminate since the number being determined is irrational. To three places after the decimal point the number is 1.414. In the numerical example just given the reader may wonder how we decided to use 4 as the first digit after the decimal and have things work out so that $(1.4)^2 < 2$ and $(1.5)^2 > 2$. The straightforward way to do this is merely to compute $(1.1)^2$, $(1.2)^2$, $(1.3)^2$, $(1.4)^2$, $(1.5)^2$, etc. and see where the change occurs from being less than or equal to 2 to being greater than 2.

Let us next explain why the procedure just described generates a number y whose square is x. The process is such that

$$(a_r \cdots a_0.b_1 \cdots b_u)^2 \leq x < (a_r \cdots a_0.b_1 \cdots (b_u + 1))^2 \qquad (1\text{–}98)$$

for every u. Now

$$a_r \cdots a_0.b_1 \cdots (b_u + 1) = a_r \cdots a_0.b_1 \cdots b_u + 10^{-u}. \qquad (1\text{–}99)$$

Then by the distributive and associative laws

$$
\begin{aligned}
(a_r \cdots a_0.b_1 &\cdots (b_u + 1))^2 \\
&= [a_r \cdots a_0.b_1 \cdots b_u + 10^{-u}][a_r \cdots a_0.b_1 \cdots b_u + 10^{-u}] \\
&= (a_r \cdots a_0.b_1 \cdots b_u)[a_r \cdots a_0.b_1 \cdots b_u + 10^{-u}] \\
&\quad + 10^{-u}[a_r \cdots a_0.b_1 \cdots b_u + 10^{-u}] \\
&= (a_r \cdots a_0.b_1 \cdots b_u)^2 + 2(a_r \cdots a_0.b_1 \cdots b_u)10^{-u} + 10^{-2u}.
\end{aligned}
\qquad (1\text{–}100)
$$

Consider now the interval of the line in Figure 1–7 whose end points are determined by $(a_r \cdots a_0.b_1 \cdots b_u)^2$ and $(a_r \cdots a_0.b_1 \cdots (b_u + 1))^2$. This interval contains the point corresponding to x, and from $(1\text{–}100)$ the length of the interval is

$$2(a_r \cdots a_0.b_1 \cdots b_u)10^{-u} + 10^{-2u}. \qquad (1\text{–}101)$$

The length of this interval decreases by a factor of about 10 each time u is increased by 1. Therefore, at each step in the above process the length of the interval containing x is reduced by a factor of 10 and the difference

$$x - (a_r \cdots a_0.b_1 \cdots b_u)^2 \qquad (1\text{--}102)$$

is less than (1–101), which gets closer and closer to 0 as u is increased. In finding a y such that $y^2 = 2$, the lengths of the intervals at each step are respectively 3, 0.29, 0.0283, 0.002829, and these do decrease by about a factor of 10 at each step.

The number y whose square is x is called the *square root* of x. The notation used for the square root is

$$y = x^{1/2} \quad \text{or} \quad y = \sqrt{x}. \qquad (1\text{--}103)$$

We shall see that the use of a fractional exponent in $x^{1/2}$ is a very appropriate notation; $x^{1/2}$ is read x to the one half.

The procedure used above to find a number whose square is a positive number x can also be used to construct a number whose third power (also called the cube) or fourth power, etc., is x. A number y such that $y^n = x$ where n is a natural number greater than or equal to 2 is called an *nth root* of x. Such a number $y > 0$ always exists when $x > 0$, and we use the following notation to denote the nth root:

$$y = x^{1/n} \quad \text{or } y = \sqrt[n]{x}. \qquad (1\text{--}104)$$

The number y determined by the computational method developed previously is always positive, and there is only one positive real number y such that $y^n = x$. Does it follow that y is the only real number such that $y^n = x$? We shall now see that this depends on whether n is even or odd (see p. 47 for the definition of even and odd natural numbers). Recall that the product of two negative numbers is positive. Thus if $y^2 = x$ then $(-y)^2 = (-1)^2 y^2 = y^2 = x$ also. Therefore, for any $x > 0$ there are two real numbers, one positive and one negative, whose square is x. This is also true whenever n is even, since if n is even we can write $n = 2m$ and if $y^n = x$ then $(-y)^n = [(-1)^2]^m y^n = y^n = x$. Hence if n is even, there are two real numbers, one positive and one negative, whose nth power is x. For example, $3^2 = 9$ and $(-3)^2 = 9$. Also $2^4 = 16$ and $(-2)^4 = 16$. If n is odd, however, there is only one real number, which is positive, whose nth power is x, since -1 raised to an odd power is negative, and hence $(-y)^n = -x$ and not x. For example, $2^3 = 8$ but $(-2)^3 = -8$. Since when n is even there are two real numbers y and $-y$ whose nth power is x if $x > 0$, we must be careful, because of this nonuniqueness, in working with roots. By convention $\sqrt[n]{x}$ and $x^{1/n}$ will be taken to mean the same thing, and will *always* be assumed to be the positive nth root of x. When n is even, $-x^{1/n}$ is also an nth root of x.

In the above we were careful to consider only numbers $x > 0$. Let us now suppose that $x < 0$. Can we still find a number y such that $y^2 = x$? A difficulty is encountered here. The square of any number which is different from 0 is positive, and $0^2 = 0$. Thus there does not exist any real number whose square is a negative number, that is, there is no real number which is the square root of a negative number. If we wished to have the square root of a negative number be a number, we would have to extend the real number system to include some new numbers. This can indeed be done, and the new numbers are called, due to historical accident, *imaginary numbers*, although there is nothing imaginary about them. The combined system of real and imaginary numbers is called the *complex number system*. The system of complex numbers is very important for many applications, but in this text we shall deal only with real numbers.

The same reasoning which showed that there is no real number y such that $y^2 = x$ when $x < 0$ also shows that there is no real number y such that $y^n = x$ when $x < 0$ and n is even. Thus there does not exist any nth root of a negative number when n is even. The situation is different, however, when n is odd. In this case there is a unique negative number whose nth power is x when x is negative. In fact, we see immediately that if $y = (-x)^{1/n}$, $-x > 0$, then $-y$ is an nth root of x, that is, $(-y)^n = x$. For example $27^{1/3} = 3$, that is, $3^3 = 27$. Also $(-3)^3 = -27$. We have now considered cases where $x > 0$ and where $x < 0$. The only possibility not yet examined is that where $x = 0$. Note that $0^n = 0$. Thus 0 is an nth root of 0 and is, in fact, the only number whose nth power is 0.

Our above discussion has shown that taking the nth root of a number is not as well behaved as the other arithmetic operations we have studied. There may be two different nth roots or there may not be any, depending on the sign of x and on whether n is even or odd. Thus we must be very careful in working with roots. We shall now proceed to use the notion of a root to generalize the definition of an exponent to include any rational number. In the following *we shall make the very important restriction that the numbers being raised to a power are always positive.* We do this because we shall be taking nth roots of the numbers and these roots would not exist if the numbers were negative and n was even. To avoid always having to be concerned with the sign of the numbers and with whether n is odd or even, we shall simply require that the numbers be positive. The odd or even problem with n still remains, because if n is even there exist two different nth roots while if n is odd there is only one. *To eliminate the nonuniqueness we shall deal only with the positive nth roots of the numbers involved,* and in accordance with the notation introduced previously, we shall denote the positive nth root of any positive number x by $x^{1/n}$.

To begin let us show that if $x_1, \ldots, x_k$ are k positive numbers then

$$(x_1 x_2 \cdots x_k)^{1/n} = x_1^{1/n} x_2^{1/n} \cdots x_k^{1/n} \tag{1–105}$$

so that the nth root of a product is the product of the nth roots. To prove (1–105), let $y_1 = x_1^{1/n}, \ldots, y_k = x_k^{1/n}$ and $z = (x_1 \cdots x_k)^{1/n}$. Then $y_1^n = x_1, \ldots, y_k^n = x_k$ and $z^n = x_1 \cdots x_k$. Thus

$$y_1{}^n y_2{}^n \cdots y_k{}^n = z^n = x_1 \cdots x_k \, , \qquad (1\text{–}106)$$

or by the properties of integral exponents

$$(y_1 y_2 \cdots y_k)^n = z^n \, . \qquad (1\text{–}107)$$

Now there is only one positive number whose nth power is $x_1 \cdots x_k$. Thus $y_1 y_2 \cdots y_k = z$, which is (1–105).

Consider now x^m where m is a natural number. By (1–105), taking $x_1 = x$, $\cdots$, $x_k = x$, and $k = m$, we see that

$$(x^m)^{1/n} = x^{1/n} \cdots x^{1/n} = (x^{1/n})^m, \quad x > 0 \, . \qquad (1\text{–}108)$$

Thus $(x^m)^{1/m}$ and $(x^{1/n})^m$ are the same number. In words, the nth root of the mth power of x is the same as the mth power of the nth root of x. Because of (1–108), we can next introduce a new symbolism $x^{m/n}$ by using the definition

$$x^{m/n} = (x^m)^{1/n} = (x^{1/n})^m \, . \qquad (1\text{–}109)$$

We can interpret $x^{m/n}$ to be x raised to a power which is a rational number. In this way we can generalize our concepts of the power of a positive number to cases where the exponent can be any positive rational number. In particular, $x^{1/n}$ can be looked upon as x raised to the $1/n$ power. Thus we have now given meaning to expressions such as $(1.3256)^{4.789}$. What does this mean? It means the 1000th root of 1.3256 raised to the 4789 power, or the 4789 power of the 1000th root of 1.3256. Originally, our notion of a power was a very simple one; x^n meant $x \cdots x$, x appearing n times. We now have introduced a much more complicated notion of a power; $x^{1.25}$ does not mean x multiplied by itself 1.25 times (this has no meaning). Instead $x^{1.25}$ is the 100th root of x raised to the 125 power—a rather complicated idea.

Let us now show that the use of the notation $x^{m/n}$ leads to results which are consistent with interpreting the exponent as a rational number. Since $n/n = 1$, it should be true that $x^{n/n} = (x^{1/n})^n = x$. This is indeed true since, by definition, the nth power of $x^{1/n}$ is x. It should also be true that for any natural number p

$$x^{m/n} = x^{mp/np} \qquad (1\text{–}110)$$

since m/n and mp/np are the same rational number. This is true, but to prove it we must first develop some additional results.

Consider $(x^{1/n})^{1/m}$. Write

$$y = x^{1/n}; \qquad z = y^{1/m} = (x^{1/n})^{1/m} \, . \qquad (1\text{–}111)$$

Then $x = y^n$ and $y = z^m$, so $x = (z^m)^n = z^{mn}$. Therefore $z = x^{1/mn}$, so by (1–111), $(x^{1/n})^{1/m} = x^{1/mn}$. In precisely the same way we can show that $(x^{1/m})^{1/n} = x^{1/mn}$. Hence we have proved that

$$(x^{1/n})^{1/m} = (x^{1/m})^{1/n} = x^{1/mn}, \qquad x > 0. \tag{1-112}$$

Consider now $x^{mp/nq}$ where m, n, p and q are natural numbers. Then we shall show that

$$x^{mp/nq} = (x^{m/n})^{p/q} = (x^{p/q})^{m/n}, \qquad x > 0. \tag{1-113}$$

Define

$$z = (x^{m/n})^{p/q}; \qquad y = x^{m/n}. \tag{1-114}$$

Then $z = y^{p/q} = (y^p)^{1/q}$ so $z^q = y^p$. Now

$$y^p = (x^{m/n})^p = (x^{1/n})^{mp} = (x^{mp})^{1/n}, \tag{1-115}$$

so

$$z^q = (x^{mp})^{1/n}.$$

Thus by the definition of the nth root

$$(z^q)^n = z^{nq} = x^{mp}. \tag{1-116}$$

But this means that z is the nqth root of x^{mp}, that is, $z = x^{mp/nq}$. From the definition of z in (1–114), the first equation of (1–113) follows. The second follows in precisely the same way.

From (1–113), we can immediately verify the correctness of (1–110), since from (1–113)

$$x^{mp/np} = (x^{m/n})^{p/p}. \tag{1-117}$$

However, we have shown that $y^{p/p} = y$. Thus (1–110) follows from (1–117).

The notion of a rational exponent can now be generalized easily from the case where an exponent is a positive rational number to that where it is any rational number. This is done in the same way that exponents were generalized from natural numbers to being any integer. We have previously defined $\alpha^0 = 1$ for any rational number α. We shall now extend this and define $x^0 = 1$ for any real number x. Furthermore, by $x^{-m/n}$ we shall mean $1/x^{m/n}$, $x > 0$. With these definitions, x^α, $x > 0$, now has meaning to us for any rational number α. Precisely the same laws of exponents hold when the exponents are rational numbers that apply when the exponents are integers. In particular

$$x^{\alpha\beta} = (x^\alpha)^\beta = (x^\beta)^\alpha, \quad x > 0, \tag{1-118}$$

and

$$x^{\alpha+\beta} = x^\alpha x^\beta, \quad x > 0. \tag{1-119}$$

For example, (1–118) implies that $(2.15)^{1.36} = (2.15^{1.7})^{0.8}$, and (1–119) implies that $(5.4)^{2.3} = (5.4)^{3.4}(5.4)^{-1.1}$. These are proved by considering all the cases involved. We have proved (1–118) for $\alpha > 0$ and $\beta > 0$ in obtaining (1–113). Let us now prove (1–119) for $\alpha > 0$, $\beta > 0$, say $\alpha = m/n$ and $\beta = p/q$. Then (1–119) reads

$$x^{(mq+np)/nq} = x^{m/n}x^{p/q} . \tag{1–120}$$

Write

$$u = x^{m/n} = (x^m)^{1/n}; \qquad v = x^{p/q} = (x^p)^{1/q} . \tag{1–121}$$

Then $u^n = x^m$ and $v^q = x^p$ and

$$(u^n)^q = u^{nq} = x^{mq}; \qquad (v^q)^n = v^{nq} = x^{np} , \tag{1–122}$$

so

$$(uv)^{nq} = x^{mq+np}$$

or

$$uv = x^{m/n}x^{p/q} = x^{(mq+np)/nq} ,$$

which is what we wished to show. To complete the proof of (1–118) and (1–119) cases where one or both of α and β are negative or 0 must be considered. We shall ask the reader to do this in the problems.

How is x^α computed numerically, given α and x? From what we now know it would first be necessary to express α in the form m/n, 0 or $-m/n$. If $\alpha = 0$, $x^\alpha = 1$. If $\alpha = m/n$ we must compute $(x^{1/n})^m$. To compute $x^{1/n}$ the procedure introduced at the beginning of the section would be used. If $\alpha = -m/n$, we compute $1/(x^{1/n})^m$. This computational procedure is exceedingly clumsy, because it may well involve taking roots where n is large. The procedure introduced at the beginning of the section is a very inefficient procedure for doing this. After computing $x^{1/n}$, however, it may be necessary to raise this number to a very high power m, which is also cumbersome to do. Later we shall develop much more efficient methods for evaluating x^α numerically. It is also possible to generalize the meaning of exponents to include irrational numbers. The procedure for doing this, however, is not so obvious and, in fact, it cannot be done until we have covered the material in the next several chapters.

1–16 SIMPLE ALGEBRAIC MANIPULATIONS WITH REAL NUMBERS

The sum, difference, product or quotient (division by 0 being excluded) of any two real numbers is another real number. Consequently, any expression involving only the four arithmetic operations or raising a positive number to a rational power must be a real number. Such expressions may look very complicated, but with sufficient computation, it can be determined to whatever accuracy is desired the real numbers they represent. When such expressions involve only specific numbers they are referred to as *arithmetic expressions*. When one or more symbols appear instead of specific numbers, the expressions are called *algebraic expressions*. Thus

$$\frac{(3.124)^{2.15}\sqrt{2}}{\frac{2}{3}\left[1.421\left(\frac{6}{0.0037}\right)\right]}\;;\qquad \frac{3}{7}\left[\frac{1}{1+\dfrac{4}{16+\dfrac{3}{1+\sqrt{3}}}}\right]$$

are arithmetic expressions, while

$$x^2 + 2;\qquad \frac{x^2 + y^2}{xy + z + \dfrac{2}{x - y}}\;;\qquad \frac{x^2 + 3y^2 + 24}{17x - 3y + 61}$$

are algebraic expressions. Often it is desirable to convert an algebraic expression from one form to another without changing its value and without substituting specific numbers for the symbols which appear. This is referred to as *algebraic manipulation*, and it can be carried out in a straightforward way using the commutative and associative laws for addition, and the commutative, associative and distributive laws for multiplication. The branch of mathematics known as algebra is basically devoted to a study of algebraic manipulation. Algebra differs from arithmetic in that arithmetic deals only with specific numbers and not with expressions involving symbols. In this chapter we have been concerned with both arithmetic and algebra. We have already gained quite a bit of familiarity with the way one does algebraic manipulation, especially in our derivations of the laws of exponents.

The following are some standard algebraic manipulations which we frequently have occasion to use. The reader is asked to derive these in the problems.

(1) $x = x + y - y = (x + y) - y.$ \hfill (1–123)

(2) $(x_1 + \cdots + x_m)(y_1 + \cdots + y_n)$

$$\begin{aligned}
&= x_1(y_1 + \cdots + y_n) + \cdots + x_m(y_1 + \cdots + y_n)\\
&= y_1(x_1 + \cdots + x_m) + \cdots + y_n(x_1 + \cdots + x_m)\\
&= x_1 y_1 + \cdots + x_1 y_n + \cdots + x_m y_n \,.
\end{aligned}$$ \hfill (1–124)

(3) $(x + y)^2 = x^2 + 2xy + y^2.$ \hfill (1–125)

(4) $(x - y)^2 = x^2 - 2xy + y^2\,.$ \hfill (1–126)

(5) $(x + y)(x - y) = x^2 - y^2\,.$ \hfill (1–127)

(6) $x/y = xz/yz,\quad y \neq 0, z \neq 0\,.$ \hfill (1–128)

(7) $x = 1/(1/x), \quad x \neq 0.$ (1–129)

(8) $x/x = 1, \quad x \neq 0$. (1–130)

(9) $(xy)/z = y(x/z), \quad z \neq 0$. (1–131)

(10) $x = -(-x)$. (1–132)

(11) $-x/y = x/-y, \quad y \neq 0$. (1–133)

When two expressions are connected by an equals sign, the result is called, as we have explained earlier, an *equation*. The above equations are frequently used in performing algebraic manipulations. The following provide some additional simple examples of algebraic manipulations.

EXAMPLES. 1. $\dfrac{x^2 - y^2}{(x + y)^2} = \dfrac{(x - y)(x + y)}{(x + y)(x + y)} = \dfrac{x - y}{x + y}, \quad x + y \neq 0$.

2. $x^2 - 6x + 6 = x^2 - 6x + 9 - 9 + 6 = (x - 3)^2 - 3$.

The process we have just illustrated is referred to as "completing the square."

3. $(x + y)^2 - (x - y)^2 = x^2 + 2xy + y^2 - x^2 + 2xy - y^2 = 4xy.$

4. $\dfrac{1}{x + y - \dfrac{1}{x - y}} = \dfrac{x - y}{(x - y)\left[x + y - \dfrac{1}{x - y}\right]} = \dfrac{x - y}{x^2 - y^2 - 1}$,

$$x - y \neq 0, \quad x^2 - y^2 - 1 \neq 0 .$$

5. $\dfrac{1}{x} + \dfrac{1}{y} + \dfrac{1}{z} = \dfrac{y + x}{xy} + \dfrac{1}{z} = \dfrac{yz + xz + xy}{xyz}, \quad x \neq 0, \quad y \neq 0, \quad z \neq 0$.

By making transformations similar to those just illustrated, it is sometimes possible to reduce rather complex looking expressions to a much simpler form.

We shall use frequently equations involving symbols such as those we have written above. It is desirable to examine in a bit more detail precisely what such an equation may mean. For example, when in (1–125) we write

$$(x + y)^2 = x^2 + 2xy + y^2 , \qquad (1\text{–}134)$$

what does this mean? It means that $(x + y)^2$ and $x^2 + 2xy + y^2$ are the same number. However, here we encounter a problem which does not appear when specific numbers are used rather than symbols, because there now arises the question as to what numbers the symbols in (1–134) represent. The characteristic of (1–134) is that $(x + y)^2$ and $x^2 + 2xy + y^2$ are the same number regardless of what real numbers we imagine x and y to represent. In other words, if we replace x by any real number and y by any real number, then (1–134) holds. Equation (1–134) is what is referred to as an *identity*. It is true regardless of what numbers we substitute for x and y.

Not all the equations involving symbols which shall be of interest to us will be identities, however. Consider the equation

$$y^2 + x^2 = 2 - x . \qquad (1\text{–}135)$$

It is not true here that, if we select an arbitrary real number y and an arbitrary real number x and compute $y^2 + x^2$ and $2 - x$, we obtain the same number. For example, if $y = 2$ and $x = 3$, $y^2 + x^2 = 13$ and $2 - x = -1$. Clearly, $13 \neq -1$. What does (1–135) mean then? In general, when we write an equation involving one or more symbols, we shall not necessarily imply that it holds for all possible values of these symbols. Thus when we write an equation involving two symbols, say x and y, we will usually mean that there will be a certain collection of pairs of values of x and y, say $(x_1, y_1), (x_2, y_2), \cdots$, such that, for example, if x is replaced by the number x_1 and y by the number y_1 we do indeed obtain an equality. However, the equation will only be valid for these special pairs of numbers. The set of pairs of numbers, the first representing a value of x and the second a value of y, for which the equation holds is called the *truth set* for the equation. Similarly, if we write an equation involving just a single symbol, such as

$$x^3 + 27x^2 - 36x = 14 , \qquad (1\text{–}136)$$

it will not in general be true that $x^3 + 27x^2 - 36x$ is 14 if we replace x by an arbitrary real number. The set of numbers $x_1, x_2, \cdots$, having the characteristic that if x is replaced by one of these numbers then $x^3 + 27x^2 - 36x$ is 14, we again call the truth set for the equation. An important problem in algebra is that of finding the truth set for any given equation. When we write an equation involving one or more symbols and we do not have in mind a specific value for the symbols, but instead imagine that they can take on any values in their truth sets, then it is typical to refer to the symbols as *variables*. Thus x and y in (1–134) and (1–135) and x in (1–136) would be referred to as variables in the equation. The values which the variable or variables in an equation can take on if the equation is to be true is simply the truth set for the equation.

We can now see that an identity such as (1–134) is nothing but an equation whose truth set consists of all pairs of real numbers. In this sense, then, there is no difference between an identity and any other equation. For this reason, mathematicians do not often make any special effort to distinguish between identities and equations which are not identities. A special sign $\equiv$ exists in mathematics to be used in place of $=$ to represent an identity.

Although it might improve the clarity of presentation significantly to always use a ≡ sign when it is appropriate, this is seldom done. Instead, the equals sign is almost always used and the reader must determine from the content whether or not the equation is an identity. We shall follow the standard practice in this text and almost always use the equals sign only.

REFERENCES

1. Albert, A. A., *College Algebra*. McGraw-Hill, New York, 1946.

2. Bell, E. T., *Men of Mathematics*. Simon & Schuster, New York, 1937.
An interesting and easy-to-read book devoted to the lives and works of a number of great mathematicians.

3. Courant, R. and H. Robbins, *What Is Mathematics?* Oxford University Press, New York, 1941.
A very interesting book which surveys many areas of mathematics and contains much material not normally found in textbooks. It is a good elementary discussion of the real number system. Although written for persons with little mathematical background, it is really quite advanced.

4. Dantzig, T., *Number—The Language of Science*. Doubleday Anchor Books, Garden City, New York, 1954.
A popular book for many years, now available in paperback form. It deals with the development of the number concept through the ages.

5. Hogben, L., *Mathematics in the Making*. Doubleday, Garden City, New York, 1960.
A book somewhat similar in purpose to Dantzig's above. This work is well illustrated and contains many full color photographs and drawings.

6. Labarre, A. E. Jr., *Elementary Mathematical Analysis*. Addison-Wesley, Reading, Mass., 1961.

7. Landau, E., *Foundations of Analysis*. Chelsea, New York, 1961.
A rigorous and abstract axiomatic development of the real number system.

8. Newman, J. R. ed., *The World of Mathematics*, 4 vols., Simon & Schuster, New York, 1954.
A four-volume work about mathematics and mathematicians intended for the layman. It consists of many articles written by a variety of individuals, including some things written by great mathematicians themselves. This work has received a rather wide distribution through book clubs, and the reader will probably find some of the material in it interesting. The articles "Counting" by L. Conant and "From Numbers to Numerals and from Numerals to Computation" by Smith and Ginsburg are recommended.

9. Niven, I., *Numbers: Rational and Irrational*. Random House, New York, 1961.

10. Smith, D. E., *History of Mathematics*, Vol. II. Dover, New York, 1958.
A work tracing the historical development of the number system. The current edition is a paperback reprint of a two-volume work published many years ago. Although this was for many years a standard reference on the history of mathematics, it is a somewhat dull and confusing book to read.

PROBLEMS

Section 1–2

1. Construct an addition table which can be used to read off the sum of any two natural numbers each of which can have any value 1, 2, ... , 10. Assume that the familiar notation (1–1) is used for the natural numbers. Determine the sum of any two numbers by counting, using the method introduced in Figure 1–1.

2. Construct an addition table which can be used to read off the sum of any two natural numbers each of which can have any value 1, ... , 5. Assume that the natural numbers are to be represented using the Egyptian symbols given in Table 1–1. Determine the sum of any two numbers by counting, using the method introduced in Figure 1–1.

3. Re-solve Problem 3 using the Mayan symbols rather than Egyptian.

4. Re-solve Problem 3 using the Greek symbols rather than the Egyptian.

5. By counting and using a diagram like that in Figure 1–1, verify that $7 + 8$ and $8 + 7$ are the same natural number.

6. Construct a multiplication table which can be used to read the product of any two of the first five natural numbers. Construct the table by reducing each multiplication to a counting problem as in Figure 1–2.

7. Construct a multiplication table which can be used to read the product of any two of the first three natural numbers. Use the Egyptian symbols given in Table 1–1 for these numbers, and construct the table by counting using the Egyptian symbols.

8. Re-solve Problem 7 using the Mayan symbols.

9. Construct a suitable figure and use counting to show that

$$(6 + 4)(3) = (6)(3) + (4)(3) .$$

10. If you knew that (1–5) and (1–7) held for all natural numbers, could you show from these two equations that

$$(m + n)q = mq + nq$$

for all natural numbers m, n and q?

11. If you knew that (1–7) held for all natural numbers, could you show that

$$q(m + n + p) = qm + qn + qp$$

for all natural numbers m, n, p and q?

Section 1–3

1. Discuss the relation between the rational number concept and the division of units into smaller units, such as feet into inches and quarts into pints.

2. Why does it make sense to write $2\frac{3}{16} = \frac{35}{16}$, and to write $\frac{35}{16} = \frac{70}{32}$?

3. What dictated the need, even in early times, to adopt some standard units of measure, thus simultaneously requiring the introduction of rational numbers?

4. Draw a straight line. Select a unit of length and an origin from which measurements are to be made. Then locate the points on the line which represent the following numbers: $5/2$, $1/4$, $23/8$, $5/3$, $6/1$, $11/4$ and $36/7$.

5. Go through the details of the reasoning which suggests that $16/3$ is the number which should be multiplied by 3 to yield 16.

6. Express each of the following numbers in the form (1–8): $120/6$, $11/3$, $20/4$, $17/11$, $46/19$.

7. Write each of the following in least terms: $32/16$, $14/7$, $96/24$, $2/8$, $25/175$, $4/7$.

8. A natural number n is said to be a prime number if its only divisors are 1 and n, that is, if 1 and n are the only two values for the natural number m which make n/m a natural number. Determine the first ten prime numbers.

Section 1–4

1. Make up a different example from that given in the text to illustrate how addition of rational numbers could have originated naturally in early times.

2. Add each of the following pairs of rational numbers and express the sum in least terms.

(a) $\dfrac{3}{2}, \dfrac{2}{5}$; (b) $\dfrac{17}{4}, \dfrac{2}{16}$; (c) $\dfrac{5}{11}, \dfrac{2}{12}$; (d) $\dfrac{21}{2}, \dfrac{32}{5}$; (e) $\dfrac{14}{2}, \dfrac{11}{6}$.

3. If it is given that addition and multiplication of natural numbers is commutative, show from the definition (1–9) that addition of rational numbers is therefore commutative also. Hint: What does (1–9) become for $(p/q) + (m/n)$?

4. Derive a formula similar to (1–9) for adding together three rational numbers. Obtain this formula by using (1–9) twice, that is, first two of the numbers are added together and then the third one is added to this. In this way add together the following sets of three rational numbers.

(a) $\dfrac{1}{2}, \dfrac{4}{7}, \dfrac{6}{3}$; (b) $\dfrac{5}{11}, \dfrac{4}{5}, \dfrac{3}{7}$; (c) $\dfrac{1}{8}, \dfrac{2}{5}, \dfrac{3}{1}$.

5. Use the results obtained in Problem 4 to show that addition of rational numbers is associative if the natural numbers obey certain laws. What laws must the natural numbers obey if addition of rational numbers is to be associative?

6. Devise an example different from that given in the text which suggests that multiplication of rational numbers should be defined as in (1–10).

7. Multiply together the following pairs of rational numbers and express the results in least terms.

(a) $\dfrac{4}{3}, \dfrac{1}{2}$; (b) $\dfrac{1}{3}, \dfrac{5}{8}$; (c) $\dfrac{4}{11}, \dfrac{7}{9}$; (d) $5, \dfrac{6}{7}$; (e) $\dfrac{8}{13}, \dfrac{13}{8}$.

8. Use the definition (1–10) to show that, if multiplication of natural numbers is commutative, so is multiplication of rational numbers.

9. Use (1–10) twice to derive a formula for multiplying together three rational numbers. Multiply the given three numbers in each of the following cases.

(a) $\dfrac{5}{7}, \dfrac{2}{3}, \dfrac{6}{11}$; (b) $\dfrac{4}{5}, \dfrac{1}{2}, \dfrac{5}{7}$; (c) $\dfrac{6}{1}, \dfrac{3}{8}, \dfrac{2}{17}$.

10. Use the results of Problem 9 to show that, if multiplication of natural numbers is associative, so is multiplication of rational numbers.

11. Check numerically the correctness of the distributive law for

$$\frac{11}{12}\left(5 + \frac{4}{7}\right) = \frac{11}{12}(5) + \frac{11}{12}\left(\frac{4}{7}\right).$$

12. Given that multiplication of rational numbers is commutative and that the distributive law holds in the form $\alpha(\beta + \gamma) = \alpha\beta + \alpha\gamma$, show that it is also true that $(\beta + \gamma)\alpha = \beta\alpha + \gamma\alpha$.

13. Given that the distributive law and the associative law for addition hold for rational numbers, show that

$$\alpha(\beta + \gamma + \delta) = \alpha\beta + \alpha\gamma + \alpha\delta .$$

14. Make up a practical example which would suggest that division of rational numbers should be carried out as in (1–11).

15. Show that to divide the rational number β by the rational number α, one simply multiplies β by $1/\alpha$.

16. If a rational number is written as a natural number plus a proper fraction, this is referred to as the mixed form for writing the number. Show that it is clumsy to multiply rational numbers in mixed form. Obtain a rule for doing so by applying the distributive law twice to $(n + \alpha)(m + \beta)$. Use this result to multiply $4\frac{1}{3}$ by $2\frac{3}{7}$.

Section 1–5

1. Can you suggest any practical problems that would have led the ancients to introduce the equivalent of negative numbers?

2. Draw a straight line, select an origin and unit of length, and then locate the points representing the numbers $-1, -\frac{1}{4}, -\frac{3}{2}, -1\frac{1}{5}, -\frac{6}{1}$ and $-1\frac{7}{17}$.

3. Determine by counting, using a figure like Figure 1–8, the following natural numbers.

(a) $11 - 4$; (b) $17 - 13$; (c) $8 - 6$; (d) $7 - 1$; (e) $15 - 6$.

4. Show that the definition of $m - n = q$ is such that $m = q + n$. Illustrate with each of the numerical cases in Problem 3.

5. Determine the sum of each of the following pairs of rational numbers. Explain the reasoning used for computing the sum in each case.

(a) $\dfrac{11}{16}, -\dfrac{5}{4}$; (b) $\dfrac{5}{3}, -\dfrac{4}{7}$; (c) $\dfrac{1}{5}, -\dfrac{4}{11}$; (d) $4\dfrac{1}{3}, -5\dfrac{7}{8}$.

6. Determine the products of the following rational numbers.

(a) $\dfrac{5}{6}$, $-\dfrac{3}{2}$; (b) $-\dfrac{2}{5}$, $-\dfrac{1}{3}$; (c) $-\dfrac{6}{7}$, $\dfrac{4}{5}$; (d) $-\dfrac{11}{15}$, $-\dfrac{4}{7}$.

7. Divide the first of each of the following pairs of numbers by the second.

(a) $-\dfrac{5}{9}$, $\dfrac{4}{3}$; (b) $\dfrac{6}{13}$, $-\dfrac{5}{7}$; (c) $-\dfrac{5}{3}$, $-\dfrac{6}{7}$; (d) $-\dfrac{1}{2}$, $-\dfrac{2}{1}$.

8. Use the definition of subtraction (1–24) for any two rational numbers to derive the rule for subtracting a larger natural from a smaller one. Use this to determine

(a) $7 - 11$; (b) $5 - 16$; (c) $13 - 21$; (d) $1 - 4$; (e) $5 - 6$.

9. Show that (1–24) implies that $\alpha - \alpha = 0$. Show also that (1–24) implies that if $\alpha - \beta = \gamma$ then $\alpha = \beta + \gamma$.

10. Determine the following differences and give the justification for each operation performed.

(a) $\dfrac{5}{7} - \dfrac{14}{3}$; (b) $-\dfrac{6}{5} - \dfrac{2}{9}$; (c) $\dfrac{7}{11} - \left(-\dfrac{5}{12}\right)$; (d) $-\dfrac{6}{17} - \left(-\dfrac{3}{4}\right)$.

11. Does the operation of subtraction obey the associative and commutative laws? Provide the justification for whatever statements you make and give examples.

Section 1–6

In Problems 1 through 4, reduce the expression to a rational number of the form m/n, 0, $-m/n$. Give the justification for each operation performed.

1. $$\dfrac{\dfrac{3}{2}\left[\left(-\dfrac{4}{3}\right)\left(1 - \dfrac{6}{5}\right) + \dfrac{7}{11}\right]}{2\left[\dfrac{1}{8/5} - \dfrac{2}{1 - (13/6)}\right]}.$$

2. $$\cfrac{1}{4 - \cfrac{1}{2 - \cfrac{1}{1 - \cfrac{1}{6}}}}.$$

3. $$\dfrac{\dfrac{21}{6}\left\{ \dfrac{\left(-\dfrac{7}{11}\right)\left(3 + \dfrac{1}{11}\right)}{4 - 7\left(\dfrac{6}{12}\right)\left(\dfrac{1}{4}\right)} \right\}}{\dfrac{5}{4}\left(\dfrac{3}{2}\right)\left(-\dfrac{1}{9}\right)\left[2 + \dfrac{4}{13}\right]}.$$

4. $$\cfrac{1}{\dfrac{2}{3} + \dfrac{6}{7}\left(3 - \dfrac{1}{(5/12) - (16/3)}\right)}.$$

5. Show by inserting enclosures in various ways that the following expression is ambiguous and can be interpreted in several different ways:

$$\dfrac{3/2 - 2/4 - 1}{3 + 2/3 - 1 + 1/4}.$$

Section 1–7

1. Construct numerical examples different from those in the text to illustrate (1–29), (1–31) and (1–33). Also develop (1–35) through (1–37) in detail.

2. Show by numerical examples that the following are not true in general.
(a) $\alpha^m + \alpha^n = \alpha^{m+n}$; (b) $\alpha^m \alpha^n = \alpha^{mn}$; (c) $(\alpha\beta)^{mn} = \alpha^m \beta^n$;
(d) $(\alpha + \beta)^n = \alpha^n + \beta^n$; (e) $(\alpha^m)^{n+q} = \alpha^{mn} + \alpha^{nq}$.

In Problems 3 through 6, show that the given expressions hold in general.

3. $(\alpha\beta)^{mn} = (\alpha^m \beta^m)^n$;   **4.** $\alpha^m \alpha^n \alpha^q = (\alpha^{m+n})\alpha^q = \alpha^{m+n+q}$;

5. $(\alpha^m)^{n+q} = \alpha^{mn}\alpha^{mq} = (\alpha^n \alpha^q)^m$;   **6.** $[(\alpha^m)^n]^q = \alpha^{mnq}$.

7. Verify (1–42) for all cases not considered in the text.

8. Verify (1–43) for all cases not considered in the text.

9. Show by direct computation that

(a) $\dfrac{4^3}{4^7} = 4^{-4}$;   (b) $\dfrac{7^4}{7^2} = 7^2$.

10. Show that if α and γ are different from 0, then

$$\frac{\alpha^3 \beta^6}{\gamma^9} = \left(\frac{\gamma^{-3}\beta^2}{\alpha^{-1}}\right)^3.$$

11. Make up numerical examples to illustrate (1–35), (1–36), (1–37), (1–38) and (1–39).

12. Show that $\alpha^m + \alpha^{m+n} = \alpha^m(1 + \alpha^n)$.

13. Show by direct calculation that $2^8 = [(2^{-2})^{-2}]^2$.

14. In Problem 8 for Section 1–3, we defined what was meant by a prime natural number. Show that if m is any natural number, then m can be written in the form $m = p_1^{n_1} p_2^{n_2} \cdots p_r^{n_r}$, where $p_1, p_2, \cdots, p_r$ are prime natural numbers and $n_1, n_2, \cdots, n_r$ are natural numbers. This is referred to as the prime factorization of m. Write the numbers 6, 8, 12, 15, 18, 21, 30 and 45 in this form. Hint: If q divides m to yield a natural number h, then $m = qh$.

Section 1–8

1. Write each of the following numbers in the form (1–44).
(a) 452; (b) 61; (c) 7; (d) 18; (e) 999; (f) 1000; (g) 1001;
(h) 0; (i) 1; (j) 201; (k) 2001; (l) 20001.

2. Use repeated division to write 769 in the form (1–44).

3. Show that, if the coefficients a_i in (1–44) are not restricted to being 0 or one of the first nine natural numbers, then (1–44) is not unique, that is, there are many ways in which m can be written in the form (1–44).

4. Show that if m is divisible by 10, then in (1–54), $a_0 = 0$.

5. Show that in using a positional notation there is no compelling reason that the digits must be written side by side as in 450. The digits could be written one on top of the other. As a matter of fact, the Mayan Indians used a positional notation and this is the way they did things.

Section 1–9

1. Write each of the following rational numbers in decimal form.

(a) $\dfrac{1}{4}$; (b) $\dfrac{3}{5}$; (c) $\dfrac{17}{25}$; (d) $\dfrac{11}{40}$; (e) $\dfrac{37}{50}$; (f) $\dfrac{14}{250}$.

2. Write each of the following rational numbers in decimal form.

(a) $\dfrac{17}{4}$; (b) $\dfrac{21}{5}$; (c) $-\dfrac{11}{2}$; (d) $\dfrac{465}{50}$; (e) $\dfrac{831}{200}$.

3. Write each of the following decimals as a rational number.
(a) 0.421; (b) 0.0016; (c) 3.041; (d) 16.234; (e) 0.000100101.

4. Write each of the following numbers in the form $u \times 10^k$, where $1 \le u < 10$ and k is an integer.
(a) 0.0135; (b) 0.2056; (c) 3125.6; (d) 38207; (e) 41.625.

5. Write each of the following numbers in the form $u \times 10^k$, where $10 \le u < 100$ and k is an integer.
(a) 4719; (b) 0.000631; (c) 0.0806; (d) 3416.2; (e) 17.4.

6. Write each of the following numbers in the form $u \times 10^k$, where $0.1 \le u < 1$.
(a) 82.6; (b) 0.871; (c) 0.000062; (d) 971; (e) 1143.2.

In Problems 7 through 13 obtain the decimal representation of the given rational number.

7. $\frac{1}{15}$; 8. $\frac{1}{17}$; 9. $\frac{2}{7}$; 10. $\frac{16}{7}$; 11. $\frac{5}{3}$; 12. $\frac{2}{9}$; 13. $\frac{3}{11}$.

14. Show that the decimal representation of $\frac{1}{3}$ is the same as that of $\frac{2}{6}$, as would be expected. Try to show that, in general, the decimal representation of m/n is the same as that of pm/pn.

Section 1–10

1. Add 248 and 2999 writing the numbers in the form (1–44). Add the numbers so that the sum is generated in the form (1–44). Show how the associative and distributive laws are used, and also show how the carrying operation arises naturally.

2. Re-solve Problem 1 using the numbers 14.67 and 532.9.

3. Add together the numbers 1035, 967 and 3120 writing the numbers in the form (1–44). Add the numbers so that the sum is generated in the form (1–44). Show how the carrying operation arises naturally.

4. Derive the rules for subtracting numbers when they are written in decimal form.

5. Multiply together the numbers 261 and 1302 in the form (1–44), and show how the familiar rules for multiplying these numbers follow.

6. Re-solve Problem 5 using the numbers 13.65 and 4.21.

7. What difficulties are encountered if we attempt to obtain rules for multiplying three numbers simultaneously?

8. From the procedure developed for obtaining the decimal representation of m/n, derive the rules learned in arithmetic for dividing two natural numbers. Note that multiplying the remainder by 10 corresponds to bringing down a zero.

9. Can the division procedure be interpreted in terms of successive subtractions? Explain.

Section 1–11

1. Give the magnitude of each of the following numbers.
(a) 1.65; (b) -4.32; (c) -0.61; (d) 0.003; (e) 0; (f) -0.0135.

2. Determine the best approximation to $\frac{1}{9}$ which uses: (a) two places, (b) three places and (c) four places after the decimal point.

3. Determine the best approximation to $\frac{1}{13}$ which uses: (a) two places, (b) three places and (c) four places after the decimal point.

4. Re-solve Problem 3 using the number $\frac{7}{15}$.

5. Re-solve Problem 3 using the number $11\frac{1}{7}$.

6. Suppose that the number α is approximated by α_1 and that the error is e_1. Suppose also that the number β is approximated by β_1 and that the error is e_2. What is the error if $\alpha\beta$ is approximated by $\alpha_1\beta_1$? What is the error if $\alpha + \beta$ is approximated by $\alpha_1 + \beta_1$?

7. Suppose that $\frac{1}{13}$ is approximated by 0.0769 and $\frac{1}{3}$ by 0.3333. Determine the error made in computing $(\frac{1}{3})(\frac{1}{13})$ when the approximate rather than the actual values are used.

Section 1–12

1. Determine the octal (base 8) representation of each of the following numbers.
(a) 452; (b) 61; (c) 7; (d) 18; (e) 64.

2. Determine the septimal (base 7) representation of each of the numbers given in Problem 1.

3. Determine the binary (base 2) representation of each of the numbers given in Problem 1.

4. Write down the first 25 natural numbers using a septimal representation.

5. Write down the first 25 natural numbers using a binary representation.

6. Give the decimal representation for each of the following numbers.
(a) $(45)_8$; (b) $(16)_8$; (c) $(100)_8$; (d) $(6)_8$; (e) $(1126)_8$.

7. Give the decimal representation for each of the following numbers.
(a) $(11)_2$; (b) $(1011)_2$; (c) $(110110)_2$; (d) $(1111111)_2$.

8. Give the decimal representation for each of the following numbers.
(a) $(16)_7$; (b) $(521)_7$; (c) $(10)_7$; (d) $(666)_7$; (e) $(400)_7$.

9. To write a number using the duodecimal representation (base 12), it is necessary to introduce two new symbols, one to represent 10 and the other 11. Denote 10 by Δ and 11 by ∇. Give the duodecimal representation of the numbers in Problem 1.

10. Give the duodecimal representation of the following numbers, using the symbols introduced in Problem 9.

(a) 9;   (b) 10;   (c) 11;   (d) 131;   (e) 142;   (f) 1450.

11. Give the decimal representation of the following numbers.

(a) $(\Delta 2)_{12}$;   (b) $(\nabla\nabla)_{12}$;   (c) $(\nabla 0\Delta)_{12}$;   (d) $(\Delta 5\nabla)_{12}$.

12. Determine the octal representation of each of the following.

(a) $\dfrac{1}{4}$;   (b) $\dfrac{2}{5}$;   (c) $\dfrac{1}{7}$;   (d) $\dfrac{4}{11}$.

13. Determine the septimal representation for each of the numbers in Problem 12.

14. Determine the binary representation for each of the numbers in Problem 12.

15. Determine the duodecimal representation for each number in Problem 12.

16. Write the following in the form m/n.

(a) $(2.611)_8$;   (b) $(0.00761)_8$;   (c) $(\Delta\nabla.\Delta\Delta\Delta)_{12}$;   (d) $(0.26)_7$;
(e) $(0.4421)_5$.   (f) $(0.\nabla 0\Delta 0\nabla)_{12}$;

17. Develop an addition table which can be used to read off the sum of any two of the first ten natural numbers when the numbers and the sum are represented in octal form.

18. Re-solve Problem 17 for the septimal representation.

19. Re-solve Problem 17 for the binary representation.

20. Re-solve Problem 17 for the duodecimal representation.

21. Develop a multiplication table which can be used to read off the product of any two of the first ten natural numbers when the numbers and product are represented in octal form.

22. Re-solve Problem 21 for the septimal representation.

23. Re-solve Problem 21 for the binary representation.

24. Re-solve Problem 21 for the duodecimal representation.

25. Add together the following numbers: $(111)_2$, $(10110)_2$, $(100100)_2$ and $(111111)_2$.

26. Multiply $(101101)_2$ by $(11100110)_2$.

27. Divide $(1110010110)_2$ by $(101101)_2$.

28. Make use of the results of Problem 17 to add the following numbers: $(764)_8$, $(5321)_8$ and $(67)_8$.

29. Make use of the results of Problem 21 to multiply $(523.1)_8$ by $(777)_8$.

30. Divide $(432)_8$ by $(71)_8$.

31. Make use of the results of Problem 20 to add the following numbers: $(\nabla\Delta\nabla)_{12}$, $(9\nabla 01\Delta)_{12}$ and $(890\nabla)_{12}$.

32. Is it possible to use any rational number greater than 1 as a base for the number system? If the answer is yes, explain how, and if no, explain why not.

Section 1–13

1. Determine five different rational numbers such that the points representing these lie in the interval whose end points are the points representing 1.576 and 1.577.

2. Determine the first ten numbers (1–88) for the case where $n = 2$ and $k = 3$.

3. Prove that if m is even then $m - 1$ and $m + 1$ are odd, and if m is odd then $m - 1$ and $m + 1$ are even. Thus, if m is even, its successor is odd, and if m is odd, its successor is even, so that the natural numbers are alternatively even and odd. Thus, show that 2, 4, 6, ... are the even natural numbers and 1, 3, 5, 7, ... are the odd natural numbers.

4. Show that if m is an even natural number, then there exists a natural number p such that $m = 2p$. Show also that any natural number $2p$ is even if p is a natural number. Similarly, show that if m is an odd natural number, then there exists an integer k which is 0 or a natural number such that $m = 2k + 1$. Show that any natural number $2k + 1$ is odd when k is defined as above.

5. Use the results of Problem 4 to show that the square of an even number is even and the square of an odd number is odd.

6. Use the results of Problem 4 to show that the sum of two even or two odd numbers is even, while the sum of an even and an odd number is odd.

7. Use the results of Problem 4 to show that the product of an even number and an odd number is an even number.

Section 1–14

1. Prove that if $a = b$ and $c = d$, then $a - c = b - d$.

2. Prove that if $a = b$ and $c = d$, then $ac = bd$.

3. Prove that if $x > y > 0$ and $a > b > 0$, then $ax > by$.

4. If $x > y$ and $a > b$, what can be said about the relation between ax and by?

5. If $x > y$ and $a > b$, what can be said about the relation between x/a and y/b if $a \neq 0$ and $b \neq 0$?

6. If $a > b$, what can be said about the relation between a^2 and b^2?

7. If $x > 1$, prove that $x^2 > 1$, and $x^2 > x$.

8. If $0 < x < 1$, prove that $x^2 < 1$ and $x^2 < x$.

9. If $x > y$ and $a > b$, prove that $x + a > y + b$.

Section 1–15

In Problems 1 through 5 determine $a^{1/2}$ to three decimal places when a is the number given.

1. 3; **2.** 5; **3.** 7; **4.** 2.2; **5.** 5.7.

In Problems 6 through 10 determine $a^{1/3}$ to two decimal places when a is the number given.

6. 5; **7.** 7; **8.** 13; **9.** 17; **10.** 21.

11. Prove that there cannot be two different positive real numbers whose square is a given number a.

12. Prove (1–118) for all cases not considered in the text.

13. Prove (1–119) for all cases not considered in the text.

14. Show that if $y \neq 0$, $(x/y)^\alpha = x^\alpha/y^\alpha$.

Section 1–16

1. Prove (1–123) and (1–124).

2. Prove (1–125) through (1–127).

3. Prove (1–128) through (1–133).

4. Complete the square in:
(a) $x^2 - 3x$;   (b) $2x^2 + 3x - 1$;   (c) $x^2 - 5x + 16$.

Functions and Relations

2–1 **SETS**

Two of the most important concepts in mathematics are those of "numbers" and "functions." In Chapter 1 an attempt was made to develop the idea of numbers; this chapter will be devoted to studying functions and associated concepts. The definition of a function can be divorced completely from any connection with numbers, but numbers frequently play a basic role in the definition of functions. The most general definition of a function requires the use of some very simple ideas from a subject known as set theory, which was introduced and developed at the end of the nineteenth century by the German mathematician Georg Cantor. We shall begin by examining the material needed, and as we progress, we shall find more and more use for set-theory concepts.

The reader will recall that we used the words set and collection many times in the previous chapter without attempting any definition of these words. There exist certain concepts in mathematics, such as points in geometry, which cannot be defined in terms of other concepts, and the notion of a set is one of these. The notion of a *set of elements* or a *collection of objects* is so basic that it is not possible to define it in terms of more fundamental ideas. The objects or elements which form a particular set of interest can, in general, be anything at all. They may, for example, be people, automobiles, ideas, apples or numbers. The thing which distinguishes the elements of a particular set from everything else in the universe is some special property or properties which the elements of the set possess. The property may be nothing more than that the elements are specified as belonging to the set, but often the property is something more fundamental which really serves to define the set. For example, a particular set of interest might be the set of all human males in the United States of age 45 or older. The characteristics which distinguish the elements of this set from everything else are: (1) they must be human and male; (2) they must be in the United States and (3) they must be 45 years of age or older. These characteristics then serve as a test to determine whether a given element is a member of the set or not.

On the other hand, if we consider the set consisting of the number 117, the Milky Way and the ocean liner United States, the elements of this set do not seem to have any special properties in common except that we have arbitrarily specified that they are elements of a particular set. Nonetheless, the set consisting of these three elements is a legitimate set. Other examples of sets are: (1) the set of all natural numbers less than 50; (2) the set of all real numbers; (3) the set of all family names in a telephone book. It should be clear that the notion of a set of elements is a very general concept indeed.

We have previously used symbols to represent numbers; it is also convenient to represent sets by symbols. Usually, we shall employ the convention that upper-case italic letters such as A or B will be used to denote sets. The symbols used to represent the elements of a set will merely be the standard symbols which we normally use to represent such elements, perhaps a or b, for example, if the elements are numbers. To indicate that an element a belongs to the set A we use the notation $a \in A$. If b is not an element of A we write $b \notin A$. A set may contain either a finite or an infinite number of elements. If the set has a finite number of elements, and we wish to exhibit these explicitly, we enclose them in braces. For example, if A is the set containing the first five natural numbers, we can write

$$A = \{1, 2, 3, 4, 5\} .$$

If A is the set consisting of n elements $a_1, \ldots, a_n$, we can write

$$A = \{a_1, \ldots, a_n\} \quad \text{or} \quad A = \{a_i, i = 1, \ldots, n\} . \tag{2-1}$$

The notation introduced in the equation on the right in (2–1) is often useful. We use a symbol for the subscript rather than a specific number, and then indicate what values this subscript can take on. Thus the set containing the four elements a_1, a_2, a_3 and a_4 we could write as $A = \{a_1, a_2, a_3, a_4\}$ or $A = \{a_i, i = 1, \ldots, 4\}$.

Frequently it is inconvenient or impossible to list explicitly the elements in a set. We must then have some other way of characterizing them, and this is done by stating the properties possessed by the elements of the set. Consider the set, call it X, of elements x having the property or properties which we shall represent symbolically by $\mathcal{P}(x)$. We shall then describe X symbolically by writing

$$X = \{x | \mathcal{P}(x)\} . \tag{2-2}$$

$\mathcal{P}(x)$ will be a declarative statement of some sort which may be simple or complex, and X is the set of elements for which $\mathcal{P}(x)$ is true. For example, $\mathcal{P}(x)$ may be the statement that "x is a person living in the Waldorf Towers on Park Avenue in New York City." Then X is the set of people who live in the Waldorf Towers on Park Avenue in New York City. As another example, $\mathcal{P}(x)$ might be the statement "x is a natural number greater than 100 but less than 1000". Then X is the set of natural numbers $101, \ldots, 999$. For cases of interest to us the statements $\mathcal{P}(x)$ will often be conveniently expressible in mathematical form. Thus the statement that x is a real number greater than the positive square root of two becomes $x > 2^{1/2}$ when it is understood that x is to be a real number. This set can be conveniently characterized by writing $X = \{x | x > 2^{1/2}\}$.

At the end of the last chapter we introduced the notion of truth sets for equations. We can now use the notation just developed to represent such sets. The truth set for (1–136) is the set of numbers x having the property that $x^3 + 27x^2 - 36x = 14$, and if we denote this set by T_1, then

$$T_1 = \{x | x^3 + 27x^2 - 32x = 14\} . \qquad (2\text{–}3)$$

The truth set for (1–135) is a set of pairs of numbers (x, y) having the property that $y^2 + x^2 = 2 - x$. If the truth set for (1–135) is denoted by T_2, then

$$T_2 = \{(x, y) | y^2 + x^2 = 2 - x\} . \qquad (2\text{–}4)$$

In (2–3) and (2–4) we are implicitly assuming that x and y are real numbers. If there is any doubt about this then it should be indicated explicitly by writing "x real" or something equivalent to this.

Having discussed methods for specifying sets and the notation to be used in representing them, we are now ready to describe operations with sets. The first notion we need to introduce is that of equality.

EQUALITY. *Two sets A and B are said to be equal, written $A = B$, if they contain the same elements, that is, if every element of A is also an element of B and every element of B is also an element of A.*

If A is not equal to B we write $A \neq B$. The sets $A = \{1, 2, 3, 5\}$ and $B = \{1, 3, 4, 5\}$ are not equal because they do not contain precisely the same elements. On the other hand, $A = \{\frac{1}{2}, 2, 1\frac{3}{3}\}$ and $B = \{0.5, \frac{4}{2}, 4\frac{1}{3}\}$ are equal since they contain the same numbers as elements.

The notion of a subset is another very basic one in set theory.

SUBSET. *The set B is said to be a subset of A if every element in B is also in A.*

Note that if $B = A$ then B is a subset of A, since every element in B is in A. Thus A is a subset of itself. In this case every element in A is in the subset. In general, however, A may contain elements which are not elements of the subset B. In this case B is said to be a *proper subset* of A. Note that A is never a proper subset of itself. To indicate that B is a subset of A we write $B \subset A$. Suppose that $A = \{1, 2, 3, 4, 5\}$. Then $B = \{1, 2\}$, $C = \{3, 4, 5\}$ and $D = \{1, 4, 5\}$ are examples of proper subsets of A. If A is the set of all boys and girls in a given class, then the set B of all boys in the class is a subset of A. The notion of a subset can be used to explain in more detail what we mean by $A = B$. If the reader will reexamine the definition of equality he will see that $A = B$ if and only if $B \subset A$ and $A \subset B$. One often is faced with the problem of showing that two sets A and B are equal. The way in which this is normally done is to show that $B \subset A$ and $A \subset B$.

We are now ready to define the basic operations with sets which are of greatest use.

INTERSECTION. *The intersection of two sets A and B, written $A \cap B$, is the set of elements common to A and B, that is, $a \in A \cap B$ if and only if $a \in A$ and $a \in B$.*

For example, if $A = \{1, 2, 5, 7, 9\}$ and $B = \{2, 7, 9, 11\}$, then $A \cap B = \{2, 7, 9\}$, since only the elements 2, 7 and 9 are common to A and B. If A is the set of all persons who paid a New York State income tax in 1966 and B is the set of all persons who paid a California State income tax in 1966, then $A \cap B$ is the set of all persons who paid both a New York and California State tax in 1966.

It may be that there are no elements common to A and B. For example, A may be a set containing certain positive numbers and B a set containing certain negative numbers; there are no numbers which are both positive and negative, so $A \cap B$ has no elements in this case. It is convenient to call "something" with no elements a set, and it is referred to as the *empty* or *null* set. The null set is denoted by the symbol $\varnothing$. Thus we say that $\varnothing$ is the set which has no elements. By definition, we also consider $\varnothing$ to be a subset of every set.

Note that if $a \in A \cap B$ then $a \in A$. Thus $A \cap B \subset A$. Similarly, $A \cap B \subset B$. If $B \subset A$ then $A \cap B = B$. Let us prove this. It provides an illustration of the way one proves that two sets are equal. We have seen that it is always true that $A \cap B \subset B$. To show that $A \cap B = B$ it is then only necessary to show that $B \subset A \cap B$. This follows by definition if $B = \varnothing$. If $B \neq \varnothing$, let x be an element of B. Since $B \subset A$ then $x \in A$. Thus $x \in B$ and $x \in A$ so $x \in A \cap B$ when $x \in B$. Therefore $B \subset A \cap B$.

Just as one can define the intersection of two sets, one can define the intersection of any finite number of sets $A_1, \ldots, A_k$. The intersection of these sets, written $A_1 \cap \cdots \cap A_k$ is the set of elements common to all the sets $A_1, \ldots, A_k$.

UNION. *The union of two sets A and B, written $A \cup B$, is the set of elements which are in A or B or both.*

The union of A and B is the set of elements which are in at least one of the sets A or B. Thus it is always true that $A \subset A \cup B$ and $B \subset A \cup B$. If $A = \{1, 2, 3\}$ and $B = \{1, 3, 5, 7\}$, then $A \cup B = \{1, 2, 3, 5, 7\}$. Note that if $B \subset A$ it follows that $A \cup B = A$. The union of the sets $A_1, \ldots, A_k$, written $A_1 \cup \cdots \cup A_k$ is the set of those elements which are in at least one of the sets $A_1, \ldots, A_k$.

Generally speaking, when we are considering several different sets, the elements for all of these sets will be drawn from some particular universe or "master set." Thus all the sets of interest will be subsets of this universe. For example, the universe may be the set of all real numbers, and every set under consideration is a set of real numbers. The master set will be denoted by E. We can now define a new operation called complementation as follows:

COMPLEMENT OF A. *Given any set A which is a subset of E, the complement of A with respect to E, written A^c, is the set of all elements in E which are not in A.*

If $E = \{1, 2, 3, 4, 5\}$ and $A = \{1, 4\}$, then $A^c = \{2, 3, 5\}$. Suppose that E is the set of all real numbers and A is the set of all natural numbers which are less than or equal to 100. Then A^c is the set of all real numbers different from the first 100 natural numbers.

A set containing just a single element is referred to as a *singleton*. Thus $A = \{a\}$ is a singleton and contains just the single element a. Mathematically, a and the set A containing the single element a are different things, that is, $a \neq \{a\}$. For many practical applications, however, it is unnecessary to make a distinction between a and $\{a\}$; they mean the same thing physically, if not mathematically. Many sets used in practice have the characteristic that the elements are themselves sets. Thus there can be a set of sets. As a simple example of this consider the set of all subsets of some given set A. This set will be denoted by P_A and is called the *power set* for A. If $A = \{1, 2, 3\}$, the subsets of A are $\emptyset$, $\{1\}$, $\{2\}$, $\{3\}$, $\{1, 2\}$, $\{1, 3\}$, $\{2, 3\}$, A. Hence P_A, the set of all subsets of A, is

$$P_A = \{\emptyset, \{1\}, \{2\}, \{3\}, \{1, 2\}, \{1, 3\}, \{2, 3\}, A\}$$

This is all we need to know about set theory for the present. We shall develop the subject somewhat more as we go along.

2–2 FUNCTIONS

In everyday life we frequently have occasion to associate with each element in a given set one and only one element of another set. For example, let A be the set of all students in a particular class and B be the set of family names of these students. Then associated with each element of A there is a unique element of B, which is the family name of the student who is the element of A under consideration. As another example, let A be a set of married men and B be the set of wives of the men in A. Then associated with each element of A, that is, each man in A, there is a unique element in B, namely his wife. Rules for associating with each element in one set a unique element in another set are called functions. More precisely, a function is defined as follows.

FUNCTION. *Consider any non-null set A. If there is given a rule for associating with each element of A one and only one element of another set B, then this rule is called a function from the set A to the set B.*

A function is simply another name for a rule by which we associate with each element in one set a unique element in another set. The definition just given is the general definition of a function and covers all of the cases which arise. At the moment the reader may find it hard to believe that the notion of a function could be one of the most important concepts in mathematics. The entire remainder of this text, however, will be devoted to studying functions, and even so only a very restricted class of functions will be considered. The importance of the function concept will become clear as we go along; for now, let us introduce some additional definitions.

DOMAIN. *The set A in the definition of a function is referred to as the domain of the function.*

We sometimes speak of a function being defined *on the set A or over the set A*. This simply means that A is the domain of the function.

IMAGE. *Let a be any element of the set A appearing in the definition of a function. The unique element $b \in B$ which is associated with a is called the image of a under the function.*

Thus, in the first example of this section, the image of any individual in A is his family name. In the second example, the image of any individual in A is his wife. The definition of a function does not require that every element in B must be the image of some element in A. There may quite possibly be elements in B which are not associated with any element of A. Both of the examples given at the beginning of the section had the characteristic that each element of B was the image of some element in A. The examples could easily be modified so there are elements in B which are not images of any element in A. As an illustration, suppose that in the second example, the set B is taken to be the set of all living women and not merely the wives of the men in the set A. Then there will be elements in B which are not images of elements in A (single women and women whose husbands are not in A, for example). To take still a different example, let A be some given set of men and let B be the set of all real numbers. Consider then the function which associates with each man in A his weight in pounds. Since each man's weight is a real number, this defines a function from A to B. However, not every element of B will be the image of some element in A. The subset R of B containing the elements in B which are the images of the elements in A is called the range of A. More precisely:

RANGE. *Consider the subset R of B which is the collection of all elements in B that are images of one or more elements in A. The set R is called the range of the function with respect to the domain A.*

It will be observed that there is a certain degree of arbitrariness in the selection of the set B when defining a function. Generally, it is only the range R that is important, and any set B having R as a subset will be a suitable B in the definition of a function. Furthermore, we don't change the function, that is, the rule, when we change B, so long as a B is used which contains R as a subset. The only characteristic that B must satisfy is that it contains R as a subset.

There is no implication in the definition of a function that a given element in the range will be the image of only one element in the domain. It could be the image of a large number of different elements in the domain (even an infinite number). To see how an element in R may easily be the image of more than just one element in the domain, consider the first example given in this section. Suppose that two students have the family name Smith. Then Smith, an element of the range of the function which associates with each student his family name, is the image of two different students, each of whom is named Smith. As another simple example of this phenomenon, consider the function which associates with each student in a given class the color of the shirt he is wearing. To be specific, imagine that there are 15 students, 7 of whom are wearing white shirts, 5 blue shirts and 3 red shirts. Let A be the set of these students and B the set of three colors white, blue and red. The function is, as we have indicated, the one which associates with each student the color of shirt he is wearing. Then the element white of B is the image of 7 students in A, blue is the image of 5 students and red is the image of 3 students.

A special case which is sometimes of interest is that where $B = R$, and where, in addition, each element of B is the image of only one element of A. Since $B = R$, there is no element of B which is not the image of some element in A. Thus the function defined on A has the characteristic that for every element in B there is associated precisely one element in A. Such a function is called *one to one* (written 1-1). A 1-1 function, it will be noted, implicitly defines a function whose domain is B and whose range is A, since associated with every element in B there is precisely one element in A. This function with domain B is called the *inverse* of the function with domain A. We have already given an example of a 1-1 function. It is the second example given earlier, where A is a set of married men, B is the set of wives of the men in A, and the function is the rule which associates with every man his wife. Each wife in B is the image of one and only one man in A, and hence the function is 1–1. The inverse function is simply the rule which associates with each woman in B her husband.

It is possible to represent the function concept graphically. Suppose that we represent symbolically the elements of A by solid dots and the elements of B by circles, as shown in Figure 2–1. Then the function is defined completely by showing how the dots are connected to the circles. This can be

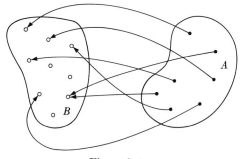

Figure 2–1

done by drawing lines as shown in Figure 2–1. There must, of course, be only one circle associated with each dot. However, a given element of B may be the image of several different elements of A, that is, two or more lines coming from A may terminate at a given circle of B. Recall also that the definition of a function does not require that every element of B be the image of some element of A. In Figure 2–1 there are some circles which do not have any lines connecting them to dots. It is the lines in Figure 2–1 which characterize the function, since they show how to associate with each element in A a unique element in B. Another way that a function might be defined, then, is as a set of ordered pairs (a, b), where $a \in A$ and $b \in B$, having the property that there is one and only one ordered pair corresponding to each element in A. In the ordered pair the first element is an element from A and the second is its image in B. A function is also sometimes referred to as a *mapping* of the set A into the set B. Mapping here simply means to associate with each element of A a unique element of B.

2–3 FUNCTIONS OF ONE VARIABLE

The elements of the sets A and B appearing in the definition of a function can be anything, as the examples given indicated. Except for the last chap-

ter, we shall in this text confine our attention to functions in which both
A and B are subsets of the real number system (the subset may, of course,
be the entire real number system). Any function whose domain and range
are subsets of the real number system is called a *real valued function of one
real variable* or simply a *function of one variable*. Functions of one variable
are very important, and are among the simplest types of functions to
study. This section will be devoted to explaining in more detail the nature
of such functions and indicating the various ways to represent them
explicitly.

Numbers appear with great frequency as elements of the domain and/
or range of a function because so many physical characteristics can be conveniently characterized by numbers. Examples are monetary values, temperatures, time, weight, lengths and speeds, to mention just a few. Functions of a single variable are frequently encountered in everyday life.
Most tables of data provide simple examples of such functions. A specific
illustration would be a table which listed the profit of General Motors for
every year over the twenty years 1946 through 1965. Such a table would
be printed as two columns of numbers. The first would give the years (represented by numbers) and the second the corresponding profits (represented
as numbers). In any given row of the table there would then be two numbers, the first giving the year and the second the profit for that year. This
table then represents a function of one variable, the function being the
rule which associates with any given year the profit made by G.M. in that
year. The domain of the function consists of 20 real numbers, 1946, 1947,
. . . , 1965, representing the 20 years under consideration. The range also
consists of 20 real numbers, representing the profits in these years. The
set B appearing in the definition of a function could then be taken to be the
set of real numbers, or any set containing the range as a subset.

Any function of one variable which has only a finite number of elements
in the domain can be represented explicitly by constructing a table with
two columns, the first listing the numbers in the domain and the second
giving their images. In any given row of this table will be found an element
of the domain and its image. Since a function is completely characterized
when one gives the elements in the domain and the image of each of these
elements, such a table provides a concrete "representation" of the function.
Tables are often convenient ways to represent functions if there are a
relatively small number of elements in the domain.

There is another convenient way that the function representing the
profits of G.M. in the twenty years 1946 to 1965 can be presented. This is
through use of a graphical method such as a bar chart, an example of which
is shown in Figure 2–2. Such a representation will also be familiar to the
reader, since such charts are often seen in newspapers and magazine articles.
Any function of one variable whose domain contains only a finite number
of elements can be represented by a bar chart. The procedure is to draw a

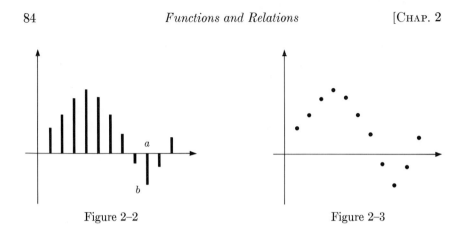

Figure 2–2   Figure 2–3

horizontal line and then locate on this line the points which correspond
to the elements of the domain. At each such point one erects a vertical bar
whose height is the image of the element in the domain corresponding to
the point under consideration. If the image is positive the vertical bar is
drawn above the horizontal line, and if negative below. Thus if a is a number in the domain and b is its image, we locate the point corresponding to a,
as shown in Figure 2–2, and then erect at this point a bar whose length is b.
We have illustrated in Figure 2–2 the case where $b < 0$. So that the heights
of the bars may be easily read, a vertical line is drawn through the point
representing 0 and a scale is placed on this line. This line is also shown in
Figure 2–2. Note that the bars in Figure 2–2 are really unnecessary, since
we could merely use dots, as shown in Figure 2–3. Figure 2–2, however, is
easier to read.

The explicit representation of a function by writing down the ordered
pairs representing an element of the domain and its image as a table can be
employed only when there are relatively few elements in the domain. If the
domain contained millions of elements, then a number of large volumes
would be required to give the table. Tables which require several volumes
have indeed been printed, but this can be justified only in very special
circumstances. Interestingly enough, the graphical representation of a
function can usually be presented conveniently even if there are many elements in the domain. Let us illustrate how this is accomplished by using a
practical example. Suppose that we collected the closing prices for some
common stock on the New York Exchange on every day that the Exchange
was in operation over a period of several years. This can be thought of as
defining a function of one variable in which the domain is the collection of
all dates, expressed as numbers, for which prices were obtained, and the
image of each date is the closing price on this date. The domain would thus
include hundreds of numbers, and the representation of this function by a
table would be a little inconvenient. If we draw a bar diagram for this
function, the bars will essentially all merge together unless a very long

sheet of paper is used and a sufficiently large unit of measure is chosen. Suppose, however, that instead of using bars and a long sheet of paper, we use a size such that the bars would essentially merge together. Imagine that instead of using bars, however, we use dots as in Figure 2–3. Then the dots are very close together, and it occurs to us simply to connect the dots together by a curve. The result will then be something which looks like Figure 2–4. This is the sort of graph which one might see in a newspaper or

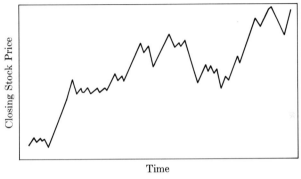

Time

Figure 2–4

in literature distributed by a stockbroker, and it provides a convenient way to represent with reasonable clarity functions of the type under consideration.

We have yet to consider the most important way of representing functions of one variable in mathematics and the sciences. The most useful representation is one where a rule is given explicitly for determining the image of each element in the domain. A very convenient way to make the rule explicit is to set down a mathematical expression or expressions having the property that given any element in the domain, they tell how to compute the image of this element. For example, consider a function whose domain is the set of all natural numbers and having the characteristic that to determine the image of any given natural number, say n, the square of n is added to 16. This can be expressed mathematically by saying that the image of n is $n^2 + 16$. If the image of n is denoted by m then $m = n^2 + 16$. From this equation we can quickly compute the image of any natural number. Thus if $n = 8$, $m = 8^2 + 16 = 80$.

Frequently, the domain for the functions of one variable which will be of interest to us will be the set of all real numbers, or the set of all real numbers corresponding to an interval on the line used to represent the numbers geometrically. The use of mathematical expressions or *formulas* to represent functions in such cases is especially appropriate. As an illustration, consider a function of one variable whose domain is the set of all

real numbers and is such that the image of any given number x is found
by adding the square of x to four times the cube of x. Thus if y is the image
of x, it follows that $y = 4x^3 + x^2$. Here we have an explicit representation
of the function. It is not always true that a single equation will suffice to
represent a function of one variable. To see this, suppose that once again
the domain is the set of all real numbers and the rule for computing the
image of any number x can be described as follows: for $x < -7$, the image
of x is x plus 7; for $-7 \leq x \leq 21$, the image of x is the square of the number $x + 7$; for $x > 21$, the image of x is twice x minus 8. In this case we
need three different equations to represent the function. If y is the image
of x, we have $y = x + 7$ when $x < -7$, $y = (x + 7)^2$ when $-7 \leq x \leq 21$,
and $y = 2x - 8$ when $x > 21$. We can then summarize the representation
of this function using the following abbreviated format

$$y = \begin{cases} x + 7, & x < -7 \\ (x + 7)^2, & -7 \leq x \leq 21 \\ 2x - 8, & x > 21 \, . \end{cases} \qquad (2\text{--}5)$$

Note that for any real number x, (2–5) tells us how to compute its image y.
Furthermore, it is possible to compute only one y for each x.

It may be well to reiterate that (2–5) tells us how to compute the image
y of any number x in the domain. Thus the symbol x represents any number in the domain, and the set of values which x can take on is the domain
of the function. The set of possible values of y is the range of the function.
In accordance with the terminology introduced in the previous chapter for
equations, the symbols x and y in (2–5) are referred to as variables; x is
called the *independent variable* and y is called the *dependent variable*. We
call x the independent variable because the value of x may be chosen
freely from the domain, whereas y is called the dependent variable because
its value is dependent on the value chosen for x. The set of possible values
of y, that is, the range, depends on the set of possible values of x, that is,
the domain. It is typical to refer to y, the image of x, as the *value of the
function at x*. It is important to observe that the particular symbols used to
denote the independent and dependent variables can be chosen arbitrarily.
Thus we would be describing precisely the same function as in (2–5) if we
instead wrote

$$\eta = \begin{cases} \xi + 7, & \xi < -7 \\ (\xi + 7)^2, & -7 \leq \xi \leq 21 \\ 2\xi - 8, & \xi > 21 \, . \end{cases} \qquad (2\text{--}6)$$

Now ξ is the independent variable and η is the dependent variable. We shall
use a variety of lower-case Roman and Greek letters as variables. In accordance with a frequently used convention, however, the Roman letters
will usually be at the end of the alphabet, say t and the letters following it.

We have just seen that a function may sometimes be compactly expressed by using one or more equations. Frequently it is inconvenient to be continually writing out these equations, and we shall therefore introduce a symbolic notation for a function of one variable just as we introduced symbols for numbers and sets. This will simplify the writing of functions in many cases, and will also allow us to discuss functions without making explicit what function it is that we are discussing. The notation we shall use to represent symbolically a function of one variable will have the format

$$y = f(x) \,. \tag{2–7}$$

Some letter, such as f, is used to symbolize the function. Immediately following this symbol we place in parentheses the symbol for the independent variable, which is x for the situation illustrated in (2–7). Then we write down the symbol for the dependent variable, y in (2–7) and place an equals sign between the two symbols as shown in (2–7). We end up with something which looks like an equation. It need not represent an equation, however. It is a symbolism for the entire function and could, for example, be a symbolic representation for the function exhibited explicitly in (2–5). Equation (2–7) is not the only notation used to represent functions. In more advanced mathematics notations are used such as $f{:}A \to B$, where A is the domain and B is the set containing the range, or simply f.

In elementary mathematics $y = f(x)$ is often given a double interpretation, symbolizing the entire function as well as indicating that y is the image of a particular element x in the domain. With this latter interpretation, $f(x)$, which is read f of x, is taken to be the symbol for the image of x under the function. The image of x is y and thus $y = f(x)$. This explains why a symbolism which looks like an equation appears in (2–7). This double interpretation of the symbolism (2–7) does not cause any problem in elementary mathematics such as is studied in this text. In more advanced mathematics it is desirable to distinguish between the notation used for the entire function and that used for the image of some particular element of the domain. The notation $f(x)$ is almost always used to represent the image of x, and a different notation is then used for the function. We shall use the double interpretation of (2–7), and no confusion will arise, but we will not always use precisely the format (2–7) to represent a function. Frequently it is unnecessary to indicate the symbol for the dependent variable, and we shall simply use $f(x)$ to denote the function. Occasionally, when no confusion will result as to whether we are referring to a variable or a function, we shall use a single letter, such as f, to denote the function. We shall call $f(x)$ the function notation, and when using this, we shall sometimes refer to the independent variable x as the *argument* of the function. It is by no means necessary always to use f in the symbolic representation of a function. We shall use a variety of letters such as f, g, h, p, q, r, F, G, H, P, Q, R, Φ, θ. Thus (2–7) could be replaced by $y = F(x)$ or $y = \Phi(x)$, for example. Different symbols can be used to differentiate between two or more different functions. Another convenient way to differentiate between functions is to use subscripts on the function symbol, for example, $f_1(x)$ and $f_2(x)$.

To characterize completely a function of one variable it is necessary to specify the domain and the rule for determining the image of each element. Thus in addition to writing $y = f(x)$, which gives the rule, we should also state what values of x are to be included in the domain. Frequently we shall write specific equations to represent functions without explicitly specifying the domain. *The convention will be adopted that unless otherwise specified the domain includes every x for which $f(x)$ is defined.* We say that $f(x)$ is defined for a given value of x if it is possible to compute from the formula symbolized by $f(x)$ a number y. Thus $f(x) = x^2$ is defined for every real number x. However, $f(x) = 1/(x - 2)$ is not defined at $x = 2$, since $f(2) = 1/0$ and division by 0 is not defined, although $f(x)$ is defined for every real number different from 2. Division by 0 is probably the most frequent reason that an expression $f(x)$ becomes undefined for certain values of its argument, but later we shall encounter other situations which can lead to $f(x)$ being undefined for some set of values of x.

It is important to realize that at any values of x where a particular expression is undefined, we are free to include these values in the domain of the function by specifying an image of each such x. Indeed, if we want these values to be included in the domain, then we must define the function for these values of x. Thus if we define a function by writing $f(x) = 1/(x - 2)$, the domain includes all real numbers except 2. If we wish to have $x = 2$ in the domain, we must define $f(2)$. It can be defined to be any real number so that, for example, we could specify $f(2) = 2.318$. Alternatively, we are not forced to define $f(2)$, so long as 2 is excluded from the domain.

It is desirable to try to understand in a little but more detail the meaning of the $f(x)$ notation. Frequently we shall encounter expressions such as $f(\alpha^2)$, $f(u - 2)$, or $f(u^2 + 4u - \alpha)$. Each of these merely symbolizes the value of the function for the argument indicated in the parentheses. Thus $f(\alpha^2)$ is $f(x)$ for $x = \alpha^2$, that is, the image of the number α^2 is the domain. Similarly, $f(u - 2)$ is the value of $f(x)$ for $x = u - 2$, that is, the image of $u - 2$. Just as we refer to x as a real number, rather than as a symbol representing a real number, we shall refer to $y = f(x)$ as a function rather than as a symbolic representation of a function.

Functions of one variable are of considerable importance in applications of mathematics, since they arise naturally in all the physical and social sciences when relations between numerically measurable characteristics of a system are considered. For example, the pressure of a gas enclosed in a container of fixed volume is a function of the gas temperature, or the postage required to mail a package to a given address is a function of the weight of the package, or one's income tax is a function of his taxable income. The physical or economic characteristics such as temperature, pressure or weight can then be interpreted to be what we have called variables, and they are therefore often referred to as variables in everyday usage.

We have noted earlier that graphs can be used to illustrate a function. The interesting question now arises as to whether, given the representation of a function $y = f(x)$ by an equation or equations, we can illustrate graphically the nature of this function. The answer, of course, is yes. To do so, however, we must make the connection between algebra and geometry, and we shall study the basis for making this connection in the next section.

2–4 ANALYTIC GEOMETRY—COORDINATE SYSTEMS

The branch of mathematics concerned with methods of representing algebraic relations geometrically and with solving geometric problems by algebra is called *analytic geometry*. The foundations of this subject were laid by two French mathematicians, Descartes (1596–1650) and Fermat (1601–1655).

The key to analytic geometry is the procedure introduced in the previous chapter for representing numbers geometrically as points on a line. Once the origin and unit of length are selected there is a unique point corresponding to each real number and a unique real number corresponding to each point. Not only does this technique serve as a geometric interpretation for numbers, but it can serve equally well to characterize points on a line arithmetically, since the arithmetic characterization of any given point is simply the real number to which it corresponds. We shall now generalize this procedure to planes rather than lines. Is it possible to characterize each point in a plane by one or more numbers? This can indeed be done as we shall now see. In the graphical interpretation of a function, such as Figure 2–3, we represented an element x in the domain and its image y by a dot, or equivalently, by a point on a plane. In other words, the ordered pair of numbers (x, y) was represented geometrically by a point on a plane. Here we have the key to arithmetizing the plane. Given any plane, we shall show that each point in the plane can be uniquely characterized by an ordered pair of numbers, and conversely, that every ordered pair of numbers can be represented geometrically by a unique point in the plane.

Consider any two different intersecting lines such as those shown in Figure 2–5, lying in the plane (we imagine that the book page represents part of the plane under consideration). Call the lines 1 and 2. These two lines can be used to provide a unique correspondence between any ordered pair of numbers and a point in the plane. Let us first show that given any ordered pair of numbers (x, y) we can locate a unique point in the plane which can be considered the geometric representation of this ordered pair. To do this we shall use the method discussed in the previous chapter to locate on line 1 the point corresponding to the number x and on line 2 the point corresponding to the number y. In order to locate these points we must select an origin for the measurements on each line. Let us agree to use the point of intersection of the two lines, which is a point common to both lines as the origin point for each. It is also necessary to select a unit of measure on each line. This need not be the same for both lines. Finally, let us agree to locate positive numbers in accordance with the arrowheads on each of the lines. Once these three things are done, a unique point on line 1 corresponding to x and a unique point on line 2 corresponding to y can be determined. First, through the point corresponding to x draw a straight line parallel to line 2 (from plane geometry, there is only one such line). Next, through the point corresponding to y draw a straight line parallel to line 1. These two lines intersect in a unique point P as shown in Figure 2–5. The point P will then be taken to be the geometric representa-

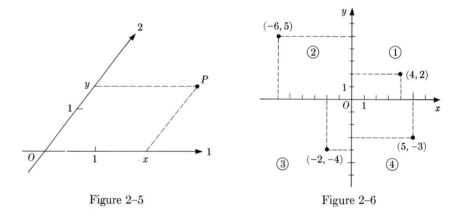

Figure 2–5   Figure 2–6

tion of the ordered pair (x, y). Given any point P in the plane, the above procedure can simply be reversed to determine a unique ordered pair (x, y) which can be considered to be the arithmetic representation of P. Through P two straight lines are drawn, one parallel to line 1 and the other parallel to line 2. The line parallel to line 2 intersects line 1 at a unique point which is the representation of a real number x, while the line parallel to line 1 intersects line 2 at a unique point which is the representation of a real number y. The ordered pair of numbers (x, y) can then be used as the arithmetic representation of the point P.

The two intersecting lines which we introduced to obtain a unique correspondence between the set of all ordered pairs (x, y) and the set of all points of the plane are called a *coordinate system*. The lines 1 and 2 are referred to as *coordinate axes*. Just as we do not know what number a set of digits, such as 12362, represents unless we know what base is being used, we are unable to determine the point in the plane corresponding to a given ordered pair, such as $(3.2, -5.6)$, unless we know what coordinate system is being used. If we select a given point, the ordered pair (x, y) which represents this point will change as the coordinate system is changed. However, once the coordinate system is chosen, then there is a direct correspondence between the points in the plane and the set of all ordered pairs.

Just as 10 is the base normally used in representing numbers, there is one standard type of coordinate system which is used much more than any other. This is the one where the coordinate axes intersect at right angles, that is, are perpendicular. Such a system, called a *rectangular* or a *Cartesian* coordinate system, is illustrated in Figure 2–6. Usually, in dealing with ordered pairs, some symbol such as x will be used to represent symbolically the first element in the ordered pair, and another symbol y will denote the second element. It is convenient to place the symbol for the first element of the ordered pair (we are using x) at the end of the horizontal axis, and the symbol for the second element (we are using y) at the end of the vertical axis as shown in Figure 2–6. These axes are then referred to as the x-axis and the y-axis respectively. The point of intersection of the coordinate axes is called the origin of the coordinate system and is denoted by 0. By the convention introduced previously, points corresponding to positive numbers lie to the right of the origin on the x-axis and above the origin on the y-axis. In Figure 2–6 we have shown the points corresponding to the ordered pairs $(4, 2)$, $(-6, 5)$, $(-2, -4)$ and $(5, -3)$. It is only by convention that the positive directions on the axes are as indicated in Figure 2–6.

In the future we shall frequently refer to an ordered pair (x, y) as *the point* instead of the arithmetic representation of a point. Thus we shall say "consider the point (x, y)." Similarly, we shall sometimes refer to x and y as points and by this we shall mean the points on a line representing x and y. What we are saying, then, is that often we shall not distinguish between points and their arithmetic representation. From an arithmetic point of view, a given plane can be looked upon simply as the collection of all ordered pairs (x, y). At first it may seem rather strange to the reader to characterize a plane in this way, since it really tells us nothing about what a plane looks like geometrically, but it is a very convenient thing to do. (In a similar way we will sometimes characterize a straight line arithmetically merely as the set of all real numbers.)

The coordinate system consisting of an x-axis and a y-axis is referred to as an xy-coordinate system, and we sometimes refer to the plane generated by the set of all points (x, y) as the xy-plane. For any point (x, y), x and y

are called the *coordinates of the point; x* is called the *x*-coordinate or *abscissa* of the point and *y* the *y*-coordinate or *ordinate* of the point. Note that in Figure 2–6 the coordinate axes divide the plane into four regions numbered 1, 2, 3, and 4, which are called *quadrants* of the plane. The quadrants are typically designated by numbering counter-clockwise starting with the quadrant in the upper right. We shall in this text deal exclusively with rectangular coordinate systems. Such systems are also frequently re-ferred to as orthogonal coordinates, while coordinates such as those shown in Figure 2–5 are called oblique coordinates. We shall usually use the same unit of length on both coordinate axes, although this it is not generally necessary. There are cases, however, where it is necessary to use the same unit on both axes, and we shall indicate this when appropriate.

There is a certain amount of ambiguity about the arithmetic representa-tion of points on the coordinate axes. We have been representing points on the *x*- and *y*-axes by single numbers, that is, by *x* or *y*. However, points on these axes are also points in the plane and should therefore be represent-able as an ordered pair. This is indeed true, since a point on the *x*-axis can be represented by the ordered pair $(x, 0)$ and a point on the *y*-axis by $(0, y)$. The question then arises as to whether a point on the *x*-axis should be represented by *x* or $(x, 0)$ and by *y* or $(0, y)$ for points on the *y*-axis. Either can be considered to be correct. When we think of a point on the *x*-axis merely as representing a number which is the coordinate of another point not lying on the axes, we shall simply use *x*. If we think of a point on the *x*-axis as being a special point in the plane, rather than representing the coordinate of another point, then we shall frequently use $(x, 0)$. A plane is what is normally thought of as being two-dimensional, while a line has only one dimension. We shall refer to planes as *two-dimensional spaces*— an ordered pair of numbers is needed to represent arithmetically any point in a plane. A straight line will be referred to as a *one-dimensional space*— only a single number is needed to represent arithmetically any point on a line. The concept of dimension is very important in more advanced mathe-matics, but we shall not attempt to give a precise definition of it here. However, it is worth noting that, intuitively speaking, the *x*- and *y*-axes are one-dimensional spaces lying in or embedded in a two-dimensional space, the *xy*-plane. The coordinate axes are examples of what are called subspaces, that is, spaces of lower dimension contained in a given space.

Having seen how to arithmetize planes, we can now return to the graph-ical or geometric representation of functions. Consider an arbitrary function of one variable, say $y = f(x)$. For any particular number *x* in the domain, there is determined a unique ordered pair (x, y), where $y = f(x)$ is the image of *x*. This ordered pair can be represented geometrically as a point in the *xy*-plane. The collection of all such points generated as *x* takes on each value in the domain is referred to as the *graph of the function* or the *locus of the function* $y = f(x)$. The graph of $y = f(x)$ is then a set *G* of points in the xy-plane, and the set G is a subset of the xy-plane. Sets whose elements are points (the points may be points on a line or points in a plane) are called *point sets*. One of our main uses for set theory will be to study point sets. By using the notation introduced in (2–2), we see that the graph of $y = f(x)$ can be represented as

$$G = \{(x, y)|y = f(x), \quad \text{all } x \text{ in the domain}\} . \tag{2–8}$$

We might also note that if $y = f(x)$ is a single equation and the domain in (2–8) contains all x for which $f(x)$ is defined, then G the graph of the function is nothing but the truth set for the equation $y = f(x)$. To see this, denote by T the truth set for $y = f(x)$. If $(x, y) \in G$, then y is the image of x and $y = f(x)$. Hence $(x, y) \in T$ or $G \subset T$. Conversely, if $(x, y) \in T$, then x must be a number for which $f(x)$ is defined, and hence x is in the domain of the function. But since $(x, y) \in T$, $y = f(x)$ and thus y is the image of x. Therefore $(x, y) \in G$ and $T \subset G$. It follows that $T = G$, which is what we wished to show. We are now ready to study the graphs of some simple functions.

2–5 THE STRAIGHT LINE

One of the simplest functions whose domain consists of all real numbers is

$$y = x . \tag{2–9}$$

The image of x is x itself. Let us attempt to illustrate geometrically the graph of this function. To do this we shall first select several values of x, say 7, 5, 3, 0, -1, -2, -4 and -6. The image of any one of these numbers, 7 for example, is by (2–9) equal to 7, so that the point representing 7 and its image is (7, 7). The ordered pairs corresponding to the above values of x are then (7, 7), (5, 5), (3, 3), (0, 0), $(-1, -1)$, $(-2, -2)$, $(-4, -4)$ and $(-6, -6)$. Let us locate each of these points in the xy-plane as shown in Figure 2–7. The task of locating the points with respect to the coordinate system is often referred to as *plotting* the points. The points are indicated by dots in Figure 2–7. If we place a ruler or straightedge along these points, we find that they are all along the edge of the ruler. Let us then use the ruler to draw a straight line through all of these points, as shown in Figure 2–7. Now the function (2–9) is defined for every x. If we consider any other number x and plot the point (x, x), we find that it lies on the line drawn. Furthermore, we see intuitively that every point on the line is represented arithmetically by a point (x, x), and hence is part of the graph of (2–9). Thus we see that the graph of the function $y = x$ is a straight line which passes through the origin of the coordinate system and makes a 45-degree angle with the x-axis. It is important to note that, although the line is terminated at both ends in Figure 2–7 because of lack of space, it really

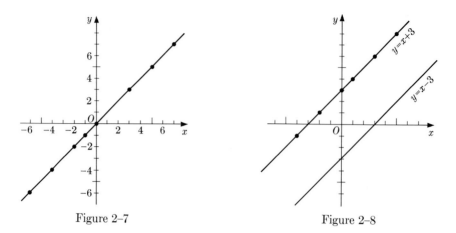

Figure 2–7   Figure 2–8

extends unendingly in both directions.

Consider next the following function, which differs slightly from (2–9):

$$y = x + 3 . \tag{2–10}$$

If we select several values of x, say 5, 3, 1, 0, -2 and -4, and proceed as above, we obtain the ordered pairs (5, 8), (3, 6), (1, 4), (0, 3), (-2, 1) and (-4, -1). These are plotted in Figure 2–8. If we place a ruler along them, we again find that they all line up with the edge of the ruler and hence lie on a straight line. Any other point (x, $x + 3$) also lies on this line. Therefore, the graph of (2–10) also corresponds to what we think' of geometrically as a straight line. It crosses (intersects) the y-axis at $y = 3$ and again makes a 45-degree angle with the x-axis.

If instead of (2–10) we consider $y = x - 3$, it follows that the graph of this function is a straight line which makes a 45-degree angle with the x-axis, but which now intersects the y-axis at $y = -3$. This line is also shown in Figure 2–8. The three lines shown in Figures 2–7 and 2–8 are what would be called parallel lines in geometry. Note that if the y-coordinate of each point on the graph of $y = x$ is increased by 3, we obtain the graph of $y = x + 3$. We can then say that by *translating* (moving) the graph of $y = x$ three units up the y-axis, we obtain the graph of $y = x + 3$. More generally, the graph of any function of the form $y = x + b$, where b is a given number, is a straight line which is parallel to the graph of $y = x$ and intersects the y-axis at $y = b$.

Let us now consider the function

$$y = 2x . \tag{2–11}$$

Once again we select several values of x, say 4, 2, 0, -1 and -3, and compute the images of each of these to obtain the ordered pairs (4, 8), (2, 4), (0, 0), (-1, -2) and (-3, -6). These are plotted in Figure 2–9. The points all fall along the edge of a ruler, and hence lie on a straight line. Furthermore, if we plot any other ordered pair $(x, 2x)$ we find that it lies on the same line. Thus the graph of (2–11) is a straight line which passes through the origin of the coordinate system. The line is quite similar to that shown in Figure 2–7; however, the angle it makes with the x-axis is not the same.

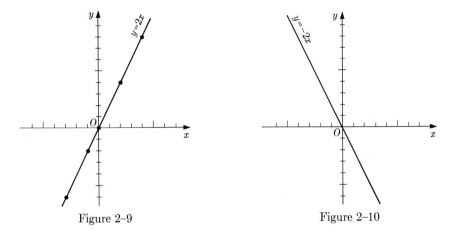

Figure 2–9   Figure 2–10

Suppose that we select any two different points (x_1, y_1) and (x_2, y_2) lying on the line shown in Figure 2–9. Since these points are in the graph of $y = 2x$, it must be true that $y_1 = 2x_1$ and $y_2 = 2x_2$. Subtracting the first of these equations from the second we obtain

$$y_2 - y_1 = 2(x_2 - x_1)$$

or

$$\frac{y_2 - y_1}{x_2 - x_1} = 2 . \tag{2–12}$$

Note that $x_2 - x_1$ is the change in the value of x in going from the first of these points to the second, and $y_2 - y_1$ is the corresponding change in y. Then the left-hand side of (2–12) is the ratio of the change in y to the change in x. From (2–12), we see that this ratio always has the value 2 regardless of what points (x_1, y_1) and (x_2, y_2) on the line are selected. If we take $x_2 = x_1 + 1$, so that there is a one-unit increase in x, then $y_2 = y_1 + 2$ and there is a two-unit increase in y, regardless of what x_1 happens to be. When we compute $(y_2 - y_1)/(x_2 - x_1)$ for any two points on the line in Figure 2–7, we obtain the value 1 independently of the points chosen.

Consider next the function $y = -2x$. Going through the same procedure as above we find that its graph is the straight line shown in Figure 2–10. If we compute $(y_2 - y_1)/(x_2 - x_1)$ in this case for any two points lying on the line we obtain -2. Thus y decreases by 2 units for every unit increase in x. If we analyze any function

$$y = ax, \tag{2-13}$$

where a is a specified real number, we find that its graph is a straight line through the origin with the property that if (x_1, y_1) and (x_2, y_2) are any two points on this line

$$\frac{y_2 - y_1}{x_2 - x_1} = a \tag{2-14}$$

so that y changes by a units when x increases by one unit. The number a in (2-13) is called the *slope of the line*. It tells us how much y changes for a one-

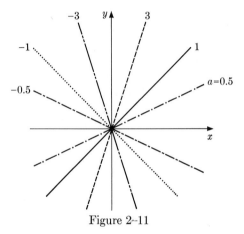

Figure 2-11

unit increase in x. Graphs of (2-13) for several different values of a are shown in Figure 2-11.

Finally, we shall examine functions of the type

$$y = ax + b, \tag{2-15}$$

where a and b are arbitrary but specified real numbers. Since $y = ax + b$ differs from $y = ax$ only in that the image of x in $y = ax$ is increased by b for every x, our previous work shows that the graph of $y = ax + b$ is a straight line which is parallel to that for $y = ax$ and crosses the y-axis at $y = b$. Furthermore, if (x_1, y_1) and (x_2, y_2) are any two points in the graph of (2-15) then $y_1 = ax_1 + b$ and $y_2 = ax_2 + b$ so

$$\frac{y_2 - y_1}{x_2 - x_1} = a$$

and the graph of (2-15) has slope a, as we would expect, since it is parallel to that of $y = ax$.

Our geometric notion of a straight line is a rather intuitive one, since we essentially think of it as something that is obtained by moving a pencil along the edge of a ruler. We have now seen that the graph of any function of the form (2–15) conforms to what we think of as a straight line. We can use this observation to make more precise the notion of a straight line and to characterize a straight line algebraically. To do this we simply define the graph of (2–15) to be what we shall call a straight line, and we often refer to $y = ax + b$ as the equation of a straight line. If L is the graph of the function (2–15), it is also the truth set for the equation(2–15), and L can be written

$$L = \{(x, y)|y = ax + b, \quad \text{all real } x\} . \tag{2–16}$$

We can think of the equation (2–15) as an algebraic representation of a straight line. Just as we refer to (x, y) as a point, we shall often refer to an equation (2–15) as a straight line rather than as a representation of a straight line. We shall also refer to an equation of the form (2–15) as a *linear equation*. In the future, straight lines will often simply be called lines. Only straight lines will be referred to in this way. We imagined that in the equation $y = ax + b$ the numbers a and b had fixed but arbitrary values. If a and/or b is changed we obtain a different straight line. Any equation of the form $y = ax + b$ then represents not just a single line, but a whole class or *family* of lines which consists of the set of all lines that can be generated by assigning all possible values to a and b. The arbitrary constants a and b are referred to as *parameters* in the equation $y = ax + b$, and an equation of this form is said to represent a *two-parameter family of lines*. The difference between the notion of a parameter and a variable is that a particular symbol is an equation is called a parameter if it is imagined that it has a specific fixed value for the problem under consideration. It is called a variable if its value is not prespecified but if it can instead have any value in the truth set for the equation.

We have noted previously that every point in the xy-plane can be represented arithmetically by a unique ordered pair (x, y). We might now ask whether, given an arbitrary straight line in the xy-plane, there exists a unique equation $y = ax + b$ which represents this line. Let us now investigate this question. First we must be able to characterize geometrically the line we have under consideration, and to do this we must have a diagram showing the line and the coordinate system to be used, like that in Figure 2–12. Recall from geometry that a line is determined by two different points, so that if we select two points on the line these should uniquely characterize the line. Suppose then that we select two points on the given line and denote them by (x_1, y_1) and (x_2, y_2). We then wish to ascertain if these points determine a unique equation $y = ax + b$, that is, if there exist unique values of a and b such that the graph of $y = ax + b$ will be the line under consideration. This will be the case if we can determine a unique

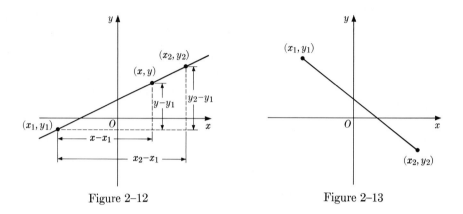

Figure 2–12   Figure 2–13

function $y = ax + b$ whose graph contains the points (x_1, y_1) and (x_2, y_2). If there is such a function it follows that

$$y_1 = ax_1 + b; \quad y_2 = ax_2 + b . \tag{2–17}$$

Subtracting the first equation from the second, we obtain $y_2 - y_1 = a(x_2 - x_1)$, and if $x_2 - x_1 \neq 0$, we find on dividing by $x_2 - x_1$ that a unique value of a is determined, which is $a = (y_2 - y_1)/(x_2 - x_1)$. This is, of course, what a must be, since it is the slope of $y = ax + b$, which is to be the slope of the given line, which in turn is $(y_2 - y_1)/(x_2 - x_1)$.

If the value obtained for a is now substituted in the first equation of (2–17), it follows that

$$y_1 = \frac{y_2 - y_1}{x_2 - x_1} x_1 + b$$

or

$$b = y_1 - \frac{y_2 - y_1}{x_2 - x_1} x_1 = \frac{y_1 x_2 - y_2 x_1}{x_2 - x_1} , \tag{2–18}$$

and b is uniquely determined. The reader should check that the same value of b is obtained if the value of a is substituted into the second equation of (2–17). Thus we have shown that in every case, except where $x_2 = x_1$, we can determine a unique function $y = ax + b$ whose graph is the given straight line. In the event that $x_2 = x_1$ it is clear that the given line is parallel to the y-axis and crosses the x-axis at $x = x_1$. This line is not the graph of a function if x is assumed to be the independent variable, since all points on the line have $x = x_1$ and hence the domain would contain only the value x_1. However, there are an infinite number of different values of y associated with x_1, and the vertical line is then the set of points

$$L = \{(x, y) | x = x_1, \quad \text{all real } y\} . \tag{2–19}$$

We see therefore that every line in the plane can be represented either by an equation of the form $y = ax + b$, or by an equation of the form $x = x_1$. Later we shall introduce an alternative representation of a line which combines both of these cases in a single equation. We have shown, then, that any given straight line can be represented algebraically.

The problem of finding the equation of a straight line which passes through two given points (x_1, y_1) and (x_2, y_2) with $x_1 \neq x_2$ is one that is encountered rather frequently. Let us now give a simple procedure by which the equation of the line can be quickly derived. The two given points determine the slope of the line which is $(y_2 - y_1)/(x_2 - x_1)$. Consider any other point (x, y) on the line. The slope is the same regardless of which two points on the line are used to compute it, and hence if (x, y) and (x_1, y_1) are used we conclude that

$$\frac{y - y_1}{x - x_1} = \frac{y_2 - y_1}{x_2 - x_1} \qquad (2\text{--}20)$$

for every point (x, y) on the line. Thus on multiplying through by $x - x_1$

$$y = \frac{y_2 - y_1}{x_2 - x_1} x + \frac{y_1 x_2 - y_2 x_1}{x_2 - x_1}, \qquad (2\text{--}21)$$

which is the equation for the line. We might note that (2–20) also follows directly from similar triangles as shown in Figure 2–12. As an example, suppose that we wish to find the equation of the line passing through the points $(4, -2)$ and $(-1, 6)$. Either of the points can be used as (x_1, y_1) in (2–20); let us use $(-1, 6)$. Equation (2–20) is the easy one to remember, so let us obtain the equation of the line from it. We have

$$\frac{y - 6}{x + 1} = \frac{-2 - 6}{4 + 1} \quad \text{or} \quad y - 6 = -\frac{8}{5}x - \frac{8}{5}.$$

Thus the desired equation is

$$y = \frac{22}{5} - \frac{8}{5} x.$$

Now that we know a quick way to determine the equation of the line passing through two given points, let us see how to sketch quickly the line representing any equation $y = ax + b$. All we need are two points on the graph, for then we can sketch the line passing through these two points. We have already noted that the line passes through the point $(0, b)$ lying on the y-axis, so we only need one more point. To obtain this, one can chose any convenient value of x, say x_1, and then compute its image $y_1 = ax_1 + b$ to obtain another point (x_1, y_1). The point where the line crosses the x-axis is often a convenient one to use for the second point. Geometrically it is clear that there is only one such point. It is that point (x, y) in the graph having

$y = 0$. What we must do, then, is find the element of the domain x whose image is 0. Thus $ax + b = 0$ or $x = -b/a$ when $a \neq 0$, and we have determined the required value of x. Thus the line crosses the x-axis at $x = -b/a$, that is, at the point $(-b/a, 0)$. The points $(-b/a, 0)$ and $(0, b)$ are called the x- and y-*intercepts* of the line, since they tell where the line crosses the x- and y-axis. Once we have determined the x- and y-intercepts of a line, then we can quickly sketch the line. For the equation $y = 3x + 4$, the x- and y-intercepts are $(-\tfrac{4}{3}, 0)$ and $(0, 4)$, so that it crosses the x-axis at $-\tfrac{4}{3}$ and the y-axes at 4. The reader should sketch the graph of this line.

We might note that in finding the x-intercept of the graph of $y = ax + b$, we have also determined the truth set for the equation $ax + b = 0$. It is the single number $-b/a$. The equation $ax + b = 0$ is called *a linear equation in one variable* and $-b/a$ is called the *solution* to this equation. A linear equation in one variable is the simplest imaginable equation involving just a single variable. A number of problems in elementary algebra reduce to finding the solution to a linear equation in one variable. A simple example of such a problem might be the following. The selling price of a radio in a store is $65. The store obtains the selling price by using a 30 percent markup over its cost from the wholesaler, who determines his price to the store by using a 20 percent markup over what he must pay the manufacturer, and the manufacturer determines the price charged the wholesaler by placing a 30 percent markup over the production cost. What, then, is the production cost of the radio? If we let x be the production cost of the radio then

$$(1.30)(1.20)(1.30)x = 65 \quad \text{or} \quad 2.028x - 65 = 0 ,$$

and the production cost is $\tfrac{65}{2.028} = \$32.10$, which is the solution to a linear equation in one variable.

Not infrequently we are interested not in the entire line passing through two given points (x_1, y_1) and (x_2, y_2), but instead with only the line segment joining the point (x_1, y_1) to (x_2, y_2). Let us see how to represent algebraically this line segment. To be specific suppose that $x_1 < x_2$. What we have in mind is illustrated geometrically in Figure 2–13. Note that if (x, y) is on the line segment, then $x_1 \leq x \leq x_2$. Thus we see that the line segment joining the two points is nothing but the graph of the function $y = ax + b$, when the domain is limited to points x satisfying $x_1 \leq x \leq x_2$. The equation $y = ax + b$ is, of course, simply the equation of the line passing through the two given points.

2–6 PARABOLAS

We are now ready to study somewhat more complicated functions, and in this section we shall examine cases where the square of the independent variable appears. To begin, let us consider the function

$$y = x^2 , \qquad\qquad (2\text{-}22)$$

when the domain is the set of all real numbers. In order to determine the geometric representation of this function let us proceed, as in the previous section, by selecting several values of x, determining their images, and then plotting the resulting points. The values of x selected and their images are given in Table 2–1. The points are plotted in Figure 2–14. By drawing a

TABLE 2–1

$y = x^2$

x	4	3	2	1	0	−1	−2	−3	−4
y	16	9	4	1	0	1	4	9	16

smooth curve through these points we obtain the graph of the function. If any other value of x is selected and its image x^2 is determined, it will be found that the point (x, x^2) does lie on the curve shown in Figure 2–14. The

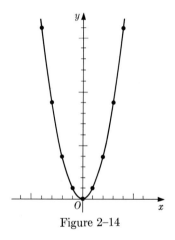

Figure 2–14

reader may now be wondering what justification we really have here, or in the previous section for that matter, for drawing a smooth curve through a small number of points and then claiming that the resulting curve is the graph of the function of interest. Certainly the point (x, y) for any x selected will be found to be on the curve. Nonetheless, it would seem that there may be at least one x for which the point does not lie on the curve. We shall not be able to give a complete justification for our procedure until the subjects of continuity and differentiability have been studied. For the present, we shall rely on intuition and assume that the procedure we have followed does indeed yield the graph of interest. The graph of $y = x^2$ is called a *parabola*.

Let us next consider slight generalizations of the function $y = x^2$, and examine the functions $y = x^2 + 2$ and $y = x^2 - 2$. If we go through the same procedure as for $y = x^2$, we obtain the solid curves shown in Figure 2–15. Suppose now that we trace the curve for $y = x^2$ on a piece of trans-

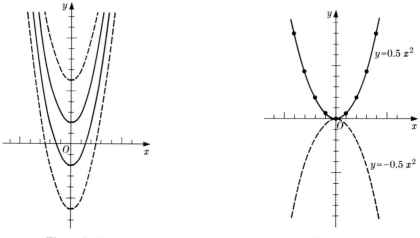

Figure 2–15   Figure 2–16

parent paper and then move it up to align with the curve for $y = x^2 + 2$. We will find that it superimposes exactly on the curve for $y = x^2 + 2$. In other words, the curve representing $y = x^2 + 2$ can be obtained from the curve for $y = x^2$ by translating each point up the y-axis by 2 units, and this does not change its shape in any way. More generally, the graph of the function

$$y = x^2 + c \qquad (2\text{--}23)$$

for any real number c differs from that of $y = x^2$ only in that it crosses the y-axis at $y = c$ instead of $y = 0$. The graphs of (2–23) are also called parabolas. In Figure 2–15, the dashed curves represent the graphs of (2–23) for $c = 6$ and -6.

To continue, let us determine the graph of the function

$$y = 0.5x^2 . \qquad (2\text{--}24)$$

On selecting several values for x and computing the image of each we obtain Table 2–2. These points are plotted in Figure 2–16, and a smooth curve has

TABLE 2–2

$y = 0.5x^2$

x	4	3	2	1	0	-1	-2	-3	-4
y	8	4.5	2	0.5	0	0.5	2	4.5	8

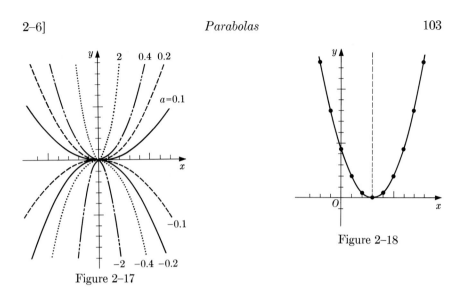

Figure 2–17

Figure 2–18

been drawn through them to yield the graph of (2–24). The graph of (2–24) is quite similar to that of $y = x^2$ except that the graph of (2–24) is more spread out. Suppose that instead of $y = 0.5x^2$ we consider $y = -0.5x^2$. The image of x for this new function is the negative of the image of x for $y = 0.5x^2$. The graph of $y = -0.5x^2$ is also shown in Figure 2–16. If we placed a mirror vertically along the x-axis, the reflection of the graph of $y = 0.5x^2$ in this mirror would appear to be that of $y = -0.5x^2$. Thus we say that the graph of $y = -0.5x^2$ can be obtained from that of $y = 0.5x^2$ by *reflecting* the latter curve in the x-axis.

We are now ready to consider functions of the form

$$y = ax^2, \quad a \neq 0, \tag{2–25}$$

where a is any specified real number different from 0. In Figure 2–17, the graphs of $y = ax^2$ for several different values of a are shown. All of these are called parabolas. If $a > 0$, the parabola opens upward, and if $a < 0$, it opens downward. The magnitude of a determines how spread out the curve is.

Let us introduce an additional complication by studying the function

$$y = 0.5(x - 3)^2. \tag{2–26}$$

Proceeding in the usual way to obtain the graph of the function, we first construct Table 2–3, plot the points so obtained, and draw a smooth curve

TABLE 2–3

$y = 0.5(x - 3)^2$

x	8	7	6	5	4	3	2	1	0	−1	−2
y	12.5	8	4.5	2	0.5	0	0.5	2	4.5	8	12.5

through them. The result is shown in Figure 2–18. If on a piece of trans-
parent paper we trace the curve for $y = 0.5x^2$ from Figure 2–16, we find
that it can be superimposed exactly on the curve in Figure 2–18. In other
words, to obtain the graph of (2–26) we merely translate the graph of $y =
0.5x^2$ by three units to the right along the x-axis. Thus replacing x^2 by
$(x - 3)^2$ did nothing but translate the curve. More generally, the graph of
any function

$$y = a(x - b)^2, \quad a \neq 0 \tag{2–27}$$

will differ from that of $y = ax^2$ only in that the curve has been translated by
b units along the x-axis, so that the point where the curve touches the x-axis
will be at $x = b$ for (2–27) rather than at $x = 0$. Some graphs of (2–27) for
several different values of a and b are shown in Figure 2–19.

For functions of the type (2–27), the vertical line $x = b$ is referred to as

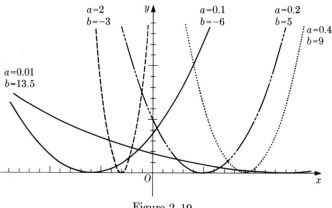

Figure 2–19

an *axis of symmetry* for the graph of the function. In general, we define an
axis of symmetry as follows:

Axis of Symmetry. *The graph of the function $y = f(x)$ is said to have the
line $x = b$ as an axis of symmetry if when $x = b + u$, $u > 0$, is in the domain, so is $x = b - u$, and furthermore $f(b + u) = f(b - u)$, for all u such
that $b + u$ is in the domain.*

If the graph of $y = f(x)$ has $x = b$ as an axis of symmetry, we frequently say
that the function has an axis of symmetry or is symmetric about $x = b$.
When the graph of $y = f(x)$ has $x = b$ as an axis of symmetry, and we know
the graph of $f(x)$ for $x > b$, we can immediately obtain the graph for $x < b$
by reflection in the axis of symmetry. If we substitute $b + u$ for x in (2–27),
we obtain $y = au^2$; we also obtain $y = au^2$ if x is replaced by $b - u$. Thus

the image of $b - u$ is the same as that of $b + u$ for any $u > 0$ and this
proves that the graph of (2–27) is symmetric.

As a final generalization, let us add an arbitrary constant c to the function in (2–27) to yield

$$y = a(x - b)^2 + c, \quad a \neq 0. \tag{2–28}$$

The graph of (2–28) differs from that of (2–27) only in that the curve is
translated along the axis of symmetry by c units so that the curve crosses

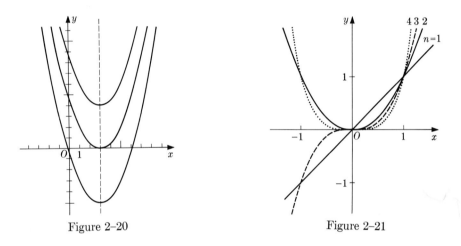

Figure 2–20   Figure 2–21

the axis of symmetry at $y = c$ instead of $y = 0$. As examples, the graphs of
$y = 0.5(x - 3)^2 + 4$ and $y = 0.5(x - 3)^2 - 5$ are shown in Figure 2–20
along with that for $y = 0.5(x - 3)^2$. The graph of any function of the form
(2–28) will be referred to as a parabola. It is also typical to refer to the function itself as a parabola, and the equation (2–28) as a parabola or the equation of a parabola. Note that, while the domain of (2–28) is the set of all
real numbers, the range does not consist of all real numbers, but instead consists of all real y, $y \geq c$ if $a > 0$ or of all real y, $y \leq c$ if $a < 0$.

An interesting and useful result which we shall now demonstrate is that
any function of the form

$$y = \alpha x^2 + \beta x + \gamma, \tag{2–29}$$

where α, β and γ are specified constants with $\alpha \neq 0$, is equivalent to a function of the form (2–28), that is, both functions have precisely the same
graph. Thus the graph of (2–29) is also a parabola. Let us then show how to
convert (2–29) to the form (2–28). The procedure we shall use is what we
have earlier called completing the square. To begin, we write (2–29) as

$$y = \alpha \left(x^2 + \frac{\beta}{\alpha} x + \frac{\gamma}{\alpha} \right),$$

which can be done, since $\alpha \neq 0$. Next let us add and subtract $(\beta/2\alpha)^2$ inside the parentheses to yield

$$y = \alpha\left(x^2 + \frac{\beta}{\alpha}x + \frac{\beta^2}{4\alpha^2} + \frac{\gamma}{\alpha} - \frac{\beta^2}{4\alpha^2}\right).$$

But from (1–125)

$$x^2 + \frac{\beta}{\alpha}x + \frac{\beta^2}{4\alpha^2} = \left(x + \frac{\beta}{2\alpha}\right)^2$$

so

$$y = \alpha\left(x + \frac{\beta}{2\alpha}\right)^2 + \left(\gamma - \frac{\beta^2}{4\alpha}\right), \tag{2–30}$$

which has the form (2–28) if

$$a = \alpha\,; \qquad b = -\frac{\beta}{2\alpha}\,; \qquad c = \gamma - \frac{\beta^2}{4\alpha}. \tag{2–31}$$

Therefore, the graph of (2–29) is a parabola with axis of symmetry $x = -\beta/2\alpha$, which crosses the axis of symmetry at $\gamma - (\beta^2/4\alpha)$. The parabola opens upward if $\alpha > 0$ and downward if $\alpha < 0$.

The need to sketch the graph of a function of the form (2–29) occurs fairly often. Once the axis of symmetry and the value of y where the parabola crosses the axis of symmetry are known, the curve can be sketched very quickly, because the sign of α tells whether it opens upward or downward. It is then only necessary to locate one or two other points on the graph to determine how spread out the curve is. The equations of (2–31) are not easy to remember. To obtain the graph of (2–29) in any particular case it is much easier actually to go through the procedure of completing the square. For example, to sketch the graph of $y = -2x^2 + 3x - 1$ we would write

$$y = -2\left(x^2 - \frac{3}{2}x + \frac{1}{2}\right) = -2\left(x^2 - \frac{3}{2}x + \frac{9}{16} + \frac{1}{2} - \frac{9}{16}\right)$$

$$= -2\left(x - \frac{3}{4}\right)^2 + \frac{1}{8}$$

The graph is therefore a parabola with axis of symmetry $x = \frac{3}{4}$, which crosses the axis of symmetry at $y = \frac{1}{8}$ and which opens downward.

A function of the form (2–29) is often referred to as a *quadratic function of* x. Unlike linear functions, it is not true for quadratic functions that, if two points (x_1, y_1) *and* (x_2, y_2) are selected in the graph of this function, then $(y_2 - y_1)/(x_2 - x_1)$ will be a constant independent of the point selected.

2–7 POWER FUNCTIONS AND HYPERBOLAS

In Section 2–5 we obtained the graph of $y = x$, and in Section 2–6 the graph of $y = x^2$. We can also easily determine the graph of

$$y = x^n \qquad (2\text{–}32)$$

where n is a natural number. A different graph is obtained for each value of n, and some of these are illustrated in Figure 2–21. Note that for n even, y is positive when x is negative. When n is even, $x = 0$ is an axis of symmetry, and $f(x) = x^n = f(-x)$. We shall call a function with the property that $f(x) = f(-x)$ for all x in the domain an *even* or *symmetric function*. When n is odd, $x = 0$ is not an axis of symmetry. Instead we have $f(-x) = -f(x)$ for all x. Functions having this property for all x in the domain are called *odd* or *antisymmetric* functions. For the graph of an odd function, the origin is called a *point of symmetry*. In general, a point of symmetry is defined as follows:

POINT OF SYMMETRY. *The point (b, c) is called a point of symmetry of the graph of $y = f(x)$ if when the point $(b + u, c + v)$, $u > 0$, is in the graph then so is the point $(b - u, c - v)$.*

When the graph of a function has (b, c) as a point of symmetry, we often say that the function itself has (b, c) as a point of symmetry. If (b, c) is a point of symmetry of $y = f(x)$, then if we draw a line through the point $(b + u, c + v)$ on the graph of $f(x)$ and the point (b, c), this line will intersect the graph again at the point $(b - u, c - v)$.

Functions of the form

$$y = a(x - b)^n + c, \quad a \neq 0, \quad n \text{ a natural number}, \qquad (2\text{–}33)$$

have, for $a > 0$, graphs whose shape is essentially the same as that of $y = x^n$. However, now $x = b$ is an axis of symmetry when n is even, with the curve crossing $x = b$ at $y = c$, and the point (b, c) is a point of symmetry when n is odd. The value of a determines how much the curves are spread out. In the problems we ask the reader to plot the graphs of some functions of the form (2–33); the reader will also be asked to explain what happens when $a < 0$.

Suppose now that we consider functions of the form

$$y = x^{m/n}, \quad x \geq 0, \qquad (2\text{–}34)$$

where m and n are natural numbers. Recall from our discussion in Chapter 1 that $x^{m/n}$ is a unique positive number when $x > 0$, and thus (2–34) does represent a function. We shall not include negative x in the domain because

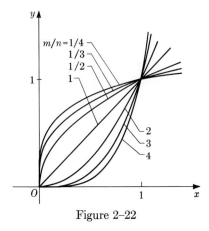

Figure 2–22

for n even there is no real number whose nth power is x. At the moment, we know only a very laborious procedure for evaluating $x^{m/n}$. Let us suppose that we did go through these computations and determined the graphs of (2–34) for several values of m/n. The curves obtained would then be those shown in Figure 2–22. The figure is drawn to a scale which illustrates clearly the interesting behavior of these functions in the interval $0 \leq x \leq 1$. Note the manner in which the curves change smoothly as m/n is changed. This provides further justification for the use of the rational exponent notation.

Let us next turn our attention to functions of the form

$$y = x^{-n}, \quad n \text{ a natural number}. \tag{2–35}$$

We can compute x^{-n} for every x except $x = 0$. Thus the domain of the

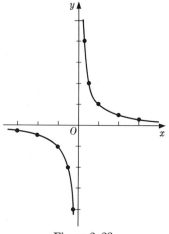

Figure 2–23

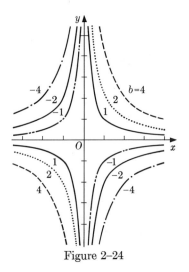

Figure 2–24

functions (2–35) will consist of all real numbers except 0. The most interesting case is that where $n = 1$ and we shall begin with it. When $n = 1$,
(2–35) becomes

$$y = \frac{1}{x} \cdot \qquad (2\text{--}36)$$

Let us proceed as we have in the past by selecting several values of x, determining their images, and plotting the resulting points. The data are given
in Table 2–4. In Figure 2–23 these points have been plotted and smooth

TABLE 2–4

$$y = 1/x$$

x	3	2	1	$\frac{1}{2}$	$\frac{1}{4}$	$-\frac{1}{4}$	$-\frac{1}{2}$	-1	-2	-3
y	$\frac{1}{3}$	$\frac{1}{2}$	1	2	4	-4	-2	-1	$-\frac{1}{2}$	$-\frac{1}{3}$

curves have been drawn through the points. The graph of this function
exhibits a behavior quite different from the other functions which we have
studied. Instead of being represented by a single curve, it consists of two
separate pieces, one lying in the first and one in the third quadrant. Each
of the two pieces is called a *branch* of the graph. The vertical line $x = 0$ (the
y-axis) is called a *vertical asymptote* of the graph of $y = 1/x$ and of the function $y = 1/x$. The function is unusual in that as x approaches 0, y becomes
either a very large positive number if $x > 0$ or a very large negative number
if $x < 0$, and the graph of $y = 1/x$ approaches the y-axis but never reaches
it. As the magnitude of x becomes very large, y gets very close to 0 and the
graph of $y = 1/x$ approaches the x-axis but never reaches it. The horizontal
line $y = 0$ (the x-axis) is called a *horizontal asymptote* of the graph of
$y = 1/x$ and of the function $y = 1/x$.

The graph of the function $y = 1/x$ is called a *hyperbola*, and the function
or equation is also often referred to as a hyperbola. Graphs of functions of
the type

$$y = \frac{b}{x}, \quad b \neq 0, \qquad (2\text{--}37)$$

where b is imagined to be a specified constant, are also called hyperbolas.
The effect of the constant b is illustrated in Figure 2–24.

The graphs of functions of the form

$$y = \frac{b}{x - a} + c \qquad (2\text{--}38)$$

differ from those of $y = b/x$ only in the location of the asymptotes. The
graphs of such functions are also referred to as hyperbolas. The graph of
(2–38) has a vertical asymptote at $x = a$ and a horizontal asymptote at
$y = c$. The graph of

$$y = \frac{1}{x-2} - 3.$$

is shown in Figure 2–25.

The functions (2–35) when $n \neq 1$ are not referred to as hyperbolas. We shall refer to them as *power functions*. The graph of these functions for several different values of n are shown in Figure 2–26. More general functions of the type

$$y = \frac{b}{(x-a)^n} + c \tag{2–39}$$

are also of interest, and the graphs of these have a vertical asymptote at $x = a$ and a horizontal asymptote at $y = c$.

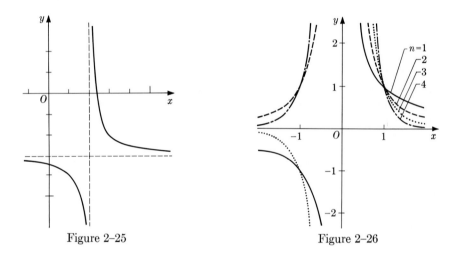

Figure 2–25   Figure 2–26

2–8 POLYNOMIALS

In Section 2–5, we studied the geometric representation of functions of the form

$$y = ax + b \tag{2–40}$$

and in Section 2–6 functions of the form

$$y = \alpha x^2 + \beta x + \gamma. \tag{2–41}$$

Note that functions of the form (2–41) are obtained from (2–40) by adding a term αx^2. In the previous section we showed how to obtain the graph of $y = ax^3$, or more generally $y = ax^n$, but we did not study functions of the form

$$y = a_3 x^3 + a_2 x^2 + a_1 x + a_0, \tag{2–42}$$

or more generally

$$y = a_n x^n + a_{n-1} x^{n-1} + \cdots + a_1 x + a_0, \quad n \text{ a non-negative integer.} \quad (2\text{–}43)$$

A function of the form (2–43) where $a_n, \ldots, a_0$ are specified numbers, is called a *polynomial*. If $a_n \neq 0$ it is called a *polynomial of degree n;* the degree of the polynomial is the largest value of j for which $a_j \neq 0$. The domain of a polynomial contains all real numbers. The functions (2–40), (2–41) and (2–42) are polynomials; (2–40) is a polynomial of first degree if $a \neq 0$, (2–41) is a polynomial of second degree if $\alpha \neq 0$, and (2–42) is a polynomial of third degree if $a_3 \neq 0$. The function $y = a_0$ is called a polynomial of degree zero, since $n = 0$ here. The numbers $a_n, \ldots, a_0$ are called the *coefficients of the polynomial* (2–43), and the jth one a_j is called the coefficient of $x^j, j = 0, 1, \ldots, n$. Note that a_0 can be considered to be the coefficient of x^0, since by our previous definition, $x^0 = 1$ for all x. If (2–43) is a polynomial of degree n, then $a_n \neq 0$. Some or all of the other coefficients may be zero, however. Thus

$$y = 3x^{16}; \quad y = 2x^2 - 1; \quad y = 4x^{25} - x^7 + 2$$

are polynomials, but

$$y = x^{1/2}; \quad y = x^3 - 2x^{3/2}; \quad y = \frac{x^2 + 2}{x^4 + 1}$$

are not polynomials. The first two are not because, in order to be a polynomial, the exponents on x must always be natural numbers or zero; the third is not a polynomial because it cannot be written in the form (2–43).

After having studied the graphs of polynomials of degrees one and two, it will no doubt seem reasonable to the reader that we should next study the graphs of third degree polynomials, that is, of functions of the form (2–42) and then go on to study nth degree polynomials. We shall not do this, however. The task of determining the graph of polynomials of degree three or higher is considerably more complicated than for those of degree one or two. Furthermore, it is only relatively rarely that there is a need to obtain an accurate graph of a polynomial of degree three or greater. Polynomials are very important functions, and we shall use them a great deal in the future, but our use for them will not require that we know precisely what their graphs look like.

Even though we will not discuss the graphs of polynomials of degree three or greater in any detail, it is instructive to see why it is so complicated to deal with them. The graph of a polynomial of degree one is a straight line, and the parameters a and b in (2–40) merely shift the line around and change its slope. The graph of a polynomial of degree two we called a parabola, and the parameters α, β and γ in (2–41) serve to move the parabola around, determine whether it opens upward or downward and determine how spread out it is. The basic shape of the graph, however, is always the same. The situation changes when we go to polynomials of degree three or greater. The parameters not only move the graph around, but they can also drastically change its shape. There is no standard shape for a polynomial of degree three. It can have a variety of shapes depending on the values of the coefficients. In Figure 2–27 is shown the graph of $y = x^3 - 2x^2 - 8x$. Note that its shape is quite different from that of $y = x^3$, as shown in Figure 2–21. If the graph of some given polynomial must be determined, it

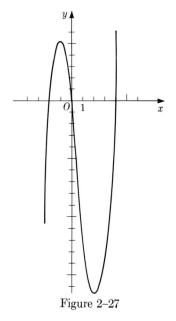

Figure 2–27

can always be done, of course, by selecting a large number of values of x, determining the image of each of these, plotting the resulting points, and drawing a smooth curve through these points. This can be very tedious, because a large number of different values of x may be needed to determine accurately the desired graph.

2–9 TRANSFORMATIONS OF EQUATIONS

In Chapter 1 we introduced the notion of the truth set for an equation, and in the past several sections we have shown how to represent graphically the truth sets for simple equations of the form $y = f(x)$ which could be looked upon as representing functions of one variable. In the next section, we shall begin to examine the problem of finding the truth sets for somewhat more complicated equations which do not, in general, represent functions. To determine the truth set for an equation, we must usually transform the equation to a different form. This must be done in such a way that the truth set for the resulting equation is precisely the same as for the original equation. We shall now study some of the most frequently used transformations and demonstrate that they do leave the truth set unchanged.

We shall wish to study arbitrary equations rather than specific equations, and to do so it will be convenient to represent the equations being discussed symbolically. Let us consider any mathematical expression involving two variables x and y. As a special case, we can imagine that it involves only a single variable, say x. Let us denote this expression symbolically by $\mathcal{G}$. Thus $\mathcal{G}$ might be $x^2 + y^2 - 1$ or $x^3(y^2 - 3) + 2$ or $x^2 - 3x + 1$. Consider then the equation $\mathcal{G} = a$, where a is a specified constant. If $\mathcal{G}$ represents $x^2 + y^2 - 1$, and $a = 0$ then $\mathcal{G} = a$ is the equation $x^2 + y^2 - 1 = 0$. Now denote by T the truth set for the equation $\mathcal{G} = a$, so that $T = \{(x, y)|\mathcal{G} = a\}$, if $\mathcal{G}$ involves x and y, and $T = \{x|\mathcal{G} = a\}$ if $\mathcal{G}$ involves x only. The set T is also referred to as the *set of solutions* to the equations $\mathcal{G} = a$. If $(x_1, y_1) \in T$ or $x_1 \in T$, then (x_1, y_1) or x_1 is called a solution of the equation $\mathcal{G} = a$. In the following we shall restrict our attention to expressions $\mathcal{G}$ such that, given any ordered pair (x, y), it is possible to compute a numerical value of $\mathcal{G}$, that is, there exist no ordered pairs for which $\mathcal{G}$ does not have meaning.

Suppose that $\mathcal{G}^*$ is another expression which is identical to $\mathcal{G}$, so that for all (x, y), $\mathcal{G}^* = \mathcal{G}$. If T^* is the truth set for $\mathcal{G}^* = a$, we shall then prove that $T^* = T$, so that the equation $\mathcal{G}^* = a$ and $\mathcal{G} = a$ both have the same truth sets. We shall refer to this as property 1. As an example, if $\mathcal{G}$ is $x^2 - y^2 - 1$, $\mathcal{G}^*$ could be $(x + y)(x - y) - 1$. We are then claiming that the truth set or set of solutions to the equation $x^2 - y^2 - 1 = a$ is the same as to $(x + y)(x - y) - 1 = a$. The proof follows immediately from what we mean by $\mathcal{G}^* = \mathcal{G}$. Let $(x_1, y_1) \in T$, so that when $x = x_1$ and $y = y_1$ then $\mathcal{G} = a$. But $\mathcal{G}^* = \mathcal{G}$ when $x = x_1$ and $y = y_1$, so $\mathcal{G}^* = a$ also, and $T \subset T^*$. Similarly, if $(x_2, y_2) \in T^*$, $\mathcal{G}^* = a$ when $x = x_2$ and $y = y_2$, so $\mathcal{G} = a$ also, and $T^* \subset T$. Hence $T^* = T$.

Let $\mathcal{K}$ be another expression involving x and y which has meaning for every pair of numbers (x, y). ($\mathcal{K}$ can be the same as $\mathcal{G}$ if desired.) As special cases, we allow $\mathcal{K}$ to involve x only, y only, or to be simply a constant. Consider next the equation

$$\mathcal{G} + \mathcal{K} = a + \mathcal{K}. \qquad (2\text{-}44)$$

Denote by T_+ the set of solutions to this equation. We can now easily show that $T_+ = T$. Suppose that $(x_1, y_1) \in T$. In $\mathcal{G}$ and $\mathcal{K}$ let us set $x = x_1$ and $y = y_1$. Then $\mathcal{G} = a$ and $\mathcal{K}$ is a specific number. Thus by the property (1-91) for equality, $\mathcal{G} + \mathcal{K} = a + \mathcal{K}$ and $(x_1, y_1) \in T_+$ so $T \subset T_+$. Next suppose that $(x_2, y_2) \in T_+$. Set $x = x_2$ and $y = y_2$ in $\mathcal{G}$ and $\mathcal{K}$. Then $\mathcal{G} + \mathcal{K} = a + \mathcal{K}$. Using (1-91) and adding $-\mathcal{K}$ to both sides of the equation we obtain $\mathcal{G} = a$, so $(x_2, y_2) \in T$ and $T_+ \subset T$. Therefore, $T = T_+$, which is what we wished to show. We shall refer to this as property 2. Property 2 says, for example, that the set of solutions to $x^2 - y^2 = 0$ is the same as the set of solutions to $x^2 - 2xy - y^2 = -2xy$ (here $-2xy$ is what we called $\mathcal{H}$ above).

Let us now study equations of the form $\mathcal{G} = 0$ (so that $a = 0$). Again the truth set will be denoted by T. Imagine that $\mathcal{G}$ can be written as the product of k other expressions, so that $\mathcal{G} = \mathcal{G}_1\mathcal{G}_2 \cdots \mathcal{G}_k$ for every pair of numbers (x, y). Denote by T_i the truth set for the equation $\mathcal{G}_i = 0$, and write $T_0 = T_1 \cup T_2 \cup \cdots \cup T_k$. Then we shall show that $T = T_0$. In words, the truth set for $\mathcal{G} = 0$ is the union of the truth sets for $\mathcal{G}_i = 0$, $i = 1, \ldots, k$. We shall refer to this as property 3. The proof goes as follows. Suppose that $(x_1, y_1) \in T_i$. Then $(x_1, y_1) \in T_0$. Imagine that in $\mathcal{G}$, $\mathcal{G}_1, \ldots, \mathcal{G}_k$ we set $x = x_1$ and $y = y_1$. It follows that $\mathcal{G}_i = 0$ and hence $\mathcal{G}_1\mathcal{G}_2 \cdots \mathcal{G}_k = 0$, so $\mathcal{G} = 0$, since $\mathcal{G} = \mathcal{G}_1 \cdots \mathcal{G}_k$. Consequently $(x_1, y_1) \in T$ and $T_0 \subset T$. Next imagine that $(x_2, y_2) \in T$. Set $x = x_2$ and $y = y_2$ in $\mathcal{G}$, $\mathcal{G}_1, \ldots, \mathcal{G}_k$. Then $\mathcal{G} = 0$ and hence $\mathcal{G}_1 \cdots \mathcal{G}_k = 0$. But then at least one $\mathcal{G}_i = 0$, since the product of numbers all of which are not 0 is different from 0. Therefore $(x_2, y_2) \in T_0$ and $T \subset T_0$. We conclude that $T = T_0$, which is what we wished to show. Property 3 says, for example, that the set of solutions to $x^2 - y^2 = 0$ is the union of the set of solutions to $x - y = 0$ and $x + y = 0$, since $x^2 - y^2 \equiv (x + y)(x - y)$. This is useful to know because it is easy to determine the solutions to the latter two equations.

Let us next imagine that we multiply the equation $\mathcal{G} = 0$ by some expression $\mathcal{H}$ to yield $\mathcal{H}\mathcal{G} = 0$. Let T_m be the set of solutions to $\mathcal{H}\mathcal{G} = 0$. In general, it need not be true that $T = T_m$. This is a very important fact to keep in mind. It may be true that $T \subset T_m$ and $\mathcal{H}\mathcal{G} = 0$ has more solutions than $\mathcal{G} = 0$, or it may be true that $T_m \subset T$ and $\mathcal{H}\mathcal{G} = 0$ has fewer solutions than $\mathcal{G} = 0$. We shall investigate the situation in more detail. If a value of $\mathcal{H}$ can be computed for every pair (x, y), then by property 3 above $T_m = T \cup T_h$, where T_h is the truth set for the equation $\mathcal{H} = 0$. In this case then $T \subset T_m$. We have $T = T_m$ only if $T_h \subset T$, that is, every solution to $\mathcal{H} = 0$ is also a solution to $\mathcal{G} = 0$. In particular, if $T_h = \varnothing$, so that there is no solution to $\mathcal{H} = 0$, then $T = T_m$. An important case where $T_h = \varnothing$ is that where $\mathcal{H}$ stands for a constant λ, $\lambda \neq 0$. We have shown then that we can multiply the equation by a constant different from 0 without changing the set of solutions. Let us call this property 4. It need not be true that $\mathcal{H}$ is a constant in order that $T_h = \varnothing$. Suppose that $\mathcal{H}$ represents $1 + x^2$. Now a value of $1 + x^2$ can be computed for every real x and $1 + x^2$ is never 0. Thus the equations $x^2 + y^2 - 1 = 0$ and $(1 + x^2)(x^2 + y^2 - 1) = 0$ have the same set of solutions. It is easy to give an example where $T \subset T_m$. Let $\mathcal{G}$ represent $x^2 - 1$, so $\mathcal{G} = 0$ is $x^2 - 1 = 0$, and let $\mathcal{H}$ represent x. Then $\mathcal{H}\mathcal{G} = 0$ is $x^3 - x = 0$. Now $\mathcal{H} = 0$, that is, $x = 0$ has precisely one solution, $x = 0$. This is not a solution to $x^2 - 1 = 0$. Hence $\mathcal{H}\mathcal{G} = 0$ has a solution which is not a solution to $\mathcal{G} = 0$.

It is not always true that a value of $\mathcal{H}$ will be computable for every pair (x, y). For example, if $\mathcal{H}$ represents $1/x$, we cannot compute a value of $\mathcal{H}$ for $x = 0$. In this case $\mathcal{H}\mathcal{G} = 0$ may have fewer solutions that $\mathcal{G} = 0$. To see this suppose that $\mathcal{G} = 0$ is $x^3 - 2x^2 + x = 0$. If $\mathcal{H} = 1/x$, then $\mathcal{H}\mathcal{G} = 0$ becomes $x^2 - 2x + 1 = 0$. Note that $x = 0$ is a solution to $\mathcal{G} = 0$, but is not a solution to $\mathcal{H}\mathcal{G} = 0$. The difficulty lies in the fact that $\mathcal{H}$ is not defined at $x = 0$. In general, if (x_1, y_1) is a solution to $\mathcal{G} = 0$, it may not be a solution to $\mathcal{H}\mathcal{G} = 0$ if $\mathcal{H}$ is not defined at (x_1, y_1). (Note that it may be possible to compute a value of $\mathcal{H}\mathcal{G}$ even if it is not possible to compute a value of $\mathcal{H}$, as the example just given illustrates.) The above discussion shows that we must be quite careful when multiplying an equation by an expression which involves variables, since the set of solutions to the new equation need not be the same as that for the original equation.

We often encounter equations of the form

$$\mathcal{G}^2 = \mathcal{H} \tag{2–45}$$

where $\mathcal{G}$ and $\mathcal{H}$ are expressions involving x and y (or x only, or y only, or neither). We shall show that the set of solutions T to (2–45) is $T = T_1 \cup T_2$, where T_1 is the set of solutions to $\mathcal{G} = \mathcal{H}^{1/2}$ and T_2 is the set of solutions to $\mathcal{G} = -\mathcal{H}^{1/2}$. We shall call this property 5. To give the proof, note that any solution to $\mathcal{G} = \mathcal{H}^{1/2}$ or $\mathcal{G} = -\mathcal{H}^{1/2}$ is a solution to (2–45), since by (1–92), if $\mathcal{G} = \mathcal{H}^{1/2}$ then $\mathcal{G}^2 = \mathcal{G}\mathcal{H}^{1/2}$ and $\mathcal{G}\mathcal{H}^{1/2} = (\mathcal{H}^{1/2})^2 = \mathcal{H}$, so $\mathcal{G}^2 = \mathcal{H}$. A similar result follows when $\mathcal{G} = -\mathcal{H}^{1/2}$. Hence $T_1 \cup T_2 \subset T$. Suppose now that (x_1, y_1) is any solution to (2–45). Thus when $x = x_1$ and $y = y_1$ in $\mathcal{G}$ and $\mathcal{H}$ we have $\mathcal{G}^2 = \mathcal{H}$. Now $\mathcal{G}^2 \geq 0$ and therefore $\mathcal{H} \geq 0$. Thus $\mathcal{H}^{1/2}$ exists. Furthermore, $\mathcal{G}$ is a number whose square is $\mathcal{H}$. The only two real numbers whose square is $\mathcal{H}$ are $\mathcal{H}^{1/2}$ or $-\mathcal{H}^{1/2}$. Hence, it must be true that $\mathcal{G} = \mathcal{H}^{1/2}$ or $\mathcal{G} = -\mathcal{H}^{1/2}$, that is, $(x_1, y_1) \in T_1 \cup T_2$. It follows that $T \subset T_1 \cup T_2$, and consequently $T = T_1 \cup T_2$, which is what we wished to show. If (2–45) has no solutions (as would be the case if $\mathcal{H}$ were always negative), then $\mathcal{G} = \mathcal{H}^{1/2}$ and $\mathcal{G} = -\mathcal{H}^{1/2}$ cannot have solutions either, since if either one of them did so would (2–45). Thus $T = T_1 = T_2 = \varnothing$ and $T = T_1 \cup T_2$ in this case also.

By use of properties 2 and 5, we can now prove that the set of solutions to $x^2 + y^2 = 1$ is the union of the graphs of the two functions

$$y = (1 - x^2)^{1/2}; \qquad y = -(1 - x^2)^{1/2}. \tag{2–46}$$

To see this note that by property 2 the set of solutions to $x^2 + y^2 = 1$ is the same as those to the equation $y^2 = 1 - x^2$, since we merely add $-x^2$ to both of the equation, that is, $\mathcal{H}$ is $-x^2$. But then it follows at once from property 5 that the set of solutions to $y^2 = 1 - x^2$, and hence to $x^2 + y^2 = 1$, is given by the union of the sets of solutions to (2–46), which are precisely the graphs of the functions (2–46).

Occasionally it is desirable to transform an equation by squaring both sides. Let us examine this briefly. Suppose that we start with the equation $\mathcal{G} = \mathcal{H}$ and form the new equation $\mathcal{G}^2 = \mathcal{H}^2$. Denote by T the set of solutions to the original equation and by T_s the set of solutions to the new equation. We can note at once that every solution to $\mathcal{G} = \mathcal{H}$ must be a solution to $\mathcal{G}^2 = \mathcal{H}^2$, so that $T \subset T_s$. However, $\mathcal{G}^2 = \mathcal{H}^2$ may have solutions which are not solutions to $\mathcal{G} = \mathcal{H}$. By property 2 the set of solutions to $\mathcal{G}^2 = \mathcal{H}^2$ is the same as the set of solutions to $\mathcal{G}^2 - \mathcal{H}^2 = 0$. However

$$\mathcal{G}^2 - \mathcal{H}^2 = (\mathcal{G} + \mathcal{H})(\mathcal{G} - \mathcal{H})$$

and by property 3, the set of solutions to $\mathcal{G}^2 - \mathcal{H}^2 = 0$ is the union of the sets of solutions to $\mathcal{G} + \mathcal{H} = 0$ and $\mathcal{G} - \mathcal{H} = 0$, which by property 2 are the sets of solutions to $\mathcal{G} = \mathcal{H}$ and $\mathcal{G} = -\mathcal{H}$. Thus the set of solutions to $\mathcal{G}^2 = \mathcal{H}^2$ contains the solutions to $\mathcal{G} = -\mathcal{H}$ as well as to $\mathcal{G} = \mathcal{H}$. If $\mathcal{G} = -\mathcal{H}$ has no solutions, then $T = T_s$, but if $\mathcal{G} = -\mathcal{H}$ has solutions it need not be true that $T = T_s$. We must, therefore, be careful in squaring any equation to determine whether or not new solutions are introduced. For example, the set of solutions to $y = (1 - x^2)^{1/2}$ is not the same as the set of solutions to $y^2 = 1 - x^2$.

We have now studied some of the most frequently used procedures for transforming equations from one form to another, and we have examined the conditions under which the set of solutions remains unchanged. Not every possible transformation has been considered, but the discussion has illustrated how it can be determined whether or not the set of solutions remains unchanged. The process of transforming equations is used with great frequency and the reader should attempt to understand what is involved. The above discussion has been somewhat more abstract than our previous developments, but its meaning should become clearer as we use the material in the future. In Section 2–5, when determining the truth set for the equation $ax + b = 0$, and in Section 2–6, when transforming (2–29), we implicitly made use of the results of this section. The reader should now go back and make these explicit, thus verifying that the results are what we claimed.

Let us conclude this section by illustrating how the results just obtained can be used to determine the truth set or the set of solutions for an equation. Consider the following equation

$$\alpha x^2 + \beta x + \gamma = 0, \quad \alpha \neq 0, \tag{2–47}$$

which is often referred to as a *quadratic equation*. The problem of finding the set of solutions to a quadratic equation arises frequently, and the set of solutions is by no means obvious when the quadratic equation is written in the form (2–47). However, we shall convert (2–47) to an alternative form such that the set of solutions for the new equation can easily be found. The conversion will be made in such a way that the set of solutions to the new equation is precisely the same as to (2–47), and in this way the set of solutions to (2–47) will be determined.

To proceed, we note that since $\alpha \neq 0$, it follows from property 4, with $\lambda = 1/\alpha$, that the set of solutions to (2–47) is the same as the set of solutions to

$$x^2 + \frac{\beta}{\alpha} x + \frac{\gamma}{\alpha} = 0 . \tag{2–48}$$

By property 2, the set of solutions to (2–48) is the same as the set of solutions to

$$x^2 + \frac{\beta}{\alpha} x = - \frac{\gamma}{\alpha} . \tag{2–49}$$

Using property 2 again, we note that the set of solutions to (2–49) is the same as the set of solutions to

$$x^2 + \frac{\beta}{\alpha} x + \left(\frac{\beta}{2\alpha}\right)^2 = - \frac{\gamma}{\alpha} + \left(\frac{\beta}{2\alpha}\right)^2 . \tag{2–50}$$

However

$$x^2 + \frac{\beta}{\alpha} x + \left(\frac{\beta}{2\alpha}\right)^2 \equiv \left(x + \frac{\beta}{2\alpha}\right)^2 \tag{2–51}$$

and thus by property 1, the set of solutions to (2–50) is the same as the set of solutions to

$$\left(x + \frac{\beta}{2\alpha}\right)^2 = - \frac{\gamma}{\alpha} + \left(\frac{\beta}{2\alpha}\right)^2 . \tag{2–52}$$

Now consider the quantity

$$\delta = - \frac{\gamma}{\alpha} + \left(\frac{\beta}{2\alpha}\right)^2 = \frac{\beta^2 - 4\alpha\gamma}{4\alpha^2} . \tag{2–53}$$

If $\beta^2 - 4\alpha\gamma < 0$, then $\delta < 0$ and there do not exist any solutions to (2–52), because there is no real number whose square is a negative number. Thus if $\beta^2 - 4\alpha\gamma < 0$, the quadratic equation (2–47) does not have any solution. If $\beta^2 - 4\alpha\gamma \geq 0$ then $\delta \geq 0$, and in this case, by property 5, the set of solutions to (2–52) is the union of the sets of solutions to

$$x + \frac{\beta}{2\alpha} = \delta^{1/2} \quad \text{and} \quad x + \frac{\beta}{2\alpha} = - \delta^{1/2} . \tag{2–54}$$

But by property 2, the sets of solutions to the equations in (2–53) are respectively the same as the sets of solutions to

$$x = - \frac{\beta}{2\alpha} + \delta^{1/2} \quad \text{and} \quad x = - \frac{\beta}{2\alpha} - \delta^{1/2} . \tag{2–55}$$

Now the equations (2–55) simply say that x must be the real number on the right-hand side of the equation. Thus each of these equations has precisely one solution. If $\delta^{1/2} > 0$, the solution to the first will be different from the solution to the second equation in (2–55). Furthermore, $\delta^{1/2} > 0$ if and only if $\beta^2 - 4\alpha\gamma > 0$. Therefore, if $\beta^2 - 4\alpha\gamma > 0$, the quadratic equation (2–48) has precisely two solutions. However, if $\beta^2 - 4\alpha\gamma = 0$, then $\delta^{1/2} = 0$, and each of the equations in (2–55) has the same solution $-\beta/2\alpha$. In this case then the quadratic equation has precisely one solution $-\beta/2\alpha$.

We have by the above procedure obtained the set of solutions to the quadratic equation (2–47). The process of finding the solutions to an equation is sometimes referred to as *solving* an equation. Thus we have solved the general quadratic equation. The procedure used to do this was nothing but the completion of the square, which we have used before. A quadratic equation never has more than two solutions, but it may have only one or no solutions, depending on the values of the coefficients and, in particular, on the value of $\beta^2 - 4\alpha\gamma$, which is referred to as the *discriminant* of the quadratic equation. When $\beta^2 - 4\alpha\gamma > 0$ note that $\delta^{1/2}$ can be written

$$\delta^{1/2} = \frac{1}{2\alpha}(\beta^2 - 4\alpha\gamma)^{1/2} \text{ if } \alpha > 0; \qquad \delta^{1/2} = -\frac{1}{2\alpha}(\beta^2 - 4\alpha\gamma)^{1/2} \text{ if } \alpha < 0.$$

$$(2\text{--}56)$$

If we denote by λ_1 and λ_2 the two solutions to the quadratic equation when $\beta^2 - 4\alpha\gamma > 0$, then regardless of whether $\alpha > 0$ or $\alpha < 0$, these two solutions are, as we see from substituting (2–56) into (2–54) in each case,

$$\lambda_1 = \frac{1}{2\alpha}[-\beta + (\beta^2 - 4\alpha\gamma)^{1/2}]; \qquad \lambda_2 = \frac{1}{2\alpha}[-\beta - (\beta^2 - 4\alpha\gamma)^{1/2}]. \quad (2\text{--}57)$$

When $\beta^2 - 4\alpha\gamma = 0$, there is only one solution, that is, $\lambda_1 = \lambda_2 = -\beta/2\alpha$. The reader should memorize (2–57), since it is often used in solving quadratic equations. In summary, if $\beta^2 - 4\alpha\gamma > 0$ there are two solutions, if $\beta^2 - 4\alpha\gamma = 0$ there is one solution, and if $\beta^2 - 4\alpha\gamma < 0$ there are no solutions to the quadratic equation (2–48). Recall that we are restricting what we call solutions to real numbers. If we allowed the solutions to be complex numbers, then a quadratic equation always has a solution, since in the complex number system it is possible to take the square root of a negative number. In this text, we are not using the complex number system, and hence when we restrict solutions to real numbers a quadratic equation may not have a solution.

We can now provide an interesting geometric interpretation of the roots of a quadratic equation. In Section 2–6 we studied the graphs of second-degree polynomials such as (2–29). If λ is a solution of the quadratic equation (2–48), then λ is in the domain of (2–29) and λ has the characteristic that its image is 0, so that the point $(\lambda, 0)$ is on the graph of (2–29). But this point lies on the x-axis. In other words, the graph of (2–29) crosses or touches the x-axis at every point in the domain which is a root of (2–48). The roots of (2–48) are then the elements of the domain of (2–29) whose image is 0. Geometrically then, the solutions of (2–48) are the points on the x-axis where the parabola (2–29) crosses or touches the x-axis. If there are two solutions the parabola cuts the x-axis at two points, as does the lowest parabola in Figure 2–15. If there is just a single solution the parabola touches the x-axis at just one point, as in Figure 2–18. If there is no solution then the parabola does not cross or touch the x-axis, as is the case with the upper parabola in Figure 2–20. The solutions of a quadratic equation $\alpha x^2 + \beta x + \gamma = 0$ are also referred to as the *roots* of the second-degree polynomial $y = \alpha x^2 + \beta x + \gamma$.

EXAMPLES. 1. Let us determine the solutions of

$$0.5x^2 - 3x - 0.5 = 0 .$$

Here $\alpha = 0.5$, $\beta = -3$ and $\gamma = -0.5$. Thus

$$\beta^2 - 4\alpha\gamma = 9 + 1 = 10 ,$$

so

$$(\beta^2 - 4\alpha\gamma)^{1/2} = 3.16 .$$

The equation has two roots, which are

$$\lambda_1 = 3 + 3.16 = 6.16; \qquad \lambda_2 = 3 - 3.16 = -0.16 .$$

The graph of $y = 0.5x^2 - 3x - 0.5$ is the lower parabola in Figure 2–20. Note that the curve does indeed cross the x-axis at $x = \lambda_1$ and $x = \lambda_2$.

2. Let us now determine the solutions to

$$0.5x^2 - 3x + 4.5 = 0 .$$

In this case $\alpha = 0.5$, $\beta = -3$ and $\gamma = 4.5$, so

$$\beta^2 - 4\alpha\gamma = 9 - 9 = 0 .$$

Thus the quadratic equation has only one solution λ_1, which is

$$\lambda_1 = -\frac{\beta}{2\alpha} = 3 .$$

The graph of $y = 0.5x^2 - 3x + 4.5$ is shown in Figure 2–18, and the parabola does touch the x-axis at the single point $x = \lambda_1$.

3. Finally, let us find the solutions to

$$0.5x^2 - 3x + 8.5 = 0 .$$

Here $\alpha = 0.5$, $\beta = -3$ and $\gamma = 8.5$. Thus

$$\beta^2 - 4\alpha\gamma = 9 - 17 = -8$$

and the quadratic equation has no root. The graph of $y = 0.5x^2 - 3x + 8.5$ is the upper parabola in Figure 2–20. It does not touch or cross the x-axis.

2–10 RELATIONS

We have been studying how functions of one variable can be represented graphically. We shall now begin studying how to represent graphically certain sets of points which are not necessarily the graphs of functions. For example, we shall be interested in representing graphically the truth sets or sets of solutions to equations such as $x^2 + y^2 = 1$. The types of point sets we wish to study are those generated by what we shall refer to as a relation between two variables x and y. A relation is defined as follows:

RELATION BETWEEN x AND y. *A relation between x and y is any rule or set of rules which serves to select from all the points in the xy-plane a certain subset G. The set of points G are those points which satisfy the rule or set of rules, and G is called the graph of the relation.*

The set G may be null in some cases or may in others contain all the points in the plane. We do not put any restriction on the nature of the rule or rules which serve to select the subset G.

It will be noted that any function of a single variable $y = f(x)$ is, according to the above definition, also a relation, since the function serves to select from the xy-plane those points which are in the graph of the function. As we shall see, however, it is by no means true that every relation is a function. The equation $x^2 + y^2 = 1$ also defines a relation between x and y, since it serves to select from all points in the xy-plane those which are solutions to this equation.

The first type of relations that we shall study are those in which the rule is a single equation involving x and y, and the graph of the relation is simply the truth set for the equation. What we wish to do then is show how to represent graphically the relation, that is, the set of solutions to the given equation. The equations to be studied will generally not represent functions, although in certain cases it will turn out that they do.

Consider first the equation

$$c_1 x + c_2 y = b \,, \tag{2–58}$$

where c_1, c_2 and b are specified numbers and c_1 and c_2 are not both zero. Let us determine the graph of this relation, that is, the set of solutions to (2–58). If $c_2 \neq 0$, then on using property 4 to multiply by $1/c_2$ and property 2 to add $-c_1 x/c_2$ to both sides of the resulting equation (all of which leave unchanged the set of solutions) we see that the set of solutions to (2–58) is the set of solutions to

$$y = \frac{b}{c_2} - \frac{c_1}{c_2} x \,. \tag{2–59}$$

However, (2–59) represents a function whose graph is a straight line with slope $-c_1/c_2$ and which intersects the y-axis at $y = b/c_2$. Therefore, when $c_2 \neq 0$, the graph of (2–58) is the straight line just described. Suppose next that $c_2 = 0$. Then $c_1 \neq 0$, since we are assuming that c_1 and c_2 are not both 0. Hence on using property 4 to multiply by $1/c_1$, we obtain $x = b/c_1$. In other words $(b/c_1, y)$ is in the graph of (2–58) for any real number y. There is an important point to observe here. When $c_2 = 0$, (2–58) becomes $c_1 x = b$, which looks like an equation in one variable x. If we think of it as an equation in one variable, it has a unique solution b/c_1. If, however, we think of it as an equation in two variables x and y, it has an infinite number of solutions $(b/c_1, y)$, where y can be any real number. Thus, we cannot necessarily tell by looking at an equation how it is to be interpreted. We must also know whether there are any variables not appearing explicitly which are imagined to be variables. In (2–58) we are assuming that y is a variable even if $c_2 = 0$. We can now observe that the set $G = \{(b/c_1, y)|\ \text{all } y\}$ is nothing but a vertical line which crosses the x-axis at $x = b/c_1$. Thus when $c_2 = 0$, the graph of (2–58) is still a line, but it is now a vertical line. Recall that we showed in Section 2–5 that every straight line can be represented algebraically by an equation of the form (2–59) or is a vertical straight line and can be represented by an equation of the form $x = x_1$. Both of these cases are represented in (2–58). *Therefore, every straight line is the graph of some relation of the form* (2–58), and (2–58) is sometimes referred to as the general equation for a straight line. In other words, every set of points

$$L = \{(x, y)|c_1 x + c_2 y = b, \quad c_1, c_2 \text{ not both } 0\} \tag{2–60}$$

is a straight line and every straight line can be represented in the form (2–60). We have thus determined the form of the graph of any relation (2–58).

Let us now consider the graphs of relations of the form

$$x^2 + y^2 = \alpha \,. \tag{2–61}$$

The nature of the set of solutions depends on the value of α. If $\alpha < 0$, there is no solution to (2–61), since the square of any real number is non-negative and the sum of two non-negative numbers is non-negative. Thus, for example, there is no solution to $x^2 + y^2 = -17$. If $\alpha = 0$, there is precisely one solution to (2–61) which is $(0, 0)$, that is, $x = 0$ and $y = 0$. The reason is that the square of any non-zero real number is positive. Thus if $x^2 + y^2 = 0$, both x^2 and y^2 must be 0, which in turn implies that x and y are 0.

We shall now consider the more interesting case where $\alpha > 0$. In this case, there always exists an infinite number of solutions to (2–61), and we shall investigate the nature of these solutions. To be specific let us first study the case where $\alpha = 1$, that is, the graph of $x^2 + y^2 = 1$. By property 2 the set of solutions to $x^2 + y^2 = 1$ is the same as the set of solutions to $y^2 = 1 - x^2$. We can see immediately that there will be no solution with $x^2 > 1$, since then $1 - x^2 < 0$. Now $x^2 \leq 1$ if and only if $-1 \leq x \leq 1$. Whenever x lies in this interval, $1 - x^2 \geq 0$ and there will exist solutions for any such x. In fact, by property 5, the set of solutions to $y^2 = 1 - x^2$ is the union of the sets of solutions to $y = (1 - x^2)^{1/2}$ and $y = -(1 - x^2)^{1/2}$. These latter two equations represent functions, and the graph of $x^2 + y^2 = 1$ is

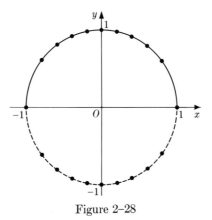

Figure 2–28

then the union of the graphs of these two functions. Since we can only compute the square root of non-negative numbers, the domain for each of the functions is the set of x for which $1 - x^2 \geq 0$. We have noted above that this is the set of x satisfying $-1 \leq x \leq 1$. Note that here $f(x)$ does not become undefined for some x because of division by 0, but rather because the square root of a negative number is involved.

Let us next determine the graphs of $y = (1 - x^2)^{1/2}$ and $y = -(1 - x^2)^{1/2}$. We shall proceed, as usual, by selecting several values of x and finding the image for each of these. The values of x and y for $y = (1 - x^2)^{1/2}$ are shown in Table 2–5. It is unnecessary to construct a separate table for $y = -(1 - x^2)^{1/2}$ since the image of x here is merely the negative of that given in Table 2–5. In Figure 2–28, we have plotted the points so obtained,

TABLE 2–5

$$y = (1 - x^2)^{1/2}$$

x	1	0.8	0.6	0.4	0.2	0	−0.2	−0.4	−0.6	−0.8	−1
y	0	0.6	0.8	0.92	0.98	1	0.98	0.92	0.8	0.6	0

and drawn a smooth curve through the points. The solid curve represents the graph of $y = (1 - x^2)^{1/2}$ while the dashed curve represents the graph of $y = -(1 - x^2)^{1/2}$. The two curves taken together yield a single, closed curve which is the graph of the relation $x^2 + y^2 = 1$. The curve looks like a circle. Indeed, if a compass is used to draw a circle with its center at the origin and a radius of one unit, it will be found that all these points lie on this circle. Furthermore, if any other point in the graph of either function is plotted, it also lies on the circle. Thus the graph of $x^2 + y^2 = 1$ corresponds to what we think of geometrically as a circle; it is a circle with its center at the origin and radius one.

If $r > 0$, the same procedure shows that the graph of $x^2 + y^2 = r^2$ also corresponds to what we think of as a circle. It is a circle with radius r and center at the origin. More generally, consider the equation

$$(x - a)^2 + (y - b)^2 = r^2 , \qquad (2\text{-}62)$$

where a and b are specified numbers. Note that if (x_1, y_1) is a solution to $x^2 + y^2 = r^2$, then if $x_2 = x_1 + a$ and $y_2 = y_1 + b$, (x_2, y_2) is a solution to (2–62). Thus it would appear that the graph of (2–62) is nothing but the graph of $x^2 + y^2 = r^2$ shifted a units along the x-axis and b units along the y-axis. This is indeed correct, as we could verify directly by going through the above procedures, since by properties 2 and 5 the graph of (2–62) is the union of the graphs of the two functions

$$y = b + [r^2 - (x - a)^2]^{1/2}; \qquad y = b - [r^2 - (x - a)^2]^{1/2} . \quad (2\text{-}63)$$

The domain of these functions is the set of values of x such that $(x - a)^2 \le r^2$. This is equivalent to $-r \le x - a \le r$ or $a - r \le x \le a + r$. Therefore, the graph of (2–62) is a circle having radius r with its center at (a, b). In Figure 2–29 are shown the graphs of

$$(x - 4)^2 + (y + 3)^2 = 9 \quad \text{and} \quad (x + 3)^2 + (y - 2)^2 = 16 .$$

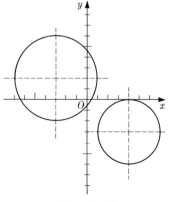

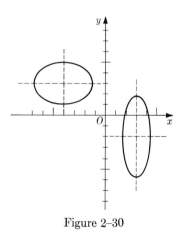

Figure 2–29   Figure 2–30

It is easy to sketch quickly the graph of any equation of the form (2–62) since it is a circle with radius r and center at (a, b). Alternatively, if we are given any circle in the xy-plane with its center is at (a, b) and radius r, the algebraic representation of the circle is (2–62). Our geometric concept of a circle is a rather intuitive one, because we think of it as a curve drawn by a compass. Since we have seen that any circle can be considered to be the graph of an equation of the form (2–62), we can now make more precise what we mean by a circle by defining a circle with center at (a, b) and radius r to be the set of points C

$$C = \{(x, y)|(x - a)^2 + (y - b)^2 = r^2\} . \qquad (2\text{–}64)$$

Let us now move on to studying the graphs of relations of the form

$$\alpha_1(x - a)^2 + \alpha_2(y - b)^2 = \beta \qquad (2\text{–}65)$$

where α_1, α_2 and β are specified positive numbers and a and b are arbitrary but specified numbers. We note immediately by property 4 that if $\alpha_1 = \alpha_2 = \alpha$, then the graph of (2–65) is a circle with radius $(\beta/\alpha)^{1/2}$. If $\alpha_1 \neq \alpha_2$, we expect that the graph of (2–65) will still roughly resemble a circle if α_1 does not differ much from α_2. This is indeed correct. To determine more precisely on the graph of (2–65) we note from properties 4, 2 and 5 (applied in this order), that the graph of (2–65) is the union of the graphs of the following two functions:

$$y = b + \left[\frac{\beta}{\alpha_2} - \frac{\alpha_1}{\alpha_2}(x - a)^2\right]^{1/2}; \qquad y = b - \left[\frac{\beta}{\alpha_2} - \frac{\alpha_1}{\alpha_2}(x - a)^2\right]^{1/2} .$$

$$(2\text{–}66)$$

The domain of these functions consists of the set of numbers x satisfying

$$a - (\beta/\alpha_1)^{1/2} \leq x \leq a + (\beta/\alpha_1)^{1/2} . \qquad (2\text{–}67)$$

The reader should verify this. In Figure 2–30, we have shown the graphs of

$$16(x - 3)^2 + 2(y + 2)^2 = 32 \quad \text{and} \quad (x + 4)^2 + 2(y - 3)^2 = 8 .$$

These are determined in the usual way and the reader should compute several points to check that the graphs are correct. The curves look like flattened-out circles, and they are called ellipses. The graph of any equation of the form (2–65) with α_1, α_2 and β positive and $\alpha_1 \neq \alpha_2$ is called an *ellipse* and (2–65) is called the equation of an ellipse.

The point (a, b) is referred to as the *center* of the ellipse whose equation is (2–65), since intuitively (a, b) lies at what we think of as the center of the interior of the graph of (2–65). If lines parallel to the x- and y-axes are drawn through (a, b) as shown by the dashed lines in Figure 2–30, these divide the ellipse into four symmetrical pieces. These two lines are referred to as axes of symmetry for the ellipse. In general, axes of symmetry are defined as follows:

AXES OF SYMMETRY. *The vertical line whose equation is $x = a$ is called an axis of symmetry for the graph of an equation if when $(a + u, y)$, $u > 0$, is a solution to the equation, then $(a - u, y)$ is also a solution. Similarly, the horizontal line whose equation is $y = b$ is called an axis of symmetry for the graph of an equation if when $(x, b + v)$, $v > 0$ is a solution to the equation, then $(x, b - v)$ is also a solution.*

It is very easy to prove, for example, that the line $x = a$ is an axis of symmetry of the graph of (2–65), since if $(a + u, y)$ is a solution, then $\alpha_1 u^2 + \alpha_2 (y - b)^2 = \beta$. However, $(a - u, y)$ is also a solution, because $(-u)^2 = u^2$. Similarly we can prove that the line $y = b$ is an axis of symmetry. A knowledge that the graph of the equation and, as we frequently say, the equation itself has an axis of symmetry simplifies the sketching of the graph of the equation, since if we know what the graph is on one side of the axis of symmetry, the graph on the other side can easily be obtained by reflection in the axis of symmetry.

To sketch rapidly an ellipse it is only necessary to draw the axes of symmetry, locate the four points where the curve crosses the axes of symmetry, and then draw in the curve which passes through these four points. We ask the reader to show in the problems that the ellipse crosses the axis of symmetry $y = b$ at $x = a + (\beta/\alpha_1)^{1/2}$ and $x = a - (\beta/\alpha_1)^{1/2}$, and crosses the axis of symmetry $x = a$ at $y = b + (\beta/\alpha_2)^{1/2}$ and $y = b - (\beta/\alpha_2)^{1/2}$. The line segments representing the parts of the axes of symmetry contained inside an ellipse are called the *axes of the ellipse*. The longer one is called the *major axis* and the shorter one the *minor axis*. The length of the horizontal axis is $2(\beta/\alpha_1)^{1/2}$ and of the vertical axis is $2(\beta/\alpha_2)^{1/2}$.

The equations for circles and ellipses represent relations whose graphs are not the graph of a function $y = f(x)$. Instead, the graph of a circle or an ellipse is the union of the graphs of two functions. It might now be helpful to point out a difference between the terminology we are using and the terminology the reader may encounter in some older calculus or analytic geometry books which are still in general use. In the older books what we have called a function is referred to as a single-valued function, and any relation whose graph is the union of two or more functions is called a multivalued function. Thus the equations for circles and ellipses would be considered to define multivalued functions. This terminology, although out of date, is still to be found in many places.

In our study of functions we have always used x as the symbol for the independent variable. Recall, however, that the symbol used is irrelevant and we could just as easily use y as the symbol for the independent variable and x as the symbol for the dependent variable. Thus instead of writing $y = x^2$ we could write $x = y^2$ and we would be representing the same function either way. We now come to an important point. The graph of $y = x^2$

will look like the graph of $x = y^2$ when we sketch it in an xy-coordinate system only if we interchange the labels on the x-and y-axes, so that the horizontal axis which we have been calling the x-axis is now called the y-axis. It is conventional, however, always to use the horizontal axis for the x-axis, so the graph of $x = y^2$ will look different from that of $y = x^2$. The graph of $x = y^2$ is shown in Figure 2–31, and as would be expected this curve is called a parabola. Note that in Figure 2–31 points on the y-axis represent elements of the domain. The reader may now wonder why we would ever consider interchanging the symbols for x and y in the function notation, and not on the coordinate axes, thus giving rise to graphs which appear turned around. The reason is that x and y may refer to physical variables which appear in some relation. This relation may possibly define a function with x as the independent variable or with y as the independent variable. In graphing relations, it is convenient always to take the x-axis as the horizontal one. In doing so, however, we must on occasion consider functions in which y is the independent variable. For example, the graph of the relation $x - y^2 = 0$ is precisely the graph of the function $x = y^2$ which has y as the independent variable. More generally, any relation

$$x - a(y - b)^2 - c = 0, \quad a \neq 0$$

is called the equation of a parabola. The graph of this equation has $y = b$ as an axis of symmetry, and the curve crosses the axis of symmetry at $x = c$.

We have noted previously that relations whose graphs are circles or ellipses have the property that their graphs can be considered to be the union of the graphs of two functions in which x is the independent variable. Equally well, however, their graphs can be considered to be the union of the graphs of two functions in which y is the independent variable. Thus, for example, the graph of $x^2 + y^2 = 1$ is the union of the graphs of the two functions $x = (1 - y^2)^{1/2}$ and $x = -(1 - y^2)^{1/2}$.

We shall conclude our discussion of graphing equations by considering one final example whose graph is the graph of a function having y as the independent variable. Let us study $x(y^2 - 1) = 1$. On multiplying by $1/(y^2 - 1)$, we see that any solution to the given equation with y different from *1* or *− 1* is an element of the graph of the function

$$x = \frac{1}{y^2 - 1}, \tag{2–68}$$

and any point in the graph of this function is a solution to the given equation. No solution to the given equation can have $y = 1$ or -1, since then $x(y^2 - 1) = 0 \neq 1$. Hence, the graph of the relation $x(y^2 - 1) = 1$ is the same as the graph of the function (2–68). The domain of (2–68) consists of all real numbers y except 1 and -1. By selecting several positive values of y and computing the images x, we obtain Table 2–6. The images of the cor-

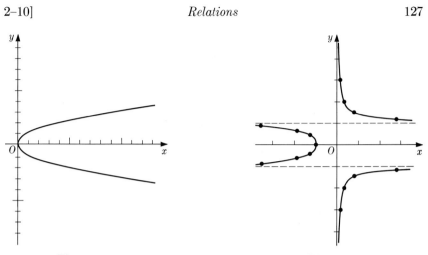

Figure 2–31   Figure 2–32

responding negative values of y are the same as the images of the positive ones. These points are plotted in Figure 2–32, and smooth curves have been drawn through the points. It will be noted that the horizontal lines $y = 1$

TABLE 2–6

$$x = \frac{1}{y^2 - 1}$$

y	0	0.5	0.7	0.85	1.16	1.5	2	3
x	-1	-1.33	-1.96	-3.58	2.78	0.8	0.33	0.125

and $y = -1$ are horizontal asymptotes and the vertical line $x = 0$ is a vertical asymptote. No special name is given to this graph. The example illustrates, however, that simple equations may have rather complicated looking graphs.

If there is more than a single solution to an equation involving two variables x and y, then the graph of such an equation will normally be represented by a curve or curves in the xy-plane. On checking back over our procedures for determining the graphs of equations, the reader will find that in every case we determined a set of one or more functions, say $y = f_1(x)$, $\ldots$, $y = f_k(x)$, having x as the independent variable, or a set of one or more functions $x = g_1(y)$, $\ldots$, $x = g_u(y)$, having y as the independent variable such that the union of the graphs of these functions was the **graph of the equation**. Usually, but not always, we can find both a set of functions with x as the independent variable and a set of functions with y as the independent variable, each set having the characteristic that the union of the graphs of the functions in the set is the graph of the equation of interest.

Whether we choose the functions with x as the independent variable or those with y as the independent variable is merely a matter of convenience.

2–11 INVERSE REPRESENTATION OF A FUNCTION

The discussion at the end of the previous section indicated that the graph of any equation can usually be thought of as the union of the graphs of one or more functions having x as the independent variable, or the union of one or more functions having y as the independent variable. This brings up an interesting idea. Given any function $y = f(x)$, does there exist a set of functions, say $x = g_1(y), \ldots, x = g_u(y)$, having y as the independent variable, such that the union of the graphs of these latter functions is precisely the graph of $y = f(x)$? The answer, normally, is yes. The set of functions $g_1(y), \ldots, g_u(y)$ form what we shall call the *inverse representation* of $y = f(x)$. Suppose that

$$G = \{(x, y) | y = f(x), \quad \text{all } x \text{ in domain}\} \tag{2–69}$$

and

$$Y_k = \{(x, y) | x = g_k(y), \; y \in D_k\}, \quad k = 1, \ldots, u, \tag{2–70}$$

where D_k is the specified domain for $g_k(y)$. (This may not be the set of all y for which $g_k(y)$ is defined.) Then if

$$G = Y_1 \cup Y_2 \cup \cdots \cup Y_k,$$

the set of functions $g_k(y)$ is said to be the inverse representation of $f(x)$.

Let us now illustrate the determination of the inverse representation of a function with some examples. The simplest possible case is that of a linear function $y = ax + b$, $a \neq 0$. By property 2, the set of solutions to this equation is the same as the set of solutions to $ax = y - b$; by property 4, the set of solutions is the same as the set of solutions to

$$x = \frac{1}{a} y - \frac{b}{a}. \tag{2–71}$$

Here we have a single linear equation which represents a function with y as the independent variable and whose graph is the same as the graph of $y = ax + b$. Therefore, the single function (2–71) is the inverse representation of $y = ax + b$. When the inverse representation of a function consists of just a single function, this single function is called *the inverse* of the given function. The only functions which have inverses are those whose inverse representation contains just a single function. The function $y = ax + b$ has an inverse, which is (2–71). When a function has an inverse, then this inverse is precisely what we meant by an inverse in Section 2–2, provided that the set B in the definition of a function is taken to be the range.

The inverse representation of a function will consist of a single function if and only if any given number y in the range is the image of only one element x in the domain. If there is an element of the range which is the image of two or more different elements of the domain, then at least two functions will be needed in the inverse representation. For example, if y^* is the image of precisely two elements of the domain, say x_1 and x_2, then the graph of $y = f(x)$ contains the points (x_1, y^*) and (x_2, y^*). If there were only one function in the inverse representation, say $g(y)$, then there would be only one point $(g(y^*), y^*)$ in the graph of this function, and it could not be the same as the graph of $y = f(x)$. It is necessary to have one function in which the image of y^* is x_1 and another in which the image of y^* is x_2. The maxi-

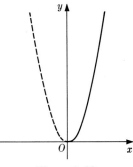

Figure 2–33

mum number of functions in the inverse representation is the maximum number of different elements in the domain which have a common image. There exist functions whose inverse representation requires an infinite number of functions.

Another example of a function which has an inverse is $y = 1/x$. Note that on multiplying by x, the set of solutions to $y = 1/x$ is the same as the set of solutions to $xy = 1$, since no solution to $xy = 1$ can have $x = 0$. However, the set of solutions to $xy = 1$ is the same as the set of solutions to $x = 1/y$ (why?). Thus the graph of $y = 1/x$ is the same as the graph of $x = 1/y$, and this latter function is the inverse of the former.

Let us now study a simple example where the inverse representation consists of two functions. Suppose that $y = x^2$. Then by property 5, the graph of $x^2 = y$ is the union of the graphs of $x = y^{1/2}$ and $x = -y^{1/2}$, and the domain of these functions is the set of all non-negative y. The graph of $x = y^{1/2}$ gives the solid curve shown in Figure 2–33 and the graph of $x = -y^{1/2}$ gives the dashed curve. These two curves form the parabola which is the graph of $y = x^2$. The inverse representation of $y = x^2$ is then the two functions $x = y^{1/2}$ and $x = -y^{1/2}$. More generally, the inverse representation of $y = a(x - b)^2 + c$, $a \neq 0$, consists of the two functions

$$x = b + \left(\frac{y-c}{a}\right)^{1/2} \quad \text{and} \quad x = b - \left(\frac{y-c}{a}\right)^{1/2}, \qquad (2\text{-}72)$$

as we can see by use of properties 2, 4 and 5. The domain of the functions (2–72) is the set of all $y \geq c$ if $a > 0$ or all $y \leq c$ if $a < 0$.

In the simple examples just given, it has been quite easy to determine the inverse representations of the functions involved. In general, however, it is not at all easy to do. For example, the reader would probably have considerable difficulty in finding the inverse representation of $y = x^3 - 3x^2 + 16x - 1$. Not only may it be difficult to determine explicitly the inverse representation, it may be impossible. The mere fact that there exists a set of functions $g_1(y), \ldots, g_u(y)$, the union of whose graphs is the graph of $y = f(x)$, does not mean we can write down an explicit formula for $g_k(y)$ which involves only a finite number of additions, subtractions, multiplications, divisions and taking roots. These are the only operations we have studied, and it is not true that every function of one variable is such that it can be represented explicitly by a formula which involves only a finite number of these operations. We shall encounter a variety of functions of this type later. Thus, even though we may know the functions $g_k(y)$ exist, we may not be able to express them using formulas of the type we have been studying.

2–12 OTHER TYPES OF RELATIONS

It is by no means true that every relation between two variables x and y can be represented by an equation. In this section we wish to study some other types of relations which occur with great frequency. We shall begin by discussing what are called *inequalities*. Let us consider the set of points H in the xy-plane having the property that

$$3x + 2y > 2. \qquad (2\text{-}73)$$

In other words, H is the set of points with the property that, if we multiply the first coordinate of any point in H by 3 and add to this 2 times the second cordinate, the number so obtained is greater than 2. This serves to define a unique set H, which is not null and is not the entire plane. We refer to (2–73) as a *linear inequality*, and the set of points H is called the *set of solutions* to the inequality (2–73). The inequality (2–73) then serves as a rule to select a certain subset of the points in the xy-plane, and this subset is the set of solutions H to (2–73). Thus (2–73) represents a relation, and the graph of this relation is H. We would now like to see how to represent H geometrically.

To do this, note that every point (x, y) must satisfy one and only one of the following relations

$$3x + 2y > 2, \quad 3x + 2y = 2, \quad 3x + 2y < 2. \qquad (2\text{-}74)$$

In other words, the line $3x + 2y = 2$ divides the plane into three mutually exclusive and collectively exhaustive sets which are the graphs of the three relations in (2–74). By mutually exclusive we mean that a point cannot be in more than one of the sets; by collectively exhaustive we mean that every point in the xy-plane is in one of them. The line $3x + 2y = 2$ is shown in Figure 2–34. No point on this line satisfies (2–73), and hence no point on the line is in H. However, the points $(2, 1)$, $(1, 2)$, $(4, -1)$, $(-1, 3)$ and $(3, -3)$ are all solutions to (2–73) and are in H. These points are plotted in Figure 2–34. In fact, if we test any point (x, y) lying to the right of the line $3x +$

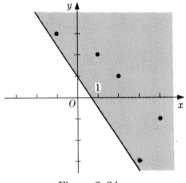

Figure 2–34

$2y = 2$, it will be found to be a solution to (2–73). The graph of the relation (2–73) is then the shaded region in Figure 2–34 and does not include the line itself. The same reasoning shows that the graph of $3x + 2y < 2$ is the unshaded part of the plane in Figure 2–34, not including the line. Thus, as is necessary, every point in the plane is in one and only one of the three sets representing the graphs of the three relations (2–74). Note that, unlike the graphs of equations, which are curves, the graphs of $3x + 2y > 2$ and $3x + 2y < 2$ correspond to what we think of intuitively as an area or region of the plane, in this case essentially half the plane. The sets

$$H_1 = \{(x, y)|3x + 2y > 2\}; \qquad H_2 = \{(x, y)|3x + 2y < 2\} \qquad (2\text{–}75)$$

will be referred to as *open half spaces*. The reason for the term *half space* follows because the set is essentially half the plane. The *open* refers to the fact that points on the line $3x + 2y = 2$, which forms the boundary of the set, are not included in the set.

Let us next find the graph of the inequality $3x + 2y \geq 2$. Any point (x, y) which, on multiplying x by 3 and adding 2 times y to this, yields a number greater than or equal to 2 is called a solution to the inequality. The set of all solutions, call it H_3, will then be the graph which we are seeking. If $(x, y) \in H_3$ then (x, y) is also a solution to $3x + 2y > 2$ or $3x + 2y = 2$, but not both. If H_1 denotes the set of solutions to $3x + 2y > 2$ and L the set of solutions to $3x + 2y = 2$, then $H_3 \subset H_1 \cup L$. However, any solution to $3x + 2y > 2$ or $3x + 2y = 2$ is also a solution to $3x + 2y \geq 2$, so $H_1 \cup L \subset H_3$. Consequently, $H_3 = H_1 \cup L$ and the set of solutions to $3x + 2y \geq 2$ is the union of the set of solutions to $3x + 2y > 2$ and the set of solutions to $3x + 2y = 2$. H_3 is then the shaded region in Figure 2–34 including the line L. H_3 is called a *closed half space*, since the boundary is now included in H_3.

Consider next the relation $x^2 + y^2 < 1$. The graph of this relation is the set of points in the xy-plane having the property that the sum of the squares

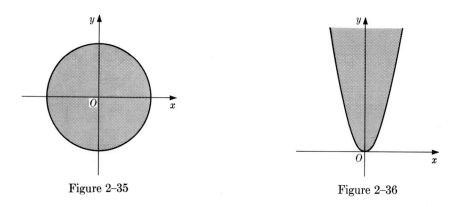

Figure 2–35   Figure 2–36

of their coordinates is less than 1. This graph is referred to as the set of solutions to the inequality. Any point lying inside the circle with center at the origin and radius 1 is then a solution to $x^2 + y^2 < 1$ and no other point is. Thus the shaded region in Figure 2–35, not including the circle $x^2 + y^2 = 1$, is the set of solutions. For obvious reasons, then, the set of points

$$I = \{(x, y) | (x - a)^2 + (y - b)^2 < r^2, \quad r > 0\} \qquad (2\text{–}76)$$

is called the inside of the circle with center (a, b) and radius r.

The set of solutions to $y \geq x^2$ is the set of points (x, y) having the characteristic that the y-coordinate is greater than or equal to the square of the x-coordinate. This set of points, which is the graph of the relation $y \geq x^2$, is the shaded area in Figure 2–36 and also includes the parabola $y = x^2$. We can now note that *any* equation relating x and y serves to divide the xy-plane into three mutually exclusive and collectively exhaustive sets. The first is the set of points satisfying the equation. The second is the set of points which satisfy the relation obtained by replacing the equals sign by a greater than sign, and the third is the set of points obtained by replacing the equals sign by a less than sign. For situations of the type we have been studying, where the graph of the equation clearly separates the plane into two distinct regions, it is easy to determine which region corresponds to the relation having the $<$ sign and which to the one having the $>$ sign. This is done simply by selecting one point not on the graph of the equation and determining which relation it satisfies. For example, to determine which side of the parabola $y = x^2$ represents the graph of $y > x^2$, we select any point not on the parabola, say $(1, 0)$, and test it. Now $1^2 > 0$. Thus $(1, 0)$ is not a solution to $y > x^2$ and the set of solutions to $y > x^2$ lies on the opposite side of the parabola from $(1, 0)$.

Consider now the two sets

$$X_1 = \{(x, y) | x^2 + y^2 \leq 1\}; \qquad X_2 = \{(x, y) | (x - 1)^2 + y^2 \leq 1\} .$$

X_1 is the set of points inside and on the circle with radius 1 and center at the origin, and X_2 is the set of points inside and on the circle with radius 1 and center at $(1, 0)$. Then $X_3 = X_1 \cup X_2$, the union of X_1 and X_2, is the shaded

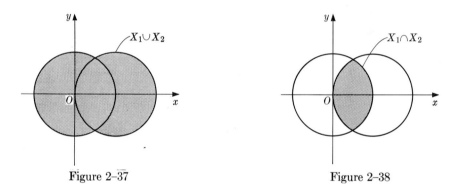

Figure 2–37   Figure 2–38

region in Figure 2–37, including the circles themselves. X_3 can be considered to be the graph of a relation which selects points that satisfy either one of the relations whose graphs are X_1 and X_2. Thus we can form new relations by taking the union of the graphs of other relations. Equally well, we can form new relations from given relations by taking the intersection of the graphs of the given relations. The set of points $X_4 = X_1 \cap X_2$ is shown in Figure 2–38 as the shaded area and includes the boundary of the shaded area. The set X_4 is also the graph of a relation. This relation selects from the xy-plane those points which are solutions to *both* of the inequalities

$$x^2 + y^2 \leq 1$$
$$(x - 1)^2 + y^2 \leq 1 . \qquad (2\text{–}77)$$

Equation (2–77) is referred to as a *system of inequalities* and X_4 is referred to as the *set of solutions* to the system of inequalities. The set of solutions to a system of inequalities is the intersection of the sets of solutions to each of the individual inequalities and is the set of points in the xy-plane having the characteristic that each point in the set is a solution to each of the inequalities involved.

Generally speaking, we shall be more interested in forming new relations by taking intersections than by taking unions. The reason for this is that many practical problems in one way or another involve situations in which one is interested in the set of points which satisfy each of a number of relations. In particular, problems involving systems of inequalities arise with

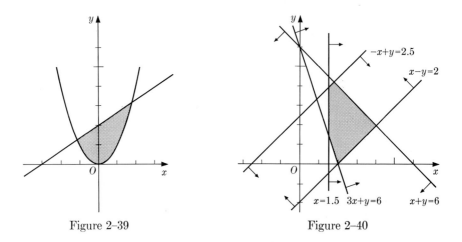

Figure 2–39   Figure 2–40

considerable frequency, and it is therefore worthwhile to study in a little more detail the geometric representation of the set of solutions for a given system of inequalities. As another example, consider the system

$$y - x^2 \geq 0$$
$$3y - 2x \leq 6 . \tag{2–78}$$

The set of solutions to (2–78) is $X_3 = X_1 \cap X_2$, where

$$X_1 = \{(x, y) | y - x^2 \geq 0\}; \qquad X_2 = \{(x, y) | 3y - 2x \leq 6\} ,$$

so that the set of solutions X_3 to (2–78) is the intersection of the sets of solutions to each of the individual inequalities. The set X_3 is the shaded region shown in Figure 2–39.

The task of finding the set of solutions to a system of linear inequalities is referred to as *solving the system of inequalities*. A system of inequalities may contain many inequalities; it is by no means true that only two will be involved as in our previous examples. As a final example, let us consider the system

$$x + y \leq 6$$
$$x \geq 1.5$$
$$3x + y \geq 6$$
$$x - y \leq 2$$
$$-x + y \leq 2.5 . \tag{2–79}$$

The set of solutions to (2–79) is the intersection of five sets, each of which is a closed half space. The set of solutions is the shaded region shown in Figure 2–40. We have shown the lines which form the boundaries of the half spaces and have indicated with arrows which side of the line represents the appropriate half space. The reader should verify that the solution set is the shaded region, by beginning with the half space representing the solutions to $x + y \leq 6$, and progressively narrowing down this region by adding one more inequality at each step. The inequalities in (2–79) are referred to as *linear inequalities*, since if the inequality signs were replaced by equal signs, we would obtain a linear equation in each case. We refer to (2–79) as a system of linear inequalities. Linear inequalities play an important role in areas such as linear programming.

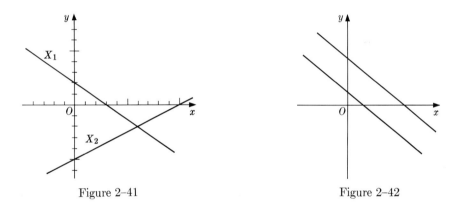

Figure 2–41   Figure 2–42

Generally, from what we have seen above, we expect the set of solutions to a system of linear inequalities to be represented by some region of the plane rather than by a curve. This need not always be true, however, since there may not be any solution, but in cases of practical interest it is usually true that the solution set will be represented by a region.

A type of practical problem which arises even more frequently than those concerned with finding the set of solutions to a system of inequalities is one in which we are interested in finding the set of points in the xy-plane which are simultaneously solutions to two equations. Suppose, for example, that we wish to find those points in the xy-plane which are simultaneously solutions to the equations

$$2x + 3y = 6$$
$$x - 2y = 10 .$$
$$(2–80)$$

The desired set of points is then the intersection of the two sets

$$X_1 = \{(x, y)|2x + 3y = 6\}; \qquad X_2 = \{(x, y)|x - 2y = 10\} ,$$

and $X_1 \cap X_2$ is called the *set of solutions* to (2–80). Each set X_1 and X_2 is a straight line as shown in Figure 2–41. Thus we see that there is only one point $x = 6$, $y = -2$ which is a solution to (2–80). We refer to (2–80) as a set or system of equations, and in particular (2–80) is called a *system of linear equations* or simultaneous linear equations, since each of the equations is linear.

A system of two linear equations need not always have a unique solution. The following system

$$x + y = 6$$
$$2x + 2y = 6 \qquad\qquad (2\text{--}81)$$

has no solution because the lines are parallel, as shown in Figure 2–42. On the other hand, the system

$$x + y = 6$$
$$2x + 2y = 12 \qquad\qquad (2\text{--}82)$$

has an infinite number of solutions, since the graphs of both equations are the same line (the upper line in Figure 2–42). In this case, the set of solutions to (2–82) is identical with the set of solutions to $x + y = 6$ (or $2x + 2y = 12$), and we say that one of the equations is *redundant*.

The above three cases cover every possibility that can arise in solving a system of two linear equations. Either the two lines intersect in a unique point, or they are parallel and there is no solution, or the two equations represent the same straight line and every point on the line is a solution. To determine the unique solution (if there is one) it is not necessary to locate graphically the point of intersection of the lines. This may easily be done algebraically by transforming the equations to a new form where the solution is exhibited explicitly. The transformations are made in such a way that the set of solutions remains unchanged. Properties 1 through 5 developed in Section 2–9 can be applied to any equation in the system without changing the set of solutions to that equation, and hence the set of solutions to the set. One more property is frequently used. We can add or subtract any one equation in the system from any other equation and the new system will have the same set of solutions as the original ones. We shall refer to this as property 6. Property 6 thus says that the following two systems have the same set of solutions

$$\mathcal{G}_1 = \mathcal{K}_1 \qquad \mathcal{G}_1 + \mathcal{G}_2 = \mathcal{K}_1 + \mathcal{K}_2$$
$$\mathcal{G}_2 = \mathcal{K}_2; \qquad \mathcal{G}_2 = \mathcal{K}_2. \qquad\qquad (2\text{--}83)$$

We ask the reader to prove property 6 in the problems.

Let us then see how to determine the unique solution, if it exists, to

$$a_1 x + a_2 y = c_1$$
$$b_1 x + b_2 y = c_2. \qquad\qquad (2\text{--}84)$$

If either a_1 or a_2 is 0, then the first equation can be immediately solved for either x or y. The value of the variable so obtained can then be substituted into the second equation to yield the value of the other variable (provided the coefficient of the other variable is not 0). The same procedure can be applied if a_1 and a_2 are different from 0, but b_1 or b_2 is 0. Now let us examine the more complicated case where a_1, a_2, b_1 and b_2 are all different from 0. Multiply the first equation by b_2 and the second by a_2 to yield

$$a_1 b_2 x + a_2 b_2 y = c_1 b_2$$
$$a_2 b_1 x + a_2 b_2 y = c_2 a_2 , \qquad (2\text{–}85)$$

and by property 4 the set of solutions to (2–85) is the same as the set of solutions to (2–84). Now subtract the second equation from the first to yield the new system

$$(a_1 b_2 - a_2 b_1)x = c_1 b_2 - c_2 a_2$$
$$a_2 b_1 x + a_2 b_2 y = c_2 a_2 , \qquad (2\text{–}86)$$

and by property 6 the set of solutions to (2–86) is the same as the set of solutions to (2–85). By definition, every solution to the system (2–86) must be a solution to each of the individual equations. However, if $a_1 b_2 - a_2 b_1 \neq 0$, it follows that the only solutions to the first equation are those having

$$x = \frac{c_1 b_2 - c_2 a_2}{a_1 b_2 - a_2 b_1} . \qquad (2\text{–}87)$$

On replacing x in the second equation by the value in (2–87), it immediately follows that there is only one solution to the second equation having the first coordinate given by (2–87), and this solution has

$$y = \frac{c_2 a_1 - c_1 b_1}{a_1 b_2 - a_2 b_1} . \qquad (2\text{–}88)$$

In this way, then, a unique solution to (2–84) is determined. If $a_1 b_2 - a_2 b_1 = 0$, there is either no solution or an infinite number of solutions, and we ask the reader to study this case in the problems. To solve (2–80) by the method just described we can, for example, multiply the second equation by 2, subtract and obtain $7y = -14$ or $y = -2$. On substituting this value of y into the second equation, we find $x = 6$. To solve a system such as (2–84), there is no need to try to remember (2–87) and (2–88). It is much easier to follow through directly the process described above, which eliminates one variable from one of the equations.

With systems of inequalities, it is possible to have a large number of inequalities in the system while still having a set of solutions which is represented geometrically by a region. Normally, however, there will be no solution (x, y) to a system of three or more linear equations. A solution to three equations could exist only if the three lines intersected in a single point, or if at least two equations represented the same line.

Let us conclude this section by studying a system of nonlinear equations. An equation which is not linear, that is, which does not have the form

$a_1x + a_2y = b$, is called *nonlinear*. A system of equations is called non-linear if at least one equation in the system is nonlinear. As an example, consider the following system involving two nonlinear equations:

$$x^2 + y^2 = 16$$
$$-(x - 1)^2 + y = -4 .$$
$$\text{(2–89)}$$

The set of solutions to the first equation is a circle with radius 4 and center at the origin, and the set of solutions to the second is a parabola which opens upward, has an axis of symmetry $x = 1$ and crosses the axis of symmetry at $y = -4$. The graphs of each of the equations are shown in Figure 2–43.

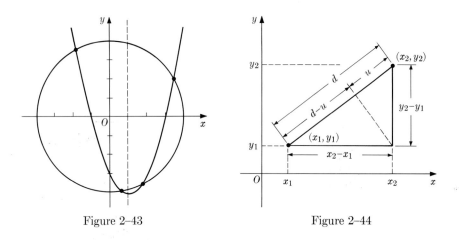

Figure 2–43   Figure 2–44

Note that the intersection of these two graphs consists of four points, and therefore there are precisely four different solutions to the system (2–89). Unlike the situation for a system of linear equations, the task of determining algebraically the solutions to (2–89) is not at all easy. We shall not consider the difficulties here. Instead, the reader is asked to investigate the matter in the problems. The variety of possible systems involving at least one non-linear equation is endless, and we shall not give additional examples in the text.

2–13 THE DISTANCE FORMULA

Suppose that two arbitrary points (x_1, y_1) and (x_2, y_2) in the xy-plane are selected and we are asked to determine the distance between these two points. At present, the only way we have of finding the distance is to place a ruler along the points and measure the distance. What we would like to develop in this section is a formula which gives the distance in terms of the coordinates of the points. To obtain such a formula, consider Figure 2–44.

The distance from (x_1, y_1) to (x_2, y_2) is simply the length d of the line segment joining these two points. The given two points determine the right triangle shown. The length of the base of the triangle is $x_2 - x_1$ and the length of the altitude is $y_2 - y_1$. We can determine the length of the base and altitude, since these are parallel to the x- and y-axes respectively. A formula which gives d in terms of x_1, x_2, y_1 and y_2 now follows immediately from the famous theorem of plane geometry known as the Pythagorean theorem. This theorem states that the square of the length of the hypotenuse of a right triangle is equal to the sum of the squares of the lengths of the other two sides. For the case under consideration this becomes

$$d^2 = (x_2 - x_1)^2 + (y_2 - y_1)^2 \tag{2–90}$$

or

$$d = [(x_2 - x_1)^2 + (y_2 - y_1)^2]^{1/2} . \tag{2–91}$$

Here we have obtained the formula desired. Given the coordinates of any two points, we can find the distance between them.

We can easily back up one step and prove the Pythagorean theorem if we take as known the properties of similar triangles. Suppose that we drop a perpendicular from the vertex of the right angle to the hypotenuse, as shown by the dashed line in Figure 2–44. There result three similar triangles. Since the lengths of the corresponding sides are proportional, we have

$$\frac{x_2 - x_1}{d - u} = \frac{d}{x_2 - x_1} \quad \text{or} \quad (x_2 - x_1)^2 = d^2 - du \tag{2–92}$$

and

$$\frac{y_2 - y_1}{u} = \frac{d}{y_2 - y_1} \quad \text{or} \quad (y_2 - y_1)^2 = du . \tag{2–93}$$

On substituting the value for du from (2–93) into (2–92), we obtain (2–90), which proves the Pythagorean theorem. We shall not attempt to carry things back any further by proving the properties of similar triangles.

We might note that in (2–91) we can interchange the subscripts 1 and 2 on the x's and y's without changing the value of d. The explanation for this is the intuitively obvious fact that the distance from (x_1, y_1) to (x_2, y_2) is the same as the distance from (x_2, y_2) to (x_1, y_1). Note also that $d > 0$ unless $x_1 = x_2$ and $y_1 = y_2$. In the derivation of (2–91) we implicitly made an important assumption which will now be made explicit. We assumed that the same unit of length was being used for measurements on both the x- and y-axes. If the units are different, then the distance measured with a ruler would not be the same as that computed from (2–91). As a final observation of interest, we see at once from (2–90) and the equation of a circle (2–62) that a circle is the set of all points which are at a fixed distance from a given point (a, b). This property can be used to define a circle geometrically.

2-14* THE SINE AND COSINE FUNCTIONS

The methods we have used previously for characterizing a function were:
1) by a table; 2) by a graph; 3) by a formula. We never characterized a
function directly by a graph. For each case studied previously, we began
with a table or a formula and deduced the graph from these. However, we
can draw an arbitrary curve in the xy-plane having the property that any
vertical line intersects the curve no more than once, and this serves to define
some function. It defines a function, since there will be determined a unique
image y for every x such that a vertical line passing through x intersects the
curve. The domain is the set of all x having the property that a vertical line
through x intersects the curve. We noted in discussing the inverse repre-

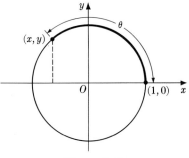

Figure 2–45

sentation of functions that not every function of one variable can be represented by an algebraic formula involving only a finite number of the four
arithmetic operations and the taking of roots. Indeed, if in the manner just
described we draw an arbitrary curve in the xy-plane to define a function, it
is very possible that there is no formula of the type just considered whose
graph will be this curve.

   In this section, we would like to introduce two functions which are widely
used in many areas, especially the physical sciences. They are called the sine
and cosine functions, and they will be defined in a manner different from
any of those listed above. These functions happen to be examples of functions which cannot be represented by formulas of the type referred to above.
To define these two new functions, consider the circle of radius 1 with center
at the origin which is shown in Figure 2–45. Recall from geometry that the
circumference of a circle is $2\pi r$, where r is the radius, with π being an irrational number which is approximately 3.14159. The circumference of the
circle in Figure 2–45 is thus 2π, since $r = 1$. Consider then the set $D =$

---

* Starred sections may be omitted without loss of continuity.

$\{\theta | 0 \leq \theta \leq 2\pi\}$. We shall initially take D to be the domain for each of the new functions to be defined. Let us now specify the rule to be used for finding the image in each case of any number θ in the domain. The independent variable in each function will be denoted by θ; x will not be used because it appears in a different context. Let us now imagine that we have a piece of wire of length 2π on which has been etched a very finely divided scale, so that it is possible to use the wire as a ruler. Next imagine that the wire is bent into a circle with radius 1 and placed on top the circle shown in Figure 2–45. Let us suppose that the wire is oriented so that the origin of its scale falls on the x-axis at the point $(1, 0)$, and the numbers on the scale increase as one moves counterclockwise.

Given any $\theta \in D$, we now locate on the scale on the wire the point corresponding to θ. But this point on the wire can be represented algebraically in the xy-coordinate system by a unique point (x, y) as shown in Figure 2–45. We can then define one function by using as the image of θ the y-coordinate of the point determined by θ, and another function can be defined by using as the image of θ the x-coordinate of the point so determined. These two functions are called the *sine* and *cosine* functions respectively. A special notation is used to denote the sine and cosine functions. The sine function is symbolized by $\sin \theta$ and the cosine function by $\cos \theta$. The double interpretation by now familiar is used here also, and $\sin \theta$ and $\cos \theta$ are also used to represent the image of a particular value of θ. Since the image of θ for the sine function is the y-coordinate of the point determined by θ and the image of θ for the cosine function is the x-coordinate, we can write

$$y = \sin \theta; \qquad x = \cos \theta . \tag{2–94}$$

Using what the reader will no doubt feel is a somewhat unusual procedure, we have defined two new functions. Note that we do not currently have available any accurate method for determining $\sin \theta$ or $\cos \theta$ for a given θ. What we must do is measure a distance θ along the circle and then measure with a ruler the x- and y-coordinates of the point so determined. Much later in our studies we shall see that it is possible to develop algebraic methods for computing $\sin \theta$ and $\cos \theta$ as accurately as desired, but it is by no means obvious at the moment how this might be done.

From the above definitions it is quite easy to determine roughly what the graphs of $\sin \theta$ and $\cos \theta$ look like, even if we cannot at the moment determine them with great precision. Let us consider $\sin \theta$ first. When $\theta = 0$, the point determined by θ is $(1, 0)$ and $y = 0$. Therefore, $\sin 0 = 0$. As θ increases, the point determined by θ moves into the first quadrant and y increases until the point lies on the y-axis. When the point lies on the y-axis and $y = 1$, we have gone one-quarter of the distance around the circle and $\theta = 2\pi/4 = \pi/2$. Hence, $\sin \pi/2 = 1$. As θ continues to increase, the point moves into the second quadrant and y begins to decrease. This con-

tinues until the point reaches $(-1, 0)$ on the x-axis. At $(-1, 0)$ we have
gone halfway around the circle and $\theta = \pi$. Here $y = 0$, and therefore,
$\sin \pi = 0$. When θ is increased again, the point moves into the third quadrant and y becomes negative. It becomes more negative until the point
$(0, -1)$ on the y-axis is reached. At this point, we have gone three-quarters
of the way around the circle so that $\theta = 3\pi/2$. Since $y = -1$ here, $\sin$
$3\pi/2 = -1$. As θ continues to increase, the point moves into the fourth
quadrant; y remains negative, but becomes less negative as θ increases.
When we have gone all the way around the circle and ended up where we
started out, $\theta = 2\pi$ and $y = 0$, so $\sin 2\pi = 0$. If we select a fairly large
number of values of θ, use a ruler to measure the y-values so obtained, plot
the points (θ, y) in a θy-coordinate system and draw a smooth curve through
them, there results the curve labeled $\sin \theta$, as shown in Figure 2–46.

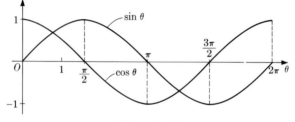

Figure 2–46

In precisely the same way we can determine what the graph of $\cos \theta$ looks
like. Note that when $\theta = 0$, the associated point is $(1, 0)$ so $\cos 0 = 1$.
When $\theta = \pi/2$ the associated point is $(0, 1)$, so $\cos \pi/2 = 0$. For $\theta = \pi$,
the associated point is $(-1, 0)$ and $\cos \theta = -1$. Then when $\theta = 3\pi/2$,
$\cos \theta = 0$ and finally when $\theta = 2\pi$, $\cos \theta = 1$. The graph of $\cos \theta$ is then the
one labeled $\cos \theta$ in Figure 2–46.

We shall now extend the domain of definition for the sine and cosine functions to include all real numbers θ. This will be done in two steps. First the
domain will be extended to include all non-negative numbers. Then the
negative numbers will also be included. Let us proceed, then, to define $\sin \theta$
and $\cos \theta$ for all $\theta \geq 0$. Consider any $\theta > 2\pi$. There exists a natural number
n such that $2\pi n \leq \theta < 2\pi(n + 1)$, so that θ lies in this interval of length
2π. If $\theta_1 = \theta - 2\pi n$, it follows that $0 \leq \theta_1 < 2\pi$. We then define $\sin \theta$ and
$\cos \theta$ to be the same as $\sin \theta_1$ and $\cos \theta_1$ so that

$$\sin \theta = \sin \theta_1; \qquad \cos \theta = \cos \theta_1, \qquad 0 \leq \theta_1 < 2\pi . \qquad (2\text{--}95)$$

In this way $\sin \theta$ and $\cos \theta$ are defined for every non-negative value of θ.
We can state the same result in another way by saying that if $\theta = \theta_1 + 2\pi n$,
where $0 \leq \theta_1 < 2\pi$ and n is any natural number, then (2–95) holds or

$$\sin (\theta_1 + 2\pi n) = \sin \theta_1; \qquad \cos (\theta_1 + 2\pi n) = \cos \theta_1, \qquad 0 \leq \theta_1 < 2\pi . \qquad (2\text{--}96)$$

Thus to obtain the graph of $\sin \theta$ for $2\pi \leq \theta < 4\pi$ we merely translate the graph of $\sin \theta$ in Figure 2–46 along the θ-axis by 2π units, so that the point originally corresponding to $\theta = 0$ now corresponds to $\theta = 2\pi$. To obtain the graph of $\sin \theta$ in the interval $4\pi \leq \theta < 6\pi$, we move the curve over another 2π units. The same procedure is used to generate the graph of $\cos \theta$ in these intervals. We have thus defined the sine and cosine functions in such a way that, for $\theta \geq 0$, they repeat themselves after every interval of length 2π. Such functions are called periodic functions. More precisely we make the following definition:

PERIODIC FUNCTION. *A function $f(x)$ is said to be periodic with period ζ, $\zeta > 0$, if for each x in the domain, $x + \zeta$ is in the domain and $f(x + \zeta) = f(x)$.*

Thus the sine and cosine functions are periodic with period 2π.

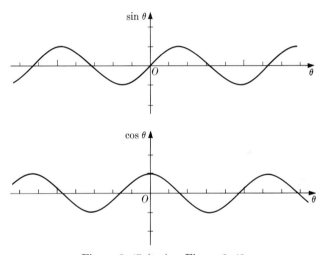

Figure 2–47 *(top)*,   Figure 2–48

We shall now extend the domain of $\sin \theta$ and $\cos \theta$ to include all negative numbers θ simply by defining $\sin \theta$ to be an odd function and $\cos \theta$ to be an even function. Therefore

$$\sin \theta = -\sin(-\theta); \qquad \cos \theta = \cos(-\theta), \qquad \theta < 0. \qquad (2\text{–}97)$$

The graphs of $\sin \theta$ and $\cos \theta$ then become those shown in Figures 2–47 and 2–48. In these figures we have employed a frequently used convention of labeling the vertical axis with the name of the function rather than the dependent variable.

We have not attempted to provide any intuitive justification for defining the sine and cosine functions as we did. For the present, the reader should simply think of the definitions as being arbitrary and merely serving as an example of yet another way of defining functions. The sine and cosine functions, which are two functions from a class of functions referred to as *trigonometric functions*, actually arise with considerable frequency in certain types of practical applications. Such functions arise naturally in problems of surveying and navigation, for example, where triangles are dealt with extensively. These applications will not be of interest to us here.

To facilitate the task of making numerical computations involving $\sin \theta$ and $\cos \theta$, tables such as those shown in Table A at the end of the text have been constructed. It is not possible to show the image of every value of θ in the table since there are an infinite number of elements in the domain. Instead, the values of $\sin \theta$ and $\cos \theta$ are tabulated for a set of values of θ, say θ_0, θ_1, θ_2, ... Normally, the θ_k are chosen so that $\theta_{k+1} - \theta_k = u$, u being a number which is independent of k. In Table A, $u = 0.02$. The number u is referred to as the *tabulation interval*, and is the interval between successive values of the argument. Let us now consider how to estimate from a table such as Table A the value of $\sin \theta$ or $\cos \theta$ for a value of θ which is different from one of the tabulated values. To do this, we determine two successive tabulated values θ_k and θ_{k+1} such that $\theta_k < \theta < \theta_{k+1}$. Then we imagine that the graph of the function of interest, say $\sin \theta$, for θ in the interval $\theta_k < \theta < \theta_{k+1}$ can be adequately approximated by the line segment joining the two points $(\theta_k, \sin \theta_k)$ and $(\theta_{k+1}, \sin \theta_{k+1})$. If (θ, y) is any point on this line segment, then by (2–20)

$$\frac{y - \sin \theta_k}{\theta - \theta_k} = \frac{\sin \theta_{k+1} - \sin \theta_k}{\theta_{k+1} - \theta_k}$$

or

$$y = \sin \theta_k + \left[\frac{\sin \theta_{k+1} - \sin \theta_k}{\theta_{k+1} - \theta_k} \right] (\theta - \theta_k) . \tag{2–98}$$

The estimate used for $\sin \theta$ is then the value of y computed from (2–98). This will only be an approximation to $\sin \theta$, but if u is small enough the approximation will be adequate. (Of course, most of the numbers in Table A are only approximations to the true values, since only three decimal places are used.) The procedure just described is referred to as *linear interpolation*. It is not necessary to tabulate $\sin \theta$ and $\cos \theta$ for θ outside the interval $0 \leq \theta < 2\pi$ because (2–95) and (2–97) can be used to compute these quantities for other values of θ. However, it is not even necessary to tabulate these functions for $0 \leq \theta < 2\pi$. Because of the symmetry of the circle, it is only necessary to tabulate them for $0 \leq \theta \leq \pi/2$ as is done in Table A. We ask the reader to explain in the problems why this is sufficient.

In this section we have used θ for the independent variable in the sine and cosine functions rather than x because x was used as the image of θ in the cosine function. In the future, however, we shall normally use x as the independent variable, writing sin x and cos x, because x will not appear in any other way.

2–15 FORMING FUNCTIONS FROM OTHER FUNCTIONS

In working with functions of one variable one often finds it helpful to construct new functions from two or more other functions. We would now like to study some very natural ways in which this can be done. Consider two functions $f_1(x)$ and $f_2(x)$ with domains D_1 and D_2 respectively. Then for every number in $D_1 \cap D_2$ we can compute a number $f_1(x)$, a number $f_2(x)$ and, therefore, a number $y = f_1(x) + f_2(x)$. This association with each $x \in D_1 \cap D_2$ of a number $f_1(x) + f_2(x)$ defines a new function, which we shall denote by $f_3(x)$, whose domain is $D_1 \cap D_2$ such that for each x

$$f_3(x) = f_1(x) + f_2(x). \tag{2–99}$$

We call $f_3(x)$ *the sum* of the functions $f_1(x)$ and $f_2(x)$. Thus we can form a new function by adding two functions. If $f_1(x)$ and $f_2(x)$ have the same domain D, then $f_3(x)$ also has the domain D. For example if $f_1(x) = x$ and $f_2(x) = x^2$ then $f_1(x) + f_2(x)$ is

$$f_3(x) = x^2 + x = \left(x + \frac{1}{2}\right)^2 - \frac{1}{4}.$$

Therefore, the graph of $f_3(x)$ is a parabola with axis of symmetry $x = -\frac{1}{2}$ which crosses the axis of symmetry at $y = -\frac{1}{4}$ and opens upward. If we had the graphs of $f_1(x)$ and $f_2(x)$, we could determine the graph of $f_3(x)$ merely by adding the ordinates of the graphs of $f_1(x)$ and $f_2(x)$ for each value of x. This is normally an inefficient way to obtain the graph of $f_3(x)$, however, although in some cases it helps to clarify things.

New functions can also be formed by multiplication. For each $x \in D_1 \cap D_2$ we can compute a number $y = f_1(x)f_2(x)$. This defines the new function, call it $g(x)$, and the rule for computing the image of $g(x)$ of x is

$$g(x) = f_1(x)f_2(x). \tag{2–100}$$

We call $g(x)$ the product of the two functions $f_1(x)$ and $f_2(x)$. For example, if $f_1(x) = f_2(x) = x$, then $g(x) = x^2$, and if $f_1(x) = x$ and $f_2(x) = (1 - 2x^2)$, then $g(x) = x - 2x^3$.

New functions can be formed equally well by division. For each $x \in D_1 \cap D_2$ for which $f_2(x) \neq 0$, we can compute a number $y = f_1(x)/f_2(x)$. This then serves to define a new function, call it $h(x)$, and the rule for evaluating $h(x)$ is

$$h(x) = \frac{f_1(x)}{f_2(x)}. \tag{2–101}$$

The function $h(x)$ is called the quotient of $f_1(x)$ by $f_2(x)$. Denote by R the set of numbers in D_2 for which $f_2(x) = 0$. The elements of R are called *roots* of $f_2(x)$. Denote by $(D_1 \cap D_2) - R$ the set of elements in $D_1 \cap D_2$ but not in R. Then $(D_1 \cap D_2) - R$ is the domain of $h(x)$.

If we have two polynomials

$$f_1(x) = a_n x^n + a_{n-1} x^{n-1} + \cdots + a_0; \quad f_2(x) = b_m x^m + b_{m-1} x^{m-1} + \cdots + b_0$$

$$(2\text{-}102)$$

then

$$h(x) = \frac{f_1(x)}{f_2(x)} = \frac{a_n x^n + a_{n-1} x^{n-1} + \cdots + a_0}{b_m x^m + b_{m-1} x^{m-1} + \cdots + b_0} \qquad (2\text{-}103)$$

is called a *rational function*. A rational function is the quotient of two polynomials. In general, a rational function is not a polynomial, but in certain cases it may be. The domain of $h(x)$ includes all real numbers except the roots of the polynomial $f_2(x)$. The roots of $f_2(x)$ are called *poles* of $h(x)$. The following are examples of rational functions

$$y = \frac{x - 1}{x^4 + x^3 - 3}; \qquad y = \frac{x^5 - 2x^2 + 5}{x^3 - 1};$$

$$y = \frac{1}{x^4 + 2x + 1}; \qquad y = \frac{x^2 + 2x + 1}{x + 1}.$$

The last rational function above is a polynomial since

$$y = \frac{x^2 + 2x + 1}{x + 1} = \frac{(x + 1)^2}{x + 1} = x + 1, \quad x \neq -1 .$$

Note that $x + 1 = 0$ at $x = -1$, so $x = -1$ is not in the domain of the rational function. We can have $y = x + 1$ for all x, however, simply by defining the image of -1 to be 0.

We have noted previously that accurately determining the graph of a polynomial can be a difficult task. The same holds true for rational functions when either the numerator or the denominator involves a polynomial of high degree. Fortunately, although rational functions are used with considerable frequency, it is only relatively rarely that it is necessary to obtain an accurate graph of such a function.

If the reader has studied the previous section, he will note that we can form a new function from the sine and cosine functions by dividing the sine function by the cosine function. The resulting function is called the *tangent* function and is symbolized by $\tan \theta$. The tangent function is another of the so-called trigonometric functions. By definition

$$\tan \theta = \frac{\sin \theta}{\cos \theta} . \qquad (2\text{-}104)$$

The domain of $\tan \theta$ includes all real numbers except those where $\cos \theta = 0$; now $\cos \theta = 0$ at $\theta = \pi/2, -\pi/2, 3\pi/2, -3\pi/2, 5\pi/2, -5\pi/2, \ldots$, so these points are not in the domain of $\tan \theta$, unless we define $\tan \theta$ at each of these. This is not normally done. The graph of $\tan \theta$ is shown in Figure 2–49. We

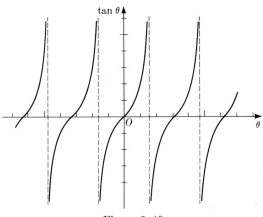

Figure 2–49

ask the reader to obtain this graph in the problems.

We now come to what is, for many purposes, the most important way of forming new functions from given functions. This is by a process referred to as *composition of functions* or as the forming of *compound functions.* Sometimes the procedure is also referred to as the method of substitution of variables. Suppose that we have two functions, $g(x)$ and $h(u)$, such that the domain of $h(u)$ contains the range of $g(x)$ as a subset. We shall now define a new function $f(x)$ whose domain D is the same as that of $g(x)$. For any $x \in D$ compute $u = g(x)$. Next compute $y = h(u)$. We shall then use y as the image of x for the function $f(x)$. In other words, $f(x) = h(u)$, where $u = g(x)$ or

$$f(x) = h[g(x)] . \qquad (2\text{–}105)$$

The image of x under the function f is simply the value of h when the argument is $g(x)$. The function $f(x)$ is called a *compound function;* it is also called the *composition* of $g(x)$ and $h(u)$. The composition process can be illustrated schematically as shown in Figure 2–50. To compute the image

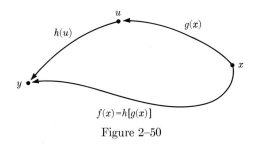

Figure 2–50

of x under f, we first compute the image u of x under g and then we compute the image of u under h. The above description may sound a little complicated, but for specific cases it is very easy to determine $f(x)$ given $g(x)$ and $h(u)$. For example, if $g(x) = x^2$ and $h(u) = 1 + u$, then

$$f(x) = h[g(x)] = 1 + g(x) = 1 + x^2 .$$

If $g(x) = 1 + x^2$ and $h(u) = u^{1/2}$, then $f(x) = (1 + x^2)^{1/2}$. To obtain $f(x)$, all we do is replace u in $h(u)$ by $g(x)$, and this is why the process is sometimes referred to as substitution of variables. The variable u is replaced by the expression $g(x)$ involving x. The above examples show that, after we have obtained $f(x)$ by a process of composition, $f(x)$ looks just like an ordinary function. There is no way of determining, given $f(x)$, that it was obtained by composition of two other functions.

The real usefulness of the composition notion will be in applying the idea in reverse. It will often be very helpful in the future to imagine that some given function is a composition of two other functions. This will often simplify the treatment of complicated functions. Consider, for example, the function $(x^2 - 3x + 1)^{25}$. We can think of this as being the composition of $g(x) = x^2 - 3x + 1$ and $h(u) = u^{25}$. The manner in which a given function can be imagined to be the result of the composition of two other functions is rot unique. For example, $y = x^2 + 2$ could be the composition of $y = u + 2$ and $u = x^2$ or of $y = (u - 5)^2 + 2$ and $u = x + 5$. Frequently, however, there will be a natural way of thinking of $f(x)$ as the composition of two other functions.

2–16 GRAPHS OF FUNCTIONS NOT REPRESENTED BY A SINGLE EQUATION

When we originally introduced the notion of a function of a single variable in Section 2–3, we pointed out that it need not be true that only a single equation will be used to represent the function explicitly. Instead, the function could be represented by different formulas for different subsets of the domain, as in (2–5). In discussing the graphs of functions, however, we have concentrated exclusively on functions which were represented by a single equation, since this is the type of function most frequently encountered. However, what we have learned can be usefully employed in illustrating geometrically the graph of a function such as (2–5).

As an example, let us determine the graph of the following function

$$y = f(x) = \begin{cases} x + 3, & x \leq -1 \\ 0.5(x - 1)^2 + 2, & -1 < x \leq 4 \\ 1/(x - 4), & x > 4 . \end{cases} \qquad (2\text{–}106)$$

To obtain the graph of this function, we merely consider each of the three intervals separately. For $x \leq -1$, $y = x + 3$. The graph of $y = x + 3$ is a straight line with slope 1 which intersects the y-axis at 3 and the x-axis at -3. The graph of $y = f(x)$ for $x \leq -1$ is then that portion of the straight line $y = x + 3$ which is generated by elements of the domain which are ≤ -1. This portion of the line is shown in Figure 2–51. For $-1 < x \leq 4$, $y = 0.5(x - 1)^2 + 2$. Now the graph of $y = 0.5(x - 1)^2 + 2$ is a parabola which opens upward, has $x = 1$ as an axis of symmetry, and crosses the axis of symmetry at $y = 2$. The graph of $y = f(x)$ for $-1 < x \leq 4$ is then that portion of the parabola generated by x lying in the interval $-1 < x \leq 4$. This portion of the parabola is shown in Figure 2–51. Finally,

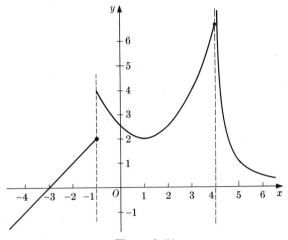

Figure 2–51

for $x > 4$, the graph of $y = f(x)$ is $y = 1/(x - 4)$. However, the graph of $y = 1/(x - 4)$ is a hyperbola, and thus the graph of $f(x)$ for $x > 4$ is that part of the hyperbola $y = 1/(x - 4)$ shown in Figure 2–51. The graph of $y = f(x)$ is then that shown in Figure 2–51. We have used dots to indicate the value of $f(x)$ at -1 and 4 where confusion could arise in looking at the figure. Thus, if we can determine the graphs of the individual parts, it is easy to illustrate geometrically the graphs of functions such as (2–106).

REFERENCES

Any book on analytic geometry and almost any calculus book covers some of the material in this chapter, although usually in a quite different manner. Some typical references are given below.

1. Labarre, A. E. Jr., *Elementary Mathematical Analysis*. Addison-Wesley, Reading, Massachusetts, 1961.

2. May, K. O., *Elements of Modern Mathematics*. Addison-Wesley, Reading, Massachusetts, 1959.

3. Morrey, C. B. Jr., *University Calculus with Analytic Geometry*. Addison-Wesley, Reading, Massachusetts, 1962.

4. Protter, M. H. and Morrey, C. B., *Calculus with Analytic Geometry, A First, Course*. Addison-Wesley, Reading, Massachusetts, 1963.

5. Smirnov, V. I., *Elementary Calculus, Vol. I of a Course in Higher Mathematics*. Addison-Wesley, Reading, Massachusetts, 1964.
    The first volume of a huge six-volume work on mathematics which has been used in Russia for many years.

6. Thomas, G. B. Jr., *Calculus with Analytic Geometry, 3rd edition*. Addison-Wesley, Reading, Massachusetts, 1960.

PROBLEMS

Section 2–1

In Problems 1 through 4, characterize each of the following sets in the form (2–2):

1. The set of all real numbers which are less than 3 but greater than -6.

2. The set of all natural numbers whose square is less than 1700.

3. The set of all real numbers having the property that the square of the number plus three times the number is equal to 17.

4. The set of all real numbers which are less than -13 or whose square is greater than 89.

5. Determine whether or not $A = B$ in each of the following cases:
  (a) $A = \{1, 3, 5, 7, 9\}$　　　　　　　　(b) $A = \{x|x \geq 2\}$
  　　$B = \{0, 1, 3, 5, 7, 9\}$;　　　　　　　　$B = \{x|x^2 \geq 4, \quad x > 0\}$;
  (c) $A = \{4, 5, 3, 2\}$　　　　　　　　　(d) $A = \{x|x^2 + 3 = 0\}$
  　　$B = \{2, 3, 4, 5\}$;　　　　　　　　　　$B = \{x|x \geq 2\}$.

6. List all of the subsets of each of the following two sets and give the power set for each:
  (a) $A = \{1, 3, 5, 8\}$;　　　　　　　　　(b) $A = \{a_1, a_2, a_3\}$.

7. Determine $A \cap B$ and $A \cup B$ in each of the following cases:
  (a) $A = \{1, 3, 5, 7\}$　　　(b) $A = \{1, 5, 7, 8, 11\}$　　　(c) $A = \varnothing$
  　　$B = \{2, 4, 5, 8, 9\}$;　　　$B = \{1, 4, 7, 9, 11\}$;　　　$B = E$;
  (d) $A = \{3, 4, 6\}$　　　　(e) $A = \{1, 3, 5, 7, 9\}$
  　　$B = \{-3, -4, -6\}$;　　　$B = \{1, 5, 9\}$.

8. Let A be the set of students at a given university who have taken the introductory physics course, and B the set of students at the same university who have taken introductory calculus. Describe in words $A \cap B$ and $A \cup B$.

9. Find the intersection of the following three sets, and show that $(A_1 \cap A_2) \cap A_3$ is the same as $A_1 \cap (A_2 \cap A_3)$.

$$A_1 = \{-3, 2, 1, 5, 7\}; \qquad A_2 = \{-2, 2, 1, 6, 7\}; \qquad A_3 = \{2, 6, 7\}.$$

10. Prove that if $B \subset A$ then $A \cup B = A$.

11. Let E be the set of all real numbers and A the set of all rational numbers. What is A^c?

12. Let E be the set of all rational numbers and A the set of all integers. What is A^c?

13. Given any two sets A and B, the set of elements which are in A but not in B is denoted by $A - B$. If A and B are as follows, determine $A - B$ and $B - A$.

$$A = \{1, 3, 4, 5, 7\}; \qquad B = \{3, 5, 7, 11, 13\}.$$

14. Explain in words what the set $(A - B) \cup (B - A)$ is. Determine this set when A and B are as defined in Problem 13.

15. Prove that $A - B = A \cap B^c$.

16. Prove that for any three sets A, B and C,

$$(A \cap B) \cap C = A \cap (B \cap C); \qquad (A \cup B) \cup C = A \cup (B \cup C).$$

These are referred to as the associative laws. Hint: The proof makes use of logic only, that is, only on the meaning of the operations.

17. Prove that for any three sets A, B and C,

$$A \cap (B \cup C) = (A \cap B) \cup (A \cap C); \qquad A \cup (B \cap C) = (A \cup B) \cap (A \cup C).$$

These are referred to as distributive laws. Verify them when

$$A = \{1, 3, 5, 7\}; \qquad B = \{1, 8, 11\}; \qquad C = \{7, 8, 10, 12\}.$$

18. Prove that if A and B are any sets,

$$(A \cap B)^c = A^c \cup B^c; \qquad (A \cup B)^c = A^c \cap B^c.$$

These are referred to as DeMorgan's laws. Verify them when A and B are the sets given in Problem 13.

19. Use the results of Problem 18 to determine $(A - B)^c$.

In Problems 20 through 26, either prove that the statement is always true or give an example which shows that it is not always true.

20. If $A \cap B = A \cap C$, then $B = C$.

21. If $A \cup B = A \cup C$, then $B = C$.

22. If $A \cup B = A \cup C$, then $B \subset C$ or $C \subset B$.

23. $(A - B) \cup C = (A \cup C) - (B \cup C)$.

24. $A = (A - B) \cup (A \cap B)$

25. $(A \cap B) \cup C = A \cap (B \cup C)$ if and only if $C \subset A$.

26. $(A \cup B) - (A \cap B) = (A - B) \cup (B - A)$.

27. Let $\mathfrak{X}$ be the set of all sets X which do not contain themselves as elements, that is, $\mathfrak{X} = \{X | X \notin X\}$. Show that $\mathfrak{X}$ does not exist. This is known as Russell's paradox. This example shows that certain restrictions must be placed on $\mathcal{P}(x)$ in

(2-2), because an arbitrary $\mathcal{P}(x)$ does not necessarily define a set. Hint: Try to decide whether $x \in x$.

28. Can you think of a set X with the property that $X \in X$?

Section 2-2

In Problems 1 through 7 determine whether the situation described represents a function.

1. Let A be a specified set of books and B be a set including the authors of all the books in A. Consider the association with each book in A its author or authors in B.

2. Let A be a set of authors and B be a set of books containing those written by the authors in A. Consider the association with each author in A the book or books he has written.

3. The correspondence between rainfall in Sydney, Australia, in a given year and the following year, over the period 1870 to 1960.

4. Let A be the set of all real numbers and B the set of all integers. Consider the rule which associates with each real number x the integer obtained by dropping everything in the decimal representation of x which comes after the decimal point.

5. The rule which associates with each father his children. Could the answer here depend on what the set B is? Suggest several possible sets B.

6. The rule which associates with each father his oldest child.

7. The rule which associates with each natural number its successor.

8. Construct an example of a function where each element in the range is the image of precisely three elements of the domain, and, in addition, where the domain contains more than three elements.

9. Let A consist of the first 100 natural numbers. Consider the rule which associates with each element n in A the number n^3. Suggest at least five different sets B for which this rule defines a function from A to B.

10. Let A and B be the set of all real numbers. Consider the rule which associates with each number x in A the number x^3. This defines a function from A to B. Show that an inverse function exists, and state the rule which describes the inverse, that is, which tells how to associate with each element in B an element in A.

11. Whether or not a function from A to B has an inverse may depend on what is used for the set B. Show that the function can never have an inverse if B is a set which is larger than the range R of the function. By larger we mean that B contains at least one element not in R. Illustrate this by considering various possible definitions for B when A is the set of all positive real numbers, and the rule is to associate with each positive number x the negative number $-x$.

Section 2-3

1. Write down in mathematical form the representations of the following functions (rules):

    (a) Square any real number, subtract from this twice the real number and add 27.

(b) Select any real number. If it is greater than 3, cube the number and subtract from it the square of the number; if the number is equal to 3, the function has the value 14; if the number is less than 3, subtract 18 from the number.

(c) Consider any real number different from 0 or 3. Multiply the number by the number minus 3, and divide the product into the number 13.

2. Determine whether or not each of the following represent functions of one variable:

(a) $y = \begin{cases} 2x, & x \geq 0 \\ x^2, & x \leq 2; \end{cases}$

(b) $y = \begin{cases} 17 & \text{if } x \text{ is irrational} \\ x^2 & \text{if } x \text{ is rational}; \end{cases}$

(c) $y = $ the larger of x^2 and $3x - 2$; (d) $y = x^{1/2}$, $x \geq 0$;

(e) $y = $ any number whose square is x;

(f) $y = \begin{cases} 14 & \text{if } x \text{ is the square of some integer} \\ 2x & \text{if } x \text{ is an odd natural number} \\ 3x^5 & \text{for all other } x \, . \end{cases}$

3. What is the largest possible domain for each of the following if they are to be interpreted as real valued functions of one real variable?

(a) $y = x^{1/2}$;   (b) $y = (x - 2)^{1/2}$;   (c) $y = 1/x$;   (d) $y = 1/(x^2 - 1)$

(e) $y = [(x - 2)(x - 3)]^{1/2}$;   (f) $y = 1/x(x - 2)(x - 3)$;

(g) $y = (x - 2)(x^2 - 2x)$.

4. Consider the function $f(x) = (x + 1)/(x - 1), f(1) = 0$. Determine each of the following:

(a) $f(3)$;   (b) $f(-6)$;   (c) $f(u + 1)$;   (d) $f(u^3 + 6)$;   (e) $f(x^2)$;

(g) $f(x^{1/2})$;   (g) $f(1/u)$;   (h) $f(\alpha u - \beta)$.

5. Consider the function

$$f(x) = \begin{cases} x + 2, & x \geq 0 \\ -x^2, & x < 0 \, . \end{cases}$$

Determine each of the following:

(a) $f(5)$;   (b) $f(-11)$;   (c) $f(\alpha - 1)$;   (d) $f(\gamma/\alpha)$;   (e) $f(u^2)$.

6. Suggest some functions of one variable which are encountered in everyday life.

7. Show that any function having only a finite number of elements in the domain and in the range can be represented by a function of one variable. Hint: Assign a number to each element. Can you give one or more examples of where this is done in practice?

In Problems 8 through 10, the results apply to any function, not merely to functions of one variable. Consider any function from A to B. If G is a subset of A, so that $G \subset A$, then by $f(G)$ we shall mean the set of elements in B which are images of the elements in G. Note that $f(G)$ is a set, not a number (the notation is a little confusing here, but it is that normally used).

8. Show that if $G \subset A$ and $H \subset A$ then $f(G \cup H) = f(G) \cup f(H)$. Give an example to illustrate this.

9. Show that if $G \subset A$ and $H \subset A$, then $f(G \cap H) \subset f(G) \cap f(H)$. Give a specific example to show that it need not be true that $f(G \cap H) = f(G) \cap f(H)$.

10. Show that $f(A) - f(G) \subset f(A - G)$. Give an example to illustrate that the sets do not have to be equal.

Section 2–4

1. Locate the following points in a rectangular coordinate system: $(3, 2)$, $(-1, 5)$, $(-2, -3)$, $(4, -1)$, $(2, 0)$, $(0, -1)$, $(0, 0)$, $(-1, 0)$, $(0, -3)$, and $(2, -7)$.

2. Locate in a rectangular coordinate system the points whose abscissa and ordinates are given below. Indicate the quadrant in which each point lies.

Abscissa	1.6	−3.5	2	−5	1	−1	2.5
Ordinate	5	2	−4	−6	1	−3.5	−1.4

3. Draw a bar diagram in a rectangular coordinate system and represent the function characterized by the following ordered pairs: $(-6, 0.2)$, $(-4, 0.8)$, $(-1, 1.2)$, $(0, 1.4)$, $(2, 1.0)$, $(4, 0.5)$, $(6, 0)$, $(10, -3)$.

4. Show that the point represented by an ordered pair of numbers depends critically on the order of the numbers. In particular, show that $(2, 5)$ and $(5, 2)$ do not represent the same point.

5. Why can we not represent any point in a plane by just a single real number? What would have to be true if this could be done?

6. Why is it convenient to take the origin for measurements for both axes of a coordinate system as the point where the axes intersect?

7. How would you characterize a plane geometrically?

8. Show that a coordinate system for a plane can be uniquely determined by selecting three points in the plane which do not lie on a straight line.

9. Suppose that we have one coordinate system, say an xy-coordinate system for a plane, and we now introduce a new coordinate system, say a uv-coordinate system such that the u-axis is identical with the x-axis, and the v-axis is parallel to the y-axis and crosses the x-axis at $x = 1$. Also assume that the direction for positive numbers is the same for the v-axis as for the y-axis. Illustrate these two coordinate systems geometrically. If (x, y) is the representation of a point in the xy-system, what is the representation of this point in the uv-system? The following are representations of some points in the xy-system. Give their representation in the uv-system: $(2, 4)$, $(0, 0)$, $(1, 0)$, $(5, -6)$, $(-4, -3)$.

Section 2–5

In Problems 1 through 9 sketch the graph of the line whose equation is given, determining the x- and y-intercepts and the slope of the line.

1. $y = 4x - 2$; **2.** $y = -3x + 4$; **3.** $y = -2x$;

4. $y = 17$; **5.** $x = 4$; **6.** $y = -0.5x - 2$;

7. $y = 0.2x + 3$; **8.** $y = 16x - 7$; **9.** $y = 0.8x - 11$.

In Problems 10 through 19 determine the equation of the straight line passing through the points given and having the slope specified (when given).

10. $(3, 1), (-2, 2)$;

11. $(1, 0)$, slope $= -1$;

12. $(-2, -1), (-4, -4)$;

13. $(3, -5)$, slope $= 2$;

14. x intercept $= 5$
y intercept $= 2$;

15. x intercept $= -3$
y intercept $= 4$;

16. passes through origin
with slope 7;

17. passes through origin
with slope -2;

18. $(5, 1), (5, -3)$;

19. $(5, 1), (-2, 1)$

20. Consider the family of lines whose equations have the form
$$y = 0.5x + b.$$
Plot several of these for different values of b. What geometrical property does this family of lines possess?

21. For each of the lines whose equations are given in Problems 1 through 9, imagine that we select some point on the line, say (x, y), and then consider another point on the line $(x + 2, y_1)$. Express y_1 in terms of y. Why is y_1 independent of x?

22. Consider a line which passes through the origin. Prove that if (x, y) is on the line, then so is $(\lambda x, \lambda y)$ for any real number λ. Also prove that if (x_1, y_1) is on the line and (x_2, y_2) is on the line, the point $(x_1 + x_2, y_1 + y_2)$ is also on the line.

23. Consider any line whose equation is $y = ax + b$. Suppose that (x_1, y_1) and (x_2, y_2) are any two points lying on the line. Show that the point
$$(x, y) = (x_1, y_1) + [\lambda(x_2 - x_1), \lambda(y_2 - y_1)]$$
is also on the line for any real λ and furthermore that every point on the line can be represented in this way.

24. Suppose that we are given three points (x_1, y_1), (x_2, y_2) and (x_3, y_3). Is there any simple way to determine algebraically if these three points lie on the same straight line?

25. Sketch the graph of the line having slope -2 which crosses the x-axis at $x = 6$. What is the y-intercept of this line?

26. Sketch the graph of the line having slope 1.5 which crosses the y-axis at $y = -3$. What is the x-intercept of this line?

27. Illustrate geometrically each of the following point sets.
    (a) $\{(x, y)|y = -2x + 4$, all real $x\}$;
    (b) $\{(x, y)|y = 0.5x - 3$, all real $x\}$;
    (c) $\{(x, y)|y = -x - 1$, all real $x\}$.

28. Sketch the line segments joining the following pairs of points.
    (a) $(0, 0), (-3, 2)$;   (b) $(-6, 5), (1, -4)$;   (c) $(4, -2), (5, 6)$;
    (d) $(-5, -6), (4, 2)$;   (e) $(-5, -5), (-5, 1)$;   (f) $(3, -2), (8, -2)$.

Section 2–6

In Problems 1 through 11 sketch the parabolas which are the graphs of the following equations. Actually plot as many points as you feel are needed to determine the general shape of the curve. In each case determine the axis of symmetry and the point where the curve crosses the axis of symmetry.

1. $y = 0.2x^2$;   **2.** $y = -0.5x^2$;   **3.** $y = 0.3x^2 + 2$;

4. $y = 0.3x^2 - 2$;   **5.** $y = -0.6(x + 2)^2 + 3$; **6.** $y = 0.4(x - 3)^2 + 2$;

7. $y = x^2 - 3x + 2$; **8.** $y = 0.2x^2 + x - 4$;   **9.** $y = -0.3x^2 - 0.1x + 1$;

10. $y = 0.5x^2 - 0.2x + 16$;   **11.** $y = 10.4x^2 - 0.8x - 2$.

12. Consider the function $y = x^2$. Let (x_1, y_1) and (x_2, y_2) be any two points lying on the graph of this function. Compute $(y_2 - y_1)/(x_2 - x_1)$ and show that this ratio is not a constant.

13. Sketch several of the parabolas in the family generated as a is allowed to take on all real values in the equation

$$y = a(x - 3)^2 .$$

14. Sketch several of the parabolas in the family generated as a is allowed to take on all real values in the equation

$$y = a(x + 2)^2 - 3 .$$

15. Sketch several of the parabolas in the family generated as c is allowed to take on all real values in the equation

$$y = 0.25(x - 2)^2 + c .$$

16. Sketch several of the parabolas in the family generated as c is allowed to take on all real values in the equation

$$y = 0.10x^2 + c .$$

17. Sketch several of the parabolas in the family generated as b is allowed to take on all real values in the equation

$$y = -0.20(x - b)^2 + 2 .$$

18. Illustrate geometrically each of the following point sets.
   (a) $\{(x, y)|y = 0.5(x + 7)^2 - 4\}$;
   (b) $\{(x, y)|y = -0.3x^2 + 6x - 5\}$;
   (c) $\{(x, y)|y = 0.01x^2 - 2x + 1\}$.

Section 2–7

1. Plot carefully the graph of $y = x^3$ and verify that it looks like the curve shown in Figure 2–21.

2. Plot carefully the graph of $y = x^4$ and show that it looks like the curve shown in Figure 2–21.

3. Consider the line $y = ax + b$. Show that any point (x_1, y_1) lying on the line is a point of symmetry for the line.

4. Prove that a parabola has no point of symmetry.

In Problems 5 through 10 sketch the graphs of the equations given.

5. $y = (x - 3)^3 + 4$;   **6.** $y = 0.5(x + 2)^3 - 5$;

7. $y = -0.5(x - 4)^3 + 2$;   **8.** $y = 0.1(x - 5)^4 + 3$;

9. $y = -0.2(x + 4)^4 - 5$;   **10.** $y = 0.01(x - 5)^5 + 3$.

11. Compute carefully the graphs of $y = x^n$ for $n = 1, 2, 3$ and 4 for x in the interval $0 \le x \le 1$ and show that they do look like the curves shown in Figure 2–22.

In Problems 12 through 22, sketch the hyperbolas which are the graphs of the equations given, and actually plot a sufficient number of points to determine the general location of the graph. Also determine the horizontal and vertical asymptotes in each case.

12. $y = \dfrac{4}{x}$;

13. $y = \dfrac{0.2}{x}$;

14. $y = \dfrac{1}{x} + 4$;

15. $y = \dfrac{0.3}{x-2} + 7$;

16. $y = \dfrac{4}{x+3} - 5$;

17. $y = \dfrac{-2}{x+7} - 11$;

18. $y = \dfrac{0.5}{x-2} - 7$;

19. $y = \dfrac{2}{0.8x-4} + 3$;

20. $y = \dfrac{-3}{0.5x+2} - 6$;

21. $y = \dfrac{-0.5}{x} + 2$;

22. $y = \dfrac{-0.3}{x}$;

In Problems 23 through 32 sketch the graphs of the power functions and determine the asymptotes.

23. $y = \dfrac{1}{x^2}$;

24. $y = \dfrac{1}{x^3}$;

25. $y = \dfrac{3}{x^2} + 2$;

26. $y = \dfrac{0.2}{x^2} - 5$;

27. $y = \dfrac{-1}{x^2}$;

28. $y = -\dfrac{1}{x^3}$;

29. $y = \dfrac{0.3}{(x-2)^2} + 7$;

30. $y = \dfrac{-0.3}{(x+2)^2} - 7$;

31. $y = \dfrac{0.1}{(x-3)^3} + 4$;

32. $y = \dfrac{-0.1}{(x+3)^3} - 4$.

Section 2–8

1. Determine which of the following are polynomials. Give the degree of each polynomial.

(a) $y = 2x^{3/2} + x^{1/2} + 7$; (b) $y = x^{-3}$; (c) $y = 6$; (d) $y = \dfrac{1}{x^2 + 2}$;
(e) $y = 4x^{16} - 5x^4 + 7$; (f) $y = 6 - x^3 + x^2 - 25x^5$;
(g) $y = 17 - 4x^7 + 6x$; (h) $y = 2x^2 + 3x + 4x^{1/3}$.

2. Write down ten different polynomials of degree 5.

3. Illustrate geometrically the graph of $y = x^4 - 2x + 1$. Determine the graph by the straightforward method of selecting a number of values for x and finding the image of each.

4. Re-solve Problem 3 when $y = 5x^4 + 3x^2 - 2x + 8$.

5. Re-solve Problem 3 when $y = x^5 - 2x^4 + x^3 + 16$.

Section 2–9

1. Given any equation of the form $\mathcal{G} + \mathcal{K} = 0$, show that $\mathcal{G} = -\mathcal{K}$ has the same set of solutions.

2. If we divide the equation $x^2 - x = 0$ by x we obtain $x - 1$. Do these two equations have the same set of solutions? How can you explain the situation?

3. If we multiply the equation $2x^2 + 1 = 0$ by x we obtain $2x^3 + x = 0$. Do these two equations have the same set of solutions? How can you explain the situation?

4. Determine the set of solutions to $(x - 2)(x - 5)(x + 4) = 0$. Explain the reasoning used in determining the solutions.

In Problems 5 through 13, determine the roots (if any) of the given quadratic equations. Illustrate the results geometrically by sketching the associated parabola.

5. $2x^2 - 4x + 2 = 0$;   **6.** $x^2 + x - 6 = 0$;   **7.** $x^2 - 4x = 0$;

8. $x^2 - 6x + 16 = 0$;   **9.** $x^2 - 7 = 0$;   **10.** $8x^2 - 4x + 3 = 0$;

11. $3x^2 - x + 1 = 0$;   **12.** $-3x^2 + 2x - 1 = 0$;   **13.** $-2x^2 + 3x + 2 = 0$;

14. Determine the roots of $(x^2 - 3x + 1)(x - 2) = 0$.

15. Determine the solutions to $(x^2 - 3x)(x^2 + 2x - 5) = 0$.

16. Determine the solutions to $(x - 3)^{1/2} = 6$.

17. Determine the solutions to $(x - 3)^{1/2} = x$.

18. Determine the solutions to $(x + 6)^{1/2} + x = 11$.

19. Determine the solutions to $2(3x + 1)^{1/2} - 4(x + 2)^{1/2} = (x - 4)^{1/2}$.

Section 2–10

1. Show that the set of points which satisfy the equations
$$c_1 x + c_2 y = b \quad \text{and} \quad \lambda c_1 x + \lambda c_2 y = \lambda b$$
for any real λ, $\lambda \neq 0$, are precisely the same set of points. Actually illustrate this by showing that $3y + 2x = 6$ and $-6y - 4x = -12$ are represented graphically by the same line.

In Problems 2 through 12 sketch the circles which are the graphs of the given relations. Determine the center and radius of the circle and sketch in the axes of symmetry which are parallel to the x- and y-axes.

2. $x^2 + y^2 = 16$;   **3.** $(x + 1)^2 + y^2 = 4$;

4. $(x - 1)^2 + y^2 = 4$;   **5.** $x^2 + (y - 1)^2 = 9$;

6. $x^2 + (y + 2)^2 = 9$;   **7.** $(x - 3)^2 + y^2 = 25$;

8. $(x + 2)^2 + (y - 3)^2 = 16$;   **9.** $(x - 3)^2 + (y - 4)^2 = 25$;

10. $x^2 + y^2 - 3y = 8$;   **11.** $x^2 + 2x + y^2 = 15$;

12. $x^2 - 4x + y^2 + 6y = 23$.

13. Show that the graph of any relation of the form
$$x^2 + \alpha x + y^2 + \beta y = \lambda$$
is a circle, provided that there is more than one point (x, y) which satisfies the relation. Determine the center of the circle and its radius. Under what conditions will there be no points which satisfy the equation?

14. Consider the equation
$$(x - 2)^2 + (y - 3)^2 = 9 \,,$$
whose graph is a circle. Actually construct a table and determine a number of points which satisfy the equation. Then, by plotting the points and drawing a smooth curve through them, determine the graph of the equation. Do not proceed, as in the chapter, by first finding the center and radius and then sketching in the curve.

15. Determine two functions the union of whose graphs is the graph of the equation $(x - 3)^2 + (y + 2)^2 = 9$. Determine the appropriate domain and range for each and sketch the graph of the functions.

In Problems 16 through 25 sketch the ellipses which are the graphs of the equations given and indicate the line segments which represents the major and minor axes.

16. $3x^2 + 4y^2 = 12;$ **17.** $\dfrac{x^2}{6} + \dfrac{y^2}{7} = 1;$

18. $4x^2 + y^2 = 8;$ **19.** $2(x - 1)^2 + 3y^2 = 12;$

20. $2(x + 1)^2 + 3y^2 = 12;$ **21.** $3(x - 4)^2 + y^2 = 6;$

22. $2(x - 3)^2 + 4(y - 4)^2 = 16;$ **23.** $3(x + 2)^2 + 5(y + 3)^2 = 30;$

24. $3x^2 + 6x + 4y^2 + 12y = 10;$ **25.** $5x^2 + 6y^2 + 12y = 16$

26. Consider any equation of the form
$$\alpha_1 x^2 + \beta_1 x + \alpha_2 y^2 + \beta_2 y = \gamma, \quad \alpha_1, \alpha_2 > 0 \,.$$
Show that if there is more than one point which satisfies the equation, then the graph of the equation is an ellipse. Determine the axes of symmetry and the points where the curve crosses the axes of symmetry. Under what conditions will there be no points which satisfy the equation?

27. Consider the equation
$$\frac{1}{4}(x - 3)^2 + \frac{1}{9}(y + 2)^2 = 1 \,,$$
whose graph is an ellipse. Construct a table and determine a number of points which satisfy the equation. Then, by plotting the points and drawing a smooth curve through them, determine the graph of the equation. Do not proceed, as in the chapter, by locating the axes of symmetry and then roughly sketching in the curve.

28. Determine the four functions (two with x being the independent variable and two with y being the independent variable) implied by the equation
$$\frac{1}{4}(x + 3)^2 + \frac{1}{9}(y - 2)^2 = 1 \,.$$
Determine the appropriate domain and range for each and sketch the graph of each.

29. Prove that if the graph of some equation has $x = a$ and $y = b$ as axes of symmetry, then (a, b) is a point of symmetry.

In Problems 30 through 44 sketch the graphs of the equation given indicating when appropriate asymptotes and axes of symmetry.

30. $x - 0.2y^2 = 0$;   **31.** $x - 0.1(y - 3)^2 = 0$;   **32.** $x - 0.3(y + 2)^2 = 0$;

33. $x + 0.3(y - 2)^2 = 6$;   **34.** $xy = 1$;   **35.** $xy^2 = 1$;

36. $xy^3 = 1$;   **37.** $y(x^2 - 1) = 1$;   **38.** $y(x^2 + 1) = 1$;

39. $x^2 - y^2 = 1$;   **40.** $y^2(x^2 - x) = x^2 + 1$;   **41.** $y = x + (1/x)$;

42. $y^2(x^2 + 1) = 1$;   **43.** $yx^2 = (x - 2)$;   **44.** $x^2 + xy + y^2 = 4$.

In Problems 45 through 50 illustrate geometrically the given point set.

45. $\{(x, y)|2x + 3y = -6\}$;   **46.** $\{(x, y)|3x - y = 7\}$;

47. $\{(x, y)|-x + 2y = -7\}$;   **48.** $\{(x, y)|-2x - 4y = 8\}$;

49. $\{(x, y)|x^2 + 3x + y^2 = 9\}$;   **50.** $\{(x, y)|x(y^2 + 4) = 16\}$.

Section 2–11

In Problems 1 through 10 determine explicitly the inverse representation of the function given. Sketch the graph of the function and illustrate the branches of the inverse representation.

1. $y = 2x + 3$;   **2.** $y = 1/x$;   **3.** $y = \dfrac{4}{x - 2} + 6$;

4. $y = x^2$;   **5.** $y = x^3$;   **6.** $y = x^4$;

7. $y = 1/x^3$;   **8.** $y = 3x^2 + 2x$;   **9.** $y = -2x^2 + 3x + 1$;

10. $y = x^2 - 2x + 4$.

11. Show that the union of the ranges of the functions $x = g_k(y)$ forming the inverse representation of $y = f(x)$ is the domain of $f(x)$. Show also that there is no overlap of the ranges of the $g_k(y)$ except at the end points of the intervals representing the ranges.

Section 2–12

In Problems 1 through 34 shade the region of the plane containing the set of points which satisfies the given relation or set of relations. Indicate, as appropriate, whether or not the boundaries of the region are included in the set.

1. $x > 2$;   **2.** $y < 3$;

3. $x + y > 2$;   **4.** $x + y \leq 2$;

5. $4x - y \leq 6$;   **6.** $2x + 3y > 7$;

7. $-3x + y \geq -2$;   **8.** $2x - y \leq -6$;

9. $x \geq 2$
    $x \leq 4$;   **10.** $x \geq 0$
                           $y \geq 0$;

11. $x \geq 0$
     $y \geq 3$;   **12.** $x + y \leq 2$
                         $3x - y \geq 4$;

13. $x + y \leq 2$
      $x \geq 0$
      $y \geq 0$;   **14.** $x + y \leq 2$
                        $x + y \geq 1$;

15. $2x + 3y \leq 4$
$\quad x + y \geq 1$
$\quad\quad x \geq 0;$

16. $3x - 2y \geq -2$
$\quad\ 2x + y \leq 3$
$\quad -3x + y \leq -4;$

17. $x + y \leq 4$
$\quad x \geq 3$
$\quad x \geq 0$
$\quad y \geq 0;$

18. $3x + 2y \leq 6$
$\quad x - 2y \leq -2$
$\quad\quad x \geq 3;$

19. $x - y \geq 0$
$\quad x + y \leq 3$
$\quad\quad x \geq 0$
$\quad\quad y \geq 0;$

20. $(x - 3)^2 + (y - 4)^2 \leq 4;$

21. $(x - 3)^2 + (y - 4)^2 \geq 4;$

22. $3(x + 2)^2 + 4(y + 1)^2 \leq 12;$

23. $y - 0.2(x - 3)^2 \leq 6;$

24. $y + 0.2(x + 3) \leq 7;$

25. $xy \geq 1;$

26. $xy \leq 1;$

27. $x^2 + y^2 \leq 1$
$\quad (x - 1)^2 + y^2 \leq 1;$

28. $x^2 + y^2 \leq 1$
$\quad x^2 + (y - 1)^2 \geq 1;$

29. $x^2 + y^2 \leq 1$
$\quad y - x^2 \leq 1;$

30. $x^2 + y^2 \leq 1$
$\quad 4xy \geq 1;$

31. $y - x^2 \geq 0$
$\quad xy \geq 1;$

32. $xy \geq 1$
$\quad x + y \leq 4;$

33. $x^2 + y^2 \leq 1$
$\quad (x - 1)^2 + y^2 \leq 1$
$\quad x^2 + (y - 1)^2 \leq 1;$

34. $y - x^2 \geq 0$
$\quad x^2 + y^2 \geq 1$
$\quad x^2 + (y - 5)^2 \geq 1.$

In Problems 35 through 40 solve the system of linear equations and illustrate the situation graphically.

35. $2x + 4y = 6$
$\quad 3x - 7y = 4;$

36. $x + y = 6$
$\quad 2x - y = -1;$

37. $3x - 2y = 4$
$\quad 6x - 4y = 11;$

38. $-2x - 6y = 14$
$\quad x - 3y = 6$

39. $x - 3y = 7$
$\quad 3x - 9y = 21;$

40. $0.5x - 0.7y = 4$
$\quad 3x - 2.5y = 6.$

41. Consider the system of linear equations (2–84). Suppose that $a_1b_2 - a_2b_1 = 0$. Develop the criteria which determine when the system has no solution or an infinite number of solutions in this case. Prove that the system cannot have a unique solution when $a_1b_1 - a_2b_2 = 0$.

42. Devise an example in which a system of three linear equations has a unique solution and illustrate geometrically.

43. Illustrate geometrically the intersection of three sets.

44. Illustrate geometrically the union of three sets.

45. Illustrate geometrically by examples the results of Problem 17, Section 2–1.

46. Illustrate geometrically by examples the results of Problem 18, Section 2–1.

47. Illustrate geometrically the set introduced in Problem 14, Section 2–1.

48. Find approximately, using graphical analysis, the set of points which satisfy the following system of equations

$$x^2 - y = 0$$
$$3x + 2y = 6 .$$

49. Show how to find the solutions to the set of equations of Problem 48 using an algebraic procedure, that is, by eliminating one of the variables. Do not attempt actually to solve the resulting equation.

50. Consider a system of equations having the general form

$$\alpha x^2 + \beta x - y = \gamma; \qquad \alpha \neq 0$$
$$ax + by = c .$$

Show by graphical examples that the system will always have either precisely two solutions, one solution or no solution. Make up a numerical example to illustrate each case. Devise a general algebraic method which could be used for determining the solutions when they exist.

51. By graphical and algebraic procedures find the solutions to the system

$$x^2 + y^2 = 1$$
$$(x - 1.5)^2 + (y - 1.5)^2 = 1 .$$

52. Discuss various cases that can arise in solving a system of equations such as

$$\alpha_1(x - a)^2 + \alpha_2(y - b)^2 = c^2, \quad \alpha_1, \alpha_2 > 0$$
$$\beta_1(x - d)^2 + \beta_2(y - e)^2 = f^2, \quad \beta_1, \beta_2 > 0 .$$

Illustrate a number of these graphically.

53. Derive a single equation in either x or y whose solutions will yield the x or y coordinates of the solutions to the system of Problem 52. Hint: Eliminate y^2 between the two equations and solve the resulting equation for y.

54. Solve graphically the system of equations

$$0.05x^2 + 0.5y^2 = 1$$
$$(x - 2)^2 + 0.10(y - 1)^2 = 1 .$$

55. Discuss various cases that can arise in solving a system of equations such as

$$xy = \alpha$$
$$(x - a)^2 + (y - b)^2 = r^2 .$$

Illustrate some of these graphically.

56. Derive a single equation in either x or y whose solutions will yield either the x or y coordinates of the solutions to the system of Problem 55.

57. Solve graphically the system of equations

$$xy = 1$$
$$x^2 + y^2 = 4 .$$

58. Prove property 6.

In Problems 59 through 64 sketch the graph of the given relations. Also determine a set of functions with x as the independent variable and a set of functions with y as the independent variable such that the graph of the relation is the union of the graphs of each of the sets of functions.

59. $(x^2 + y^2 - 4)[(x - 1)^2 + y^2 - 1] = 0;$

60. $(x^2 + y^2 - 4)[(x - 2)^2 + (y - 1)^2 - 1] = 0$;

61. $(x^2 + y^2 - 4)[3x^2 + 4(y - 2)^2 - 24] = 0$;

62. $(y - x^2)(y^2 - x) = 0$;

63. $(y - x^3)(x^2 + y^2 - 1) = 0$;

64. $(x^2 + y^2 - 4)[(x + 1)^2 + y^2 - 1] = 0$.

Section 2–13

In Problems 1 through 6 determine the distance between the points given.

1. $(2, 1)$, $(-3, 4)$; **2.** $(3, -6)$, $(4, 7)$; **3.** $(5, 2)$, $(1, 1)$;

4. $(-3, 2)$, $(-3, -8)$; **5.** $(0, 5)$, $(4, 1)$; **6.** $(6, 0)$, $(7, 2)$.

7. For two points $(x_1, 0)$ and $(x_2, 0)$ on the x-axis show that when $x_2 > x_1$ the distance formula yields $x_2 - x_1$ as the distance between the points.

8. Would the distance formula have any meaning if we did not use the same unit of distance for making measurements on both the x- and y-axes? Discuss.

Section 2–14

1. Draw a circle having a radius of about four inches. Using the radius as the unit of length, mark a scale on the edge of a sheet of paper. Have the paper long enough to so that at least 2π units can be included on the scale. Now use this scale to determine approximately 20 points in the graph of $\sin \theta$ and $\cos \theta$. Plot the points for $\sin \theta$ on one figure and those for $\cos \theta$ on another. Draw smooth curves through the points to determine the graphs of $\sin \theta$ and $\cos \theta$ in the interval $0 \leq \theta \leq 2\pi$.

2. Use the results of Problem 1 and (2–96) to determine points on the graphs of $\sin \theta$ and $\cos \theta$ in the interval $2\pi \leq \theta \leq 4\pi$, that is, increase θ by 2π for each θ used in Problem 1. Draw smooth curves through these points to obtain the graphs of $\sin \theta$ and $\cos \theta$ in the interval $2\pi \leq \theta \leq 4\pi$.

3. Use the results of Problem 1 and (2–97) to determine points on the graphs of $\sin \theta$ and $\cos \theta$ in the interval $-2\pi \leq \theta \leq 0$. Draw smooth curves through these points to obtain the graphs of $\sin \theta$ and $\cos \theta$ in the interval $-2\pi \leq \theta \leq 0$.

4. Use the definitions (2–97) to prove that $\sin \theta$ and $\cos \theta$ are periodic functions when the domain is extended to include all real numbers.

5. Prove that the sine and cosine functions are periodic with period $2\pi n$, where n is any natural number. If $f(x)$ is periodic, the smallest ς for which $f(x + \varsigma) = f(x)$ is called the least period of $f(x)$. What is the least period for the sine and cosine functions?

6. Show that if $\pi/2 < \theta \leq \pi$, then

$$\sin \theta = \cos \left(\theta - \frac{\pi}{2}\right); \qquad \cos \theta = -\sin \left(\theta - \frac{\pi}{2}\right).$$

Thus, if we can compute or use a table to find $\sin \theta$ and $\cos \theta$ for $0 \leq \theta \leq \pi/2$, it is also possible to determine $\sin \theta$ and $\cos \theta$ for $\pi/2 < \theta \leq \pi$. Hint: Show that the two triangles in Figure 2–52 (*turn page*) are congruent.

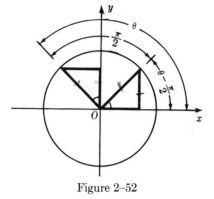

Figure 2–52

7. Use a method similar to that employed in Problem 6 to show that if $\pi < \theta \le 3\pi/2$, then
$$\sin \theta = -\sin (\theta - \pi); \qquad \cos \theta = -\cos (\theta - \pi).$$
Thus if we can compute or use a table to find $\sin \theta$ or $\cos \theta$ for $0 \le \theta \le \pi/2$, it is also possible to determine $\sin \theta$ and $\cos \theta$ for $\pi < \theta \le 3\pi/2$.

8. Use a method similar to that employed in Problem 6 to show that if $3\pi/2 < \theta \le 2\pi$, then
$$\sin \theta = -\cos \left(\theta - \frac{3\pi}{2}\right); \qquad \cos \theta = \sin \left(\theta - \frac{3\pi}{2}\right).$$

The results of this problem, along with those of Problems 6 and 7, show that if we can compute or use a table to find $\sin \theta$ and $\cos \theta$ for θ in the interval $0 \le \theta \le \pi/2$, $\sin \theta$ and $\cos \theta$ can be computed for any other value of θ.

9. Make use of the results of Problem 6, 7 and 8, along with Table A at the end of the text, to draw an accurate graph of $\sin \theta$ and $\cos \theta$ for $0 \le \theta \le 2\pi$.

10. Use Table A at the end of the text to evaluate:

(a) $\sin 0.24$;   (b) $\cos 0.50$;   (c) $\sin (-0.30)$;

(d) $\cos (-0.40)$;   (e) $\sin \left(\frac{\pi}{2} + 0.36\right)$;   (f) $\cos \left(\frac{\pi}{2} + 0.60\right)$;

(g) $\sin \left(\frac{3\pi}{2} + 0.70\right)$;   (h) $\cos \left(\frac{3\pi}{2} + 0.40\right)$.

11. Use Table A at the end of the text along with linear interpolation to evaluate:
(a) $\sin 0.215$;   (b) $\cos 1.342$;   (c) $\sin 3.61$;   (d) $\cos 2.15$.

12. Use Table A at the end of the text along with linear interpolation to evaluate
(a) $\sin (-2.69)$;   (b) $\cos 27.34$;   (c) $\sin 367.2$;   (d) $\cos (-9.73)$.

13. Illustrate geometrically what is being done when linear interpolation is used.

14. Present as much as you are able to discover about the inverse representation of the sine and cosine functions.

15. Determine a value of θ, $0 \le \theta \le \pi/2$ such that:
(a) $\sin \theta = 0.732$;   (b) $\cos \theta = 0.431$;   (c) $\sin \theta = 0.883$;   (d) $\cos \theta = 0.105$.

16. Prove that for all θ, $(\sin \theta)^2 + (\cos \theta)^2 = 1$.

Section 2-15

1. Determine the functions which are the sums of the following functions and give the domain for the sum.

(a) $f_1(x) = 3x^2 + 2x$
 $f_2(x) = 4x^3 + 1$;

(b) $f_1(x) = 2x^2 - 1$
 $f_2(x) = 3x^2 - 2x$;

(c) $f_1(x) = 3x^3 - 6x^2 + 2$
 $f_2(x) = x^3 + 6x^2 - 2x + 1$;

(d) $f_1(x) = x^3 - 3x^2 + 1$
 $f_2(x) = x^3 + 5x^2 - 2x$;

(e) $f_1(x) = 2x^{1/2}$
 $f_2(x) = 3x^2 + 2$;

(f) $f_1(x) = 1/x$
 $f_2(x) = 1/(x - 4)$.

2. Determine the functions which are the products of the following functions, and give the domain for the product functions.

(a) $f_1(x) = 2x - 1$
 $f_2(x) = x + 2$;

(b) $f_1(x) = 2x^2 + 1$
 $f_2(x) = x - 3$;

(c) $f_1(x) = 3x^2 + 1$
 $f_2(x) = 2x^2 + 2x + 1$.

3. Determine the functions which are the products of the following functions, and give the domain for the product functions.

(a) $f_1(x) = x^3 - 2x^2 + 1$
 $f_2(x) = -3x^2 + 1$;

(b) $f_1(x) = x^4 - 3x^3 + 2x^2 - 1$
 $f_2(x) = x^3 + 3x^2 - 2x + 7$.

4. Determine the functions which are the products of the following functions, and give the domain for the product functions.

(a) $f_1(x) = 1/(x - 2)$
 $f_2(x) = 1/(x - 3)$;

(b) $f_1(x) = x^{1/2}$
 $f_2(x) = x^{5/2}$;

(c) $f_1(x) = x^{1.732}$
 $f_2(x) = x^{-0.541}$

5. Determine the composition $f(x) = h[g(x)]$ in each of the following cases, and give the domain of $f(x)$. Show in each case that $f(x)$ is a polynomial.

(a) $g(x) = 1 + x^2$
 $h(u) = 1 - u^2$;

(b) $g(x) = 2x + 1$
 $h(u) = u + u^2$;

(c) $g(x) = 3x^2 - 2x + 1$
 $h(u) = 3u^2 - 2u + 1$.

6. Determine the composition $f(x) = h[g(x)]$ in each of the following cases, and give the domain of $f(x)$.

(a) $g(x) = 1/(x - 3)$
 $h(u) = 1/(u - 3)$;

(b) $g(x) = 2x + 1$
 $h(u) = (u + 3)/(u + 2)$;

(c) $g(x) = x^{1/2}$
 $h(u) = u^{2.16}$

7. Suggest at least one way in which each of the following functions can be imagined to be the composition of two other functions.

(a) $y = (x^2 - 3x)^{1/2}$;

(b) $y = \left(\dfrac{x + 2}{x - 3}\right)^4$;

(c) $y = 2(x - 1)^3 + 3(x - 1)^2 + 1$.

8. Prove that the sum of an nth degree polynomial and an mth degree polynomial is a polynomial whose degree is not greater than n if $n \geq m$. Under what circumstances will the degree of the sum be less than n?

9. Prove that the product of an nth degree polynomial and an mth degree polynomial is a polynomial whose degree is $m + n$.

10. Sketch the graph of the rational function $y = (x - 2)/(x - 3)$, indicating where appropriate any asymptotes.

12.* Use Table A at the end of the text to draw the graph of $\tan \theta$.

13.* Prove that, if $f(x)$ is periodic with period ς, then so is $a\,f(x) + b$, where a and b are any real numbers. Thus, conclude that $3 + 2 \sin x$ is a periodic function and sketch the graph of this function.

14.* Prove that, if $f_1(x)$ and $f_2(x)$ are both periodic with period ς, then $f_1(x) + f_2(x)$ is also periodic with period ς. Thus, conclude that $\sin x + \cos x$ is periodic and sketch the graph of this function.

15.* Prove that, if $f_1(x)$ and $f_2(x)$ are both periodic with period ς, then $f_1(x)f_2(x)$ is also periodic with period ς. Thus conclude that $(\sin x)(\cos x)$ is periodic and sketch the graph of this function.

16.* Prove that if $f_1(x)$ and $f_2(x)$ are both periodic with period ς, then $f_1(x)/f_2(x)$ is also periodic with period ς. Thus, conclude that $\tan x$ and $1/\sin x$ are periodic, and sketch the graph of $1/\sin x$.

17.* Is it necessarily true in Problems 14 through 16 that if ς is the least period of $f_1(x)$ and $f_2(x)$, ς is also the least period of the resulting function? Give any examples that occur to you.

18.* Suppose that $g(x)$ is periodic with period ς. Prove that the compound function $h[g(x)]$ is also periodic with period ς. Thus, conclude that $\sin(\cos x)$ is periodic·

19. Prove that if $f_1(x)$ and $f_2(x)$ are odd functions, then so is $f_1(x) + f_2(x)$. Prove also that if $f_1(x)$ and $f_2(x)$ are even functions, then so is $f_1(x) + f_2(x)$. Give examples to illustrate this.

20. Prove that if $f_1(x)$ and $f_2(x)$ are odd functions, then $f_1(x)f_2(x)$ is an even function. Similarly, prove that if $f_1(x)$ and $f_2(x)$ are even functions, then $f_1(x)f_2(x)$ is also an even function. Finally, prove that if $f_1(x)$ is even and $f_2(x)$ is odd, then $f_1(x)f_2(x)$ is odd. Give an example to illustrate each of these results.

21. Suppose that $g(x)$ and $h(u)$ are odd functions. Prove that $f(x) = h[g(x)]$ is an odd function. What can be said when both functions are even or when one is even and one is odd? Give examples to illustrate each of the cases.

Section 2–16

In Problems 1 through 10, sketch the graphs of the given functions.

1. $y = \begin{cases} x, & x \geq 0 \\ -x, & x < 0; \end{cases}$

2. $y = \begin{cases} 2x + 1, & x \geq 0 \\ 1, & x < 0 \end{cases}$

3. $y = \begin{cases} x^{1/2}, & x \geq 0 \\ (-x)^{1/2}, & x < 0; \end{cases}$

4. $y = \begin{cases} 1 + x, & x > 0 \\ 3, & x = 0 \\ 1 - x, & x < 0 \end{cases}$

5. $y = \begin{cases} 1/x, & x > 0 \\ -1/x, & x < 0 \end{cases}$

6. $y = \begin{cases} 1/x, & x > 0 \\ x^2, & x \leq 0; \end{cases}$

* Starred problems assume a familiarity with the material covered in starred sections in the text.

7. $y = \begin{cases} x, & x \geq 0 \\ x^2, & x < 0; \end{cases}$

8. $y = \begin{cases} 2 & x < 1 \\ -1, & x = 1 \\ -5, & x > 1; \end{cases}$

9. $y = \begin{cases} 1 - x, & x \leq 1 \\ 1 - x^2, & -1 < x < 1 \\ x - 1, & x > 1; \end{cases}$

10. $y = \begin{cases} x^2, & x < 1 \\ -(1 - x^2)^{1/2}, & -1 < x < 1 \\ 3 - x, & x > 1. \end{cases}$

As Problems 11 through 20, determine the inverse representations of each of the functions given in Problems 1 through 10.

CHAPTER 3

Limits and Differentiation

3–1 THE NOTION OF A LIMIT

Most of the functions whose graphs were studied in the last chapter have the characteristic that if we consider any number α in the domain, then the value $f(x)$ of the function for any x which is very close to α is close to $f(\alpha)$. Indeed, for these functions, the value of $f(x)$ gets closer and closer to $f(\alpha)$ as x gets closer and closer to α. For example, suppose that $f(x) = x^2$ and $\alpha = 2$, so that $f(\alpha) = 4$. Then if x is close to 2, $f(x)$ will be close to 4. Thus $f(2.01) = 4.0401$, $f(1.99) = 3.9601$, $f(2.001) = 4.004001$, $f(1.999) = 3.996001$, $f(2.0001) = 4.00040001$ and $f(1.9999) = 3.99960001$. What we are saying is that, for many functions, the value of the function changes smoothly as the value of x is changed. There are no sudden jumps in the function.

It is by no means true, however, that a function must necessarily exhibit the type of behavior just discussed for every value α in its domain. Let us study the following function, whose graph is shown in Figure 3–1.

$$f(x) = \begin{cases} x + 1, & x > 2 \\ 4.5, & x = 2 \\ x - 1, & x < 2 \,. \end{cases} \tag{3–1}$$

Suppose that we take $\alpha = 2$. Then $f(\alpha) = 4.5$. Consider values of x which are very close to 2 but are greater than 2. When $x > 2, f(x) = x + 1$. Thus $f(2.001) = 3.001$ and $f(2.0001) = 3.0001$. As x gets closer and closer to 2 while remaining greater than 2, $f(x)$ does not get closer and closer to $f(2) = 4.5$. Instead, $f(x)$ gets closer and closer to 3. Let us next examine the behavior of $f(x)$ for x which are very close to 2 but are less than 2. When $x < 2, \quad f(x) = x - 1.$ Hence $f(1.99) = 0.99, \quad f(1.999) = 0.999$ and $f(1.9999) = 0.9999$. Here also $f(x)$ does not get closer and closer to $f(2)$ as

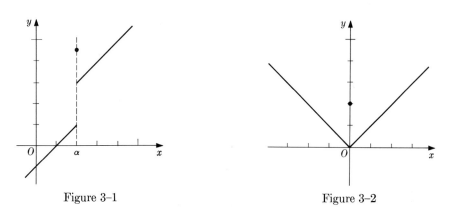

Figure 3–1   Figure 3–2

x gets closer and closer to 2 while remaining less than 2. Instead $f(x)$ gets closer and closer to 1. Not only does $f(x)$ not approach $f(2)$ as x gets closer and closer to 2, but in addition, $f(x)$ approaches different values depending on whether x is greater than 2 or less than 2. For $x > 2, f(x)$ approaches 3 as x approaches 2, while for $x < 2, f(x)$ approaches 1 as x approaches 2. This is all obvious when the graph in Figure 3–1 is examined.

There is a more subtle point, however, that is worth noting. In spite of the fact that $f(x)$ can be made arbitrarily close to 3 by properly selecting a value of $x > 2$, there is no value of x for which $f(x) = 3$, because $f(2)$ is not 3 but 4.5. Similarly, in spite of the fact that $f(x)$ can be made arbitrarily close to 1 by properly selecting a value of $x < 2$, there is no value of x for which $f(x) = 1$. The reader should give some thought to this point, since it is not easy to grasp initially.

Let us now study a similar but slightly different sort of behavior. Consider the function

$$f(x) = \begin{cases} x, & x > 0 \\ 2, & x = 0 \\ -x, & x < 0 . \end{cases} \qquad (3\text{–}2)$$

The graph of this function is shown in Figure 3–2. We shall study its behavior for values of x close to 0, that is, we shall take $\alpha = 0$ here. From (3–2), $f(0) = 2$. For x close to 0, but greater than 0, $f(x) = x$, and therefore, $f(0.001) = 0.001$, $f(0.0001) = 0.0001$ and $f(0.00001) = 0.00001$. As x approaches 0 while remaining greater than 0, $f(x)$ approaches 0, which is not $f(0) = 2$. For x close to 0, but less than 0, $f(x) = -x$. Thus $f(-0.001) = 0.001$, $f(-0.0001) = 0.0001$, and $f(-0.00001) = 0.00001$. As x approaches 0 while remaining less than 0, $f(x)$ approaches 0, just as it did for $x > 0$. Here, then, we have a situation where $f(x)$ approaches 0 as x approaches 0 regardless of whether $x > 0$ or $x < 0$, but $0 \neq f(0)$. In other words $f(x)$ is close to 0 for all x close to 0, but for such x, $f(x)$ is not close to $f(0)$.

In each of the examples studied above $f(x)$ approached some definite number β_+ as x approached α from the right, that is, for $x > \alpha$. Furthermore, $f(x)$ approached a definite number β_- as x approached α from the left, that is, for $x < \alpha$. It was not true in each case, however, that $\beta_+ = \beta_-$, and furthermore it was not in general true that $f(\alpha) = \beta_+$ or $f(\alpha) = \beta_-$. We would now like to consider still a different type of behavior which can be exhibited. Consider the function

$$f(x) = \begin{cases} \dfrac{1}{x-4}, & x > 4 \\ (x-4)^2, & x \le 4 \end{cases} \tag{3-3}$$

whose graph is shown in Figure 3–3. Suppose that we consider the value $\alpha = 4$. Then $f(\alpha) = 0$. For x greater than 4, $f(x) = 1/(x-4)$, and selecting some values of $x > 4$, but close to 4, we see that $f(4.01) = 100$, $f(4.001) = 1000$, and $f(4.0001) = 10,000$. As x approaches 4 from the right, $f(x)$ does not approach any number, but instead gets larger and larger. On the other hand, if $x < 4$, $f(x) = (x-4)^2$ and selecting some values of $x < 4$, but close to 4, we see that $f(3.99) = 0.0001$, $f(3.999) = 0.000001$, and $f(3.9999) = 0.00000001$. Thus as x approaches 4 from the left, $f(x)$ does approach a definite number 0, which is $f(0)$. The behavior just described is clearly evident on studying the graph in Figure 3–3.

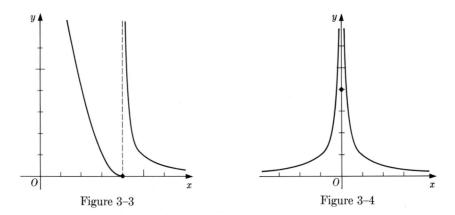

Figure 3–3   Figure 3–4

As an illustration of a slightly different sort of behavior consider

$$f(x) = \begin{cases} \dfrac{1}{x}, & x > 0 \\ 4, & x = 0 \\ -\dfrac{1}{x}, & x < 0. \end{cases} \tag{3-4}$$

The graph of this function is shown in Figure 3–4. Let us examine the case where $\alpha = 0$, so $f(\alpha) = f(0) = 4$. For $x > 0$, $f(x) = 1/x$, and selecting some values of $x > 0$ but close to 0, we see that $f(0.01) = 100$, $f(0.001) = 1000$ and $f(0.0001) = 10,000$. Thus as x approaches 0 from the right, $f(x)$ does not approach a definite number, but instead gets larger and larger. For $x < 0$, $f(x) = -1/x$, and selecting some values of $x < 0$ but close to 0, we see that $f(-0.01) = 100$, $f(-0.001) = 1000$ and $f(-0.0001) = 10,000$. Hence as x approaches 0 from the left, $f(x)$ does not approach a definite number, but instead gets larger and larger.

We began this chapter by noting that, for many of the functions studied in the previous chapter, when x is close to α, $f(x)$ is close to $f(\alpha)$. In other words, using some of the new ideas introduced during our discussion, $f(x)$ approaches $f(\alpha)$ as x approaches α from the right, and $f(x)$ approaches $f(\alpha)$ as x approaches α from the left. We next introduced examples to show that $f(x)$ can approach a number β_+ as x approaches α from the right, and a number β_- as x approaches α from the left, and it need not be true that $\beta_+ = f(\alpha)$ or $\beta_- = f(\alpha)$ or $\beta_+ = \beta_-$. Examples were then introduced to show that $f(x)$ need not approach any number as x approaches α from either the right or left. We are now ready to make an important observation. In the above examples α was always in the domain of the function. The examples have clearly illustrated, however, that the behavior of $f(x)$ as x approaches α from the right or from the left is totally independent of how $f(\alpha)$ is defined. We can now observe that the behavior of $f(x)$ as x approaches α from the right or from the left is independent of whether or not α is an element of the domain of $f(x)$. Thus if we consider the function

$$f(x) = \begin{cases} x + 1, & x > 2 \\ x - 1, & x < 2, \end{cases} \tag{3–5}$$

we note that this function differs from (3–1) only in that 2 is not in the domain of (3–5). However, the function in (3–5), just as the function in (3–1), has the characteristic that $f(x)$ approaches 3 as x approaches 2 from the right and $f(x)$ approaches 1 as x approaches 2 from the left. We would reach the same sort of conclusion if we removed α from the domain of each of the other examples studied above. Thus we conclude that the behavior of $f(x)$ for values of x close to α, but different from α, in no way depends on whether or not α is in the domain or what value $f(\alpha)$ has if α is in the domain.

We shall, in the future, be very much interested in being able to determine what value (if any) a given function $f(x)$ approaches as x approaches some given number α from the right and/or the left. We shall now introduce some terminology and notation which will allow us to describe the behavior of $f(x)$ under such circumstances. If $f(x)$ approaches a number β_+ as x approaches α from the right, we say that β_+ is the *limit* of $f(x)$ as x

approaches α from the right, and we represent this symbolically by writing

$$\lim_{x \to \alpha+} f(x) = \beta_+ . \tag{3-6}$$

If $f(x)$ approaches a number β_- as x approaches α from the left, we say that β_- is the limit of $f(x)$ as x approaches α from the left, and we represent this symbolically by writing

$$\lim_{x \to \alpha-} f(x) = \beta_- . \tag{3-7}$$

In the event that $f(x)$ approaches a number β as x approaches α from the right and $f(x)$ approaches the same number β as x approaches α from the left, we call β the limit of $f(x)$ as x approaches α, and we denote this symbolically by writing

$$\lim_{x \to \alpha} f(x) = \beta . \tag{3-8}$$

By definition, (3–8) is equivalent to writing

$$\lim_{x \to \alpha+} f(x) = \beta; \qquad \lim_{x \to \alpha-} f(x) = \beta . \tag{3-9}$$

The limits (3–6) and (3–7) are frequently referred as as *one-sided limits*, since (3–6) only tells what $f(x)$ approaches as x approaches α from the right and gives no information as to what happens to the left of α, while (3–7) indicates what $f(x)$ approaches as x approaches α from the left. The limit (3–8) is called *the limit* of $f(x)$ as x approaches α. When (3–8) holds, $f(x)$ approaches β as x approaches α from both the right and left.

We say that the limit of $f(x)$ *exists* as x approaches α if there exists a number β for which (3–8), that is, (3–9) holds. It is by no means true that the limit of $f(x)$ as x approaches α always exists. It may not exist even though both one-sided limits exist, that is, there exist numbers β_+ and β_- such that (3–6) and (3–7) hold. The limit exists only if $\beta_+ = \beta_-$. Of course, it may be true that one or both of the one-sided limits do not exist. Let us now illustrate the sorts of situations which can arise by applying our new terminology and notation to the examples studied above.

When $f(x) = x^2$ and $\alpha = 2$, we have seen that

$$\lim_{x \to 2+} f(x) = 4; \qquad \lim_{x \to 2-} f(x) = 4; \qquad \lim_{x \to 2} f(x) = 4 = f(\alpha) . \tag{3-10}$$

If $f(x)$ is given by (3–1) and $\alpha = 2$,

$$\lim_{x \to 2+} f(x) = 3; \qquad \lim_{x \to 2-} f(x) = 1 . \tag{3-11}$$

In this case, $\lim_{x \to 2} f(x)$ does not exist, since although both one-sided limits exist they do not have the same value. When $f(x)$ is given by (3–2) and $\alpha = 0$,

$$\lim_{x \to 0+} f(x) = 0; \qquad \lim_{x \to 0-} f(x) = 0; \qquad \lim_{x \to 0} f(x) = 0 . \tag{3-12}$$

If $f(x)$ is given by (3–3), and $\alpha = 4$

$$\lim_{x \to 4-} f(x) = 0 \, . \tag{3–13}$$

However, $\lim_{x \to 4+} f(x)$ does not exist, because $f(x)$ becomes larger and larger as x approaches 4 from the right. Thus $\lim_{x \to 4} f(x)$ does not exist, since in order for it to exist both one-sided limits must exist and have the same value. When $f(x)$ is given by (3–4) and $\alpha = 0$ neither of the one-sided limits exist and hence $\lim_{x \to 0} f(x)$ does not exist either. The examples studied show that situations can arise where neither one-sided limit exists, where one of these exists but not the other, and where both exist. If both exist, they may or may not have the same value. It is only in the case where both one-sided limits exist and have the same value that $\lim_{x \to \alpha} f(x)$ exists.

The notion of one-sided limits and the limit are very useful in describing how a function behaves for values of x close to some given number α. The limit concept will be fundamental in all of our future work. The reader should keep clearly in mind the fact that the notion of $\lim_{x \to \alpha+} f(x)$ or $\lim_{x \to \alpha-} f(x)$ or $\lim_{x \to \alpha} f(x)$ in no way depends on whether α is in the domain of $f(x)$ or what value $f(\alpha)$ has if α is in the domain. In this section, our discussion of limits has been completely intuitive in nature. In the next section we shall make more precise what we mean by (3–6), (3–7) and (3–8).

3–2 ANALYTIC DEFINITION OF LIMITS

We have defined $\lim_{x \to \alpha+} f(x) = \beta_+$ to mean that if we consider values of $x > \alpha$ but close to α, then as x gets closer and closer to α, $f(x)$ gets closer and closer to β_+. This has a perfectly clear intuitive meaning. However, if we claimed that $\lim_{x \to \alpha+} f(x) = \beta_+$, and someone asked us to prove it, how could this be done? The procedure used in the previous section was to evaluate $f(x)$ for several values of x close to but greater than α, and to note that $f(x)$ got closer and closer to β_+ as x got closer and closer to α. This cannot, however, be considered a proof. It is easy to think of examples where our intuitive approach is not sufficient. Suppose that we consider the function

$$f(x) = \begin{cases} 2 + x, & x \text{ rational} \\ 5 + x, & x \text{ irrational} \end{cases} \tag{3–14}$$

and take $\alpha = 2$. If several values of x are selected, say 2.01, 2.001, 2.0001, all of which are rational numbers, we see that $f(2.01) = 4.01$, $f(2.001) = 4.001$ and $f(2.0001) = 4.0001$. This would suggest that $\lim_{x \to 2+} f(x)$ exists and is equal to 4. However, if a different set of values for x were selected, say 2.010010001 $\cdots$, 2.0010001 $\cdots$, 2.000100001 $\cdots$, all of which are irrational numbers, it follows that $f(2.010010001 \cdots) = 7.010010001 \cdots$, $f(2.0010001 \cdots) = 7.0010001 \cdots$ and $f(2.000100001 \cdots)$

$= 7.000100001 \cdots$. These results suggest that $\lim_{x \to 2+} f(x)$ exists and is equal to 7. Here is an example where we obtain apparently contradictory results depending on what values of x are used.

The question then remains, does $\lim_{x \to 2+} f(x)$ exist and, if so, what is its value? The function (3–14) is a rather peculiar one. If we attempt to draw the graph of (3–14) we obtain something which looks like that shown in Figure 3–5. Figure 3–5 is somewhat misleading, however, since it makes it

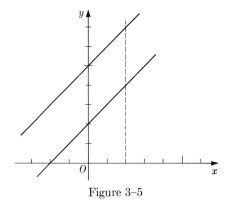

Figure 3–5

appear that two different values of y are associated with each x. This is not the case. The point (x, y) consisting of x and its image y lies on the lower line if x is rational and on the upper line if x is irrational. It is clear, however, that $f(x)$ approaches 4 as x approaches 2 from the right if x takes on only rational values and approaches 7 as x approaches 2 from the right if x takes on only irrational values. If we considered a set of x values which were alternately rational and irrational, then $f(x)$ would be alternately close to 4 and 7 and would not approach any specific number as x approached 2 from the right in this way. After this analysis, it would appear that we should say that $\lim_{x \to 2+} f(x)$ does not exist, because we can find sets of values of x such that $f(x)$ does not approach any number but oscillates, being close to 4 for some values and close to 7 for others. Figure 3–5 also suggests that $\lim_{x \to 2+} f(x)$ does not exist.

The above example has shown that our original intuitive idea must be made more precise if it is going to be able to handle all cases. What, then, do we mean by $\lim_{x \to a+} f(x) = \beta_+$? The analysis of the function of (3–14) has shown that we must require that $f(x)$ be close to β_+ for *all* $x > \alpha$ which are close to α, and not merely that $f(x)$ get closer and closer to β_+ for some specific set of values of x which get closer and closer to α. However, there is still considerable vagueness in what we mean by close and closer. For example, if $f(x) = 1 + 10^{-18} + x$, $f(x)$ gets closer and closer to 1 as x approaches 0 from the right. Shall we say, however, that $\lim_{x \to 0+} f(x) = 1$?

The reader will no doubt feel intuitively that this is not correct. He will see that the correct statement is $\lim_{x \to 0+} f(x) = 1 + 10^{-18}$. Why is this? While it is true that $f(x)$ gets closer and closer to 1 as x approaches 0 from the right, and indeed gets very close to 1, nonetheless $f(x) - 1$ is always greater than 10^{-18}. However, the difference $f(x) - 1 - 10^{-18} = x$ can be made arbitrarily small by taking x to be sufficiently close to 0. Thus $f(x) - 1 - 10^{-18} < 10^{-27}$ if $x = 10^{-28}$. In fact, $f(x) - 1 - 10^{-18} < 10^{-27}$ for *every* x satisfying $0 < x < 10^{-27}$. Similarly, $f(x) - 1 - 10^{-18} < 10^{-1000}$ for *every* x satisfying $0 < x < 10^{-1000}$. Here we have the basis for a rigorous definition of limits. Essentially, $\lim_{x \to a+} f(x) = \beta_+$ means that the magnitude of the difference $f(x) - \beta_+$ will be arbitrarily small for *all* $x > \alpha$ which are sufficiently close to α. To be still more precise, for every positive number ϵ, no matter how small ϵ may be, it is possible to find a positive number δ such that for every x, $\alpha < x < \alpha + \delta$, the magnitude of $f(x) - \beta_+$ is less than ϵ.

The rigorous definition of what we mean by $\lim_{x \to a+} f(x) = \beta_+$ can now be obtained from our discussion in the previous paragraph. Let us first introduce some useful terminology and notation. Recall that the magnitude of any number x is its distance from the origin, so that its magnitude is x if $x \geq 0$ and is $-x$ if $x < 0$. We shall denote the magnitude of x by $|x|$; $|x|$ is also sometimes referred to as the absolute value of x. Thus $|2| = 2$, $|-3| = 3$ and $|0| = 0$. Now $|x - \alpha|$ is $x - \alpha$ if $x - \alpha \geq 0$ and is $\alpha - x$ if $x - \alpha < 0$. This follows at once from our above definition. It is also true, however, that $|x - \alpha|$ is the distance between the points x and α on the x-axis. This is a useful fact to remember. Thus, $|f(x) - \beta_+|$ is the distance between $f(x)$ and β_+ when these are thought of as points on a line. The set of all points on the x-axis whose distance from a given point α is less than some specified number δ is the set

$$I_0 = \{x \mid |x - \alpha| < \delta\}. \tag{3–15}$$

The distance between x and α is less than δ if x lies less than δ units to the right of α or δ units to the left of α, that is, if x satisfies $\alpha - \delta < x < \alpha + \delta$. Thus the set I_0 in (3–15) is the same as the set

$$I_0 = \{x \mid \alpha - \delta < x < \alpha + \delta\}. \tag{3–16}$$

Hence, saying x is a number such that $|x - \alpha| < \delta$ is equivalent to saying that x satisfies $\alpha - \delta < x < \alpha + \delta$. If $|f(x) - \beta_+| < \epsilon$, then this is equivalent to $\beta_+ - \epsilon < f(x) < \beta_+ + \epsilon$.

We can now define precisely what we mean by the $\lim_{x \to a+} f(x) = \beta_+$. If, given any positive number ϵ, it is possible to find a $\delta > 0$ such that for every x satisfying $\alpha < x < \alpha + \delta$ it is true that $|f(x) - \beta_+| < \epsilon$, then $\lim_{x \to a+} f(x) = \beta_+$. It is important to note that one must be able to find or show the existence of a suitable δ for *every* positive ϵ, no matter how small ϵ may be. This association of a number δ with each $\epsilon > 0$ then defines a function, call it $g_+(\epsilon)$, whose domain is the set of all positive numbers and whose range is a subset of the positive numbers. We can then rephrase the above definition as follows, and in doing so we include the definition of $\lim_{x \to a-} f(x) = \beta_-$.

ONE-SIDED LIMITS. *If there exists a function $g_+(\epsilon)$ whose domain is the set of all positive numbers and whose range is a subset of the positive numbers, having the property that for every x satisfying $\alpha < x < \alpha + g_+(\epsilon)$ it is true that $|f(x) - \beta_+| < \epsilon$, then $\lim_{x \to a+} f(x) = \beta_+$. Similarly, if there exists a function $g_-(\epsilon)$ whose domain is the set of all positive numbers and whose range is a subset of the positive numbers, having the property that for every x satisfying $\alpha - g_-(\epsilon) < x < \alpha$ it is true that $|f(x) - \beta_-| < \epsilon$, then $\lim_{x \to a-} f(x) = \beta_-$.*

The proof that $\lim_{x \to a+} f(x) = \beta_+$ then reduces to showing the existence of a function $g_+(\epsilon)$ with the properties specified above. Here we have a rigorous definition and one which can be used in making sound mathematical proofs concerning limits.

Let us next illustrate what the above definition says geometrically, and thus show that it is consistent with our original intuitive ideas. If an $\epsilon > 0$ is selected, then when $|f(x) - \beta_+| < \epsilon$, we know that $\beta_+ - \epsilon < f(x) < \beta_+ + \epsilon$. Thus if x is an element of the domain of $f(x)$ for which $|f(x) - \beta_+| < \epsilon$, then the point $(x, f(x))$ on the graph of $f(x)$ must be in the shaded band shown in Figure 3–6. If $\lim_{x \to a+} f(x) = \beta_+$, then given any horizontal band centered at β_+ as shown in Figure 3–6, no matter how narrow it may be, it is possible to determine a $\delta > 0$ such that if we consider the vertical band determined by the vertical lines $x = \alpha$ and $x = \alpha + \delta$, the part of the graph of $f(x)$ which lies in this vertical band also lies entirely inside the horizontal band determined by the horizontal lines $y = \beta_+ + \epsilon$ and $y = \beta_+ - \epsilon$. This is illustrated in Figure 3–7.

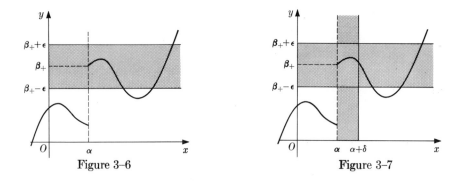

Figure 3–6　　　　　　　　　　　　　　　Figure 3–7

There are several points concerning the above definition which we should discuss in a little more detail. First of all, the reader may be wondering why in the above definition we require that for every $\epsilon > 0$ it is possible to determine a $\delta > 0$ with the properties specified, when it would appear from our previous discussions that we are really only interested in very small values of ϵ. The phrasing which uses all $\epsilon > 0$ is merely a matter of convention; it could be replaced by all $\epsilon > 10^{-1000}$. Note, however, that no harm is done by using all $\epsilon > 0$ in the definition, since the δ which can be used for 10^{-1000} can equally well serve as the δ for any larger value of ϵ. Next observe that if $\lim_{x \to \alpha+} f(x)$ exists, then there must exist a positive number γ such that every x in the interval $\alpha < x < \alpha + \gamma$ is in the domain of $f(x)$. The reason for this is that for any $\epsilon > 0$, there exists a $\delta > 0$ such that for every x satisfying $\alpha < x < \alpha + \delta$, $|f(x) - \beta_+| < \epsilon$. However, it is not possible to have $|f(x) - \beta_+| < \epsilon$ unless $f(x)$ is defined, that is, unless x is in the domain of $f(x)$. Since there is a $\delta > 0$ for every $\epsilon > 0$, there must then be a γ such that every x satisfying $\alpha < x < \alpha + \gamma$ is in the domain of $f(x)$, which is what we indicated above. This observation shows us, for example that $\lim_{x \to \alpha+} f(x)$ does not exist for any α when $f(x) = 2 + x$ and the domain includes only irrational numbers.

The final observation is that, even though $\lim_{x \to \alpha+} f(x) = \beta_+$, it need not be true that there is any element λ in the domain of $f(x)$ such that $f(\lambda) = \beta_+$. There are elements in the domain for which $f(x)$ is arbitrarily close to β_+, but there is not necessarily any element λ for which $f(\lambda) = \beta_+$. It is very important to understand this, and the reader should check back through the examples in the previous section to see that in a number of cases there is no element λ in the domain for which $f(\lambda) = \beta_+$.

In the future, we shall be mainly interested in finding *the* limit of $f(x)$ as x approaches some number α, and for the cases of interest to us the limit will normally exist. Recall that $\lim_{x \to \alpha} f(x) = \beta$ means that $\lim_{x \to \alpha+} f(x) = \beta$ and $\lim_{x \to \alpha-} f(x) = \beta$, and to show that $\lim_{x \to \alpha} f(x) = \beta$, we must show that both one-sided limits exist and have the value β. It is frequently difficult to use the mathematical definition of a one-sided limit given above to demonstrate rigorously the existence of such a limit. Fortunately, we shall almost never need to use the definition explicitly. Let us now give two very simple illustrations of the use of the mathematical definition. These will be used repeatedly later, but interestingly enough, they will be almost all we need.

Consider the function $f(x) = \lambda$, a constant. It is obvious intuitively that, in this case, for any number α

$$\lim_{x \to \alpha+} f(x) = \lim_{x \to \alpha-} f(x) = \lambda \tag{3-17}$$

and therefore

$$\lim_{x \to \alpha} f(x) = \lambda , \tag{3-18}$$

since the graph of $f(x)$ is simply a horizontal straight line which crosses the y-axis at $y = \lambda$. It is also very easy to prove these results. Let us prove that

$\lim_{x \to \alpha+} f(x) = \lambda$. We must show the existence of a function $g_+(\epsilon)$ such that if x satisfies $\alpha < x < \alpha + g_+(\epsilon)$, $|f(x) - \lambda| < \epsilon$. In our case, $f(x) - \lambda = \lambda - \lambda = 0$ always. Thus $|f(x) - \lambda|$, being 0 always, is 0 when $\alpha < x < \alpha + 1$. Therefore, for $g_+(\epsilon)$ we can simply use $g_+(\epsilon) = 1$ for all $\epsilon > 0$. This proves that $\lim_{x \to \alpha+} f(x) = \lambda$ for every α. By taking $g_-(\epsilon) = 1$, we can prove in precisely the same way that $\lim_{x \to \alpha-} f(x) = \lambda$. Hence (3–18) holds. Equation (3–18) says that the limit of a constant as x approaches α is the constant, or we can rewrite (3–18) as

$$\lim_{x \to \alpha} \lambda = \lambda, \quad \text{all } \alpha. \tag{3–19}$$

A slightly more difficult case is that where $f(x) = x$. It is obvious intuitively here that

$$\lim_{x \to \alpha+} f(x) = \lim_{x \to \alpha-} f(x) = \alpha, \tag{3–20}$$

so

$$\lim_{x \to \alpha} f(x) = \alpha \tag{3–21}$$

for every α, since the graph of $f(x)$ is a straight line through the origin. To prove that $\lim_{x \to \alpha+} f(x) = \alpha$ when $f(x) = x$, note that $|f(x) - \alpha| = x - \alpha$ when $x > \alpha$. Thus if $0 < x - \alpha < \epsilon$, then $|f(x) - \alpha| < \epsilon$. Hence if we take $g_+(\epsilon) = \epsilon$, this function has the properties needed to show that $\lim_{x \to \alpha+} f(x) = \alpha$. If we take $g_-(\epsilon) = \epsilon$, it follows that $\lim_{x \to \alpha-} f(x) = \alpha$. Thus (3–21) holds. We can rewrite (3–21) to read

$$\lim_{x \to \alpha} x = \alpha. \tag{3–22}$$

The reader should not get the impression that all proofs involving limits are as trivial as those just given. For example, if we take the slightly more complicated case where $f(x) = x^2$, the reader will not find it quite so easy to show that $\lim_{x \to \alpha+} f(x) = \alpha^2$, a result which we obtained on an intuitive basis in the previous section. We need not concern ourselves with a direct proof of this result, because we shall be able to prove it easily in another way, using the material to be introduced in the next section.

3–3 EVALUATION OF LIMITS

We shall now study several rules which make it a relatively simple matter to evaluate most, but by no means all, limits which may be of interest. Suppose that we have a function $f_1(x)$ having the property that $\lim_{x \to \alpha} f_1(x) = \beta$. Imagine now that we form the new function $f(x) = \lambda f_1(x)$. Let us investigate whether $\lim_{x \to \alpha} f(x)$ exists and, if so, what its value is. Recall that

$\lim_{x \to \alpha} f_1(x) = \beta$ means that $f_1(x)$ approaches β as x approaches α from both the right and from the left. If $f_1(x)$ approaches β under these conditions, then $\lambda f_1(x)$ should approach $\lambda\beta$, that is, $\lim_{x \to \alpha} f(x)$ exists and

$$\lim_{x \to \alpha} f(x) = \lambda\beta . \tag{3-23}$$

This can be written more conveniently as

$$\lim_{x \to \alpha} \lambda f_1(x) = \lambda \lim_{x \to \alpha} f_1(x) = \lambda\beta . \tag{3-24}$$

In words, (3–24) says that *the limit of λ times a function is λ times the limit of the function when this latter limit exists.* From (3–24) we can immediately conclude, for example, that

$$\lim_{x \to \alpha} \lambda x = \lambda \lim_{x \to \alpha} x = \lambda\alpha$$

for any real numbers α and λ. This follows from (3–22).

Let us next assume that we have two functions $f_1(x)$ and $f_2(x)$ having the property that

$$\lim_{x \to \alpha} f_1(x) = \beta_1; \qquad \lim_{x \to \alpha} f_2(x) = \beta_2 . \tag{3-25}$$

Consider the function $f(x) = f_1(x) + f_2(x)$, and let us determine what can be said about $\lim_{x \to \alpha} f(x)$. If $f_1(x)$ approaches β_1 and $f_2(x)$ approaches β_2 as x approaches α from both the right and from the left, $f_1(x) + f_2(x)$ must then get closer and closer to $\beta_1 + \beta_2$, so that $f(x)$ approaches $\beta_1 + \beta_2$. In other words, when (3–25) holds

$$\lim_{x \to \alpha} [f_1(x) + f_2(x)] = \beta_1 + \beta_2 , \tag{3-26}$$

or

$$\lim_{x \to \alpha} [f_1(x) + f_2(x)] = \lim_{x \to \alpha} f_1(x) + \lim_{x \to \alpha} f_2(x) , \tag{3-27}$$

so *the limit of the sum of two functions is the sum of the limits of the individual functions when the latter limits exist.* Precisely the same result holds for the sum of any finite number of functions, that is,

$$\lim_{x \to \alpha} [f_1(x) + \cdots + f_k(x)] = \lim_{x \to \alpha} f_1(x) + \lim_{x \to \alpha} f_2(x) + \cdots + \lim_{x \to \alpha} f_k(x) \tag{3-28}$$

when each of the limits on the right in (3–28) exists. As an example of (3–27), if $f_1(x) = x$, $f_2(x) = c$, a constant, then for any α

$$\lim_{x \to \alpha} (x + c) = \lim_{x \to \alpha} x + \lim_{x \to \alpha} c = \alpha + c , \tag{3-29}$$

because of (3–19) and (3–22).

Suppose once again that we have two functions $f_1(x)$ and $f_2(x)$ for which (3–25) holds. Let us consider the function $f(x) = f_1(x)f_2(x)$, and examine $\lim_{x \to \alpha} f(x)$ in this case. If $f_1(x)$ approaches β_1 and $f_2(x)$ approaches β_2 as x approaches α both from the right and from the left, then $f_1(x)f_2(x)$ must get closer and closer to $\beta_1\beta_2$, so that $f(x)$ approaches $\beta_1\beta_2$. Thus

$$\lim_{x \to \alpha} f_1(x)f_2(x) = \beta_1\beta_2 , \tag{3–30}$$

or

$$\lim_{x \to \alpha} f_1(x)f_2(x) = \lim_{x \to \alpha} f_1(x) \lim_{x \to \alpha} f_2(x) , \tag{3–31}$$

so *the limit of the product of two functions is the product of the limits of the individual functions when the latter limits exist.* Precisely the same result holds for the product of any finite number of functions, that is,

$$\lim_{x \to \alpha} f_1(x)f_2(x) \cdots f_k(x) = \lim_{x \to \alpha} f_1(x) \lim_{x \to \alpha} f_2(x) \cdots \lim_{x \to \alpha} f_k(x) \tag{3–32}$$

when each of the limits on the right in (3–32) exists. As an example of (3–31), we see that for any α

$$\lim_{x \to \alpha} x^2 = \left(\lim_{x \to \alpha} x\right)\left(\lim_{x \to \alpha} x\right) = \alpha^2 \tag{3–33}$$

because of (3–22). Similarly, for any natural number k, we see from (3–32) that

$$\lim_{x \to \alpha} x^k = \alpha^k . \tag{3–34}$$

Using (3–31) and (3–32) we have obtained results in (3–33) and (3–34) which are not so easily proved by use of the mathematical definition of a limit given in the previous section.

We can now obtain an important result. From (3–34) and (3–24), we see that for any natural number k and any numbers λ and α

$$\lim_{x \to \alpha} \lambda x^k = \lambda \lim_{x \to \alpha} x^k = \lambda \alpha^k . \tag{3–35}$$

Consider then any polynomial

$$f(x) = a_n x^n + a_{n-1} x^{n-1} + \cdots + a_0 .$$

On using (3–35) along with (3–28) and (3–19), we see that for any α, $\lim_{x \to \alpha} f(x) = f(\alpha)$ or

$$\lim_{x \to \alpha} (a_n x^n + a_{n-1} x^{n-1} + \cdots + a_0) = a_n \alpha^n + a_{n-1} \alpha^{n-1} + \cdots + a_0 . \tag{3–36}$$

For example,

$$\lim_{x \to 3} (2x^2 + 5x - 6) = 2(3)^2 + 5(3) - 6 = 27 .$$

Let us now obtain one final rule. Suppose that $f_1(x)$ and $f_2(x)$ are functions for which (3–25) holds, and suppose, in addition, that $\beta_2 \neq 0$. Consider the function $f(x) = f_1(x)/f_2(x)$, and let us examine $\lim_{x \to a} f(x)$. Since $f_1(x)$ approaches β_1 and $f_2(x)$ approaches β_2 as x approaches α both from the right and from the left, $f_1(x)/f_2(x)$ must get closer and closer to β_1/β_2 and thus $f(x)$ approaches β_1/β_2. Hence

$$\lim_{x \to a} f(x) = \frac{\beta_1}{\beta_2},$$

or

$$\lim_{x \to \alpha} \frac{f_1(x)}{f_2(x)} = \frac{\lim\limits_{x \to \alpha} f_1(x)}{\lim\limits_{x \to \alpha} f_2(x)}, \tag{3–37}$$

when both the limits on the right exist and the limit in the denominator is not 0, so that *the limit of the quotient of two functions is the quotient of the limits of the individual functions, when these limits exist and when the limit of the function appearing in the denominator is not zero.*

By use of (3–37) and (3–29) we immediately see that

$$\lim_{x \to 3} \frac{x + 5}{x - 2} = \frac{\lim\limits_{x \to 3} (x + 5)}{\lim\limits_{x \to 3} (x - 2)} = \frac{8}{1} = 8 .$$

Similarly, from (3–36), we see that

$$\lim_{x \to \alpha} \frac{a_n x^n + a_{n-1} x^{n-1} + \cdots + a_0}{b_m x^m + b_{m-1} x^{m-1} + \cdots + b_0} = \frac{a_n \alpha^n + a_{n-1} \alpha^{n-1} + \cdots + a_0}{b_m \alpha^m + b_{m-1} \alpha^{m-1} + \cdots + b_0} \tag{3–38}$$

provided that $b_m \alpha^m + b_{m-1} \alpha^{m-1} + \cdots + b_0 \neq 0$, that is, provided α is not a root of the polynomial $b_m x^m + b_{m-1} x^{m-1} + \cdots + b_0$. What (3–38) says is that, if $f(x)$ is a rational function and α is in the domain of this function, then

$$\lim_{x \to \alpha} f(x) = f(\alpha) . \tag{3–39}$$

The four properties given by (3–24), (3–27), (3–31) and (3–37) are extremely useful in working with limits. We shall, in the future, frequently be confronted with the problem of determining, or as we say evaluating, $\lim_{x \to a} f(x)$ for some given function $f(x)$. The problem will be to find what the limit is. We shall not normally know its value in advance. To prove that the $\lim_{x \to a} f(x) = \beta$ using the mathematical definition of a limit given in the previous section we must know ahead of time what the limit is, since the definition provides no assistance for determining β. However, the four results obtained above make it possible to determine β while simultaneously proving that β is the limit. Thus the four equations just obtained are basic in the evaluation of limits.

The reader will note that we obtained (3–24), (3–27), (3–31) and (3–37) by intuitive reasoning. We did not prove them rigorously, although this could be done by using the mathematical definition of a limit given in the previous section. The proofs are not really difficult, but they would require some time to go through in detail, and since we are not attempting in this work to prove rigorously every result, we shall omit them. Equations (3–24), (3–27), (3–31) and (3–37) also hold for one-sided limits, that is, if $x \to \alpha$ is replaced by $x \to \alpha+$ or $x \to \alpha-$. We have stated the results using the limit, since this is what we shall be most interested in later.

The reader should be careful not to read more into the above results than is really implied. For example, (3–27) holds when the limits on the right in (3–27) exist. If they do not exist, $\lim_{x \to \alpha} f(x)$ may or may not exist. Equation (3–27) does not help us to answer this when $\lim_{x \to \alpha} f_1(x)$ and $\lim_{x \to \alpha} f_2(x)$ do not exist. To see that $\lim_{x \to \alpha} f(x)$ may exist, even if those of $f_1(x)$ and $f_2(x)$ do not, suppose that $f_1(x) = 1/x$, $f_2(x) = 1 - (1/x)$ so that $f(x) = f_1(x) + f_2(x) = 1$, $x \neq 0$. Clearly then, $\lim_{x \to 0} f(x) = 1$. However, $\lim_{x \to 0} f_1(x)$ and $\lim_{x \to 0} f_2(x)$ do not exist (why?). Similar remarks apply to the other equations. In (3–37), $\lim_{x \to \alpha} f_1(x)/f_2(x)$ may exist even if $\lim_{x \to \alpha} f_2(x) = 0$. This can happen if $\lim_{x \to \alpha} f_1(x) = 0$ also. As a very simple example, suppose that $f_1(x) = x$ and $f_2(x) = x$. Then $f_1(x)/f_2(x) = 1$, $x \neq 0$, and hence $\lim_{x \to 0} f_1(x)/f_2(x) = 1$ even though $\lim_{x \to 0} f_2(x) = 0$. The reader should also be careful not to try to use the above equations in the reverse order. For example, from the fact that $\lim_{x \to \alpha} f_1(x)/f_2(x)$ exists, it cannot be concluded from (3–37) that $\lim_{x \to \alpha} f_1(x)$ and $\lim_{x \to \alpha} f_2(x)$ exist. This may or may not be true.

The procedure for using the results obtained in this section as an aid in evaluating $\lim_{x \to \alpha} f(x)$ is to imagine $f(x)$ as the sum, product, quotient of other functions whose limits can be more easily evaluated. Let us now provide some additional examples.

EXAMPLES: 1. To evaluate $\lim_{x \to 2} 1/x^2$, we can imagine that $1/x^2$ is of the form $f_1(x)/f_2(x)$ where $f_1(x) = 1$ and $f_2(x) = x^2$. From what we have shown above

$$\lim_{x \to 2} 1 = 1; \qquad \lim_{x \to 2} x^2 = 4 .$$

Hence the limit of interest exists and

$$\lim_{x \to 2} \frac{1}{x^2} = \frac{1}{4} .$$

2. Suppose that $f(x) = (x^2 - 3x + 1)(x^4 - x^2 + 2x)$. Let us determine $\lim_{x \to 1} f(x)$. We can think of $f(x)$ as being the product of two functions $f_1(x)$ and $f_2(x)$ where

$$f_1(x) = x^2 - 3x + 1; \qquad f_2(x) = x^4 - x^2 + 2x .$$

Then by (3–36)

$$\lim_{x \to 1} f_1(x) = 1 - 3 + 1 = -1; \quad \lim_{x \to 1} f_2(x) = 1 - 1 + 2 = 2 .$$

Since both of these limits exist, it follows from (3–31) that

$$\lim_{x \to 1} f(x) = (-1)(2) = -2 .$$

3. Let

$$f(x) = \frac{x^2 + 2x + \dfrac{3}{x}}{(x^2 - 2x + 1)(x^3 + 4x - 3)} .$$

We shall now evaluate $\lim_{x \to -1} f(x)$. We can think of $f(x)$ as being the quotient of $f_1(x)$ by $f_2(x)$, where

$$f_1(x) = x^2 + 2x + \frac{3}{x} ; \qquad f_2(x) = (x^2 - 2x + 1)(x^3 + 4x - 3) .$$

To evaluate $\lim_{x \to -1} f_1(x)$, note that we can think of $f_1(x)$ as being the sum of two functions $f_3(x)$ and $f_4(x)$, where

$$f_3(x) = x^2 + 2x; \qquad f_4(x) = \frac{3}{x} .$$

By (3–36)

$$\lim_{x \to -1} (x^2 + 2x) = (-1)^2 - 2 = -1 .$$

From (3–38) we see that

$$\lim_{x \to -1} \frac{3}{x} = \frac{3}{-1} = -3 .$$

Since the limits of $f_3(x)$ and $f_4(x)$ exist, so does that of $f_1(x)$ by (3–27), and

$$\lim_{x \to -1} f_1(x) = -1 + (-3) = -4 .$$

To evaluate $\lim_{x \to -1} f_2(x)$, we can note that $f_2(x)$ can be looked upon as the product of two functions $f_5(x)$ and $f_6(x)$, where

$$f_5(x) = x^2 - 2x + 1; \qquad f_6(x) = x^3 + 4x - 3 .$$

By (3–36)

$$\lim_{x \to -1} f_5(x) = (-1)^2 + 2 + 1 = 4; \qquad \lim_{x \to -1} f_6(x) = (-1)^3 - 4 - 3 = -8 .$$

Inasmuch as the limits of $f_5(x)$ and $f_6(x)$ exist then by (3–31), the limit of $f_2(x)$ exists and

$$\lim_{x \to -1} f_2(x) = 4(-8) = -32 .$$

Finally, since the limits of $f_1(x)$ and $f_2(x)$ exist and the latter is not 0, it follows from (3–37) that the limit of $f(x)$ exists and

$$\lim_{x \to -1} f(x) = \frac{-4}{-32} = \frac{1}{8} .$$

We have gone through this example in great detail to show the logic involved. After the process becomes familiar, each of the above steps would not actually be written down in solving a given problem. Instead, several steps would be carried out simultaneously.

4. Suppose that

$$f(x) = \begin{cases} \dfrac{x^2 + 3}{x - 1} & x > 0 \\ 5, & x = 0 \\ 0, & x < 0 . \end{cases}$$

Let us determine $\lim_{x \to 0} f(x)$ if it exists. For $x > 0, f(x) = (x^2 + 3)/(x - 1)$. Now by (3–38), which also holds for one-sided limits,

$$\lim_{x \to 0+} f(x) = \frac{3}{-1} = -3 ,$$

and the one-sided limit does exist and has the value -3. Note, however, that $\lim_{x \to 0} f(x)$ does not exist in this case, since $\lim_{x \to 0-} f(x) = 0$ and this is not equal to $\lim_{x \to 0+} f(x)$.

We shall conclude this section by pointing out two more properties of limits which are occasionally useful. Suppose that $\lim_{x \to a} f(x) = \beta$. Let us write $v = x - \alpha$. Then $|v|$ is the distance of x from α. Now $x = \alpha + v$, so $f(x) = f(\alpha + v)$. We can then write $f_1(v) = f(\alpha + v)$, and $f_1(v)$ is a function of the variable v. Now as x approaches α, either from the right or from the left, v approaches 0. However, $f(x)$ approaches β as x approaches α from the right and from the left, and therefore $f_1(v)$ must approach β as v approaches 0 from the right and from the left, since $f_1(v) = f(x)$. Thus $\lim_{v \to 0} f(\alpha + v) = \beta$ if $\lim_{x \to a} f(x) = \beta$. On the other hand, if $f(\alpha + v)$ approaches β as v approaches 0 from the right and from the left, then $f(x)$ approaches β as x approaches α from the right and from the left. In other words,

$$\lim_{v \to 0} f(\alpha + v) = \beta \quad \text{if and only if} \quad \lim_{x \to a} f(x) = \beta . \qquad (3\text{–}40)$$

It is often convenient to make the change of variable from x to v, or vice versa, in evaluating some limit.

The other property of limits is the following. Suppose that $\lim_{x \to a+} f_1(x) = \beta_+$ and $\lim_{x \to a+} f_2(x) = \gamma_+$. Assume also that there exists a $\delta > 0$ such that for all x, $\alpha < x < \alpha + \delta$ it is true that $f_2(x) \geq f_1(x)$. Then it follows that $\gamma_+ \geq \beta_+$. We can easily see intuitively that this must be the case, for if $\gamma_+ < \beta_+$, then since $f_2(x)$ gets closer and closer to γ_+ and $f_1(x)$ gets closer and closer to β_+ as x approaches α from the right, for x sufficiently close to α we must have $f_1(x) > f_2(x)$, which is a contradiction. This same type of argument can be used to provide a rigorous proof, but we shall not give it.

3–4 CONTINUITY

We began this chapter by noting that most of the functions studied in the previous chapter have the property that if α is in the domain, then for all x which are very close to α, $f(x)$ will be close to $f(\alpha)$. Stated more precisely, as x approaches α from the right and from the left, $f(x)$ approaches $f(\alpha)$. This is equivalent to stating that

$$\lim_{x \to \alpha} f(x) = f(\alpha) . \tag{3–41}$$

We then went on to see that it is by no means always true that (3–41) holds. A function for which (3–41) holds is said to be *continuous* at α. In order for $f(x)$ to be continuous at α, it must be true that: (1) α is in the domain, (2) $\lim_{x \to a+} f(x)$ and $\lim_{x \to a-} f(x)$ exist, and (3) both one-sided limits must be equal and have the value $f(\alpha)$. These three conditions are all summarized in the single equation (3–41). If a function is not continuous at α, it is said to be *discontinuous* at α. A function is automatically discontinuous at any values of α which are not in the domain of the function. It may, however, be discontinuous at α even if α is in the domain. This will be true if $\lim_{x \to a} f(x)$ exists but is not equal to $f(\alpha)$, or if $\lim_{x \to a} f(x)$ does not exist. A function which is discontinuous at one or more points is called a *discontinuous function*.

In Section 3–1 we introduced several discontinuous functions in the process of introducing the notion of a limit. Let us now go back and study these once again. The function given by (3–2) has the characteristic that $\lim_{x \to 0} f(x)$ exists, but is not equal to $f(0)$. The function is thus discontinuous at 0. The type of discontinuity exhibited here is called a *removable discontinuity*, since if $f(0)$ were defined to be 0 rather than 2, then the function would be continuous at 0. A function is said to have a removable discontinuity at α if it is not continuous at α, but can be made continuous at α by suitably defining $f(\alpha)$. A function has a removable discontinuity at α if and only if $\lim_{x \to a} f(x)$ exists, call it value β, and either α is not in the domain or

$\beta \neq f(\alpha)$. To remove the discontinuity it is only necessary to define $f(\alpha) = \beta$. The function given in (3–2) is continuous at every value of x other than 0.

The function defined by (3–1) has the characteristic that $\lim_{x \to 2} f(x)$ does not exist, since although both one-sided limits exist, they do not have the same value. Instead,

$$\lim_{x \to 2+} f(x) = 3; \qquad \lim_{x \to 2-} f(x) = 1 .$$

The function given by (3–1) is said to have a *jump discontinuity* at $x = 2$. This type of discontinuity occurs at α if both one-sided limits exist, but do not have the same value. It is not possible to remove a jump discontinuity by suitably defining $f(\alpha)$. No matter what value is used for $f(\alpha)$, the jump discontinuity will remain. It will be noted that the function (3–1) is continuous at every point except 2.

Consider now the function (3–3). This function is not continuous at $x = 4$, since $\lim_{x \to 4} f(x)$ does not exist. In this case it is also true that $\lim_{x \to 4+} f(x)$ does not exist; instead $f(x)$ gets larger and larger as x approaches 4 from the right. The $\lim_{x \to 4-} f(x)$ does exist, however. The type of discontinuity illustrated here is often referred to as an *infinite discontinuity*. A function is said to have an infinite discontinuity at α if $f(x)$ becomes a larger and larger positive number, increasing without bound, or becomes an arbitrarily large negative number as x approaches α from the right and/or the left.

We can now make more precise what we mean by a vertical asymptote to the graph of a function. The function $f(x)$ is said to have a vertical asymptote at α if it has an infinite discontinuity at $x = \alpha$. Thus the function (3–3) has a vertical asymptote at $x = 4$. The function is continuous at all other points. The function given by (3–4) has an infinite discontinuity at $x = 0$ and has a vertical asymptote at $x = 0$. It is continuous at all other points.

Generally speaking, the functions normally studied in mathematics and encountered in practice will either be continuous at every point in their domain or will be discontinuous only at a relatively small number of points. This has been true for each of the examples studied above. With one exception, we have illustrated the basic types of discontinuities which can occur in such cases. This exception is a discontinuity which results from the function oscillating more and more rapidly as x approaches some given number. Such behavior is illustrated by $\sin 1/x$ as x approaches 0. The reader who has studied the sine function may be interested in examining the behavior of $\sin 1/x$ near $x = 0$. We shall not attempt to study such oscillatory discontinuities, since the reader will almost certainly never encounter one in applications.

Certain functions have a domain which includes only a subset of the real numbers, and by the way we have defined continuity they are automatically discontinuous at all numbers not in the domain. Thus $x^{1/2}$ is defined only for $x \geq 0$ and would, according to our previous definition, be considered to be discontinuous at every negative number. The statement that $x^{1/2}$ is discontinuous for $x < 0$ is not very meaningful or illuminating, since $x^{1/2}$ is not defined for any $x < 0$. Normally, the information that $f(x)$ is discontinuous at α is of interest only if $f(x)$ is defined at all values of x, $\alpha < x < \delta$, or all values of x, $\alpha - \delta < x < \alpha$, or both, for some positive δ. Although, as we noted above, most functions are not discontinuous at more than a relatively few points in their domain, it is possible for a function to be defined for every real number and yet be discontinuous at each element of the domain. The function given by (3–14) provides such an example. As might be expected, however, functions of this type are not encountered in applications.

A function whose domain includes all real numbers and which is continuous at each point in the domain is said to be continuous everywhere. It follows from (3–36) that polynomials form a class of functions which are continuous everywhere. Often we shall be interested in functions which are continuous over an interval. Basically, there are two types of intervals that will be of interest to us. One of these is referred to as an *open interval*. An open interval with end points a and b is the set of points on the x-axis, which we shall denote symbolically by I_{ab}^0, defined as

$$I_{ab}^0 = \{x | a < x < b\} . \tag{3–42}$$

This is the set of points shown in Figure 3–8, not including the points a and b. A function is said to be continuous over the open interval I_{ab}^0 if it is continuous at each point x in the interval.

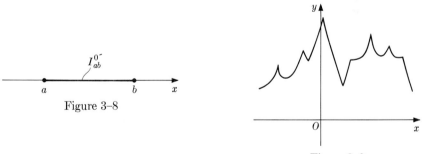

$$I_{ab}^{0}$$

a b x

Figure 3–8

Figure 3–9

The other type of interval is called a *closed interval*. A closed interval with end points a and b is defined to be the set of points

$$I_{ab}^c = \{x | a \leq x \leq b\} . \tag{3–43}$$

The geometric representation of I_{ab}^c is the same as I_{ab}^0 except that I_{ab}^c includes the end points a and b. A closed interval contains its end points while an open one does not. Note that

$$I_{ab}^c = I_{ab}^0 \cup \{a\} \cup \{b\} . \tag{3-44}$$

Every point in I_{ab}^0 is called an *interior point* of I_{ab}^c. A function $f(x)$ is said to be continuous over the closed interval I_{ab}^c if it is continuous at every point in I_{ab}^0 and if $\lim_{x \to a+} f(x) = f(a)$ and $\lim_{x \to b-} f(x) = f(b)$. At the end points a and b, the usual definition of continuity $\lim_{x \to a} f(x) = f(a)$ and $\lim_{x \to b} f(x) = f(b)$ is not used. The reason for this special treatment of the end points is to have the definition of continuity over I_{ab}^c be such that points outside of I_{ab}^c need not be considered in deciding whether $f(x)$ is continuous or not. This definition is quite satisfactory so long as only points in I_{ab}^c are considered.

Intervals exist that are closed at one end and open at the other, for example, the intervals $I_{ab}^0 \cup \{a\}$ or $I_{ab}^0 \cup \{b\}$. We shall not, however, have much need for intervals of this sort. We shall also call the sets $I_{a\infty}^c = \{x|x \geq a\}$, $I_{-\infty a}^c = \{x|x \leq a\}$, $I_{a\infty}^0 = \{x|x > a\}$ and $I_{-\infty a}^0 = \{x|x < a\}$ intervals. The first two are called closed intervals since they contain their single end point a, and the other two are called open intervals since they do not contain their single end point a. If a function is continuous over some interval, the graph of this function over the interval is called a *continuous curve*. For example, the curve shown in Figure 3–9 is a continuous curve and is the graph of a continuous function. A continuous curve does not have any jumps in it. However, it can have corners, that is, it does not have to be smooth.

If $f_1(x)$ and $f_2(x)$ are continuous at α, then $\lim_{x \to \alpha} f_1(x) = f_1(\alpha)$ and $\lim_{x \to \alpha} f_2(x) = f_2(\alpha)$. Thus by (3–27), if $f(x) = f_1(x) + f_2(x)$, $\lim_{x \to \alpha} f(x) = f_1(\alpha) + f_2(\alpha) = f(\alpha)$, and $f(x)$ is continuous at a. Thus if $f_1(x)$ and $f_2(x)$ are continuous at α, we see that the sum of these two functions is also continuous at α. This property is often expressed by saying that *the sum of continuous functions is continuous*. In a similar way it follows from (3–31) that if $f_1(x)$ and $f_2(x)$ are continuous at α then so is the product of these functions, that is, *the product of continuous functions is continuous*. Finally, from (3–37), we see that if $f_1(x)$ and $f_2(x)$ are continuous at α and $f_2(\alpha) \neq 0$, then $f_1(x)/f_2(x)$ is continuous at α, or *the quotient of continuous functions is continuous whenever the denominator is not zero*. These results can often be conveniently employed in proving that rather complicated functions are continuous, as we shall show in the examples which follow.

Except for the function studied in the last section of the previous chapter, each of the functions studied there was continuous at each point in its domain. We have already shown that polynomials and rational functions have this property. The only other functions studied there were $x^{m/n}$, $\sin \theta$, $\cos \theta$ and $\tan \theta$. To see that $\sin \theta$ and $\cos \theta$ are continuous, we only need note that if (x_0, y_0) is the point determined by θ_0, the coordinates of the points (x, y) determined by values of θ close to θ_0 have x close to x_0 and y close to y_0, and as θ approaches θ_0, x approaches x_0 and y approaches y_0. We have to use this sort of geometric argument here, since this is the way in which $\sin \theta$ and $\cos \theta$ were defined. Since $\tan \theta = \sin \theta / \cos \theta$, it follows from the fact that the quotient of continuous functions is continuous wherever the denominator is not zero that $\tan \theta$ is continuous at every point in its domain.

It is obvious from the graphs of the functions $x^{m/n}$ that each is continuous for all $x > 0$. We cannot, however, prove this using the rules developed in the previous section. To make the proof, we must go back to the definition of a limit. We shall give the proof to illustrate, in a somewhat more complicated situation than has been studied previously, how the definition can be used to prove the existence of a limit. To begin, let us consider the function $x^{1/n}$. We shall now show that $\lim_{x \to a+} x^{1/n} = \alpha^{1/n}$ if $\alpha > 0$. When $x > \alpha$, $x^{1/n} > \alpha^{1/n}$, and $|x^{1/n} - \alpha^{1/n}| = x^{1/n} - \alpha^{1/n}$. This quantity will be less than ϵ when $x^{1/n} - \alpha^{1/n} < \epsilon$ or $x^{1/n} < \alpha^{1/n} + \epsilon$. However, if $0 < u^n < v^n$, then $u < v$. Hence, if $(x^{1/n})^n = x < (\alpha^{1/n} + \epsilon)^n$ and $x > \alpha$, then $|x^{1/n} - \alpha^{1/n}| < \epsilon$. Consequently, if we take $g_+(\epsilon) = (\alpha^{1/n} + \epsilon)^n - \alpha$, this function serves to show that $\lim_{x \to a+} x^{1/n} = \alpha^{1/n}$. In precisely the same way, we can show that $\lim_{x \to a-} x^{1/n} = \alpha^{1/n}$ if $\alpha > 0$. Thus $\lim_{x \to a} x^{1/n} = \alpha^{1/n}$ when $\alpha > 0$, and $x^{1/n}$ is continuous for all $x > 0$. Inasmuch as the product of continuous functions is continuous, $(x^{1/n})^m = x^{m/n}$ is continuous for all $x > 0$, and this is what we wished to show.

EXAMPLES. 1. The functions $3x^2 + 2$ and $\sin x$ are continuous everywhere, and thus so is $f(x) = 3x^2 + 2 + \sin x$, since the sum of continuous functions is continuous.

2. The functions $x^{1.746}$ and $(x + 2)/(x + 3)$ are continuous for all $x > 0$; therefore

$$f(x) = x^{1.746} + \frac{x + 2}{x + 3}$$

is continuous for all $x > 0$, since the sum of continuous functions is continuous.

3. The functions $2x^{3.1416} + 5$ and $(x^2 - 1)/(x^2 + 1)$ are continuous for $x > 0$ (why?); hence

$$f(x) = \frac{(x^2 - 1)(2x^{3.1416} + 5)}{x^2 + 1}$$

is continuous for $x > 0$, since the product of continuous function is continuous.

4. The functions $x^{1/3}$ and $\sin x$ are continuous for $x > 0$, and therefore $x^{1/3} \sin x$ is continuous for $x > 0$, since the product of continuous functions is continuous.

5. The functions $2x^{4.16}$ and $x^2 - 3x + 2$ are continuous for $x > 0$ and $2x^{4.16}$ is positive for such x. Thus the function $(x^2 - 3x + 2)/2x^{4.16}$ is continuous for $x > 0$, since the quotient of continuous functions is continuous at all points where the denominator is not zero.

When determining $\lim_{x \to \alpha} f(x)$, it is frequently convenient to imagine that $f(x) = h[g(x)]$, so that $f(x)$ is the composition of $g(x)$ and $h(u)$. Let us now see why this is so. Suppose that $\lim_{x \to \alpha} g(x) = \beta$ and that $h(u)$ is continuous at $u = \beta$. As x approaches α from the right and from the left, $g(x)$ approaches β, that is, $u = g(x)$ approaches β. But for all u which are sufficiently close to β, $h(x)$ can be made arbitrarily close to $h(\beta)$. Hence as x approaches α, $h[g(x)]$ approaches $h(\beta)$, or $\lim_{x \to \alpha} f(x) = h(\beta)$. We can write this in a more revealing way as

$$\lim_{x \to \alpha} h[g(x)] = h[\lim_{x \to \alpha} g(x)] , \tag{3-45}$$

when $h(u)$ is continuous at β. To determine $\lim_{x \to \alpha} h[g(x)]$ we only need to evaluate $\lim_{x \to \alpha} g(x)$ and the desired limit is then $h[\lim_{x \to \alpha} g(x)]$. Note that we have not assumed in the above that $g(x)$ is continuous at α. It need not be true that $\beta = g(\alpha)$ or that α is in the domain of $g(x)$. We have not proved (3-45) rigorously, but this could be done using the definition of the limit. The intuitive argument given will suffice for our purposes. Equation (3-45) also holds, of course, for one-sided limits, that is, if $x \to \alpha$ is replaced by $x \to \alpha+$ or $x \to \alpha-$.

If $g(x)$ is continuous at α so that $\lim_{x \to \alpha} g(x) = g(\alpha)$, then (3-45) reduces to

$$\lim_{x \to \alpha} h[g(x)] = h[g(\alpha)] , \tag{3-46}$$

and in this case $f(x) = h[g(x)]$ is continuous at $x = \alpha$. Thus if $g(x)$ is continuous at $x = \alpha$ and $h(u)$ is continuous at $u = g(\alpha)$, then $h[g(x)]$ is continuous at $x = \alpha$. This is frequently stated by saying that *the composition of continuous functions is continuous*.

We can often evaluate $\lim_{x \to \alpha} h[g(x)]$ even if $h(u)$ is not continuous at $\beta = \lim_{x \to \alpha} g(x)$. If $\lim_{u \to \beta} h(u) = \gamma$, then since $g(x)$ approaches β as x approaches α and $h(u)$ approaches γ as u approaches β, it would appear that $\lim_{x \to \alpha} h[g(x)] = \gamma$. This is frequently true; however, it is not necessarily true. The reason for this is that, if $h(x)$ is not continuous at β, then $\lim_{u \to \beta} h(u) = \gamma$ is not necessarily $h(\beta)$, even if β is in the domain of $h(u)$. Now as $x \to \alpha$, there is no guarantee that, for values of x arbitrarily close to α, it will not be true that $g(x) = \beta$. For such x, $h(u)$ need not be close to γ or even be defined. Thus $\lim_{x \to \alpha} h[g(x)]$ may not exist even though $\lim_{x \to \alpha} g(x)$ and $\lim_{u \to \beta} h(u)$ exist. For example, suppose that $g(x) = 3$ for

x a rational number and $g(x) = 3 - x$ for x irrational; then $\lim_{x \to 0} g(x) = 3$. Assume also that $h(u) = u - 3$, $u > 0$, $h(u) = 3 - u$ for $u < 0$, so that $\lim_{u \to 3} h(u) = 0$. However, let $h(3) = 6$. In this case $\lim_{x \to 0} h[g(x)]$ does not exist, because

$$h[g(x)] = \begin{cases} 6, & x \text{ rational} \\ -x, & x < 3, \text{ irrational} \\ x, & x > 3, \text{ irrational} . \end{cases}$$

If there exists a $\delta > 0$ such that for all x, $0 < |x - \alpha| < \delta$, $g(x) \neq \beta$, then $\lim_{x \to \alpha} h[g(x)] = \gamma$. The difficulties arise when $g(x) = \beta$ for x values arbitrarily close to α. Let us now give some examples to illustrate the usefulness of the material developed in the preceding paragraphs.

EXAMPLES. 1. Inasmuch as $u^{1/2}$ is continuous for all $u > 0$ and $x^2 + 2$ is continuous and positive for all x, $(x^2 + 2)^{1/2}$ is everywhere continuous, because the composition of continuous functions yields a continuous function.

2. The functions $\cos \theta$ and $x^2 - 3x - 1$ are continuous everywhere and therefore $\cos(x^2 - 3x - 1)$ is continuous everywhere, since the composition of continuous functions is continuous.

3. Since u^2 is continuous everywhere, it follows from (3–45) that

$$\lim_{x \to 2} \left[\frac{x-1}{x^2+2} \right]^2 = \left[\lim_{x \to 2} \left(\frac{x-1}{x^2+2} \right) \right]^2 = \left(\frac{2-1}{4+2} \right)^2 = \frac{1}{36} .$$

We could have evaluated this limit without (3–45) by noting that

$$\left[\frac{x-1}{x^2+2} \right]^2 = \frac{(x-1)^2}{(x^2+2)^2} = \frac{x^2 - 2x + 1}{x^4 + 4x^2 + 4}$$

and using (3–38). This latter procedure, however, is much more complicated than that required when using (3–45).

4. Inasmuch as $u^{1/2}$ is continuous for $u > 0$, it follows from (3–45) that

$$\lim_{x \to -1} \left(\frac{2x+4}{x^3+5} \right)^{1/2} = \left[\lim_{x \to -1} \left(\frac{2x+4}{x^3+5} \right) \right]^{1/2} = \left(\frac{2}{4} \right)^{1/2} = \frac{1}{\sqrt{2}} .$$

Note that we could not conveniently evaluate the above limit from our previous rules without using (3–45).

5. Since $\sin \theta$ is continuous for all θ, it follows from (3–45) and Table A at the end of the text that

$$\lim_{x \to 4} \sin \left(\frac{x^{1/2}}{2x - 12} \right) = \sin \left[\lim_{x \to 4} \left(\frac{x^{1/2}}{2x - 12} \right) \right] = \sin \frac{4^{1/2}}{-4} = \sin \left(-\frac{1}{2} \right)$$

$$= -0.479 .$$

3–5 CALCULUS

We shall begin in the next section the study of a subject known as the *calculus* or *analysis*. The calculus is typically subdivided into two parts which are referred to as differential calculus and integral calculus. Differential calculus is concerned in a general way with problems involving differentiation, while integral calculus is concerned with problems of integration. We shall study differentiation for the remainder of this chapter, and in the next integration will be introduced.

The foundations of the calculus were developed independently by Isaac Newton, an Englishman, and Gottfried Leibniz, a German, toward the end of the seventeenth century. Newton, one of the most remarkable geniuses in the history of science, developed the calculus while studying the motions of the planets. This, in turn, led to his development of the law of gravitation and, in addition, the fundamental laws of mechanics which describe the motions of all material bodies (provided that they are not too small or moving too fast). Newton made important discoveries in other areas such as optics, and in later life did an outstanding job of running the British mint. Leibniz was also a remarkable man, and although he did not make such significant contributions as Newton in other areas of science, he had an amazing understanding of most phases of human knowledge as they existed in his time. The development of the calculus brought about revolutionary changes not only in mathematics, but in physics and engineering as well. Today, calculus finds important applications in business and the social sciences as well as in the physical sciences and engineering.

The basis for developing the differential calculus is the notion of the limit of a function, which we have been studying in this chapter. It is interesting to observe that, historically, the theory of limits and the precise concept of a function were developed long after the calculus was introduced. Newton and Leibniz carried out their developments more or less intuitively, and it is a real tribute to their abilities that they accomplished so much in this way without being misled by the crude approaches they employed. The reader should not get the impression, however, that Newton and Leibniz suddenly created a whole new branch of mathematics called the calculus without anyone ever having thought of such things before. Many of the basic ideas had been in existence for a number of years, and some for centuries, since the Greeks, especially Archimedes and Eudoxus, had made important contributions. Newton and Leibniz did, however, provide the synthesis and the key techniques which provided a general procedure for solving problems using the calculus.

3–6 THE DERIVATIVE OF A FUNCTION

Consider the graph of some continuous function $f(x)$ such as that shown in Figure 3–10. Let us select a particular value of x, say α, which thus de-

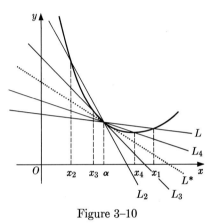

Figure 3–10

termines a point $(\alpha, f(\alpha))$ in the graph of $f(x)$. Since $f(x)$ is continuous at α, we know that $f(x) - f(\alpha)$ can be made arbitrarily small in magnitude by selecting x to be sufficiently close to α. Let us then select a number of other values of x, the kth of which will be denoted by x_k. Then corresponding to x_k there is a point $(x_k, f(x_k))$ in the graph of $f(x)$. These points are shown in Figure 3–10. We shall now obtain a set of straight lines, the kth of which will be denoted by L_k, and is the unique line passing through the two points $(\alpha, f(\alpha))$ and $(x_k, f(x_k))$. The slope of line L_k is

$$\frac{f(x_k) - f(\alpha)}{x_k - \alpha}. \tag{3–47}$$

This is true regardless of whether $x_k > \alpha$ or $x_k < \alpha$. As we consider values x_k which get closer and closer to α, we see that the corresponding lines L_k get closer and closer together and apparently merge into a single line which we have denoted by L^* in Figure 3–10. What is the slope of L^*? For points x_k on the x-axis which are close to α, the slope of L_k, given by (3–47), is close to the slope of L^*. However, we cannot determine the slope of L^* from (3–47) by setting $x_k = \alpha$, since (3–47) then becomes $0/0$ and division by 0 is undefined. Intuitively, the reason that we cannot find the slope of L^* from (3–47) by replacing x_k with α is that L^*, unlike the other lines, does not pass through two points on the graph of $f(x)$. It only passes through $(\alpha, f(\alpha))$, and this point alone does not determine a unique line. Instead L^* is that line passing through $(\alpha, f(\alpha))$ and having the characteristic that its slope is the limiting slope of the lines L_k as x approaches α. This suggests, then, that to determine the slope of L^* we must evaluate a limit. Let us now investigate this in more detail.

Associated with any number x different from α in the domain of $f(x)$ there is a number $[f(x) - f(\alpha)]/(x - \alpha)$, which is the slope of the line, call it L, passing through the points $(\alpha, f(\alpha))$ and $(x, f(x))$ in the graph of $f(x)$. This association defines a new function which will be denoted by $g(x)$, whose domain differs from that of $f(x)$ only in that α is not in the domain of $g(x)$. By definition

$$g(x) = \frac{f(x) - f(\alpha)}{x - \alpha}. \qquad (3\text{--}48)$$

Having introduced $g(x)$, we see that our above analysis suggests that the slope of L^* is $\lim_{x \to \alpha} g(x)$. If this limit exists and has the value β, we can indeed find a line passing through $(\alpha, f(\alpha))$ with slope β, and by definition of β, the line passing through $(\alpha, f(\alpha))$ and $(x, f(x))$, with slope $g(x)$, will have a slope which is arbitrarily close to β when x is sufficiently close to α. This shows that we should be able to determine the slope of L^* by computing the limit of a function.

The above geometrical analysis has suggested that $\lim_{x \to \alpha} g(x)$, when is $g(x)$ defined in terms of another function $f(x)$ by (3–48), may have an interesting geometric interpretation, and therefore it seems to be of interest to study in more detail the nature of this limit. It was through reasoning of this type that Leibniz was led to develop the calculus. Let us for the moment completely forget about the geometric discussion given above and instead concentrate our attention on evaluating the limit

$$\lim_{x \to \alpha} g(x) = \lim_{x \to \alpha} \frac{f(x) - f(\alpha)}{x - \alpha} \qquad (3\text{--}49)$$

for some arbitrarily specified function $f(x)$. We can suppose that the geometric discussion only prompted us to study limits of the form (3–49). We shall, however, return later to the geometric discussion and consider it in more detail.

As we shall see, the limit (3–49) may not exist even though $f(x)$ is continuous. When it does exist, the limit need not be in any way related to $f(\alpha)$, that is, a knowledge of $f(\alpha)$ will give us no information as to what the limit (3–49) is. We can also note that (3–37) cannot be used to evaluate (3–49) since $\lim_{x \to \alpha} (x - \alpha) = 0$. This does not imply that the limit (3–49) does not exist. It simply means that we cannot immediately apply (3–37) to find it. In order to evaluate (3–49) it is usually convenient to introduce the change of variable $x = \alpha + v$ and, according to (3–40), evaluate $\lim_{v \to 0} g(\alpha + v)$ instead of $\lim_{x \to \alpha} g(x)$. The task of evaluating (3–49) is then equivalent to evaluating the limit

$$\lim_{v \to 0} \frac{f(\alpha + v) - f(\alpha)}{v} . \qquad (3\text{–}50)$$

The function $g(x)$ given by (3–48) is referred to as the *difference quotient* for the function $f(x)$. When the difference quotient function has a limit as x approaches α, this limit, that is, this number, is called the *derivative of* $y = f(x)$ at $x = \alpha$, and is written $f'(\alpha)$, $df(\alpha)/dx$, or $(dy/dx)_\alpha$. Thus by definition

$$f'(\alpha) = \lim_{v \to 0} \frac{f(\alpha + v) - f(\alpha)}{v} . \qquad (3\text{–}51)$$

The notations other than $f'(\alpha)$ appear rather cumbersone at first glance, but they are useful, as we shall see later. (Newton's notation and terminology are no longer used, but the dy/dx notation, sometimes called differential notation, was developed by Leibniz.) If the limit (3–50) exists, that is, if $f'(\alpha)$ exists, we say that $f(x)$ is differentiable at α. Before continuing let us give an example illustrating the evaluation of the derivative of a function.

EXAMPLE. Suppose that $f(x) = x^2$. We shall show that $f'(\alpha)$ exists for all α, and we shall determine $f'(\alpha)$ explicitly. To compute $f'(\alpha)$ we must evaluate (3–50) when $f(x) = x^2$. Note that $f(\alpha + v) = (\alpha + v)^2$ and $f(\alpha) = \alpha^2$. Thus

$$f(\alpha + v) - f(\alpha) = (\alpha + v)^2 - \alpha^2 = \alpha^2 + 2\alpha v + v^2 - \alpha^2 = 2\alpha v + v^2 ,$$

and when $v \neq 0$,

$$\frac{f(\alpha + v) - f(\alpha)}{v} = 2\alpha + v .$$

Now

$$\lim_{v \to 0} 2\alpha = 2\alpha; \qquad \lim_{v \to 0} v = 0 .$$

Thus on using (3–27)

$$\lim_{v \to 0} \frac{f(\alpha + v) - f(\alpha)}{v} = \lim_{v \to 0} (2\alpha + v) = 2\alpha = f'(\alpha) .$$

Therefore, for every α, $f'(\alpha)$ exists and has the value 2α.

Let us now show that a function can be continuous at α but not be differentiable there. Consider the function $f(x) = |x|$, that is, $f(x) = x$.

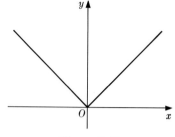

Figure 3–11

$x \geq 0$, $f(x) = -x$ for $x < 0$. The graph of $f(x)$ is shown in Figure 3–11. Note that $\lim_{x \to 0+} x = 0$ and $\lim_{x \to 0-} (-x) = 0$. Hence $\lim_{x \to 0} f(x) = f(0) = 0$ and $f(x)$ is continuous at $x = 0$. We shall show, however, that $f(x)$ is not differentiable at 0. To show that $\lim_{x \to 0} g(x)$ does not exist, we shall evaluate $\lim_{x \to 0+} g(x)$ and $\lim_{x \to 0-} g(x)$, and show that while both these one-sided limits exist, they do not have the same value. For $x > 0$

$$g(x) = \frac{x - 0}{x} = 1, \qquad \text{so} \qquad \lim_{x \to 0+} g(x) = 1 .$$

For $x < 0$

$$g(x) = \frac{-x - 0}{x} = -1, \qquad \text{so} \qquad \lim_{x \to 0-} g(x) = -1 .$$

Since the two one-sided limits do not have the same value, $\lim_{x \to 0} g(x)$ does not exist and $f(x) = |x|$ is not differentiable at $x = 0$.

We can easily give a geometric interpretation to this fact. If we select a set of values of x, some positive and some negative, as in Figure 3–10, we see that the line L_k passing through $(0, 0)$ and $(x_k, f(x_k))$ is $y = x$ if $x_k > 0$ and is $y = -x$ if $x_k < 0$. As x approaches 0 from the right, the L_k approach $y = x$, while as x approaches 0 from the left the L_k approach $y = -x$. There is no unique line L^* which is approached by the L_k as x approaches 0 from the right and from the left. Note that at $x = 0$ the graph of $f(x)$ has a corner. In general, $f'(\alpha)$ will not exist if $f(x)$ has a corner at $x = \alpha$.

If $\lim_{x \to \alpha+} g(x)$ exists, then we say that $f(x)$ has a right-side derivative at α. If $\lim_{x \to \alpha-} g(x)$ exists, then we say that $f(x)$ has a left-side derivative at α. In order for $f(x)$ to be differentiable at α, it must possess both a right-side derivative and a left-side derivative and these must be equal. The function $f(x) = |x|$ possesses both right- and left-side derivatives at 0, but they are not equal.

In studying $f(x) = |x|$ we have seen that a function may be continuous at α but not have a derivative at α. However, *if $f(x)$ is differentiable at α*

then it must be continuous at α. We shall now prove this. To make the proof note first that if $f'(\alpha)$ exists, then α is in the domain of the function (why?). Furthermore, if $v \neq 0$

$$f(\alpha + v) - f(\alpha) = \frac{f(\alpha + v) - f(\alpha)}{v} v$$

or

$$f(\alpha + v) = f(\alpha) + \frac{f(\alpha + v) - f(\alpha)}{v} v .$$

However,

$$\lim_{v \to 0} \frac{f(\alpha + v) - f(\alpha)}{v} = f'(\alpha) \quad \text{and} \quad \lim_{v \to 0} v = 0 .$$

Hence by (3–31) and (3–27)

$$\lim_{v \to 0} f(\alpha + v) = f(\alpha) + f'(\alpha)(0) = f(\alpha) ,$$

or $\lim_{x \to \alpha} f(x) = f(\alpha)$, and this is precisely what is meant by the statement that $f(x)$ is continuous at α. Thus differentiability implies continuity, but continuity does not necessarily imply differentiability.

If $f(x)$ has a derivative for each x in the open interval I^0_{ab}, then $f(x)$ is said to be differentiable in this interval. When $f(x)$ is differentiable in I^0_{ab}, then for each x in this interval there is associated a number $f'(x)$ which is the derivative of $f(x)$. This association then defines a function of one variable whose domain is I^0_{ab}, which we shall call *the derivative function* and which we shall denote by $f'(x)$. From the previous example, we see that if $f(x) = x^2$, then $f'(x) = 2x$ and the domain of the derivative function includes all real numbers. The process of differentiation thus serves to generate from a given function a new function, which is called the derivative function. The domain for the derivative function will not necessarily be the same as that for the given function, because there may be elements in the domain of the given function where this function is not differentiable.

3–7 TANGENTS

We shall now return to the geometrical interpretation of derivatives. The discussion of the last section has shown that, if $f(x)$ has a derivative at $x = \alpha$, then the graph of $f(x)$ cannot have a corner at α such as the one at $x = 0$ in Figure 3–11. If the function is differentiable over some open interval, then the graph of the function will be represented by a smooth curve in this interval. The graph could not look like that shown in Figure 3–9, where the curve has many corners and spikes in it. As we shall see below, all the functions studied in Chapter 2, with the exception of the one examined in the last section, possess derivatives at every point in their domains. The justification for drawing smooth curves through a few plotted points to obtain approximately the graph of the function really rested in the fact that the functions were differentiable (and thus also continuous).

Let $x = \alpha$ be a point at which $f(x)$ is differentiable. Consider the unique line having slope $f'(\alpha)$ which passes through the point $(\alpha, f(\alpha)$ on the graph of $f(x)$. *This line, whose equation is*

$$y = f(\alpha) + f'(\alpha)(x - \alpha) , \tag{3-52}$$

is called the tangent or tangent line to the graph of $f(x)$ at $x = \alpha$. The slope of the tangent is $f'(\alpha)$. *By definition, we say that the slope of the graph of $f(x)$ at $x = \alpha$ is the slope of its tangent.* The point $(\alpha, f(\alpha))$ is referred to as the point of tangency between the curve and its tangent at $x = \alpha$. The slope of the graph of $f(x)$, or as we shall often say, the slope of $f(x)$ at $x = \alpha$, is by definition $f'(\alpha)$, the derivative of $f(x)$ at α.

EXAMPLE. Consider once again the function $f(x) = x^2$. At $x = \alpha$, $f'(\alpha) = 2\alpha$. Thus $f(x)$ has a tangent at every point α, and from (3–52) the equation of the tangent line is

$$y = \alpha^2 + 2\alpha(x - \alpha) = 2\alpha x - \alpha^2 .$$

If $\alpha = 1.5$, the tangent line has the equation

$$y = 3x - 2.25 .$$

This tangent line is illustrated along with the graph of $f(x)$ in Figure 3–12. The slope of $f(x) = x^2$ at $x = 1.5$ is therefore $2(1.5) = 3$.

Let us now return to the geometric discussion which originally motivated our introduction of the derivative. Suppose that $f(x)$ is a function for which $f'(\alpha)$ exists. Consider then the points $(\zeta, f(\zeta))$ and $(\alpha, f(\alpha))$ in the graph of $f(x)$, where ζ is any number different from α in the domain of $f(x)$. These two points determine a unique straight line whose equation is

$$y = f(\alpha) + \left[\frac{f(\zeta) - f(\alpha)}{\zeta - \alpha} \right] (x - \alpha) . \tag{3-53}$$

Each such line is called a *secant line*, and every secant line (3–53) passes through the point $(\alpha, f(\alpha))$. As ζ approaches α, the slope of the secant line L approaches the slope of the tangent L^* to $f(x)$ at α, since $f'(\alpha)$ exists. Inasmuch as both the tangent and all the secant lines pass through $(\alpha, f(\alpha))$, and the slope of the secant line approaches the slope of the tangent line as

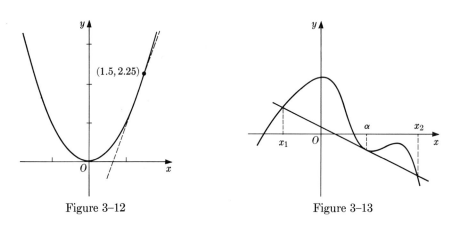

Figure 3–12   Figure 3–13

ξ approaches α, we can say intuitively that the tangent line L^* is the limit of the secant lines as ζ approaches α.

Normally, for x close to α, the graph of $f(x)$ will lie entirely on one side of the tangent line to $f(x)$ at α, that is, the graph of $f(x)$ will lie in one of the closed half-spaces produced by the tangent line. This is illustrated in Figure 3–12. In Figure 3–12, the *entire* graph of $f(x)$ lies in one closed half space produced by the tangent. In general, there is no reason why the tangent line at α may not cut the graph of $f(x)$ one or more times, as shown in Figure 3–13. In Figure 3–13, however, note that for $x_1 < x < x_2$, the graph of $f(x)$ lies in one closed half-space produced by the tangent. It can occur, nonetheless, that the tangent line actually cuts the graph of $f(x)$ at α, as shown in Figure 3–14. If this occurs, then the graph of $f(x)$ for

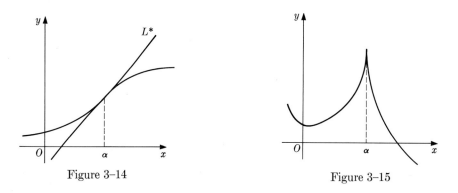

Figure 3–14   Figure 3–15

$x < \alpha$ but close to α lies in one closed half-space produced by the tangent L^*, while the graph of $f(x)$ for $x > \alpha$ but close to α lies in the other closed half-space.

Whenever $f'(\alpha)$ exists, then $f(x)$ has a tangent line at α. Normally, when $f'(\alpha)$ does not exist, we say that $f(x)$ does not have a tangent at α. Thus we say that $f(x) = |x|$ does not have a tangent at $x = 0$. The secants do not approach a unique line as ζ approaches 0, but instead for all $\zeta > 0$, the secant is $y = x$, and for all $\zeta < 0$, the secant is $y = -x$. There is one case in which it is convenient to say that $f(x)$ has a tangent at α even though $f'(\alpha)$ does not exist. This is illustrated in Figure 3–15. Consider the point $(\alpha, f(\alpha))$. In this case, all the secant lines passing through this point approach a unique vertical line $x = \alpha$, and thus it seems appropriate to call $x = \alpha$ the tangent to $f(x)$ at α. However, $f'(\alpha)$ does not exist in this case (why?). When the tangent is a vertical line at $x = \alpha$, we then say that $f(x)$ has *infinite slope* at α, which merely means that the tangent is vertical.

3–8 RATE OF CHANGE

We now wish to introduce another extremely important interpretation of the derivative. When we have a variable y related to another variable x by the function $y = f(x)$, we are often faced with the problem of determining how much y will change when x is changed by a specified amount from a given value α. At $x = \alpha$, $y = f(\alpha)$. Suppose now that x is changed to a new value $\alpha + v$. The new value of y is simply $f(\alpha + v)$, and the change in y, defined to be the new value minus the old one, is $f(\alpha + v) - f(\alpha)$. Thus if we can evaluate $f(x)$ easily, we have no trouble in determining the change in y. Let us next study the quantity

$$\frac{f(\alpha + v) - f(\alpha)}{v}, \tag{3–54}$$

which we have previously called the difference quotient. This is the change in y divided by the change in x, and is the slope of the secant passing through the points $(\alpha, f(\alpha))$ and $(\alpha + v, f(\alpha + v))$. We shall call the number (3–54) *the average rate of change of y with respect to x when x is changed from α to $\alpha + v$.*

For example, let y be the distance an individual traveled in his car as a function of time as he drove from home to work. If we take α to be the time at which he left home and v the time required to reach work, $f(\alpha + v) - f(\alpha)$ is the distance he traveled in going to work. Then (3–54) is the distance traveled divided by the travel time, or simply the average speed in miles per hour at which the individual was traveling. Hence if one hour were required to drive twenty miles, the average speed was twenty miles per hour. The average speed is, according to our above definition, the average rate of change of distance with respect to time. The actual speed of the auto during the trip no doubt varied widely, falling to 0 when the car was stopped for a red light and perhaps reaching 65 miles per hour on a freeway. Equation (3–54) gives the average speed for the entire trip, but tells us nothing about the auto's speed at any particular instant of time.

The above discussion brings up an interesting question. What do we mean by the speed of a car at some particular instant in time? Presumably, it is the reading on the speedometer (if it is accurate), but what does this reading really mean? Speed tells us how fast the car is going, that is, if its speed is fifty miles per hour, it will travel fifty miles in one hour. This is true, however, only if the speed remains constant for one hour. Suppose that the speed is always changing due to red lights, other cars and so forth. At each instant the speedometer gives a reading. What does it mean? To develop a precise understanding of the notion of the speed of a car at a given instant of time, let us suppose that the odometer on the car (the device which gives the distance traveled) is very accurate. Let us place beside the odometer an accurate clock. As the car moves along, let us imagine that we take a movie which records simultaneously the readings of the odometer and the clock. We can then plot a graph, giving the distance traveled as a function of time, which might look like the one shown in Figure 3–16. Let

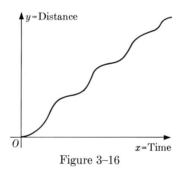

Figure 3–16

us use this graph to make precise what we mean by the speed of the car at some instant of time, say $x = \alpha$.

The average speed of the car over the time interval extending from α to $\alpha + v$ is given by (3–54), if we denote the function whose graph is Figure 3–16 by $y = f(x)$. As v is made smaller and smaller, the average speed should come closer and closer to what we intuitively think of as the instantaneous speed at $x = \alpha$, since when v is small enough the speed of the car will have remained essentially constant from α to $\alpha + v$, and, therefore, the average speed will be essentially equal to the instantaneous speed. It is now clear that what we are carrying out here is precisely the same sort of process we went through in studying how secants approach the tangent line. We can, then, give a rigorous meaning to the instantaneous speed of the car at $x = \alpha$ by saying that it is the limit of (3–54) as v approaches α. This limit is $f'(\alpha)$ when $f'(\alpha)$ exists, $f(x)$ giving the total distance traveled as a function of time. Thus the notion of instantaneous speed really involves a limiting process, and this makes it difficult for persons not familiar with mathematics to understand clearly the meaning of instantaneous speed. (It might be pointed out that the speedometer of a car does not go through a limiting process of the type described above to give a reading. Instead it works on a gearing principle which roughly gives as a reading the average speed over some short interval, not the instantaneous speed.) Thus if $y = f(x)$ represents the distance that a car travels as a function of time, the derivative function $f'(x)$ gives its speed as a function of time. This example then shows that the derivative function can have an important physical interpretation.

The rate of change of distance with respect to time is what we call the speed of the car (or whatever the moving object happens to be). The notion of the rate of change of one variable with respect to another arises in most areas of application and is a very important concept. In general, given any function $y = f(x)$ having the characteristic that $f'(\alpha)$ exists, *we define the rate of change of y with respect to x at $x = \alpha$ to be $f'(\alpha)$*. Speed is one example of a rate of change which is used in everyday life. Acceleration is another, acceleration being the rate of change of velocity with respect to time. The rate of usage of electrical energy, frequently expressed as kilowatts, is still a different example. In each of the examples just given, time was the independent variable, and although time is frequently the independent variable, it is by no means true that it must be. The atmospheric pressure varies with altitude and the rate of change of pressure with altitude can usefully be considered. As another example, the quantity of some product which the public will demand in a given time period is a function of its price, and economists are often interested in the rate of change of the quantity demanded with price. Thus we see that the rate of change concept appears frequently in everyday life. To have a precise understanding of this concept, it is necessary to understand the notion of a derivative.

The mathematical definition of the rate of change of y with respect to x at $x = \alpha$ implicitly assumes that arbitrarily small changes in x can be considered, since $v = x - \alpha$ must be allowed to become arbitrarily close to 0 in the limiting process. Interestingly enough, it is not possible to make arbitrarily small changes in variables occurring in the real world. There are certain minimal changes that can be made, which may, for example, involve adding one more atom or molecule. Even time cannot be changed by arbitrarily small amounts due to the limitations of the measuring processes. In other words, the basic nature of the real world is not such that arbitrarily small changes in variables can, in fact, be made, and therefore the limiting processes of mathematics cannot be rigorously carried over to the real world. In practice, only ratios of the form (3–54) can be dealt with. However, v can often be made so small that for all practical purposes (3–54) is $f'(\alpha)$. What we are saying, then, is that the mathematical notion of the rate of change of y with respect to x is an idealization of the sorts of situations encountered in the real world, and can be looked upon as an approximate procedure for treating everyday problems. It turns out to be an extremely useful idealization and approximation, because it is much easier to work with the derivative function than it is to work with difference quotients.

3–9 **EVALUATION OF DERIVATIVES**

We have thus far been discussing derivatives and their interpretation without giving much attention to the details of evaluating the derivative, if it exists, of a given function. We shall now turn our attention to the problem of actually computing derivatives. Our aim will be to develop a set of rules which will make it unnecessary to go through the detailed evaluation of the limit (3–51). Equation (3–51) will be used to determine the derivatives of certain simple functions, but once we have obtained these results we shall be able to obtain the derivatives of very complicated functions by applying the rules which we are now going to develop.

At first thought, it might seem that the properties of limits given in (3–24), (3–27), (3–32) and (3–37) carry over directly to derivatives, so that, for example, the derivative of the product of two functions is the product of their derivatives. This is not true. Some of the results for limits do have direct analogs for derivatives, while others do not. In this section we shall apply the properties of limits obtained in Section 3–3 to obtain some very helpful properties of derivatives. Before turning to these properties let us differentiate two very simple functions. By using the derivatives of these functions we shall be able to illustrate the applicability of the results developed and simultaneously show how to obtain the derivative of any polynomial or rational function.

Suppose that $f(x) = \lambda$, a constant. Then

$$f'(\alpha) = \lim_{v \to 0} \frac{f(\alpha + v) - f(x)}{v} = \lim_{v \to 0} \frac{\lambda - \lambda}{v} = 0$$

for all α. Thus the domain of the derivative function includes all real numbers, and

$$f'(x) = 0 \quad \text{when} \quad f(x) = \lambda . \tag{3–55}$$

Next consider $f(x) = x$. Then

$$f'(\alpha) = \lim_{v \to 0} \frac{\alpha + v - \alpha}{v} = \lim_{v \to 0} 1 = 1$$

for all α, so that the domain of the derivative function includes all real numbers, and

$$f'(x) = 1 \quad \text{when} \quad f(x) = x . \tag{3–56}$$

We have here proved that the derivative of a constant λ is 0 and the derivative of x is 1.

Let us now proceed to derive the analogs of the properties of limits obtained in Section 3–3. *Suppose that $f(x)$ is a given function, and we form a new function $g(x) = \lambda f(x)$, where λ is a constant. Then $g'(x)$ exists for all x for which $f'(x)$ exists, and*

$$g'(x) = \frac{d}{dx}\lambda f(x) = \lambda f'(x) . \tag{3–57}$$

In words, *the derivative of a constant times a function is equal to the constant times the derivative of the function.* To prove this, we observe that, for any fixed x,

$$\frac{g(x+v) - g(x)}{v} = \frac{\lambda f(x+v) - \lambda f(x)}{v} = \lambda \frac{f(x+v) - f(x)}{v} .$$

However, when $f'(x)$ exists, we see from (3–24) that $g'(x)$ exists and

$$g'(x) = \lim_{v \to 0} \frac{g(x+v) - g(x)}{v} = \lambda \lim_{v \to 0} \frac{f(x+v) - f(x)}{v} = \lambda f'(x) .$$

Thus, for example, from (3–56) and (3–57) we see that if $f(x) = \lambda x$, then $f'(x) = \lambda$.

Assume next that we are given two functions $f_1(x)$ and $f_2(x)$ and that we form the new function $g(x) = f_1(x) + f_2(x)$. Then $g'(x)$ exists for all x for which $f_1'(x)$ and $f_2'(x)$ both exist, and

$$g'(x) = \frac{d}{dx}[f_1(x) + f_2(x)] = f_1'(x) + f_2'(x) . \tag{3–58}$$

In words, *the derivative of a sum is the sum of the derivatives.* To prove this note that, for a fixed x,

$$\frac{g(x+v) - g(x)}{v} = \frac{f_1(x+v) + f_2(x+v) - f_1(x) - f_2(x)}{v}$$

$$= \frac{f_1(x+v) - f_1(x)}{v} + \frac{f_2(x+v) - f_2(x)}{v} .$$

When $f_1'(x)$ and $f_2'(x)$ both exist, we see from (3–27) that $g'(x)$ exists, and

$$g'(x) = \lim_{v \to 0} \frac{g(x+v) - g(x)}{v}$$

$$= \lim_{v \to 0} \frac{f_1(x+v) - f_1(x)}{v} + \lim_{v \to 0} \frac{f_2(x+v) - f_2(x)}{v}$$

$$= f_1'(x) + f_2'(x) ,$$

which is what we wished to show.

EXAMPLES. 1. If $f_1(x) = x$ and $f_2(x) = \lambda$, then by (3–55), (3–56) and (3–58)

$$\frac{d}{dx}(x + \lambda) = 1 \quad \text{for all } x .$$

2. If $f_1(x) = a_1x$ and $f_2(x) = a_2x^2$, then, since we showed previously that the derivative function for x^2 is $2x$, it follows from (3–57) that

$$f_1'(x) = a_1; \qquad f_2'(x) = 2a_2x .$$

Therefore, by (3–58)

$$\frac{d}{dx}(a_1x + a_2x^2) = a_1 + 2a_2x \quad \text{for all } x .$$

Observe that it follows at once from (3–28) that if $f_j'(x)$ exists for each j, $j = 1, \ldots, n$, then

$$\frac{d}{dx}[f_1(x) + \cdots + f_n(x)] = f_1'(x) + \cdots + f_n'(x) . \qquad (3\text{--}59)$$

Equations (3–57) and (3–58) have precisely the same form as the corresponding results on limits. We shall now turn to a case where the property of limits does not carry over directly to derivatives. *Consider again two functions $f_1(x)$ and $f_2(x)$ and suppose that we form the new function $g(x) = f_1(x)f_2(x)$. Then $g'(x)$ exists for all x for which both $f_1'(x)$ and $f_2'(x)$ exist and*

$$g'(x) = \frac{d}{dx}[f_1(x)f_2(x)] = f_1(x)f_2'(x) + f_2(x)f_1'(x) . \qquad (3\text{--}60)$$

In words, *the derivative of the product of two functions is equal to the first times the derivative of the second plus the second times the derivative of the first.* Note that the derivative of a product is not equal to the product of the derivatives, which would be the case if (3–31) carried over directly. To prove (3–60), note that for fixed x

$$\frac{g(x + v) - g(x)}{v} = \frac{f_1(x + v)f_2(x + v) - f_1(x)f_2(x)}{v} . \qquad (3\text{--}61)$$

To convert the right-hand side of (3–61) into a form whose limit is easily evaluated, we add and subtract $f_1(x + v)f_2(x)$ in the numerator to yield

$$\frac{g(x + v) - g(x)}{v}$$

$$= \frac{f_1(x + v)f_2(x + v) - f_1(x + v)f_2(x) + f_1(x + v)f_2(x) - f_1(x)f_2(x)}{v}$$

$$= f_1(x + v)\frac{f_2(x + v) - f_2(x)}{v} + f_2(x)\frac{f_1(x + v) - f_1(x)}{v} . \qquad (3\text{--}62)$$

Suppose now that $f_1'(x)$ and $f_2'(x)$ exist. Since $f_1'(x)$ exists, f_1 is continuous at x and therefore $\lim_{v \to 0} f_1(x + v) = f_1(x)$. Hence, from (3–31)

$$\lim_{v \to 0} \left[f_1(x + v) \frac{f_2(x + v) - f_2(x)}{v} \right] = f_1(x) f_2'(x) ,$$

and by (3–24)

$$\lim_{v \to 0} \left[f_2(x) \frac{f_1(x + v) - f_1(x)}{v} \right] = f_2(x) f_1'(x) .$$

Using these results and (3–27), we see that, since the limits of both terms on the right in (3–62) exist, $g'(x)$ exists and

$$g'(x) = f_1(x) f_2'(x) + f_2(x) f_1'(x) ,$$

which is (3–60).

We shall now use (3–60) to obtain an interesting result. Recall that the derivative function for x^2 is $2x$. Now consider $g(x) = x^3$. We can write x^3 as the product of $f_1(x) = x$ and $f_2(x) = x^2$, so that $g(x) = f_1(x) f_2(x)$. Furthermore, $f_1'(x) = 1$ and $f_2'(x) = 2x$ for all x. Thus, by (3–60) $g'(x)$ exists for all x and

$$g'(x) = x(2x) + x^2(1) = 2x^2 + x^2 = 3x^2 .$$

Hence, by use of (3–60) and results which we have obtained previously, it has been shown that $dx^3/dx = 3x^2$. This process can be continued. The function $g(x) = x^4$ can be written as the product of $f_1(x) = x$ and $f_2(x) = x^3$. Since $f_1'(x) = 1$ and $f_2'(x) = 3x^2$ for all x, $g'(x)$ exists for all x, and from (3–60)

$$g'(x) = x(3x^2) + x^3 = 4x^3 ,$$

so that $dx^4/dx = 4x^3$.

The above results suggest that for any natural number n, $dx^n/dx = nx^{n-1}$. Can we prove that this is true for every natural number n? The answer is yes, but we must introduce a new method of proof called a *proof by recursion*, or more frequently a *proof by induction*, to do so. Suppose that we have an unending sequence of mathematical statements $A_1, A_2, A_3, \ldots$, one associated with each natural number. Assume that we know A_1 is true, and we also know that if A_n is true then A_{n+1} is true regardless of what natural number n happens to be. Note that we are not assuming that we know A_n is true; all we know is that *if* A_n is true, then A_{n+1} is true. Under these conditions, each of the statements must be true, because first of all A_1 is true. Then since A_2 is true if A_1 is, it follows that A_2 is true. But if A_2 is true, then A_3 is also true, and so on. Thus all the statements will be true if we can prove that A_1 is true and if we can also show that, regardless of what natural number n happens to be, *if* A_n is true, then A_{n+1} is also true. This method of proof is called a proof by induction. We have not proved the method of proof by induction. Whether or not it can be proved depends on what is taken as given concerning the natural numbers. The basis of the proof by induction is that we can reach any natural number n by starting at 1 and moving to the successor of 1, that is, 2, then to the successor of 2, that is, 3, and so on until n is reached.

We can now prove by induction that

$$\frac{d}{dx} x^n = nx^{n-1}, \quad n \text{ a natural number} . \tag{3–63}$$

We have already shown that (3–63) holds for $n = 1$. All that remains is to show that *if* (3–63) holds for $n = k$, then (3–63) also holds for $n = k + 1$, regardless of what natural number k happens to be. To do this, note that $x^{k+1} = x(x^k)$. If the derivative of x^k exists, then by (3–60) the derivative of x^{k+1} exists. Furthermore, if the derivative of x^k is kx^{k-1}, then by (3–60), the derivative of x^{k+1} is

$$\frac{d}{dx} x^{k+1} = x(kx^{k-1}) + x^k(1) = (k + 1)x^k .$$

Thus it is indeed true that, if (3–60) holds for $n = k$, it also holds for $n = k + 1$. Since (3–60) does hold for $n = 1$, it follows by the induction principle that it holds for all natural numbers. This is what we wished to prove.

Given (3–63) we can see immediately on using (3–57) and (3–59) that if $f(x)$ is a polynomial, say

$$f(x) = a_n x^n + a_{n-1} x^{n-1} + \cdots + a_0 ,$$

then $f'(x)$ exists for every x and

$$f'(x) = na_n x^{n-1} + (n - 1)a_{n-1} x^{n-2} + \cdots + a_1 . \tag{3–64}$$

The derivative function of an nth degree polynomial is thus a polynomial of degree $n - 1$.

EXAMPLES. 1. If $y = x^5$, then by (3–63), $dy/dx = 5x^4$. The equation for the tangent to $y = x^5$ at $x = 2$, the general equation for which is (3–52), reduces to

$$y = 32 + 80(x - 2) = 80x - 128 ,$$

since $f(2) = 32$ and $f'(2) = 80$. The reader should illustrate this situation graphically.

2. If $y = 3x^2 + 2x - 6$, then

$$\frac{dy}{dx} = 2(3)x + 2 - 0 = 6x + 2 .$$

When $f(x)$ is a quadratic function, the derivative function is represented by a linear equation. From (3–52), the tangent to $f(x)$ at $x = 0$ is

$$y = -6 + 2x,$$

since $f(0) = -6$ and $f'(0) = 2$. The reader should illustrate this situation graphically.

3. If $y = x^3$, $dy/dx = 3x^2$, and from (3–52), the equation of the tangent to the curve at $x = 0$ is $y = 0$, since $f(0) = 0$ and $f'(0) = 0$. The reader should illustrate this case graphically and should observe that here we have a case where the tangent crosses the graph of $f(x)$ at the point of tangency.

Suppose that from a given function $f(x)$ we form the new function $g(x) = 1/f(x)$. Then $g'(x)$ exists for all x such that $f'(x)$ exists and $f(x) \neq 0$. Furthermore

$$g'(x) = \frac{d}{dx}\left[\frac{1}{f(x)}\right] = -\frac{f'(x)}{[f(x)]^2}, \quad f(x) \neq 0. \tag{3–65}$$

In words, *the derivative of $1/f$ is the negative of f' divided by f^2.* Let us now prove (3–65). Note that

$$\frac{g(x + v) - g(x)}{v} = \frac{\dfrac{1}{f(x + v)} - \dfrac{1}{f(x)}}{v} = \frac{f(x) - f(x + v)}{vf(x)f(x + v)}$$

$$= -\frac{\dfrac{f(x + v) - f(x)}{v}}{f(x)f(x + v)}. \tag{3–66}$$

If $f'(x)$ exists, then

$$\lim_{v \to 0} \frac{f(x + v) - f(x)}{v} = f'(x).$$

Furthermore, when $f'(x)$ exists, f is continuous at x and thus $\lim_{v \to 0} f(x + v) = f(x)$. Consequently, from (3–24),

$$\lim_{v \to 0} f(x)f(x + v) = [f(x)]^2.$$

Now if in addition $f(x) \neq 0$, then $[f(x)]^2 \neq 0$, and from (3–37) we conclude that $g'(x)$ exists. Then from (3–66), $g'(x)$ is given by (3–65), which is what we wished to prove.

Given (3–65), we can immediately compute dx^{-n}/dx when $x \neq 0$ and n is a natural number. We see on using (3–63) that

$$\frac{dx^{-n}}{dx} = -\frac{\dfrac{dx^n}{dx}}{x^{2n}} = -\frac{nx^{n-1}}{x^{2n}} = -nx^{-n-1}. \tag{3–67}$$

We have here obtained an interesting result, since (3–67) is of the same form as (3–63). In other words, for any integer $k \neq 0$

$$\frac{d}{dx} x^k = k x^{k-1} . \tag{3–68}$$

We might note that (3–68) also holds for $k = 0$ if $x \neq 0$ when we use the definition $x^0 = 1$. Equation (3–68) holds for all x when $k > 0$ and for all $x \neq 0$ when $k \leq 0$. The reader should remember (3–68).

EXAMPLE. Consider the hyperbola $y = 1/x = x^{-1}$. By (3–68), for $x \neq 0$, $dy/dx = -x^{-2} = -1/x^2$. From (3–52), the tangent to $y = 1/x$ at $x = 2$ is

$$y = 0.5 - 0.25(x - 2) = 1 - 0.25x .$$

The tangent to $y = 1/x$ at $x = -1$ is

$$y = -1 - (x + 1) = -2 - x .$$

The hyperbola and these two tangents are illustrated in Figure 3–17.

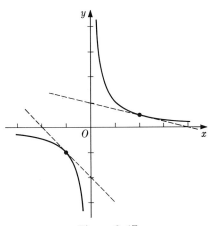

Figure 3–17

By combining (3–60) and (3–65), one additional useful result may be obtained. *If $g(x) = f_1(x)/f_2(x)$, $g'(x)$ exists for all x such that $f_1'(x)$ and $f_2'(x)$ both exist and, in addition, $f_2(x) \neq 0$. Furthermore,*

$$g'(x) = \frac{d}{dx}\left[\frac{f_1(x)}{f_2(x)}\right] = \frac{f_2(x)f_1'(x) - f_1(x)f_2'(x)}{[f_2(x)]^2} . \tag{3–69}$$

To prove (3–69), let $f_3(x) = 1/f_2(x)$. Then by (3–65), $f_3'(x)$ exists when $f_2'(x)$ exists and $f_2(x) \neq 0$. Thus by (3–60), $g'(x)$ exists if $f_1'(x)$ also exists and

$$g'(x) = f_3(x)f_1'(x) + f_1(x)f_3'(x) . \tag{3–70}$$

Then by (3–65)

$$f_3'(x) = -\frac{f_2'(x)}{[f_2(x)]^2},$$

which when substituted into (3–70) along with the definition of $f_3(x)$ yields (3–69).

By use of (3–69) and the results obtained previously, we can differentiate any rational function. Note that a rational function possesses a derivative at every point where the denominator is not zero and that the derivative function of a rational function is a rational function.

EXAMPLE. Let us compute $f'(x)$ when

$$f(x) = \frac{4x^2 - 2x + 1}{x + 3}.$$

If we write

$$f_1(x) = 4x^2 - 2x + 1; \qquad f_2(x) = x + 3,$$

then

$$f_1'(x) = 8x - 2; \qquad f_2'(x) = 1$$

for all x. Thus by (3–69), $f'(x)$ exists for all $x \neq -3$ and

$$f'(x) = \frac{(x + 3)(8x - 2) - (4x^2 - 2x + 1)(1)}{(x + 3)^2}$$

$$= \frac{4x^2 + 24x - 7}{x^2 + 6x + 9},$$

which is also a rational function.

In this section we have obtained several useful rules for differentiating functions. The reader should memorize (3–57), (3–58), (3–60), (3–65), (3–68) and (3–69), since they are used with great frequency in practice.

3–10 THE CHAIN RULE

One additional rule for differentiation, known as the chain rule, is very useful in practice. The chain rule tells how to express the derivative of a compound function $h[g(x)]$ in terms of the derivatives of $h(u)$ and $g(x)$. We shall prove that *if* $f(x) = h[g(x)]$, *then* $f'(x)$ *exists if* $g'(x)$ *exists and, in addition,* $h'(u)$ *exists for* $u = g(x)$. Furthermore,

$$f'(x) = \frac{d}{dx} h[g(x)] = h'[g(x)]g'(x) . \tag{3–71}$$

In words, the derivative of a compound function $h[g(x)]$ is equal to the product of the derivatives of $h(u)$ and $g(x)$, where $h'(u)$ is evaluated at

$u = g(x)$. Although it may not appear obvious at the moment, (3–71) is one of the most useful, if not *the* most useful, rules for differentiating complex functions. We shall see in the following why this is the case. Let us now prove that (3–71) is true.

To carry out the proof, let us first note that, given any function $f(x)$, if $f'(x)$ exists, then we can define a function $\gamma(v)$ as

$$\gamma(v) = \frac{f(x + v) - f(x)}{v} - f'(x) \tag{3–72}$$

for all $v \neq 0$ such that $x + v$ is in the domain of f. Note that $\gamma(0)$ is not defined in (3–72), but since $f'(x)$ exists, $\lim_{v \to 0} \gamma(v) = 0$ (why?). Let us then include 0 in the domain of $\gamma(v)$ by defining $\gamma(0)$ to be 0. Then $\gamma(v)$ is continuous at $v = 0$. The function $\gamma(v)$ will be useful in proving (3–71).

To carry out the proof, we begin, as always, by constructing the difference quotient for $f(x)$. Let us first introduce some notation and define w as

$$w = g(x + v) - g(x) , \tag{3–73}$$

so that if $u = g(x)$, then

$$u + w = g(x + v) . \tag{3–74}$$

Thus

$$\frac{f(x + v) - f(x)}{v} = \frac{h[g(x + v)] - h[g(x)]}{v} = \frac{h(u + w) - h(u)}{v} .$$

Since, by assumption, $h'(u)$ exists, we have on using (3–72)

$$h(u + w) - h(u) = [h'(u) + \gamma(w)]w ,$$

so that by (3–73)

$$\frac{f(x + v) - f(x)}{v} = [h'(u) + \gamma(w)] \left(\frac{w}{v} \right)$$

$$= [h'(u) + \gamma(w)] \frac{g(x + v) - g(x)}{v} . \tag{3–75}$$

Now recall that $\gamma(w)$ is continuous at $w = 0$, and by (3–73), $\lim_{v \to 0} w = 0$. Thus by the rule (3–45) for computing the limit of a compound function,

$$\lim_{v \to 0} \gamma(w) = \gamma[\lim_{v \to 0} w] = \gamma(0) = 0 .$$

Hence

$$\lim_{v \to 0} [h'(u) + \gamma(w)] = h'(u) ,$$

since $h'(u)$ does not depend on v. Therefore, since

$$\lim_{v \to 0} \frac{g(x + v) - g(x)}{v} = g'(x) ,$$

we see on applying (3–31) to (3–75) that $f'(x)$ exists and (3–71) holds, which is what we wished to prove.

The differential notation provides a convenient way to write (3–71) which the reader may find easier to remember. It is simply

$$\frac{dy}{dx} = \frac{dy}{du}\frac{du}{dx} . \tag{3–76}$$

Let us now give some examples which illustrate the usefulness of the chain rule. The chain rule is employed to differentiate some complex function by imagining that the function is a compound function $h[g(x)]$ and then applying (3–71). By use of (3–71) it is only necessary to evaluate the simpler derivatives $h'(u)$ and $g'(x)$. Sometimes it is necessary to apply the chain rule several times, for example, by also considering $g(x)$ to be a compound function.

EXAMPLES. 1. Let us compute the derivative of

$$f(x) = (2x + 3)^{17} .$$

If we did not know the chain rule we could obtain $f'(x)$ by multiplying out $(2x + 3)^{17}$ and then differentiating the resulting seventeenth-degree polynomial. Alternatively, we could apply (3–60), writing $f(x) = (2x + 3)$ $(2x + 3)^{16}$; then (3–60) would be applied again to $(2x + 3)^{16}$, and so forth. Both of these procedures are very clumsy, but it is very easy to compute $f'(x)$ using the chain rule. Suppose that we write $g(x) = 2x + 3$ and $h(u) = u^{17}$. Then $f(x) = h[g(x)]$. Now $g'(x) = 2$ for all x and $h'(u) = 17u^{16}$ for all u. When $u = 2x + 3$, $h'(2x + 3) = 17(2x + 3)^{16}$. Thus

$$f'(x) = 17(2x + 3)^{16}(2) = 34(2x + 3)^{16} ,$$

and $f'(x)$ exists for all x.

2. Next we shall compute the derivative of

$$f(x) = \left(\frac{x - 2}{x + 3}\right)^5 .$$

To evaluate $f'(x)$ without using the chain rule would again be very clumsy. One way to do this would be to multiply out $(x - 2)^5$ and $(x + 3)^5$ and differentiate the resulting rational function. However, $f'(x)$ can easily be determined using the chain rule. Let

$$g(x) = \frac{x - 2}{x + 3} ; \qquad h(u) = u^5 .$$

Then by (3–69) and (3–63) respectively,

$$g'(x) = \frac{(x + 3)(1) - (x - 2)(1)}{(x + 3)^2} = \frac{5}{(x + 3)^2} ; \qquad h'(u) = 5u^4 .$$

Then by (3–71)

$$f'(x) = h'\left(\frac{x-2}{x+3}\right) g'(x) = 25 \frac{(x-2)^4}{(x+3)^6}.$$

Since $h'(u)$ exists for all u and $g'(x)$ for $x \neq -3$, $f'(x)$ exists for all x, $x \neq -3$.

We have previously seen how to differentiate x^k, where k is any integer. Using the chain rule, we shall now obtain the derivative of $x^{m/n}$, m and n being natural numbers. Recall that we can be sure that $x^{m/n}$ is defined only when $x \geq 0$. We shall here restrict x to being positive; at $x = 0$ we could only compute a one-sided derivative. If n is odd, $x^{m/n}$ is defined for $x < 0$, and in the problems we ask the reader to prove that the results we obtain below hold for $x < 0$ if n is odd. Let us then study

$$f(x) = x^{m/n}, \quad x > 0.$$

Consider now the function

$$g(x) = [f(x)]^n = (x^{m/n})^n = x^m.$$

We know from previous work that $g'(x) = mx^{m-1}$. However, by the chain rule

$$g'(x) = n[f(x)]^{n-1}f'(x).$$

Hence

$$n[f(x)]^{n-1} f'(x) = mx^{m-1}$$

or

$$f'(x) = \frac{m}{n} \frac{x^{m-1}}{(x^{m/n})^{n-1}} = \frac{m}{n} \frac{x^{m-1}x^{m/n}}{(x^{m/n})^n} = \frac{m}{n} \frac{x^{m-1}x^{m/n}}{x^m}$$

$$= \frac{m}{n} x^{(m/n)-1}. \tag{3–77}$$

Here we have obtained $f'(x)$ and we can see that it has precisely the same form as (3–68). There is one point of rigor that was ignored in the above derivation. We never showed that $f'(x)$ actually exists. This must be done in order to use the chain rule, and we ask the reader to show in the problems that $f'(x)$ does exist.

From (3–65) we can immediately obtain the derivative of $x^{-m/n}$, since on using (3–77)

$$\frac{d}{dx} x^{-m/n} = -\frac{\frac{m}{n} x^{(m/n)-1}}{x^{2m/n}} = -\frac{m}{n} x^{(-m/n)-1}. \tag{3–78}$$

We can combine (3–78), (3–77) and (3–68) into a single equation and write

$$\frac{d}{dx} x^\alpha = \alpha x^{\alpha-1}, \quad x > 0, \quad \alpha \text{ any rational number}. \tag{3-79}$$

We have not as yet given any meaning to x^α when α is irrational, and hence we are unable to consider derivatives of x^α for this case. A generalization to the case of irrational α will come later. Note in particular that (3-79) implies

$$\frac{d}{dx} x^{1/2} = \frac{1}{2} x^{-1/2}; \qquad \frac{d}{dx} x^{-1/2} = -\frac{1}{2} x^{-3/2}. \tag{3-80}$$

EXAMPLES. 1. $\dfrac{d}{dx} x^{4.715} = 4.715 x^{3.715}, \quad x > 0$.

2. By the chain rule

$$\frac{d}{dx} (4x - 1)^{5.13} = 5.13(4x - 1)^{4.13}(4) = 20.52(4x - 1)^{4.13}.$$

3. Let us differentiate

$$y = \sqrt{\frac{x+3}{x+2}}.$$

Write

$$y = u^{1/2}; \qquad u = \frac{x+3}{x+2}.$$

Then

$$\frac{dy}{du} = \frac{1}{2} u^{-1/2}; \qquad \frac{du}{dx} = \frac{(x+2)(1) - (x+3)(1)}{(x+2)^2} = -\frac{1}{(x+2)^2}.$$

Hence from the chain rule

$$\frac{dy}{dx} = \frac{dy}{du}\frac{du}{dx} = -\frac{1}{2(x+2)^2}\left(\frac{x+3}{x+2}\right)^{-1/2}.$$

The reader should check that the derivative exists for $x > -2$ and $x < -3$.

3-11 DERIVATIVE OF INVERSE

Suppose that $y = f(x)$ has a derivative at $x = \alpha$ and $f'(\alpha) \neq 0$. Consider now the inverse representation of $f(x)$ introduced in Section 2-11. Let us assume that at α the inverse representation of $f(x)$ is given by $x = g_k(y)$ and that the domain of $g_k(y)$ is $y_k \leq y \leq y_{k+1}$. We shall suppose (without loss of generality) that $\beta = f(\alpha)$ satisfies $y_k < \beta < y_{k+1}$. We would now like to show how $g_k'(\beta)$ can be determined from a knowledge of $f'(\alpha)$. The problem is very simple when viewed geometrically. Suppose that the graph of $y = f(x)$ looks like that shown in Figure 3-18. The curve between x_k

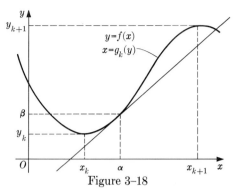

Figure 3–18

and x_{k+1} is the graph of $y = f(x)$ and is also the graph of $x = g_k(y)$. Now the tangent line to the curve at (α, β) is unique and does not depend on whether we think of the curve as being the graph of $f(x)$ or $g_k(y)$. When we think of the curve as being the graph of $f(x)$, the equation for the tangent is

$$y - \beta = f'(\alpha)(x - \alpha) . \qquad (3\text{–}81)$$

If we think of the curve as being the graph of $g_k(y)$, then the equation of the tangent should be

$$x - \alpha = g_k'(\beta)(y - \beta) . \qquad (3\text{–}82)$$

Equations (3–81) and (3–82) should both represent the same line. By dividing by $f'(\alpha)$, which we have assumed is not 0, (3–81) can be converted to the form

$$x - \alpha = \frac{1}{f'(\alpha)} (y - \beta) . \qquad (3\text{–}83)$$

Comparing (3–83) and (3–82), we see that it must be true that

$$g_k'(\beta) = \frac{1}{f'(\alpha)} . \qquad (3\text{–}84)$$

This result can be proved analytically without use of geometric reasoning. Note that

$$y = f[g_k(y)], \qquad y_k \le y \le y_{k+1} \qquad (3\text{–}85)$$

and $dy/dy = 1$. Hence by the chain rule, at (α, β)

$$\frac{dy}{dy} = 1 = f'(\alpha)g_k'(\beta) ,$$

which yields (3–84). There is one point of rigor which has not been filled in above, and this concerns the existence of $g_k'(\beta)$. The geometric argument makes it quite clear that $g'_k(\beta)$ exists when $f'(\alpha)$ exists and is not 0. We shall not bother to give the analytic proof. A convenient way to write (3–84) using differential notation is

$$\frac{dx}{dy} = \frac{1}{\dfrac{dy}{dx}} \,. \tag{3–86}$$

We shall later make use of (3–84) to obtain one result of great importance, but here we shall give only a simple example of its usefulness.

EXAMPLE. If $f(x) = x^2$, then for $x > 0$, the inverse representation of $f(x)$ is $g(y) = y^{1/2}$. Now $f'(x) = 2x$. Hence $g'(y) = 1/2x$. However, for this to make sense, we must replace x by y using $x = y^{1/2}$. Hence,

$$g'(y) = \frac{1}{2}\, y^{-1/2} \,,$$

which is a result we can verify directly by differentiating $g(y)$.

3–12* DIFFERENTIATION OF THE TRIGONOMETRIC FUNCTIONS

The trigonometric functions $\sin \theta$ and $\cos \theta$ possess derivatives for all values of θ. We encounter a certain difficulty in attempting to determine these derivatives because our definition of these functions in Section 2–14 was geometric in nature and we never have provided a way to compute $\sin \theta$ and $\cos \theta$ to any desired accuracy. To obtain rigorously the derivatives of the sine and cosine functions it would be necessary to introduce a considerable amount of additional material. We shall not attempt to do this, but will instead give an intuitive geometric argument to obtain them.

Consider

$$g(v) = \frac{\sin (\theta + v) - \sin \theta}{v} \,. \tag{3–87}$$

The numbers representing the numerator and denominator of the difference quotient are shown in Figure 3–19, where we have shown the unit circle used to define the trigonometric functions θ, v and $\sin(\theta + v) - \sin \theta$. As v gets smaller and smaller, the triangle ABC becomes closer and closer to being similar to the triangle OAD as marked, since for v very small AB becomes perpendicular to OA. Therefore, as v approaches 0, BC/AB approaches OD/OA or OD, since OA has length 1. Now OD is simply $\cos \theta$. Furthermore, for v very small the length of the line segment AB is essentially v and BC is precisely $\sin(\theta + v) - \sin \theta$. Thus it would appear that

$$\lim_{v \to 0} \frac{\sin (\theta + v) - \sin \theta}{v} = \cos \theta \,.$$

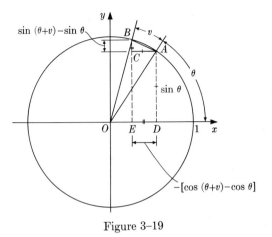

Figure 3–19

This is indeed correct, as we could prove by more rigorous means, and *for all θ the derivative of* $\sin \theta$ *is* $\cos \theta$, so that

$$\frac{d}{d\theta} \sin \theta = \cos \theta, \quad \text{all } \theta . \tag{3–88}$$

The intuitive argument leading to the derivative of $\cos \theta$ can also be obtained from Figure 3–19. Note that the length of the side AC of the triangle ABC is $-[\cos(\theta + v) - \cos \theta]$. The minus sign appears because $\cos(\theta + v) - \cos \theta$ is negative here. Using the same similar triangles, we see that AC/AB approaches AD/OA or AD, since OA has length 1. But AD has length $\sin \theta$. Furthermore, AB is essentially v and AC has length $-[\cos(\theta + v) - \cos \theta]$. Hence it should be true that

$$\lim_{v \to 0} -\frac{\cos(\theta + v) - \cos \theta}{v} = \sin \theta$$

or

$$\lim_{v \to 0} \frac{\cos(\theta + v) - \cos \theta}{v} = -\sin \theta .$$

This is indeed correct, and *for all θ, the derivative of* $\cos \theta$ *is* $-\sin \theta$, so that

$$\frac{d}{d\theta} \cos \theta = -\sin \theta, \quad \text{all } \theta . \tag{3–89}$$

Given these two results it is possible to obtain directly the derivative of $\tan \theta$. We ask the reader to do this in the problems.

EXAMPLES. 1. By use of a good table of $\sin \theta$, it can easily be seen numerically that $g(v)$ given by (3–87) gets closer and closer to $\cos \theta$. For example, for $\theta = 0.700$, $g(0.005) = 0.7632$, $g(0.003) = 0.7637$ and $g(0.001) = 0.7640$, whereas $\cos \theta = \cos 0.7 = 0.7648$. This, of course, does not prove that what we obtained above is correct.

2. From the chain rule

$$\frac{d}{dx} \sin x^2 = (\cos x^2)(2x) = 2x \cos x^2, \quad \text{all } x .$$

Here we used $g(x) = x^2$ and $h(u) = \sin u$.

3. Note that $\cos(\sin x)$ is a function whose domain includes all x. On writing $g(x) = \sin x$ and $h(u) = \cos u$, it follows from the chain rule that this function is differentiable for all x and

$$\frac{d}{dx} \cos(\sin x) = -[\sin(\sin x)]\cos x .$$

3–13 MAXIMA AND MINIMA

A type of practical problem frequently encountered in both the physical and social sciences is one in which it is desired to determine the maximum or minimum value of a function under certain conditions. For example, a firm wishes to operate in such a way as to maximize profits, or an airline is interested in determining the precise flight path that a jet should follow in going from one city to another so as to minimize fuel consumption. Maximization and minimization problems are often referred to collectively as *optimization problems.* Many optimization problems are very difficult to solve. In this section we wish to show how the theory of differentiation can be usefully employed to solve the simplest type of optimization problem— those problems concerned with optimizing a function of just a single variable.

We shall concentrate our attention on determining the maximum or minimum value of some function $f(x)$ over a specified closed interval I^c_{ab}. It will be assumed that $f'(x)$ exists for each x in the interval. This is almost always a valid assumption for the types of problems encountered in practice. What we wish to do is determine the value or values of x in I^c_{ab} for which $f(x)$ takes on its largest or smallest value. Note that all values of x in the interval are being considered. We shall not study cases in which x can take on only special values, such as integral values.

Let us first define precisely what we mean by the maximum or absolute maximum of $f(x)$ over the interval.

ABSOLUTE MAXIMUM. *Consider the function $f(x)$ and let I^c_{ab} be a subset of its domain. Then $f(x)$ is said to take on its absolute maximum for $x \in I^c_{ab}$ at $x^* \in I^c_{ab}$ if $f(x) \leq f(x^*)$ for every $x \in I^c_{ab}$.*

The absolute maximum is sometimes referred to as the *global maximum* of $f(x)$ over I_{ab}^c. We can define the notion of absolute minimum in precisely the same way.

ABSOLUTE MINIMUM. *The function $f(x)$ is said to take on its absolute minimum over I_{ab}^c at $x_* \in I_{ab}^c$ if $f(x) \geq f(x_*)$ for all $x \in I_{ab}^c$.*

We refer to the absolute maximum or minimum of $f(x)$, whichever is appropriate, as *the optimal value of $f(x)$* or *the optimum*, and the value or values of x which yield the optimal value of $f(x)$ as *the optimal values of the variable*. If $f(x)$ is the function shown in Figure 3–20, and I_{ab}^c is that shown, then $f(x^*)$, x^*, $f(x_*)$ and x_* are illustrated on the figure.

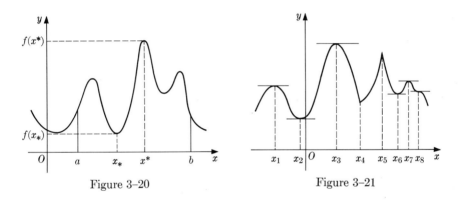

Figure 3–20   Figure 3–21

Let us now proceed to show how the optimal values of x can be determined in the case where $f(x)$ is differentiable. No procedures exist by which the optimal values of x can be determined directly. Instead, the procedure we are about to develop will locate what are referred to as relative maxima and minima of $f(x)$ or, more generally, what are called stationary values of $f(x)$. From a knowledge of the stationary values of $f(x)$ and the points at which these stationary values are taken on, we can then proceed to determine the optimal values. A relative maximum is defined as follows (the changes necessary to define a relative minimum are obvious).

RELATIVE MAXIMUM. *The function $f(x)$ is said to take on a relative maximum at x_0, x_0 being in the interior of I_{ab}^c, if there exists a $\delta > 0$ such that for every x in I_{ab}^c whose distance from x_0 is less than δ, $f(x) \leq f(x_0)$.*

Intuitively $f(x)$ takes on a relative maximum at x_0 if, for all x very close to x_0, $f(x) \leq f(x_0)$. Thus relative maxima correspond to mountain peaks of the graph of $f(x)$. Similarly, relative minima correspond to valleys. Note that the above definition of a relative maximum did not require that $f(x)$ be either differentiable or continuous at x_0. Consider Figure 3–21. The function $f(x)$ takes on a relative maximum at x_1, x_3, x_5 and x_7, and a relative minimum at x_2, x_4 and x_6. Note that if $f(x) = \lambda$, a constant, then according to the above definition $f(x)$ takes on a relative maximum (and a relative minimum) at every x. This case is clearly a degenerate one where there are no peaks and valleys, and is not of practical interest.

It will be noted from Figure 3–21 that for each x where $f(x)$ takes on a relative maximum or minimum and where, in addition, $f(x)$ is differentiable, the tangent line to the curve at this point is horizontal. From (3–52) we see immediately that this implies that $f'(x) = 0$ at such points. Thus it would appear that, if $f(x)$ is differentiable at every point in I_{ab}^c, then it should be true that $f'(x_0) = 0$ at each point x_0 where $f(x)$ takes on a relative maximum or minimum. This is indeed correct, and we shall now prove it analytically. We shall prove the following. *Suppose that $f(x)$ takes on a relative maximum at x_0 and suppose also that $f'(x_0)$ exists. Then $f'(x_0) = 0$.*

To prove this result note that the definition of a relative maximum implies that, for all v whose magnitude is sufficiently small, say $|v| < \delta$,

$$f(x_0 + v) \le f(x_0) \quad \text{or} \quad f(x_0 + v) - f(x_0) \le 0 . \tag{3–90}$$

Then for $v > 0$, (3–90) implies that

$$\frac{f(x_0 + v) - f(x_0)}{v} \le 0 . \tag{3–91}$$

However, since $f'(x_0)$ exists, then the limit of the left-hand side of (3–91) as v approaches 0 through positive values must be $f'(x_0)$. But since (3–91) holds for all $v > 0$, it follows from p. 185 that

$$\lim_{v \to 0+} \frac{f(x_0 + v) - f(x_0)}{v} = f'(x_0) \le 0 , \tag{3–92}$$

so $f'(x_0) \le 0$.

Suppose next that $v < 0$. Then, on dividing (3–90) by v and noting that division by a negative number changes the direction of the inequality, we have

$$\frac{f(x_0 + v) - f(x_0)}{v} \ge 0 . \tag{3–93}$$

Taking the limit of (3–93) as v approaches 0 through negative values, we conclude that $f'(x_0) \ge 0$. Thus we have shown that $f'(x_0) \le 0$ and $f'(x_0) \ge 0$. This will be true if and only if $f'(x_0) = 0$. *Precisely similar arguments show that if $f(x)$ takes on a relative minimum at a point x_0 where $f'(x_0)$ exists, then $f'(x_0) = 0$.*

What have we proved? We have shown that *if $f(x)$ is differentiable at each point in I_{ab}^c, then every value of x where $f(x)$ takes on a relative maximum or minimum in the interior of I_{ab}^c must be a solution to the equation $f'(x) = 0$, that is, the only values of x at which $f(x)$ can take on a relative maximum or minimum are the roots of the derivative function.* The task of finding the points where $f(x)$ takes on a relative maximum or minimum is thus considerably simplified, because we only need to look at the roots of $f'(x)$. The fact that $f'(x_0) = 0$ if $f(x)$ takes on a relative maximum at x_0 implies that the tangent to the graph of $y = f(x)$ at x_0 is the horizontal straight line $y = f(x_0)$. We have noted previously that this should be the case.

It is important to note that it is not necessarily true that $f(x)$ will take on a relative maximum or minimum at every root of $f'(x) = 0$. For example, $f'(x_8) = 0$ in Figure 3–21, but $f(x)$ does not take on a relative maximum or minimum at x_8. The tangent line is horizontal, but it cuts the graph of $f(x)$ at x_8. While we are not sure that $f(x)$ will take on a relative maximum or minimum at every root of $f'(x)$, we are sure that when $f(x)$ is differentiable, every point at which it takes on a relative maximum or minimum will be a root of $f'(x)$. The values of x for which $f'(x) = 0$ are frequently referred to as *stationary points* or critical values of $f(x)$, and the corresponding values of $f(x)$ are referred to as *stationary values* or critical values of the function. For the function whose graph is shown in Figure 3–21, the points x_1, x_2, x_3, x_6, x_7 and x_8 would all be solutions to $f'(x) = 0$ and are all stationary points of $f(x)$. At each of these points except x_8, $f(x)$ takes on a relative maximum or minimum. The points x_4 and x_5, where $f(x)$ takes on a relative minimum and maximum respectively, are not roots of $f'(x)$. However, $f(x)$ is not differentiable at x_4 and x_5.

Let us now return to the problem of finding the optimal value of $f(x)$, say the absolute maximum, over I^c_{ab}. If $f(x)$ has an absolute maximum over this interval, then it must be taken on at one of the points a or b or at an interior point of the interval. Let us next prove that, if the absolute maximum occurs at an interior point of I^c_{ab}, then the point x^* where it is taken on also yields a relative maximum of $f(x)$. If x^* is an interior point, let δ_1 be its distance from a and δ_2 its distance from b, and take δ to be smaller than δ_1 and δ_2. Then all x whose distance from x^* is less than δ lie in I^c_{ab}. Since $f(x)$ takes on its absolute maximum at x^*, $f(x) \leq f(x^*)$ for all $x \in I^c_{ab}$. Hence, for all x whose distance from x^* is less than δ, $f(x) \leq f(x^*)$. But by the definition of a relative maximum, $f(x)$ then takes on a relative maximum at x^*. The above reasoning has thus shown that the absolute maximum of $f(x)$ is either taken on at one of the end points of the interval or at an interior point where $f(x)$ takes on a relative maximum. Now if $f(x)$ is differentiable at every point in the interval, every point at which $f(x)$ takes on a relative maximum is a root of $f'(x)$. Hence, in such a case, the absolute maximum of $f(x)$ is taken on at one of the end points of the interval or at one or more roots of $f'(x)$.

We now have the background needed to develop a procedure for finding the absolute maximum of $f(x)$ over I^c_{ab}. Since, when $f(x)$ is differentiable, the absolute maximum can only occur at one of the roots of $f'(x)$ or at an end point of the interval, all we need to do is determine each of the roots of $f'(x)$ lying in I^c_{ab}, call them $\lambda_1, \ldots, \lambda_k$, and then compute $f(\lambda_1), \ldots,$

$f(\lambda_k)$, $f(a)$, $f(b)$. The absolute maximum of $f(x)$ over I_{ab}^c is then the largest of these numbers, and the point or points where the absolute maximum is taken on is simply that element (or elements) of $\{\lambda_1, \lambda_2, \ldots, \lambda_k, a, b\}$ which yields this largest value of $f(x)$. Note that with this procedure we do not need to determine whether any particular root λ_u of $f'(x)$ yields a relative maximum of $f(x)$, a relative minimum or neither. To find the absolute minimum of $f(x)$ over I_{ab}^c it is only necessary to determine the smallest of the numbers $f(\lambda_1), \ldots, f(\lambda_k), f(a), f(b)$. Note that the absolute maximum (or minimum) may occur at one of the end points in the interval where $f'(x) \neq 0$. Figure 3–22 illustrates such a case, where the absolute maximum is taken on at $x = a$.

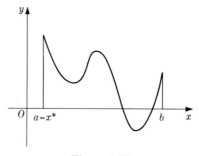

Figure 3–22

In the above analysis we have not considered the question of whether $f(x)$ actually has an absolute maximum or minimum over I_{ab}^c. Could it be that $f(x)$ does not? This can occur if $f(x)$ is not continuous. However, if $f(x)$ is continuous it can be proved that I_{ab}^c contains points x^* and x_* where $f(x)$ takes on its absolute maximum and minimum respectively, that is, $f(x)$ does indeed have an absolute maximum and minimum. Thus, if $f(x)$ is differentiable at every point in I_{ab}^c, it does have an absolute maximum and minimum. As an example of a case where $f(x)$ does not have an absolute maximum in a given interval, let

$$f(x) = \begin{cases} 3 + x, & 0 \le x < 1 \\ x - 1, & 1 \le x \le 2 \end{cases} \tag{3-94}$$

and suppose that we are trying to determine the absolute maximum of $f(x)$ over the interval $0 \le x \le 2$. Note that $\lim_{x \to 1-} f(x) = 4$. However, $f(1) = 0$. We can find values of x for which $f(x)$ is arbitrarily close to 4, and hence it would appear that the absolute maximum of $f(x)$ is 4. However, there is no value of x in the interval though for which $f(x) = 4$. Another example of a function which has no absolute maximum over the interval $0 \le x \le 2$ is $f(x) = 1/(x - 1)$, $f(1) = 0$. In this case $f(x)$ can be made arbitrarily large and hence there is no largest value of $f(x)$. For most practical applications, it is clear from the nature of the problem that $f(x)$ will have an absolute maximum or minimum, and all that remains is to find the points where it is taken on.

In the following section we shall give some simple practical examples illustrating how the theory developed in this section can be applied. Before going on, however, it is worth pointing out that the theory developed here is useful only if we can conveniently determine all the roots of $f'(x)$. In general, this is by no means an easy problem. If the roots of $f'(x)$ cannot be readily determined, then other methods are more appropriate for solving a problem involving the optimization of $f(x)$. In particular, if the problem were to be solved numerically using a computer, an alternative procedure, which will be described later, would be used.

3–14 EXAMPLES OF OPTIMIZATION PROBLEMS

1. Suppose that we have a piece of wire 20 inches long. This wire is to be bent to form a rectangle (whose perimeter is then 20 inches). It is possible to form many different rectangles from this piece of wire each of which has a perimeter of 20 inches. For example, one might have a base 8 inches in length and an altitude of 2 inches, while another might have a base of 6 inches and an altitude of 4 inches. Suppose that out of all possible rectangles that can be formed in this way we wish to find the dimensions of the one having the largest area.

Let us now show how the theory developed in the previous section can be applied to solve this problem. The area of any rectangle having a base of length x inches and an altitude of length y inches is xy square inches. We are interested in rectangles whose perimeter is 20 inches. Thus $2x + 2y = 20$. Consequently, whatever the value chosen for x, y must be given by $10 - x$. Hence x must satisfy $0 \leq x \leq 10$ and the area can now be expressed as a function of x. It is

$$f(x) = x(10 - x) . \tag{3–95}$$

What we then wish to do is find that x lying in the interval $0 \leq x \leq 10$ which yields the largest value of $f(x)$. The problem has now been cast into the form studied in the previous section.

To proceed we find the roots of $f'(x)$ lying in the interval of interest. Note that $f(x)$ possesses a derivative for all x and thus the theory developed in the previous section applies. Furthermore

$$f'(x) = 10 - x + x(-1) = 10 - 2x .$$

The only solution to $f'(x) = 0$ is $x = 5$, which does indeed lie in the interval $0 \leq x \leq 10$. To determine the maximum area, we evaluate the area $f(x)$ at $x = 5$ and at the end points of the interval $x = 0$ and $x = 10$. We see from (3–95) that $f(0) = f(10) = 0$ and $f(5) = 25$. Thus the rectangle having maximum area out of all those which have a perimeter of 20 inches is a square with 5-inch sides. The area of this rectangle (square) is 25 square inches. It is obvious geometrically that $f(x)$ takes on its absolute maximum for all x (not just x satisfying $0 \leq x \leq 10$) at $x = 5$, since the graph of $f(x)$ is a parabola with $x = 5$ as an axis of symmetry which crosses the axis of symmetry at $y = 25$ and opens downward.

2. Let us determine the point on the line $2x + 3y = 6$ which is closest to the origin. The point closest to the origin is the point whose distance from the origin is as small as possible. The distance from any point (x, y) in the plane from the origin is $[x^2 + y^2]^{1/2}$. If this point lies on the given line then

$$y = 2 - \frac{2}{3}x.$$

Hence the distance of a point $(x, 2 - \frac{2}{3}x)$, which lies on the given line, from the origin is

$$f(x) = \left[x^2 + \left(2 - \frac{2}{3}x \right)^2 \right]^{1/2}.$$

and we have expressed the distance in terms of x. We wish to determine that value of x which minimizes $f(x)$. Here the interval over which x is to be allowed to range has not been defined in a natural way. Geometrically, however, it is obvious that $-100 \leq x \leq 100$, since it is easy to find points inside this interval which are closer to the origin than those with $x = 100$ or -100.

Note that $x^2 + (2 - \frac{2}{3}x)^2 > 0$ for all x, and therefore $f(x)$ is differentiable for all x. Furthermore, by the chain rule,

$$f'(x) = \frac{1}{2} \left[2x + 2 \left(2 - \frac{2}{3}x \right) \left(-\frac{2}{3} \right) \right] \left[x^2 + \left(2 - \frac{2}{3}x \right)^2 \right]^{-1/2}.$$

Now $[x^2 + (2 - \frac{2}{3}x)^2]^{1/2} > 0$ for all x. Therefore the set of x which satisfies $f'(x) = 0$ satisfies

$$x + \left(2 - \frac{2}{3}x \right) \left(-\frac{2}{3} \right) = 0 \quad \text{or} \quad \frac{13}{9}x - \frac{4}{3} = 0.$$

Hence there is only one root of $f'(x) = 0$, which is $x = 12/13$. We have noted above that the solution will not occur at the end points of the interval. Hence the unique point on the line which is closest to the origin has $x = 12/13$ and $y = 2 - \frac{2}{3}x = 18/13$, that is, the point $(12/13, 18/13)$. The reader should illustrate this geometrically.

3. An oil company sells millions of quarts of motor oil per year in tin-plate cans. The cost of the can itself is not negligible, and a significant part of the cost of the can comes from the cost of the tin plate used in making it. The cans must have the form of right circular cylinders as shown in Figure 3–23, but there is freedom in selecting the dimensions of the can, that is, r and h. It is desired to determine the dimensions of a one-quart can which

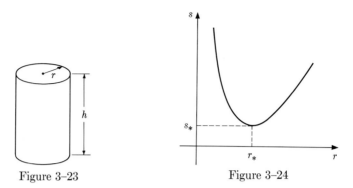

Figure 3–23 Figure 3–24

require the smallest amount of tin plate in its manufacture.

The minimum thickness of the tin plate is determined independently of the dimensions of the can, and therefore the problem reduces to minimizing the number of square inches of tin plate of a given thickness needed to produce the can. For simplicity, let us neglect problems of wastage due to cutting the patterns from the tin plate. Then the tin plate needed will be minimized if the surface area of the can (including the top and bottom) is minimized, provided that we make the additional simplifying restriction that the tin plate needed for the seam on the side of the can and that needed for crimping the top and bottom to the side does not vary significantly with the dimensions of the can. This is not quite true. We could easily take into account the material needed for seams, but for this simple example, we shall not bother to do so. In the problems the reader is asked to treat this aspect of the problem. Finally, we shall assume that the can can be completely filled. Our problem then reduces to finding the right circular cylinder of minimum surface area which has a volume of one quart. Let us now solve this problem.

The volume v of the cylinder shown in Figure 3–23 is equal to the product of the area of its base πr^2 times its height h, that is, $v = \pi r^2 h$. Consequently, when the volume v is specified, once the radius of the base is selected, h is determined by $h = v/\pi r^2$. The surface area of the side of the can is simply $2\pi rh$ (its length times its height) and the area of the top and bottom combined is $2\pi r^2$. The surface area s for a given h and r is then

$$s = 2\pi r^2 + 2\pi rh ,$$

or if we replace h by $v/\pi r^2$, we can express s in terms of r for any specified v, that is

$$s = f(r) = 2\pi r^2 + \frac{2v}{r} . \tag{3–96}$$

We wish to determine the r which minimizes (3–96) when v is one quart. Practical considerations would make it impossible to use an r of less than 1 inch or greater than 10 inches. Thus, we wish to determine that r satisfying $1 \leq r \leq 10$ which yields the absolute minimum of $f(r)$.

Note that $f(r)$ is differentiable at each point in the interval under consideration and

$$f'(r) = 4\pi r - \frac{2v}{r^2}.$$

There is only one r for which $f'(r) = 0$, which is

$$r = \left(\frac{v}{2\pi}\right)^{1/3}. \tag{3-97}$$

If r and h are being measured in inches, then the unit of volume will be cubic inches. Hence to determine r from (3–97) we cannot set $v = 1$ quart. There are 57.75 cubic inches in a quart. Therefore we should set $v = 57.75$ Then

$$r = \left(\frac{57.75}{2\pi}\right)^{1/3} = 2.095.$$

This value of r is within the interval of interest. Furthermore, as the reader can easily check, $f(2.095)$ is smaller than $f(1)$ or $f(10)$. Hence the optimal r is $r_* = 2.095$ inches, and the corresponding height of the can is

$$h_* = \frac{57.75}{\pi(2.095)^2} = 4.170 \text{ inches}.$$

We have now found the optimal dimensions for the can. The graph of $f(r)$, the surface area, as a function of r is shown in Figure 3–24.

It is important to note that, in the formulation of the above problem, it was specified that the can must be a right circular cylinder. A more general problem would be that of finding the shape of a container which has the minimum surface area for a given volume. This latter problem is much more difficult than the one we have studied, and it cannot be solved by the methods developed above. It is a problem in what is called the calculus of variations, a subject which will not be studied here. (Incidentally, the answer is a sphere.)

4. A large mining company is about to start digging an open-pit copper mine. The thickness of copper-bearing ore has been determined from geological data to be about 2000 feet. The areal extent of the ore is 5 square miles or $5(5.280 \times 10^3)^2 = 1.39 \times 10^8$ square feet. The ore bed can be looked upon as a parallelepiped whose altitude is 2000 feet and whose base has an area of 1.39×10^8 square feet, as shown in Figure 3–25. The volume of ore in this mine is then $2(1.39) \times 10^{11} = 2.78 \times 10^{11}$ cubic feet or 1.03×10^{10} cubic yards. The concentration of copper in the ore is essentially uniform throughout the bed, and one cubic yard of ore yields 5 pounds of refined copper. Copper sells for $0.35 per pound and the cost of processing

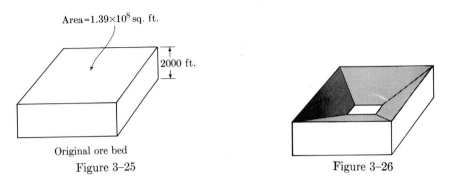

Area=1.39×10^8 sq. ft.

2000 ft.

Original ore bed

Figure 3–25

Figure 3–26

each cubic yard of ore to obtain the metallic copper is $0.87. The **deeper** workmen dig down into the ore vein, the more expensive it is to mine a cubic yard of ore. The mine must be developed in a certain pattern (with a fixed slope to the sides, etc.), as shown in Figure 3–26, and from this geometry the number of cubic yards of ore which will be removed by the time a given depth is reached can be computed. If d is the depth in yards to which the digging has been carried, the engineers have computed that the number of cubic yards of ore removed is $1.55 \times 10^7 \, d^{1/2}$. From this and the economics of the situation the engineers have determined the total cost of mining the ore and transporting it to the smelting plant as a function of the depth to which the vein is dug. This cost K is

$$K = 3.07 \times 10^5 \, d . \qquad (3\text{–}98)$$

The mining company would like to maximize the profit received from this mining venture. It is not necessarily true that profits will be maximized by digging down 2000 feet to the bottom of the vein. Since digging costs per cubic yard increase with depth, it may be desirable not to mine as much copper as possible, but instead to terminate the digging at some depth less than 2000 feet. It is desired to determine the depth at which to terminate the digging so that the company's profit will be maximized. Let us now see how to solve this problem.

The procedure is to express the profit as a function of the depth at which digging is terminated, and then the theory we have been studying can be applied. The total profit from the operation is equal to the revenues received from sale of the copper less the costs incurred. We shall now determine the profit. The company receives $0.35 per pound of copper, and one cubic yard yields 5 pounds of copper. Thus one cubic yard of ore brings $5(0.35) = \$1.75$. The number of cubic yards produced if digging is terminated at a depth d is $1.55 \times 10^7 \, d^{1/2}$. Hence the total revenue generated is

$$1.75(1.55 \times 10^7) \, d^{1/2} .$$

Consider now the costs incurred in producing the metallic copper. There are two components of this cost. The digging and transportation cost to the smelter is one of these, and the other is the cost of refining the ore, that is, obtaining the copper metal from the ore. The cost of digging and transportation as a function of the depth at which digging is terminated is given by (3–98). Let us now determine the refining cost. The refining cost is \$0.87 per cubic yard, so that the total refining cost when digging is terminated at a depth d is

$$0.87(1.55 \times 10^7)\, d^{1/2}\,.$$

Consequently the profit $f(d)$ as a function of d is

$$
\begin{aligned}
f(d) &= 1.75(1.55 \times 10^7)\, d^{1/2} - 0.87(1.55 \times 10^7)\, d^{1/2} - 3.07 \times 10^5\, d \\
&= 1.36 \times 10^7\, d^{1/2} - 3.07 \times 10^5\, d\,.
\end{aligned}
\tag{3–99}
$$

We have now determined the company's profit in dollars as a function of the depth at which digging is terminated.

We wish to determine the value of d in yards satisfying $0 \le d \le 666\tfrac{2}{3}$ which maximizes (3–99). Note that $666\tfrac{2}{3}$ is the depth of the vein in yards. Now

$$f'(d) = 0.68 \times 10^7\, d^{-1/2} - 3.07 \times 10^5\,.$$

There is just one root of $f'(d)$, which is

$$d = \left(\frac{6.8}{3.07} \times 10^1\right)^2 = (22.2)^2 = 490 \text{ yards}\,.$$

Now

$$f(0) = 0,\quad f(490) = 1.51 \times 10^8,\quad f(666\tfrac{2}{3}) = 1.48 \times 10^8\,.$$

Therefore the maximum profit occurs for $d = 490$ yards, or 1470 feet, and digging should be terminated at this point. The maximum profit is about 151 million dollars. This is a large number, but it should be kept in mind that it would take perhaps 20 years to dig a mine of this size, so that the annual profit is about 7 million dollars.

5. The theory we have developed is often especially useful for obtaining interesting theoretical results. Let us illustrate with an example taken from economics. Consider a firm which produces a single product. The firm would like to decide how much of this product should be produced during the coming year in order to maximize its profits over this period. Let q be the quantity produced, and suppose that the revenues generated on selling q units amount to $r(q)$. Also, let $c(q)$ be the total cost of producing the q units. Then the profit obtained as a result of producing q units is

$$f(q) = r(q) - c(q)\,. \tag{3–100}$$

Suppose that Q is the maximum quantity which can be produced. Then it is desired to find a q satisfying $0 \leq q \leq Q$ which maximizes $f(q)$. Now

$$f'(q) = r'(q) - c'(q)$$

and the roots of $f'(q)$ are the values of q for which

$$r'(q) = c'(q) . \tag{3-101}$$

If the optimal quantity to produce q^* is not 0 or Q, then q^* must satisfy (3–101), which says that the rate of change of revenues with respect to q is equal to the rate of change of costs. In economics, $r'(q)$ is called the marginal revenue at q, and $c'(q)$ is called the marginal cost. Thus what we have shown is that, if q^* is not 0 or Q, then q^* occurs where the marginal revenue is equal to the marginal cost. In economics texts the statement is often found that production should be adjusted to the point where marginal revenue is equal to marginal cost.

In general, the price per unit that the firm charges for its product may need to be reduced as production is increased if all units are to be sold. Suppose, however, that any quantity $q \leq Q$ can be disposed of at the fixed market price p. In this case $r(q) = pq$, since the revenue received will be the price (which is independent of q) times the quantity sold, and $r'(q) = p$. Thus (3–101) becomes in this case

$$p = c'(q) , \tag{3-102}$$

and it follows that, when the firm has no control over the price, production should be adjusted so that the marginal cost is equal to the price per unit of the product.

3–15 DERIVATIVES OF HIGHER ORDER

If $f(x) = x^2$, then $f'(x) = 2x$ for all x. Note that if we desire we can compute the derivative of $f'(x)$ to obtain $df'(x)/dx = 1$ for all x. If $f'(x)$ has a derivative at $x = \alpha$, we call the derivative of $f'(x)$ at α the *second derivative* of $f(x)$ at $x = \alpha$, and denote it by $f''(\alpha)$, $(d^2y/dx^2)_\alpha$ or $d^2f(\alpha)/dx^2$. Thus by definition

$$f''(\alpha) = \lim_{v \to 0} \frac{f'(\alpha + v) - f'(\alpha)}{v} . \tag{3-103}$$

If $f''(\alpha)$ exists then $f'(x)$ is continuous at $x = \alpha$, and hence there exists a $\delta > 0$ such that $f'(\alpha)$ exists for each x whose distance from α is less than δ. Thus $f''(\alpha)$ cannot exist without $f'(x)$ being defined not only at $x = \alpha$ but in some neighborhood of α as well. Just as we could think of $f'(x)$ as a function of x, which we called the derivative function, *we can think of $f''(x)$ as a function of x, which we can call the second derivative function.* If any confusion may arise, we should call $f'(x)$ the first derivative function.

EXAMPLES. 1. If $y = x^n$,   then

$$\frac{dy}{dx} = nx^{n-1}; \qquad \frac{d^2y}{dx^2} = n(n-1)x^{n-2}, \quad n \geq 2.$$

2. If $f(x) = 4x^4 - 17x^3 + x - 1$, then

$$f'(x) = 16x^3 - 51x^2 + 1$$

and

$$f''(x) = 48x^2 - 102x.$$

The second derivative function of $f(x)$ when $f(x)$ is a polynomial of degree n is a polynomial of degree $n - 2$.

3. If $f(x) = x + 3$, then $f'(x) = 1$ and $f''(x) = 0$.

4. If $f(x) = 6$, then $f'(x) = 0$ and $f''(x) = 0$. Whenever $f'(x) = 0$ for all x, $f''(x)$ always exists and is also 0 for all x.

5. If $f(x) = \sin x$, $f'(x) = \cos x$ and $f''(x) = -\sin x$, for all x.

Just as we can compute $df'(x)/dx = f''(x)$ when $f'(x)$ is differentiable, we can similarly compute the derivative of $f''(x)$ when it exists. We denote $df''(x)/dx$ by $f'''(x)$ or d^3y/dx^3 and call it the third derivative of $f(x)$. In the same way, we can define the nth derivative of $f(x)$, when it exists, as the derivative of the $(n - 1)$th derivative of $f(x)$. The nth derivative of $f(x)$ will be denoted by $f^{(n)}(x)$ or d^ny/dx^n. We use $f^{(n)}(x)$ because it becomes inconvenient to use primes after the third derivative; parentheses are placed around n so that it is not interpreted as the nth power of $f(x)$. Thus, by definition

$$f^{(n)}(x) = \lim_{v \to 0} \frac{f^{(n-1)}(x+v) - f^{(n-1)}(x)}{v} \qquad (3\text{--}104)$$

or

$$\frac{d^ny}{dx^n} = \frac{d}{dx}\frac{d^{n-1}y}{dx^{n-1}}. \qquad (3\text{--}105)$$

It is common to refer to $f^{(n)}(x)$ as the derivative of order n of $f(x)$ as well as the nth derivative of $f(x)$. We shall find it convenient when using the notation $f^{(n)}(x)$ to use the definition $f^{(0)}(x) = f(x)$.

EXAMPLES. 1. The polynomial

$$y = 3x^4 + 2x^3 - x + 1$$

possesses derivatives of all orders for all x, and

$$\frac{dy}{dx} = 12x^3 + 6x^2 - 1; \qquad \frac{d^2y}{dx^2} = 36x^2 + 12x;$$

$$\frac{d^3y}{dx^3} = 72x + 12; \qquad \frac{d^4y}{dx^4} = 72;$$

$$\frac{d^ny}{dx^n} = 0, \quad n = 5, 6, 7, \ldots .$$

2. If $f(x) = x^n$, then

$$f'(x) = nx^{n-1};$$
$$f''(x) = n(n - 1)x^{n-2};$$
$$f'''(x) = n(n - 1)(n - 2)x^{n-3}, \ldots ;$$
$$f^{(n)}(x) = n(n - 1) \cdots (2)(1);$$
$$f^{(k)}(x) = 0, \quad k = n + 1, \quad n + 2, \ldots$$

Products of the form $n(n - 1) \cdots (2)(1)$ arise frequently in mathematics, and a special symbol $n!$ is used to represent this product; $n!$ is read n factorial. Thus by definition

$$n! = n(n - 1) \cdots (2)(1)$$

so that, for example,

$$5! = 5(4)(3)(2)(1) = 120 .$$

Also, by definition $0! = 1$. By use of the factorial symbol, a product such as

$$n(n - 1) \cdots (n - k + 1), \quad k = 1, \ldots, n$$

can be written $n!/(n - k)!$ since

$$(n - k)! = (n - k)(n - k - 1) \cdots (2)(1) .$$

Hence

$$n(n - 1) \cdots (n - k + 1) = \frac{n!}{(n - k)!} .$$

This notation provides a convenient way to write the derivatives of $f(x) = x^n$. They become

$$f^{(k)}(x) = \frac{n!}{(n - k)!} x^{n-k}, \quad k = 1, \ldots, n; \qquad f^{(k)}(x) = 0, \quad k > n . \qquad (3\text{–}106)$$

3. Using the results of Example 2 we can easily obtain a useful result known as the binomial expansion or the binomial theorem. Consider the function $f(x) = (x + a)^n$. This function is a polynomial of degree n, as could be verified by multiplying out $(x + a)^n$. Thus

$$(x + a)^2 = x^2 + 2xa + a^2; \qquad (x + a)^3 = x^3 + 3x^2a + 3xa^2 + a^3 ,$$

or in general

$$(x + a)^n = b_n x^n + b_{n-1} x^{n-1} + \cdots + b_1 x + b_0 = f(x) . \quad (3\text{--}107)$$

We shall now show that it is easy to obtain an explicit expression for the coefficients b_j. They could, of course, be obtained by repeatedly multiplying $x + a$ by itself, but this is a complicated way to obtain them, since it is possible to give an easily remembered formula.

By the chain rule

$$f^{(k)}(x) = \frac{n!}{(n-k)!} (x + a)^{n-k}, \quad k = 1, \ldots, n . \quad (3\text{--}108)$$

Equation (3–108) also holds if $k = 0$. However, on differentiating the polynomial in (3–107), we see that $f^{(k)}(x)$ is also given by

$$f^{(k)}(x) = \frac{n!}{(n-k)!} b_n x^{n-k} + \frac{(n-1)!}{(n-1-k)!} b_{n-1} x^{n-k-1} + \cdots + k!\, b_k .$$
$$(3\text{--}109)$$

The two expressions (3–108) and (3–109) are equal for all x. At $x = 0$ we see from (3–108) that

$$f'(0) = \frac{n!}{(n-k)!} a^{n-k} ,$$

and from (3–109)

$$f'(0) = k!\, b_k .$$

Thus

$$k!\, b_k = \frac{n!}{(n-k)!} a^{n-k}$$

or

$$b_k = \frac{n!}{k!(n-k)!} a^{n-k}, \quad k = 0, 1, \ldots, n . \quad (3\text{--}110)$$

Here, by use of differentiation, we have obtained an explicit expression for the coefficients b_j in (3–107). We have shown that

$$(x + a)^n = x^n + n x^{n-1} a + \frac{n(n-1)}{2} x^{n-2} a^2$$

$$+ \frac{n(n-1)(n-2)}{3!} x^{n-3} a^3 + \cdots + n x a^{n-1} + a^n. \quad (3\text{--}111)$$

Equation (3–111) is called the binomial expansion or binomial theorem, and is a frequently useful result.

From a given function $f(x)$ we can, by successive differentiation, generate a sequence of functions $f^{(1)}(x)$, $f^{(2)}(x)$, $f^{(3)}(x)$, $\ldots$, which are the derivative functions of $f(x)$. The domains of all of these functions are not necessarily the same, but for many functions, such as polynomials, they are. For a variety of applications the nature of these derivative functions is of considerable interest.

3–16 OTHER USES FOR DERIVATIVES

In Chapter 2 we studied how a function $f(x)$ could be represented graphically. The derivative function $f'(x)$ can often be usefully employed in determining the graphs of relatively complicated functions $f(x)$. Note that if $f'(\alpha) > 0$, then for v small enough

$$\frac{f(\alpha + v) - f(\alpha)}{v} > 0,$$

and when $v > 0$ we conclude that $f(\alpha + v) > f(\alpha)$. Hence wherever $f'(x) > 0$ we see that $f(x)$ will increase as the value of x increases. Similarly, whenever $f'(x) < 0$, $f(x)$ will decrease as the value of x increases. Let us illustrate how this information can be utilized by obtaining the graph of

$$y = x^3 - 2x^2 - 8x.$$

Now

$$\frac{dy}{dx} = 3x^2 - 4x - 8.$$

The graph of $f'(x)$ is thus a parabola which opens upward. It crosses the x-axis at

$$x = \frac{1}{6}[4 + (16 + 96)^{1/2}] = 2.43 \text{ and } x = \frac{1}{6}[4 - (16 + 96)^{1/2}] = -1.096,$$

as we see on applying (2–57). Since the parabola opens upward we see that $f'(x) > 0$ if $x > 2.43$ or $x < -1.096$ and $f'(x) < 0$ if $-1.096 < x < 2.43$. Thus $f(x)$ should increase with increasing x for all $x < -1.096$. Then at $x = -1.096$, $f(x)$ should change from increasing to decreasing, that is, $f(x)$ should have a relative maximum at $x = -1.096$. The function continues to decrease with increasing x until $x = 2.43$; then $f(x)$ begins to increase with x for all $x > 2.43$. Thus $f(x)$ should take on a relative minimum at $x = 2.43$. On computing $f(2.43) = -17$ and $f(-1.096) = 5$, and on noting that $f(0) = 0$, we can quickly obtain the graph of $f(x)$ by selecting several other values of x and evaluating $f(x)$. The graph of $f(x)$ is shown in Figure 2–27.

As another application of derivatives recall that for small v

$$\frac{f(\alpha + v) - f(\alpha)}{v} \doteq f'(\alpha)$$

or

$$f(\alpha + v) \doteq f(\alpha) + f'(\alpha)v , \tag{3-112}$$

where $\doteq$ means approximately equal. Equation (3–112) is often useful for computing approximately $f(\alpha + v)$ or $f(\alpha + v) - f(\alpha)$. For example, suppose that we know α^n and would like to evaluate $(\alpha + v)^n$ where the magnitude of v is very small with respect to α. If $f(x) = x^n$ then $f'(x) = nx^{n-1} = nf(x)/x$. Hence according to (3–112)

$$(\alpha + v)^n \doteq \alpha^n + n\frac{\alpha^n}{\alpha}v .$$

We use α^n/α because it may be easier to divide α^n by α than to compute α^{n-1} directly. Thus

$$(1.002)^{25} \doteq 1 + 25(0.002) = 1.050 ,$$

as we see by taking $\alpha = 1$ and $v = 0.002$. A very useful approximation is then

$$(1 + v)^n \doteq 1 + nv \tag{3-113}$$

for v having a small magnitude.

We have noted that (3–112) should hold to a good approximation if v is small. Now interestingly enough, it can be proved, although we shall not do so here, that if $f(x)$ is continuous at each point in the closed interval $\alpha \leq x \leq \beta$ and if $f(x)$ possesses a derivative at each interior point of this interval, then there exists at least one ξ, $\alpha < \xi < \beta$ such that

$$\frac{f(\beta) - f(\alpha)}{\beta - \alpha} = f'(\xi) , \tag{3-114}$$

or on writing $\beta = \alpha + v$,

$$f(\alpha + v) = f(\alpha) + f'(\xi)v , \tag{3-115}$$

and this equation holds exactly. The difference between (3–115) and (3–112) is that $f'(\xi)$ appears in (3–115) and $f'(\alpha)$ appears in (3–112). What (3–115) says is that (3–112) can be made to hold exactly if we evaluate $f'(x)$ not at

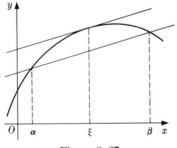

Figure 3–27

α but at some suitable ξ lying between α and $\alpha + v$ (when $v > 0$). Equation (3-115) is called *the theorem of the mean* and is very useful in theoretical developments. It should be noted that (3-115) holds even if $v < 0$ (why?). From a geometrical point of view, it is fairly obvious that the theorem of the mean is true, since all (3-114) says is that, given any secant line to the graph of $f(x)$, then if $f(x)$ is differentiable, there is a value ξ of x lying between α and β where the slope of the curve is equal to the slope of the secant. This is illustrated in Figure 3-27.

We shall encounter more and more uses for the derivative concept as we proceed through the remainder of the text.

REFERENCES

1. Allen, R. G. D., *Mathematical Analysis for Economists*. Macmillan, London 1938.
Discusses some applications of the theory of derivatives in economics.

2. Bell, E. T. *Men of Mathematics*. Simon and Schuster, New York, 1937.
Chapter 6 is devoted to the life of Newton and Chapter 7 to that of Leibniz.

3. Boyer, C. B., *The Concepts of the Calculus—A Critical and Historical Discussion of the Derivative and the Integral*. Hafner, New York, 1949.
An interesting and readable history of the development of the calculus. The book has been reissued (1959) as a Dover paperback under the title *The History of the Calculus and Its Conceptual Development*.

4. Hardy, G. H., *A Course of Pure Mathematics*, 10th ed. Cambridge University Press, Cambridge, 1955.
A book which has been popular for many years. Gives an advanced discussion of limits

5. Kuratowski, K., *Introduction to Calculus*. Addison-Wesley, Reading, Mass. 1962.
A compact but very good text by the well-known Polish topologist.

6. Landau, E., *Differential and Integral Calculus*. Chelsea, New York, 1951.
An example of an everywhere continuous–nowhere differentiable function is to be found on p. 73. The example is not elementary.

7. Morrey, C. B., Jr., *University Calculus with Analytic Geometry*. Addison-Wesley, Reading, Mass., 1962.

8. Smirnov, V. I., *Elementary Calculus*. Addison-Wesley, Reading, Mass., 1964.

9. Thomas, G. B., Jr., *Calculus and Analytic Geometry*, 3rd ed. Addison-Wesley, Reading, Mass., 1960.

10. Thomas, G. B., Jr., *Limits*. Addison-Wesley, Reading, Mass., 1963.

PROBLEMS

Section 3-1

In Problems 1 through 12 determine whether or not

$$\lim_{x \to 3+} f(x), \quad \lim_{x \to 3-} f(x), \quad \lim_{x \to 3} f(x)$$

exist, and what their values are if they do exist. Do this by sketching the graph of $f(x)$. Indicate whether or not any one of the limits has the value $f(3)$ when 3 is in the domain of $f(x)$.

1. $f(x) = x + 2;$

2. $f(x) = \dfrac{1}{x};$

3. $f(x) = (x - 3)^2;$

4. $f(x) = \begin{cases} x + 2, & x \neq 3 \\ 8, & x = 3; \end{cases}$

5. $f(x) = \begin{cases} x + 3, & x > 3 \\ x - 2, & x < 3; \end{cases}$

6. $f(x) = \begin{cases} (x - 3)^2, & x > 3 \\ (x - 3)^3, & x < 3; \end{cases}$

7. $f(x) = \begin{cases} x, & x > 3 \\ 6 - x, & x < 3; \end{cases}$

8. $f(x) = \begin{cases} x + 1, & x > 3 \\ 4, & x = 3 \\ 2x - 1, & x < 3; \end{cases}$

9. $f(x) = \begin{cases} \dfrac{1}{x - 3}, & x > 3 \\ (x - 3)^2, & x < 3; \end{cases}$

10. $f(x) = (x - 3)^{1/2};$

11. $f(x) = \dfrac{1}{x - 3}$

12. $f(x) = \begin{cases} \dfrac{1}{(x - 3^2}, & x > 3 \\ \dfrac{1}{x - 3}, & x < 3. \end{cases}$

Section 3–2

1. Consider the function

$$f(x) = \begin{cases} 3 + x, & x \text{ rational} \\ 3 - x^2, & x \text{ irrational}. \end{cases}$$

Does $\lim_{x \to 0^+} f(x)$ exist? Use an intuitive argument. Do not attempt to prove rigorously whatever statement you make.

2. Prove that $\lim_{x \to a^+} (x + 3) = \alpha + 3$.

3. Prove that $\lim_{x \to a^+} x^2 = \alpha^2$. Hint: $x^2 - \alpha^2 = (x - \alpha)(x + \alpha)$, and if x is close to α, $x + \alpha < 2\alpha + 1$ since $x < \alpha + 1$.

4. Prove that

$$|a + b| \leq |a| + |b|$$

by considering the various possibilities with respect to the signs of a and b. Construct numerical examples to illustrate the case where the equality holds and that where the inequality holds.

5. Prove that $|ab| = |a|\,|b|$.

6. Prove that $|1/a| = 1/|a|$, $a \neq 0$, and $|a/b| = |a|/|b|$, $b \neq 0$.

7. Prove that $\lim_{x \to a^+} 1/x = 1/\alpha$, where $\alpha > 0$.

8. Let $f(x) = x + 1 + 10^{-100}$. Why isn't it true that $\lim_{x \to 0} f(x) = 1$?

9. Let $f(x) = x$, x irrational. Does $\lim_{x \to 0} f(x)$ exist?

10. Show that the definition of $\lim_{x \to a} f(x) = \beta$ is equivalent to stating that $\lim_{x \to a} f(x) = \beta$ means that there exists a function $g(\epsilon)$ whose domain is the set of all positive numbers, such that for all x, $0 < |x - \alpha| < g(\epsilon)$, then $|f(x) - \beta| < \epsilon$. Why is $0 < |x - \alpha| < g(\epsilon)$ used rather than $|x - \alpha| < g(\epsilon)$?

Section 3–3

In Problems 1 through 10 make use of the results developed in this section to determine the limits indicated.

1. $\lim_{x \to 3} \dfrac{x + 2}{x - 1}$;

2. $\lim_{x \to 1} \dfrac{1}{(x + 2)^2}$;

3. $\lim_{x \to 0} \dfrac{(2x + 1)^2}{x - 3}$;

4. $\lim_{x \to 1} \dfrac{3x + 2x - 1}{4x + 6}$;

5. $\lim_{x \to 2} \dfrac{2x + 3}{x^3 - 4x + 2}$;

6. $\lim_{x \to 0} \dfrac{x^4 - 2}{x^3 + x + 1}$;

7. $\lim_{x \to 1} \dfrac{\dfrac{1}{x} + 2x}{\dfrac{3}{x} - x^2}$;

8. $\lim_{x \to 3} \left(x^2 + 2x - \dfrac{1}{x} \right)\left(x^3 + \dfrac{1}{x - 4} \right)$;

9. $\lim_{x \to 0} \dfrac{(x^2 - 2x + 1)(3x + 2)^3}{\left(x - \dfrac{1}{x - 1} \right)(2 + 3x^2)}$;

10. $\lim_{x \to -1} \dfrac{\dfrac{1}{(x - 2)^2}\left(1 + \dfrac{1}{3x - 1} \right)}{\left(x^2 - \dfrac{1}{x} \right)\left(3x^2 + \dfrac{2}{x} \right)}$.

11. Compute

(a) $\lim_{x \to 0} \dfrac{\dfrac{1}{x} + 2x}{\dfrac{3}{x} - x^2}$;

(b) $\lim_{x \to 1} \dfrac{\dfrac{1}{x} - 1}{x - 1}$.

12. Compute

(a) $\lim_{x \to 2} \dfrac{\dfrac{1}{x - 2} + 3}{\dfrac{2}{x - 2} + 5x}$;

(b) $\lim_{x \to 2} \dfrac{\dfrac{1}{(x + 1)^2} - \dfrac{1}{9}}{x - 2}$.

13. Use the definition of a limit to prove (3–24).

14. Use the definition of a limit to prove (3–26). Hint: $|f_1(x) + f_2(x) - \beta_1 - \beta_2| \le |f_1(x) - \beta_1| + |f_2(x) - \beta_2|$, by the result of Problem 4 for Section 3–2.

15. Construct an example different from the one given in the text to show that $\lim_{x \to a} [f_1(x) + f_2(x)]$ may exist even if the corresponding limits of $f_1(x)$ and $f_2(x)$ do not.

16. Construct an example to show that $\lim_{x \to a} f_1(x) f_2(x)$ may exist even if the corresponding limits of $f_1(x)$ and $f_2(x)$ do not.

17. Construct an example different from that given in the text to show that $\lim_{x \to a} f_1(x)/f_2(x)$ may exist even if $\lim_{x \to a} f_2(x) = 0$.

Section 3–4

In Problems 1 through 10 determine any points at which the function is not continuous and discuss the nature of the discontinuity. Sketch the graph of the function for values of x close to each point of discontinuity.

1. $f(x) = \dfrac{1}{x(x-3)}$;

2. $f(x) = \dfrac{3x+2}{x^2-3x+1}$;

3. $f(x) = \dfrac{2x+1}{x^3-x}$;

4. $f(x) = \begin{cases} \dfrac{x^2-4}{x-2}, & x \ne 2 \\ 2, & x = 2 \end{cases}$;

5. $f(x) = \begin{cases} \dfrac{1}{x(x-3)}, & x > 1 \\ 1, & x = 1 \\ 2x, & x < 1 \end{cases}$;

6. $f(x) = |x|$;

7. $f(x) = \dfrac{x}{|x|}$;

8. $f(x) = x + |x|$;

9. $f(x) = \begin{cases} \dfrac{1}{x-3}, & x > 3 \\ 4, & x = 3 \\ (x-3)^2, & x < 3 \end{cases}$;

10. $f(x) = \begin{cases} 4-x, & x \text{ an integer} \\ x, & x \text{ not an integer} \end{cases}$.

11. Show that $\cos(\sin x^2)$ is continuous for all x.

12. Show that $(x^2 + 3x - 1)(x^{25} - 1)$ is continuous for all x.

In Problems 13 through 20 compute the limits indicated, justifying the validity of each step.

13. $\lim\limits_{x \to 1} \left(\dfrac{x^2 + 2x + 1}{x+3} \right)^{1/2}$;

14. $\lim\limits_{x \to 0+} \left(\dfrac{2x+3}{x^2+1} \right)^{1/2}$;

15. $\lim\limits_{x \to 0} \left(\dfrac{2x+3}{x^2-1} \right)^{1/3}$;

16. $\lim\limits_{x \to 1} \left(\dfrac{x^3 + x^2 + 1}{2x + \dfrac{3}{x}} \right)^{1/4}$;

17. $\lim\limits_{x \to 0} \sin \dfrac{x^2+1}{x-1}$;

18. $\lim\limits_{x \to 0} \dfrac{\sin x + [\sin(x+2)]^2}{x-3}$;

19. $\lim\limits_{x \to 1} \sin(\cos(x-1))$;

20. $\lim\limits_{x \to \pi/2} \sin(\cos(\sin x))$

21. Plot the graph of $x \sin 1/x$ and discuss the behavior of this function near $x = 0$.

Section 3–6

1. Let $f(x) = x^2$, and $\alpha = 2$. Consider the set of x-values, $x_1 = 3$, $x_2 = 1$, $x_3 = 2.5$, $x_4 = 1.75$, $x_5 = 2.25$, $x_6 = 1.90$ and $x_7 = 2.05$. Determine the secant L_k passing through the points $(\alpha, f(\alpha))$ and $(x_k, f(x_k))$ for each k. Illustrate these graphically. To what number does the sequence of slopes seem to be converging? Is this $f'(\alpha)$?

In Problems 2 through 10 use the definition of the derivative to find $f'(x)$ for all x where $f'(x)$ exists.

2. $f(x) = 3x;$ **3.** $f(x) = 2x^2;$ **4.** $f(x) = 2x^2 + 3x;$

5. $f(x) = x^3;$ **6.** $f(x) = \dfrac{1}{x};$ **7.** $f(x) = \dfrac{1}{x-3};$

8. $f(x) = x^2 + \dfrac{1}{x};$ **9.** $f(x) = \dfrac{1}{x^2};$ **10.** $f(x) = \dfrac{x}{x+3}.$

11. Show that if $f(x) = \sqrt{x}, f'_+(0)$ does not exist.

12. Let $f(x) = \begin{cases} x^2, & x \geq 0 \\ x, & x < 0. \end{cases}$

Does $f'(0)$ exist? Prove whatever answer you give. Illustrate the situation graphically.

13. Let $f(x) = \begin{cases} x^2, & x > 0 \\ 0, & x \leq 0. \end{cases}$

Does $f'(0)$ exist? Prove whatever answer you give. Illustrate the situation graphically.

14. Let $f(x) = -2 + |x|$. Does $f'(0)$ exist? Prove whatever answer you give. Illustrate the situation graphically.

15. Let $f(x) = 1/x, x \neq 0$. Show that, regardless of how $f(0)$ might be defined, $f(x)$ does not have a derivative at $x = 0$.

16. Let $f(x) = \begin{cases} x, & x \geq 1 \\ 3 + x, & x < 1. \end{cases}$

Does $f'(1)$ exist? Prove whatever answer you give, and illustrate the situation geometrically. Does either one-sided derivative exist?

17. Let $f(x) = \begin{cases} x, & x \neq 1 \\ 3, & x = 1. \end{cases}$

Does $f'(1)$ exist? Prove whatever answer you give, and illustrate the situation geometrically. Does either one-sided derivative exist?

18. Let $f(x) = \begin{cases} x, & x > 1 \\ 2, & x = 1 \\ 4 + x, & x < 1. \end{cases}$

Does $f'(1)$ exist? Prove whatever answer you give, and illustrate the situation geometrically. Does either one-sided derivative exist?

19. Prove that if $f(x) = 0$ for all x, then $f'(x)$ exists for all x and $f'(x) = 0$ for all x.

Section 3–7

1. Determine the equations of the lines tangent to $y = x^2$ at $x = -1, x = 0,$ $x = 0.5$ and $x = 3$. Illustrate each of these graphically.

2. Determine the equation of the line tangent to $y = x^5$ at $x = 0$. Show that this line crosses the graph of $y = x^5$ at the point of tangency.

3. Determine the equations of the lines tangent to $y = 1/x$ at $x = 4$ and at $x = -2$. Illustrate each of these graphically.

4. What information does $f'(\alpha)$ give us about the graph of $f(x)$ at α?

5. Why might it be reasonable intuitively to refer to $f'(\alpha)$ as the "slope" of the graph of $f(x)$ at α?

6. Consider the function

$$y = \begin{cases} 3 - (2 - x)^{1/3}, & x \leq 2 \\ 3 - (x - 2)^{1/3}, & x > 2 \,. \end{cases}$$

Sketch the graph of this function and show geometrically that it has a vertical tangent at $x = 2$.

7. Consider the line $y = ax + b$. Show that, for each x, the tangent to this line is the line itself.

Section 3–8

1. The distance in miles traveled by a car as a function of time is $25t^2$, where t is in hours. What is the speed of the car in miles per hour at $t = 0.1, 0.5$ and 1?

2. What is the acceleration of the car referred to in Problem 1 at each of the indicated times?

3. In a certain country, a person's income tax T, in dollars, is related to his taxable income I, in dollars, by $T = 0.2\,I$. What is the rate of change of T with respect to I? What is the intuitive interpretation of this rate of change?

4. For a function $y = f(x)$, which does not have a derivative at α, can we talk about the rate of change of y with respect to x at $x = \alpha$? Consider as an example the case where $f(x) = |x|$ and $\alpha = 0$.

Section 3–9

In Problems 1 through 20 evaluate the derivative of the given function for every x where it exists. Give the justification for each step made in determining the derivative function.

1. x^4;

2. $3x^5$;

3. $-3x^7$;

4. $2x^2 - 3x + 1$;

5. $2x^2 - 6x^2 + x + 1$;

6. $x - 3x^2 + x$;

7. $x^6 - 6x^5 + 2x - 1$;

8. $\dfrac{1}{x^3}$;

9. $3x^2 + \dfrac{2}{x}$;

10. $\dfrac{1}{x^2 - 3}$;

11. $\dfrac{2x + 1}{4x - 2}$;

12. $\dfrac{3x^2 - x + 2}{2x + 1}$;

13. $\dfrac{2x^2 + 1}{3x^2 - 2}$;

14. $\dfrac{3x^2 - 2x + 1}{4x^2 - 2x^2}$;

15. $\dfrac{3x^2 + \dfrac{1}{x}}{4x^3 - 2}$;

16. $(3x^2 + 2x + 1)(2x + 3)$; **17.** $\dfrac{x + \dfrac{3}{x^3}}{2 - \dfrac{3}{1 + x^2}}$; **18.** $\dfrac{3x^3 + 2x - \dfrac{1}{x^4}}{2x + \dfrac{3}{x^2}}$;

19. $\dfrac{1}{(x - 2)(x - 3)}$; **20.** $\dfrac{x + 2}{(x^2 - 3)(x^2 + 2)}$.

21. If $f'(x)$ exists, prove by induction that $g'(x)$ exists when $g(x) = [f(x)]^n$, n a natural number, and $g'(x) = n[f(x)]^{n-1} f'(x)$.

In Problems 22 through 24 use the results of Problem 21 to determine the derivative function for the given function.

22. $(2x + 3)^{17}$; **23.** $\left(\dfrac{2x - 1}{x^2 + 2}\right)^3$; **24.** $\left(\dfrac{2x + \dfrac{1}{x}}{x - x^3}\right)^4$.

25. How might the results of Problem 21 be used to evaluate the derivative of $x^{1/2}$?

Section 3–10

In Problems 1 through 15 differentiate the given function and provide the justification for each step.

1. $x^{3.265}$; **2.** $x^{-4.032}$;

3. $\left(x + \dfrac{1}{x}\right)^{16.41}$; **4.** $\left(\dfrac{x + 3}{2x - 1}\right)^2$;

5. $[(x + 1)^{3.16}(2x - 3)^{-4.27}]^{11\ 92}$; **6.** $[(x^2 + 1)(3x^2 - 2)]^{3.667}$;

7. $(2x + 1)^{4/11}$; **8.** $x^{3/16} - \dfrac{1}{x}$;

9. $\left(x + \dfrac{3}{x}\right)^{1/2}$; **10.** $\left(\dfrac{2x + 1}{x - 3}\right)^{1/2}$;

11. $x^{1/2} + x^{-1/2}$; **12.** $[(x - 3)(x - 2)(x - 1)]^{1/2}$;

13. $\dfrac{(x - 3)^{1/3}}{(2x + 1)^{1/2}}$; **14.** $\dfrac{x}{1 + \dfrac{x}{1 + \dfrac{x}{1 + x^2}}}$;

15. $\left[\dfrac{(x - 3)^{1/5}\left(\dfrac{1}{x} + 2\right)^{1/3}}{(x - 3)^2}\right]^{1/2}$.

16. Prove that (3–77) holds when $x < 0$ if n is odd.

17. Sketch the graph of $y = x^{1/3}$. Show that at $x = 0$ this function has a vertical tangent and hence infinite slope.

18. Prove that if $f(x) = h[g(x)]$ and $f'(x)$ and $h'(u)$, $u = g(x)$, exist and $h'(u) \neq 0$, then $g'(x)$ exists if $g(x)$ is continuous at x. Hint: From (3–75),

$$\frac{g(x+v) - g(x)}{v} = \frac{\dfrac{f(x+v) - f(x)}{v}}{h'(u) + \gamma(w)}.$$

Use this result to justify the derivation of (3–77).

Section 3–11

1. Use the results of this section to determine the derivative function for each of the functions which make up the inverse representation of $y = x^3$.

2. Determine the inverse representation of

$$y = \frac{x+2}{x-3}.$$

Compute the derivative function for each of the functions which make up the inverse representation using the results of this section and by differentiating directly the functions of the inverse representation.

Section 3–12*

In Problems 1 through 12 determine the derivative of the given function and indicate the domain for the derivative function.

1. $\sin 2x$;

2. $\cos(3x + 1)$;

3. $\tan x$;

4. $\cos 1/x$;

5. $(\cos x)^2$ (usually written $\cos^2 x$);

6. $1/\sin x$;

7. $\sin\left(\dfrac{x+2}{x+3}\right)$;

8. $\cos(\cos x)$;

9. $\cos(\sin x^2)$;

10. $1/(\cos x)(\sin x)$;

11. $\sin(\cos(\sin x))$;

12. $\sin(1/\sin x)$.

Sections 3–13 and 3–14

1. Determine the point or points where $f(x) = 10x + (2/x)$ takes on its absolute minimum over the interval $1 \leq x \leq 10$. Illustrate the situation geometrically.

2. Determine the point or points where $f(x) = -x^2 + 2x + 1$ takes on its absolute maximum for all real x and illustrate the situation geometrically.

3. Find the point or points where $f(x) = x^3 - 3x^2 + 2x + 1$ takes on its absolute maximum over the interval $0 \leq x \leq 10$.

4. Find the point or points where $f(x) = 3x^3 - 2x + 6$ takes on its absolute maximum over the interval $-10 \leq x \leq 10$.

5. Find the point or points where $f(x) = x^3 - 4x$ takes on its absolute minimum over the interval $-2 \leq x \leq 2$.

6. Consider the function

$$f(x) = \begin{cases} x, & x \leq 1 \\ 2 - x, & x > 1 . \end{cases}$$

Determine the point or points where $f(x)$ takes on its absolute maximum for x in the interval $-10 \leq x \leq 10$. Show that it does not occur where $f'(x) = 0$ and explain. Illustrate the situation geometrically.

7. Re-solve the oil-can example under the assumption that $\frac{1}{4}$ inch of material is needed for the seam on the side of the can. Also, because of material needed to crimp the top and bottom to the side, the radius of the top and bottom must be $\frac{1}{4}$ inch greater than the final radius of the can, and the side must be $\frac{1}{2}$ inch greater in altitude than the height of the finished can.

8. Let R be the set of all pairs of positive real numbers whose sum is 50. Find that pair x_1 and x_2 in R such that $x_1 x_2$ is as large as possible.

9. Let R be the set of all right triangles whose perimeter is 100. Find the dimensions of that triangle in R which has the greatest area.

10. Find that point (x, y), $x > 0$, lying on the graph of $y = 1/x$ which is closest to the origin. Illustrate geometrically.

11. Find that point (x, y), $x > 0$, lying on the graph of $y = x^2$ which is closest to the point $(1, 0)$. Illustrate geometrically.

12. Find the point or points on the circle $x^2 + y^2 = 1$ which are closest to the point $(3, 4)$. Also determine the point or points on the circle which are farthest away from $(3, 4)$. Illustrate geometrically.

13. A piece of wire 30 inches in length is cut into two pieces. One of these is formed into a square and the other into a circle. How should the wire be cut if the sum of the areas of the square and the circle are maximized?

14. For the mining example plot a graph of the function representing the total profit as a function of the depth at which digging is terminated.

15. For the mining example determining the cost of mining a cubic yard as a function of depth.

16. What would be the solution to the mining example if the price per pound of copper is $0.40?

17. Re-solve Problem 16 under the assumption that the price per pound of copper is $0.30.

18. A large petroleum company is about to start marketing on the West Coast, a region which it has not served previously. A decision is about to be made on the number of stations that should be opened in heavily populated city areas. To make the problem simple, suppose that all stations are to be of the same size. Assume that the initial cost of a station is $100,000 and that each station costs $2000 per month to operate; this includes labor, power, taxes, and so forth. The business done per station will decrease as the number of stations in a given area is increased, but the total number of customers served will increase as the number of stations is increased. Let M be the total number of persons living in populated areas on the West Coast, and assume that, if x stations are built in city areas, the total number of customers y who will be attracted to the company's stations will be

$$y = \frac{M}{2} \left(\frac{x}{1 + x} \right).$$

Each customer will purchase $100 worth of products per year and the cost of these products will be $50. How many stations should the company plan to build in city areas if $M = 2 \times 10^7$ and it desires to maximize total profits over a five-year period? Hint: Costs here include the costs of building the stations, plus the costs of operating the stations for five years, plus the costs of the products sold.

19. For Problem 18 plot the total profit as a function of x. Also determine how the number of customers served per station varies with x.

20. A firm is about to invest 20×10^6 in two new products. The revenue received from the first product will be $10 \times 10^6 \, y^{1/2}$ if y dollars are invested in this product, and will be $5 \times 10^6 \, z$ for the second product if z dollars are invested in this product. How much should be invested in each product so as to maximize the total revenues received for the given total investment?

21. A large company is planning to build a new office building in New York. Assume that a total of 500,000 square feet of space is needed. The average cost per square foot to build the building increases as the height of the building increases. However, the lower the building the more land that will be required. Assume that land costs $15 per square foot. Also assume that the average building cost per square foot is $12x^{1/40}$, where x is the number of stories in the building. How many stories should the building contain if the number of square feet of land to be purchased must be 20 percent greater than the number of square feet on any floor? Assume that each floor has the same number of square feet. Assume also that the decision is to made on the basis of minimizing the combined land cost and building cost.

Section 3–15

In Problems 1 through 15 find the second derivative function for the given function. Determine the domain of the second derivative function.

1. $3x^3 + 2x - 1$;

2. $\dfrac{x - 1}{x + 1}$;

3. $\dfrac{x^2 - 2}{x + 3}$;

4. $(x^2 - 2)(x^3 + 3x - 1)$;

5. $\sin x$;

6. $\tan x$;

7. $(\sin x)(\cos x)$;

8. $\sin(\cos x)$;

9. $(\sin x)/x$;

10. $x \sin x$;

11. $x^{4.271}$;

12. $x^{1.304}$;

13. $(x + 2)(x \sin x)$;

14. $\dfrac{1}{x^3 - 1}$;

15. $x + \dfrac{1}{x}$.

16. Consider the function

$$f(x) = \begin{cases} \dfrac{x^2}{2}, & x \le 0 \\ \dfrac{x^2}{4}, & x > 0. \end{cases}$$

Determine the functions $f'(x)$ and $f''(x)$ and determine the domain for each. Sketch the graphs of $f(x)$, $f'(x)$, and $f''(x)$.

17. Prove the binomial theorem by induction.

18. Determine all derivatives of $y = x^5$.

19. Determine all derivatives through order 4 of
(a) $\sin x$;   (b) $x^4 - 3x^2 + 1$.

20. We have noted that $d^k x^n/dx^k = 0$ for n a natural number and $k > n$. What can be said about $d^k x^\alpha/dx^k$, where α is a rational number which is not a natural number? Are any of the derivative functions of x^α zero for all $x \neq 0$?

In Problems 21 through 29 use the binomial theorem to "expand" the given expressions.

21. $(x + 1)^4$;   **22.** $(x - 1)^4$;   **23.** $(2x + 3)^5$;   **24.** $(x + a)^5$;

25. $(x - a)^5$;   **26.** $(1.001)^3$;   **27.** $(x + y)^4$;   **28.** $(xy - 1)^3$;

29. $(2x - 3y)^4$.

Section 3–16

In Problems 1 through 6 sketch the graph of the given function.

1. $y = x^3 - 2x^2 + 1$;   **2.** $y = 3x^3 + x^2 - 5$;

3. $y = x^3 - 1$;   **4.** $y = x^3 - 2x^2 + 6$;

5. $y = x^3 - 2x^2 + x + 1$;   **6.** $y = x^5 - 7x^2 + 2x + 6$.

In Problems 7 through 11 compute $f(\alpha + v) - f(\alpha)$ exactly and also approximately using (3–112).

7. $f(x) = x^3 - 1$, $\alpha = 0$, $v = 0.1$;   **8.** $f(x) = \dfrac{x - 1}{x + 2}$, $\alpha = -1$, $v = -0.2$;

9. $f(x) = \dfrac{\sin x}{x}$, $\alpha = 1, v = 0.12$;   **10.** $f(x) = \tan x$, $\alpha = 0, v = 0.15$;

11. $f(x) = \dfrac{1}{(x - 2)^2}$; $\alpha = -1.9$, $v = -0.05$

12. Given that the area of a circle of radius 1 is π, use (3–112) to estimate the area of a circle having radius 1.05. Also compute the area exactly and determine the error involved in using (3–112).

13. Consider $f(x) = x^2$. Determine the equation of the secant passing through the points $(0, 0)$ and $(1, 1)$. Find the point ξ, $0 < \xi < 1$, such that $f'(\xi)$ is the slope of the secant. Illustrate geometrically.

14. Consider $f(x) = x^{1/2}$. Determine the equation of the secant passing through the points $(0, 0)$ and $(4, 2)$. Find the point ξ, $0 < \xi < 4$ such that $f'(\xi)$ is the slope of the secant. Illustrate geometrically.

15. Construct an example where the mean value theorem does not hold.

CHAPTER 4

Sequences and Integration

4-1 SEQUENCES

We shall begin this chapter by introducing a concept of the limit of a function which is somewhat different than that studied in the previous chapter. In Chapter 3 we studied functions $f(x)$ of a type where the domain of the function included every value of x or every value of x in some interval. Such functions are called *functions of a continuous variable*. Here we shall study functions of one variable whose domain is the set of natural numbers, that is, functions which are defined only when the argument is a natural number. A function $f(x)$ whose domain is the set of all natural numbers is called an *infinite sequence* or simply a sequence.

INFINITE SEQUENCE. *An infinite sequence is a function whose domain is the set of all natural numbers and whose range is a subset of the real numbers.*

We shall normally refer to an infinite sequence as simply a sequence. In dealing with sequences it is convenient to introduce some notation which differs from usual functional notation. Instead of using $f(n)$, we shall denote the image of the natural number n by a_n (or b_n, c_n, etc.). We can represent a sequence graphically by plotting the points (n, a_n) as shown in Figure 4–1. However, there is another representation which is sometimes convenient. We merely plot the numbers a_n on the x-axis, indicating, as shown in Figure 4–2, the particular a_n to which a given point corresponds. The infinite sequence is characterized by the set $A = \{a_n | n = 1, 2, \ldots\}$, and often this sequence is represented symbolically as $\{a_n\}$. This notation is a little confusing; it does not mean a set whose single element is a_n, but rather an abbreviated way of writing A. We shall follow this convention and denote a sequence by $\{a_n\}$. A particular element a_n of $\{a_n\}$ is called the *nth term* of the sequence. We could use a_n to represent the entire sequence as well as the

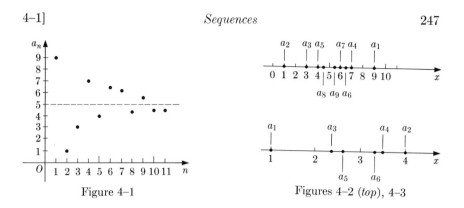

Figure 4–1   Figures 4–2 (*top*), 4–3

*n*th term, just as we give a double interpretation to $f(x)$. This would be confusing here, however, and this is why $\{a_n\}$ will be used to represent the sequence.

Our interest in sequences will lie in the behavior of the terms as n becomes larger and larger. In particular, we shall study sequences whose behavior is something like the following. Suppose that we consider the sequence $\{a_n\}$ with

$$a_n = 3 + (-1)^n \frac{2}{n}, \quad n = 1, 2, 3, \ldots, \tag{4–1}$$

so that $a_1 = 1$, $a_2 = 4$, $a_3 = 2\frac{1}{3}$, $a_4 = 3\frac{1}{2}$ and so forth. If we plot the terms of this sequence on a diagram such as that shown in Figure 4–2, we obtain Figure 4–3. Note that for n odd $a_n < 3$ and for n even $a_n > 3$. However, as n gets larger and larger a_n gets closer and closer to 3. Intuitively, we might say that a_n *approaches* 3 as n gets larger and larger. Let us examine in a little more detail what we mean when we say that a_n approaches 3. We have noted above that, no matter how large n is, a_n is never equal to 3. As n increases, however, the distance between 3 and a_n gets smaller and smaller. Indeed, given any number $\epsilon > 0$, no matter how small, all but a finite number of terms of the sequence lie at a distance no greater than ϵ from 3. Stated yet another way, the interval $3 - \epsilon \leq x \leq 3 + \epsilon$ for any $\epsilon > 0$ contains all of the terms of the sequence except for a finite number. We shall introduce a special terminology to characterize this sort of behavior, and will say that 3 is *the limit* of the sequence $\{a_n\}$ defined by (4–1). To indicate that a number α is the limit of a sequence $\{a_n\}$ we shall write

$$\lim_{n \to \infty} a_n = \alpha, \tag{4–2}$$

which is read the limit of the sequence $\{a_n\}$ is α. The symbolism $n \to \infty$ is used to remind us that a_n approaches α as n becomes very large. The $n \to \infty$ is superfluous and could be omitted.

Intuitively, (4–2) means that the a_n cluster more and more closely about α as n increases and that $|a_n - \alpha|$ can be made arbitrarily small as n increases. In other words, all terms with very large n will be very close to α. A more precise way of expressing this intuitive notion is to say that, given any $\epsilon > 0$, it is possible to find a value of n, call it n_0, such that every term with $n > n_0$ lies at a distance less than ϵ from α. The definition (4–2) does not imply that each term is necessarily closer to α than the previous one, that is, that

$$|a_{n+1} - \alpha| < |a_n - \alpha|, \quad \text{all } n .$$

For example, if

$$a_n = \begin{cases} 1 + \dfrac{5}{n}, & n \text{ odd} \\[2ex] 1 - \dfrac{1}{n}, & n \text{ even}, \end{cases} \tag{4–3}$$

which is illustrated in Figure 4–4, a_{2k} is always closer to 1 than a_{2k+1}, and

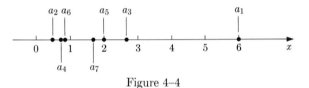

Figure 4–4

indeed, a_2 is closer to 1 than a_9. Nonetheless, we feel intuitively that we should say that $\{a_n\}$ has the limit 1 here, since as n increases, the terms cluster more and more closely about 1, and any interval $1 - \epsilon < x < 1 + \epsilon$ contains all but a finite number of terms of the sequence for any $\epsilon > 0$.

Just as with limits of functions of a continuous variable, we need a precise definition of (4–2) in order to develop any rigorous mathematical theory. The key to the rigorous definition is the observation that, if (4–2) holds, then for any $\epsilon > 0$, the interval $\alpha - \epsilon < x < \alpha + \epsilon$ must contain all but a finite number of terms in the sequence. In other words, given any $\epsilon > 0$, we must be able to show that there exists an n_0 for this ϵ such that for *all* $n > n_0$, $|a_n - \alpha| < \epsilon$. Thus if (4–2) holds, there exists a function $g(\epsilon)$, whose domain contains all positive numbers, such that for all $n > g(\epsilon)$, then $|a_n - \alpha| < \epsilon$, that is, the distance from a_n to α is less than ϵ. The reader should note its similarity to (and differences from) the corresponding definition for the limit of a function of a continuous variable. Thus we can give the following precise definition for the limit of a sequence.

LIMIT OF A SEQUENCE. *The number α is said to be the limit of the sequence $\{a_n\}$ if there exists a function $g(\epsilon)$, whose domain is the set of all positive numbers, with the characteristic that if $n > g(\epsilon)$ then $|a_n - \alpha| < \epsilon$.*

To show that (4–2) holds, we must show the existence of a function $g(\epsilon)$

with the properties stated in the above definition. We shall not have to use this general definition very frequently, since we shall not prove rigorously all the results about sequences but will instead rely mainly on intuitive arguments.

4–2 DIVERGENT SEQUENCES AND POINTS OF ACCUMULATION

A sequence which has a limit is said to be *convergent*. It is by no means true that all sequences are convergent. Just as a function of a continuous variable may not have a limit as x approaches α, a sequence may also have no limit. To understand more clearly what is implied by a sequence having a limit or being convergent, it is instructive to study some examples of sequences which do not have limits. Sequences which are not convergent are said to be *divergent* or to diverge. Consider, for example, the sequence $\{a_n\}$ defined by

$$a_n = \begin{cases} 1 + \dfrac{1}{n}, & n \text{ even} \\[2ex] 3 - \dfrac{1}{n}, & n \text{ odd}. \end{cases} \tag{4–4}$$

The behavior of this sequence is illustrated geometrically in Figures 4–5

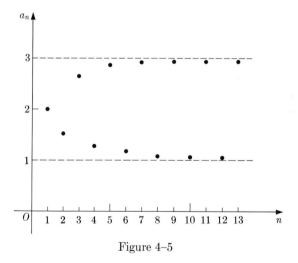

Figure 4–5

and 4–6. The first few terms are $a_1 = 2$, $a_2 = 1\frac{1}{2}$, $a_3 = 2\frac{2}{3}$, $a_4 = 1\frac{1}{4}$, $a_5 = 2\frac{4}{5}$ and $a_6 = 1\frac{1}{6}$. Note that as n increases, the terms with n even cluster about 1 and the terms with n odd cluster about 3. Here we have an example of a divergent sequence. As n gets larger and larger a_n does not approach any number in the sense described in the previous section. Instead the a_n with a_n even get closer and closer to 1, but those for a_n odd get closer and closer to 3. However, neither 1 nor 3 can be considered as the limit of $\{a_n\}$, because it is not true that all but a finite number of terms of the

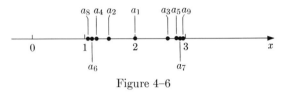

Figure 4–6

sequence lie in the interval $1 - \epsilon < x < 1 + \epsilon$ or $3 - \epsilon < x < 3 + \epsilon$ for any positive number ϵ, no matter how small ϵ may be.

The points 1 and 3 on the line in Figure 4–6 are special points, however, since an infinite number of terms of the sequence are at a distance of less than ϵ from 1 and an infinite number are at a distance of less than ϵ from 3 no matter how small $\epsilon > 0$ may be. Note that this implies that there are an infinite number of terms lying in the interval $0.999 < x < 1.001$ and an infinite number of terms lying in the interval $2.999 < x < 3.001$. The fact that a given interval contains an infinite number of terms of the sequence does not imply that there are necessarily only a finite number of terms outside of the interval. The reader should note this carefully, since it is not always easy to grasp initially. The points 1 and 3 are called *points of accumulation* or cluster points of the sequence $\{a_n\}$. Let us formalize the definition of this concept.

POINT OF ACCUMULATION. *The number α is called a point of accumulation of the sequence $\{a_n\}$ if given any $\epsilon > 0$ there are an infinite number of terms of the sequence whose distance from α is less than ϵ.*

Note that if $\{a_n\}$ has a limit α, then according to the above definition, α will be a point of accumulation of the sequence. A sequence will have a limit only if it has no more than one point of accumulation. As we shall see later, however, it may not have a limit even though it has only one point of accumulation.

In general, a sequence can have many different points of accumulation. Sometimes points of accumulation are called limit points, but this terminology is a little confusing since a sequence may have limit points but no limit. We have seen that a sequence may diverge because it has more than one point of accumulation. This, however, is not the only reason that a sequence may not have a limit. Consider the sequence $\{a_n\}$ with $a_n = n$. Here $a_1 = 1$, $a_2 = 2$, $a_{100} = 100$ and $a_{1000} = 1000$. In this case the terms get larger and larger as n increases and the a_n clearly do not get closer and closer to any number. Thus this sequence does not have a limit and it also diverges. Similar but slightly different behavior is illustrated by the sequence $\{a_n\}$ with $a_n = (-1)^n n$ so that $a_1 = -1$, $a_2 = 2$, $a_3 = -3$, $a_4 = 4, \ldots$. Now $|a_n|$ increases as n increases, but a_n is negative for n odd and positive for n even. This is also clearly a divergent sequence.

We can now easily construct an example of a sequence which has only one point of accumulation but which does not converge. Consider the sequence $\{a_n\}$ with

$$a_n = \begin{cases} \dfrac{n}{10}, & n \text{ odd} \\[2ex] (-1)^{n/2}\dfrac{1}{n}, & n \text{ even.} \end{cases} \qquad (4\text{–}5)$$

Then $a_1 = 0.1$, $a_2 = -0.5$, $a_3 = 0.3$, $a_4 = 0.25$, $a_5 = 0.5$, $a_6 = -0.167$, $a_7 = 0.7$, $a_8 = 0.125$, $a_9 = 0.9$, $a_{10} = -0.1$, $a_{11} = 1.1$, $a_{12} = 0.083, \ldots$. These terms are plotted in Figure 4–7. In this case 0 is a point of accumulation and is the only point of accumulation. However, it is not true that $\{a_n\}$ has a limit 0, because for n odd a_n increases with n and gets farther and farther away from 0.

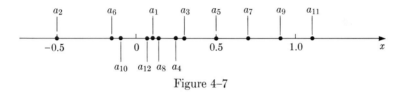

Figure 4–7

In this section we have shown through examples the sort of behavior that will be exhibited by divergent sequences. If $\{a_n\}$ diverges then either $\{a_n\}$ has two or more points of accumulation or some $|a_n|$ become arbitrarily large as n increases or both of these phenomena occur.

4–3 DETERMINATION OF LIMITS

We shall be mainly interested in sequences which converge, and our interest will center about the problem of determining the limit of any such sequence. The definition of the limit of a sequence is not very useful for this purpose, since to use this definition α must be known in advance. What we need are some rules like those introduced for finding the limit of a function of a continuous variable. In fact, the precise analogs of these rules apply to sequences. The four rules for sequences are as follows. First, *if $\{a_n\}$ converges to α, and if $\{b_n\}$ is a sequence with $b_n = \lambda a_n$ for all n, then $\{b_n\}$ converges also and its limit is $\lambda\alpha$.* This rule can be expressed by writing

$$\lim_{n \to \infty} \lambda a_n = \lambda \lim_{n \to \infty} a_n = \lambda\alpha . \qquad (4\text{–}6)$$

Second, *if $\{a_n\}$ converges to α and $\{b_n\}$ converges to β, then if $\{c_n\}$ is a sequence with $c_n = a_n + b_n$, $\{c_n\}$ converges also and its limit is $\alpha + \beta$.* This rule can be expressed by writing

$$\lim_{n \to \infty} (a_n + b_n) = \lim_{n \to \infty} a_n + \lim_{n \to \infty} b_n = \alpha + \beta . \qquad (4\text{–}7)$$

Third, *if $\{a_n\}$ converges to α and $\{b_n\}$ converges to β, then if $\{c_n\}$ is a sequence* with $c_n = a_n b_n$, $\{c_n\}$ *converges also and its limit is* $\alpha\beta$. This rule can be expressed by writing

$$\lim_{n\to\infty} a_n b_n = \left(\lim_{n\to\infty} a_n\right)\left(\lim_{n\to\infty} b_n\right) = \alpha\beta \,. \tag{4-8}$$

Finally, *if* $\{a_n\}$ *converges to* α *and* $\{b_n\}$ *converges to* β, $\beta \neq 0$, *then if* $\{c_n\}$ *is a sequence with* $c_n = a_n/b_n$, *when* $b_n \neq 0$, *and* c_n *defined arbitrarily when* $b_n = 0$, *then* $\{c_n\}$ *converges and its limit is* α/β. This can be expressed by writing

$$\lim_{n\to\infty} \frac{a_n}{b_n} = \frac{\displaystyle\lim_{n\to\infty} a_n}{\displaystyle\lim_{n\to\infty} b_n} = \frac{\alpha}{\beta} \,. \tag{4-9}$$

One minor point concerning this final rule should be noted. If $\{b_n\}$ converges to β and $\beta \neq 0$, then for all n sufficiently large $b_n \neq 0$, because all b_n will be at a distance of no more than ϵ from β for any $\epsilon > 0$. If we take $\epsilon = |\beta|$ we see that all b_n will be different from 0 when n is large enough. A finite number of b_n, however, may be 0, and for these we cannot write $c_n = a_n/b_n$. Here we merely define c_n to be anything we like, say $c_n = 1$. This has absolutely no influence on the limit of $\{c_n\}$, of course, since the limit depends only on the behavior of c_n for arbitrarily large n.

The above rules say: (1) If each term of a sequence is multiplied by a constant λ the limit is multiplied by λ; (2) The limit of a sum is the sum of the limits; (3) The limit of a product is the product of the limits; (4) The limit of a quotient is the quotient of the limits when the limit in the denominator is not 0. It is easy to see intuitively that these rules are correct, since, for example, if all terms a_n with n large are very close to α and all terms b_n with n large are very close to β, then all terms $c_n = a_n + b_n$ will be close to $\alpha + \beta$, and if the a_n get closer and closer to α while the b_n get closer and closer to β, then the c_n will get closer and closer to $\alpha + \beta$. Hence, $\{c_n\}$ should converge when $\{a_n\}$ and $\{b_n\}$ do and its limit should be $\alpha + \beta$. These four rules could be proved rigorously from the precise definition of the limit of a sequence, but we shall not take the time to do so here.

The four rules given above make it easy to determine the limits of most of the sequences which will be of interest to us. These rules are applied in precisely the same way as in evaluating limits of functions of a continuous variable. To apply the above rules there are two very simple limits we shall have to determine. If $\{a_n\}$ is a sequence with $a_n = \lambda$, a constant, so that every term in the sequence has the value λ, then $\{a_n\}$ converges and its limit is λ. Thus

$$\lim_{n\to\infty} \lambda = \lambda \,. \tag{4-10}$$

This is easy to prove from the definition of a limit since $|a_n - \lambda| = 0$ for all λ. Thus $|a_n - \lambda| < \epsilon$, $\epsilon > 0$ for every $n \geq 1$. Consequently, for $g(\epsilon)$ we can simply use $g(\epsilon) = 1$, and this function serves to prove that (4–10) holds. Consider next the sequence $\{a_n\}$ with $a_n = 1/n$. Then $\{a_n\}$ converges and its limit is 0, that is,

$$\lim_{n \to \infty} \frac{1}{n} = 0 . \tag{4–11}$$

This is also easy to prove, since

$$|a_n - 0| = \left| \frac{1}{n} - 0 \right| = \left| \frac{1}{n} \right| = \frac{1}{n} ,$$

and $1/n < \epsilon$ when $n > 1/\epsilon$. Therefore, if we take $g(\epsilon) = 1/\epsilon$, $|a_n - 0| < \epsilon$ for all $n > g(\epsilon)$ and this function serves to prove that (4–11) is true.

Given (4–10) and (4–11) we can now use the four rules presented above to evaluate the limits of more complicated sequences. Thus by (4–6), $\lim_{n \to \infty} \lambda/n = 0$ for any λ, and by (4–8)

$$\lim_{n \to \infty} \frac{1}{n^2} = \left(\lim_{n \to \infty} \frac{1}{n} \right) \left(\lim_{n \to \infty} \frac{1}{n} \right) = 0 , \tag{4–12}$$

or more generally for any natural number m,

$$\lim_{n \to \infty} \frac{1}{n^m} = 0 . \tag{4–13}$$

If $\{a_n\}$ is a sequence with $a_n = 3 + (2/n)$, then by (4–7) and (4–6)

$$\lim_{n \to \infty} \left(3 + \frac{2}{n} \right) = \lim_{n \to \infty} 3 + 2 \lim_{n \to \infty} \frac{1}{n} = 3 + 2(0) = 3 .$$

Consider next the sequence $\{a_n\}$ with

$$a_n = \frac{3n - 1}{5n + 2} .$$

To determine whether this sequence has a limit and, if so, what its value is, we attempt to use (4–10), (4–11) and the four rules given above. To convert a_n into a form which involves some sequences whose limits we know it is convenient to first divide by n, writing

$$a_n = \frac{3 - \dfrac{1}{n}}{5 + \dfrac{2}{n}} .$$

Now if we write $b_n = 3 - (1/n)$ and $c_n = 5 + (2/n)$, then $a_n = b_n/c_n$. However, we at once see from (4–7) and (4–6) that $\{b_n\}$ converges to 3 and $\{c_n\}$ converges to 5. Thus by (4–9), $\{a_n\}$ converges and its limit is $\frac{3}{5}$. It might be instructive for the reader to compute several terms of $\{a_n\}$ and plot these.

As an additional example, consider the sequence $\{a_n\}$ with

$$a_n = \frac{4n^2 + 2n - \dfrac{1}{n}}{3n^2 - 6n + 2} .$$

To convert this to a form involving sequences whose limits we know, we first divide the numerator and denominator by n^2 to yield

$$a_n = \frac{4 + \dfrac{2}{n} - \dfrac{1}{n^3}}{3 - \dfrac{6}{n} + \dfrac{2}{n^2}}.$$

If we now write

$$b_n = 4 + \frac{2}{n} - \frac{1}{n^3} \; ; \qquad c_n = 3 - \frac{6}{n} + \frac{2}{n^2},$$

then $a_n = b_n/c_n$. By (4–6), (4–7) and (4–13) we immediately see that $\{b_n\}$ converges to 4 and $\{c_n\}$ converges to 3. Thus, by (4–9), $\{a_n\}$ converges and has the limit $4\!\!\!/_3$.

There is one more interesting sequence which we shall study now. The limit, however, will not be obtainable using the above rules. Consider the sequence $\{a_n\}$ with $a_n = r^n$, where $-1 < r < 1$. We shall prove that $\{a_n\}$ converges to 0, that is,

$$\lim_{n \to \infty} r^n = 0, \quad |r| < 1 . \tag{4–14}$$

To prove this, consider $|r^n - 0| = |r^n|$. However, $|r^n| = |r|^n$ (why?). Now since $|r| < 1$, we see on multiplying this inequality by $|r|$ that $|r|^2 < |r| < 1$ or, in general, $|r|^n < 1$. Thus, if $|r| \neq 0$, we can write $|r|^n = 1/u^n$, where $u = 1/|r|$ and $u > 1$. Hence we shall have $|r|^n < \epsilon$ if $1/u^n < \epsilon$ or $u^n > 1/\epsilon$. Next write $u = 1 + \beta$, where $\beta > 0$. Then by the binomial theorem (3–111) $u^n = (1 + \beta)^n > 1 + n\beta$, since all remaining terms in binomial expansion are positive. Thus if $1 + n\beta > 1/\epsilon$ or

$$n > \frac{1}{\beta} \left(\frac{1}{\epsilon} - 1 \right) = g(\epsilon) , \tag{4–15}$$

then $u^n > 1/\epsilon$ and $|r^n - 0| < \epsilon$. Therefore, if we take $g(\epsilon)$ as defined in (4–15), $|r^n - 0| < \epsilon$ when $n > g(\epsilon)$ and this proves (4–14). The result (4–14) is obvious intuitively, since, for example, if $r = 0.5$, $(0.5)^2 = 0.25$, $(0.5)^3 = 0.125$ and $(0.5)^4 = 0.0625$. The result was a little tricky to prove rigorously, however, for we had to make use of the binomial expansion in a somewhat subtle way.

4–4* INFINITE SERIES

One interesting application of the theory of sequences and limits of sequences is to the theory of what are called *infinite series*. We are familiar with computing sums of a finite number of terms such as $a_1 + \cdots + a_n$. In practical applications situations are frequently encountered where it is desired to compute the sum of an infinite number of terms $a_1 + a_2 + \cdots$, and in cases of interest this sum will be a finite number. For example, consider the sum

$$1 + \frac{1}{2} + \frac{1}{4} + \frac{1}{8} + \frac{1}{16} + \cdots$$

where each term is $\frac{1}{2}$ the preceding one, that is, $a_{n+1} = a_n/2$. Now $1 + \frac{1}{2} = 1.5, 1.5 + \frac{1}{4} = 1.75, 1.75 + \frac{1}{8} = 1.875, 1.875 + 1/16 = 1.9375$ and $1.9375 + 1/32 = 1.96875$. It would appear that as we add more and more terms, the sum will not become arbitrarily large, but will get closer and closer to a number which, from the computations made, appears to be about 2. How could the need to compute such a sum arise in practice? Let us give a simple example. Suppose that we drop a rubber ball from a height h_1 onto a flat surface. The ball will bounce back up into the air again. Assume that it rises a distance h_2 and then falls back to the surface again and bounces up a distance h_3, and so on. How far will the ball travel before coming to rest? The distance will be

$$h_1 + 2h_2 + 2h_3 + 2h_4 + \cdots,$$

which can be looked upon as the sum of an infinite number of terms. This sum will be finite, however, since we know from experience that h_2 will be less than h_1 and h_3 less than h_2. This illustrates how such a problem could arise in the study of natural phenomena.

Although the example just given is very simple, the notion of the sum of an infinite number of terms arises in many applications. Let us now make precise what we mean by the sum of an infinite number of terms. Suppose that we have a sequence $\{a_n\}$. Let us now form a new sequence $\{s_n\}$ by writing

$$s_1 = a_1; \quad s_2 = s_1 + a_2 = a_1 + a_2; \quad s_3 = s_2 + a_3 = a_1 + a_2 + a_3,$$

or in general

$$s_{n+1} = s_n + a_{n+1} = a_1 + a_2 + \cdots + a_{n+1}. \tag{4-16}$$

Suppose now that $\{s_n\}$ converges to some limit, call it α. Intuitively, from the way the s_n are defined, we would like to think of α as being the sum of all the terms in the sequence $\{a_n\}$. Here, then, we have the basis for giving a precise definition of the sum of an infinite number of terms $a_1 + a_2 + \cdots$. *We shall define the sum to be the limit of the sequence $\{s_n\}$ defined above when this limit exists. The sequence $\{s_n\}$ defined by (4-16) is called an infinite series. The series is said to converge if $\{s_n\}$ converges and is said to diverge if $\{s_n\}$ diverges. The limit α of $\{s_n\}$ is said to be the sum of the infinite series. The infinite series has a sum only when $\{s_n\}$ converges. We call the term s_n from $\{s_n\}$ the nth partial sum of the infinite series and a_n is called the nth term of the infinite series.*

According to the above definition, the limit α of $\{s_n\}$ is what we shall mean by the sum of all the terms in $\{a_n\}$. To indicate this it is typical to write

$$\alpha = a_1 + a_2 + a_3 + \cdots. \tag{4-17}$$

Frequently, however, $a_1 + a_2 + a_3 + \cdots$ is given a double meaning just as is $f(x)$. This expression not only is used to represent the limit of the sequence $\{s_n\}$ but is also used to represent the sequence itself. Thus statements will be found such as, consider the infinite series $a_1 + a_2 + \cdots$. What this means is consider the sequence $\{s_n\}$.

In studying infinite series we are often interested in showing that the series converges. This is not always easy. We shall show, however, that if the infinite series $\{s_n\}$ converges then it is necessarily true that

$$\lim_{n \to \infty} a_n = 0. \tag{4-18}$$

Thus, if (4–18) does not hold, we are sure that the series does not converge. (It is not necessarily true, however, that the series will converge if (4–18) holds. There exist divergent series for which (4–18) holds.) Let us now prove that if $\{s_n\}$ converges then (4–18) holds. Note from (4–16) that

$$a_n = s_n - s_{n-1}. \tag{4-19}$$

Now if $\{s_n\}$ converges to α, then $\lim_{n \to \infty} s_n = \alpha$. If $b_n = s_{n-1}$ and $b_1 = 0$, then $\lim_{n \to \infty} b_n = \alpha$ also, since if the s_n cluster about α so will the b_n. But $a_n = s_n - b_n$. Hence, since $\{s_n\}$ and $\{b_n\}$ converge, we see from (4–7) that so does $\{a_n\}$ and

$$\lim_{n \to \infty} a_n = \lim_{n \to \infty} s_n - \lim_{n \to \infty} b_n = \alpha - \alpha = 0,$$

which is (4–18).

We shall study only one infinite series in any detail. This series is known as the geometric series and is an unending sum of the type

$$1 + r + r^2 + r^3 + \cdots, \tag{4-20}$$

that is, the infinite series generated by the sequence $\{a_n\}$ where $a_n = r^{n-1}$. Here

$$s_n = 1 + r + \cdots + r^{n-1}. \tag{4-21}$$

We can find an explicit expression for s_n as follows. If (4–21) is multiplied by r we obtain

$$r s_n = r + r^2 + \cdots + r^n. \tag{4-22}$$

On subtracting (4–22) from (4–21) we have

$$(1 - r)s_n = 1 - r^n \quad \text{or} \quad s_n = \frac{1}{1 - r}(1 - r^n), \quad r \neq 1. \tag{4-23}$$

This holds for all $r \neq 1$. When $r = 1$, $s_n = 1 + 1 + \cdots + 1 = n$. Thus we have found an explicit expression for s_n in every case.

Let us next investigate the convergence of $\{s_n\}$. If $|r| \geq 1$, then $|r^n| \geq 1$ for all n, so that the distance of a_n from 0 is greater than or equal to 1 and (4–18) does not hold. Thus the series diverges for $|r| \geq 1$. Consider next the case where $|r| < 1$. We proved in the previous section that when $|r| < 1$ then $\lim_{n \to \infty} r^n = 0$. Hence $\{r^n\}$ converges to 0, and from (4–23), (4–7) and (4–6), $\{s_n\}$ converges and

$$\lim_{n \to \infty} s_n = \frac{1}{1-r} \left[\lim_{n \to \infty} 1 - \lim_{n \to \infty} r^n \right] = \frac{1}{1-r}. \qquad (4\text{–}24)$$

We have then proved that the series (4–20) diverges when $|r| \geq 1$, but converges for $|r| < 1$. Furthermore, when it converges its sum is $1/(1 - r)$. Consequently, we can write

$$1 + r + r^2 + r^3 + \cdots = \frac{1}{1-r}, \quad |r| < 1. \qquad (4\text{–}25)$$

This is a result which is frequently used in practice. Thus we see that the infinite series $1 + 1/2 + 1/4 + \cdots$ studied at the beginning of this section does converge and that its sum is 2, since $r = 1/2$ here. This is what we suspected from our numerical computations.

Given the concept of an infinite series, we can now note that any non-terminating decimal $0.b_1b_2b_3 \cdots$ is really the infinite series

$$b_1 \times 10^{-1} + b_2 \times 10^{-2} + b_3 \times 10^{-3} + \cdots.$$

Thus infinite series are important in the study of numbers themselves.

We are now in a position to prove the statement made in Chapter 1 that any nonterminating periodic decimal represents a rational number. Let $\alpha = 0.b_1 \cdots b_k c_1 \cdots c_v c_1 \cdots c_v \cdots$ be a nonterminating periodic decimal in which the sequence of digits $c_1 \cdots c_v$ is repeated unendingly. Now note that α can be written

$$\begin{aligned}
\alpha &= b_1 \times 10^{-1} + \cdots + b_k \times 10^{-k} + c_1 \times 10^{-(k+1)} + \cdots + c_v \times 10^{-(k+v)} \\
&\quad + c_1 \times 10^{-(k+v+1)} + \cdots + c_v \times 10^{-(k+2v)} + \cdots \\
&= (b_1 \cdots b_k) \times 10^{-k} + (c_1 \cdots c_v) \times 10^{-(k+v)}[1 + 10^{-v} + 10^{-2v} + \cdots],
\end{aligned} \qquad (4\text{–}26)$$

where $b_1 \cdots b_k$ and $c_1 \cdots c_v$ are natural numbers with the decimal representations as written. Now

$$1 + 10^{-v} + 10^{-2v} + \cdots$$

is a geometric series with $r = 10^{-v}$. This series converges and its sum is $1/(1 - 10^{-v}) = 10^v/(10^v - 1)$. Thus

$$\alpha = \frac{(b_1 \cdots b_k)(10^v - 1) + (c_1 \cdots c_v)}{10^k(10^v - 1)}, \qquad (4\text{–}27)$$

which is the quotient of two natural numbers and hence is a rational number. For example,

$$0.142857142857\cdots = 142857 \times 10^{-6}[1 + 10^{-6} + 10^{-12} + \cdots]$$

$$= \frac{142857}{10^6 - 1} = \frac{142857}{999999} = \frac{1}{7}.$$

This same procedure can be used to show, for example, that

$$0.249999\cdots = 0.2500\cdots.$$

We ask the reader to do this in the problems.

4–5 SUMMATION NOTATION

In the past we have often written summations such as $a_1 + a_2 + \cdots + a_n$ where symbols rather than specific numbers are used. It is inconvenient to be continually writing out summations like this, and to avoid doing so it is desirable to introduce a simplified notation for summations. One way to do this would be merely to introduce a new symbol, say α, to represent the summation, so that $\alpha = a_1 + a_2 + \cdots + a_n$. Then α would be used instead of writing out the summation. The difficulty here is that α does not tell us explicitly what the summation is. We must remember this. It is desirable to have a notation which indicates the summation explicitly. To characterize the sum of n numbers $a_1, \ldots, a_n$, all we really need to do is use a symbol which represents any one of the numbers being summed, say a_j, then indicate precisely what the elements are, that is, what values j takes on, and finally introduce a symbol to indicate that the elements are to be summed.

A capital Greek sigma, Σ, called a summation sign, is used in mathematics to represent summation. The sum $a_1 + a_2 + \cdots + a_n$ is then abbreviated

$$\sum_{j=1}^{n} a_j. \tag{4–28}$$

Immediately after the summation sign we place the symbol which represents any one of the numbers being summed. Next, if we want to sum a_j for $j = 1, 2, \ldots, n$, this is indicated by giving the smallest value of j under the summation sign, writing $j = 1$, and the largest value on top of the summation sign. It is convenient, as we shall see, to write $j = 1$ on the bottom of the summation sign rather than merely 1. Equation (4–28) is read the sum from j equals 1 to j equals n of a_j. In general, then, a summation such as $a_m + a_{m+1} + \cdots + a_n$ can be abbreviated $\Sigma_{j=m}^{n} a_j$. When writing summations in the body of the text, we move the symbolism normally placed above and below the summation sign to the side as was done here. The reason for this is to avoid an unequal spacing of the lines in the printed text. Thus by definition

$$\sum_{j=m}^{n} a_j = a_m + a_{m+1} + \cdots + a_n, \quad m < n. \tag{4–29}$$

Any one of the numbers a_j for specified j is called a *term* in the summation. The symbol j in (4–29) is called *the summation index*, and m and n are referred to as the limits of the summation. The symbol used for the summation index is irrelevant. Thus $\Sigma_{j=m}^{n} a_j$, $\Sigma_{i=m}^{n} a_i$, and $\Sigma_{r=m}^{n} a_r$ all mean $a_m + \cdots + a_n$. Let us now provide some examples of the summation notation.

EXAMPLES. 1. The sum $1 + 2 + \cdots + n$ of the first n natural numbers can be written using the summation notation as $\Sigma_{j=1}^{n} j$. Here $a_j = j$. Similarly, the sum $1^2 + 2^2 + \cdots + n^2$ of the squares of the first n natural numbers can be written as $\Sigma_{j=1}^{n} j^2$. Here $a_j = j^2$.

2. $\displaystyle\sum_{j=1}^{n} (1 + j) = (1 + 1) + (1 + 2) + \cdots + (1 + n)$.

3. $\displaystyle\sum_{j=-3}^{2} a_j = a_{-3} + a_{-2} + a_{-1} + a_0 + a_1 + a_2$.

The summation index does not have to take on only values which are natural numbers. It can take on any integer value. Suppose that we wish to form the sum of elements a_j for a special set of subscripts j, where j is in a given set J. We can denote this sum by $\Sigma_{j\epsilon J} a_j$. If $J = \{-5, 0, 6, 11, 100\}$, then

$$\sum_{j\epsilon J} a_j = a_{-5} + a_0 + a_6 + a_{11} + a_{100}.$$

4. $\displaystyle\sum_{j=1}^{n} a_{ij} = a_{i1} + a_{i2} + \cdots + a_{in}$.

This example shows why it is desirable to write at the bottom of the summation sign $j = 1$ rather than merely 1. If only 1 were written, it would not be clear whether $\Sigma_1^n a_{ij}$ meant the above sum or $a_{1j} + \cdots + a_{nj}$ or something else.

5. $\displaystyle\sum_{j=1}^{n} f_j(x) = f_1(x) + f_2(x) + \cdots + f_n(x)$.

6. $\displaystyle\sum_{j=1}^{n} \lambda = n\lambda$, where λ is a constant. Here $a_j = \lambda$. Note that the sum is $n\lambda$, not λ.

We shall now discuss several properties of the summation operation which are used with great frequency. Note that

$$\lambda a_m + \cdots + \lambda a_n = \lambda(a_m + \cdots + a_n) \, .$$

Thus

$$\sum_{j=m}^{n} \lambda a_j = \lambda \sum_{j=m}^{n} a_j \, . \tag{4-30}$$

A common factor in each term in the summation can be factored out and taken outside the summation sign.

Next note that, by the associative law,

$$a_m + \cdots + a_r + a_{r+1} + \cdots + a_n$$
$$= (a_m + \cdots + a_r) + (a_{r+1} + \cdots + a_n) \, .$$

Thus

$$\sum_{j=m}^{n} a_j = \sum_{j=m}^{r} a_j + \sum_{j=r+1}^{n} a_j, \quad m < r < n \, . \tag{4-31}$$

It is possible to split up a summation into two parts, and (4-31) shows how to do this. It is convenient to introduce the definition

$$\sum_{j=m}^{m} a_j = a_m \, , \tag{4-32}$$

and with this definition (4-31) holds, even if $r = n - 1$.

Finally, observe that by the commutative and associative laws

$$(a_m + b_m) + \cdots + (a_n + b_n) = (a_m + \cdots + a_n) + (b_m + \cdots + b_n) \, .$$

Therefore

$$\sum_{j=m}^{n} (a_j + b_j) = \sum_{j=m}^{n} a_j + \sum_{j=m}^{n} b_j \, . \tag{4-33}$$

Hence, if each term in a summation can be looked upon as the sum of two parts, the summation can be broken up as shown in (4-33).

EXAMPLES. 1.

$$\sum_{j=1}^{n} 4j^2 = 4 \sum_{j=1}^{n} j^2 \, .$$

2. $\displaystyle\sum_{j=1}^{10} (1 + j)^2 = \sum_{j=1}^{7} (1 + j)^2 + \sum_{j=8}^{10} (1 + j)^2 \, .$

3. $\displaystyle\sum_{j=1}^{n} (1+j)^2 = \sum_{j=1}^{n} (1+2j+j^2) = n + 2\sum_{j=1}^{n} j + \sum_{j=1}^{n} j^2$.

4. An nth degree polynomial $a_n x^n + \cdots + a_0$ can be conveniently written using the summation notation as $\sum_{j=0}^{n} a_j x^j$.

5. The summation notation is often used to represent infinite series. The infinite series generated by the sequence $\{a_n\}$ would be written $\sum_{n=1}^{\infty} a_n$, using the symbol ∞ as an upper limit for the summation index to indicate that there is no upper limit. The symbol $\sum_{n=1}^{\infty} a_n$ is often used to represent both the infinite series and its sum when the series converges.

4–6 AREA AND THE DEFINITE INTEGRAL

We now shall begin the study of integral calculus. Just as the concept of the limit of a function of a continuous variable was the basis for developing differential calculus, the notion of the limit of a sequence will be the basis for the development of the integral calculus. Initially, the integral calculus will appear to be totally unrelated to differential calculus. Interestingly enough, however, we shall later see that there is an intimate connection between differential and integral calculus, and it is because of this connection that the two combined form such a powerful tool for solving practical problems.

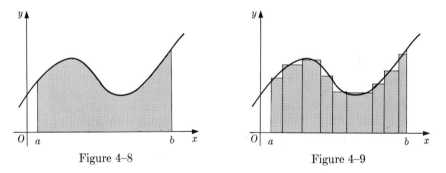

Figure 4–8   Figure 4–9

Suppose that $f(x)$ is a continuous function and imagine that its graph looks like that shown in Figure 4–8. Consider the set of points satisfying the inequalities

$$y - f(x) \leq 0$$
$$y \geq 0 \tag{4-34}$$
$$a \leq x \leq b .$$

The set of points satisfying these inequalities is the shaded region of Figure 4–8. Intuitively, we think of this set of points as a two-dimensional set. Just as a one-dimensional set, such as the line segment I_{ab}^c, has associated with it a length, a two-dimensional set has associated with it a number which is called its area. What do we mean by area? Intuitively, area provides a measure of the content of a two-dimensional set of points. The problem of computing areas is studied initially in plane geometry. The unit of area is defined so that a square, each of whose sides is one fundamental unit of length, contains an area of one unit. Such a square is called a unit square. Thus a square, each of whose sides is of length one foot, has an area of 1 square foot. The area of any other region is then, from an intuitive point of view, equal to the number of unit squares it contains. In general, of course, the number of unit squares contained in a given region will not be a natural number, and it will be necessary to cut some unit squares into odd-shaped pieces in order to completely cover the region of interest.

This gives an intuitive discussion of how one of the ancients might have proceeded to find the area of some given region. The way areas are computed in geometry depends on the precise set of axioms used. In some developments, one of the axioms is that the area of a rectangular region is equal to the product of the length of the base and the altitude. Then the areas of other regions bounded by straight lines, such as triangular regions, are determined. We shall be interested here in determining the areas of regions bounded by curves, such as that shown in Figure 4–8. In our development we shall take as known or as an axiom the formula for computing the area of a rectangle.

Suppose now that we wish to compute the area of the shaded region shown in Figure 4–8. It is not at all obvious initially how we can determine the area exactly, even though we feel intuitively that we understand what the area of the shaded region means. A little thought, however, suggests a procedure for computing the area approximately. We can approximate the shaded area by the sum of the areas of a number of rectangular regions, as shown in Figure 4–9. The shaded area of Figure 4–8 can then be approximated by the area of the shaded region shown in Figure 4–9, this latter area being the sum of the areas of the individual rectangular regions. This technique for approximating the areas of regions bounded by curves was used by Archimedes around 250 B.C.

We can now systemize the above approximation procedure and simultaneously gain more information. Indeed, we shall be led to a method for computing the area exactly. Suppose that we subdivide the interval I_{ab}^c into n subintervals, each of length $h = (b - a)/n$, by the set of $n - 1$ equally spaced points

$$x_k = a + \frac{k}{n}(b - a), \quad k = 1, \dots, n - 1. \tag{4–35}$$

Also write $x_0 = a$ and $x_n = b$. Let y_k^* and y_{*k} be the absolute maximum and minimum, respectively, of $f(x)$ for x in the kth subinterval, that is, for x satisfying $x_{k-1} \leq x \leq x_k$. Using the kth subinterval as a base, let us form

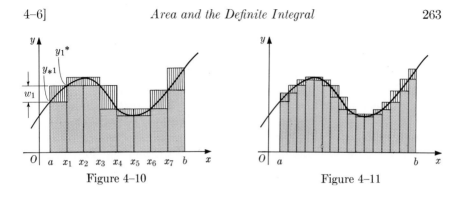

Figure 4–10   Figure 4–11

two rectangles, one of whose altitude is y_k^* and the other whose altitude is y_{*k}. We do this for each k, $k = 1, \ldots, n$, and the result will look like that shown in Figure 4–10. Denote the rectangles having y_k^* as their altitudes as the upper rectangles and the ones with y_{*k} as their altitudes as the lower rectangles. The area of the kth lower rectangle, that is, the one whose base is the kth subinterval, is $y_{*k}h$; the area of the upper kth rectangle is y_k^*h. The lower rectangles are shaded in Figure 4–10.

If we write $w_k = y_k^* - y_{*k}$ then the area of the upper kth rectangle can be written

$$y_k^*h = y_{*k}h + w_k h \qquad (4\text{--}36)$$

and is equal to the area of the lower kth rectangle plus the area of another rectangle with a base whose length is the length of the kth subinterval and whose altitude has length w_k. The rectangles whose areas are $w_k h$ are the crosshatched rectangles in Figure 4–10. Now note that for all k, $y_{*k}h \le y_k^*h$, so the area of the kth lower rectangle is not greater than the area of the kth upper rectangle. Suppose that we next sum the areas of the lower rectangles. This sum is

$$s_{Ln} = \sum_{k=1}^{n} y_{*k}h = \frac{b-a}{n} \sum_{k=1}^{n} y_{*k}. \qquad (4\text{--}37)$$

Similarly the sum of the areas of the upper rectangles is

$$s_{Un} = \sum_{k=1}^{n} y_k^*h = \frac{b-a}{n} \sum_{k=1}^{n} y_k^* \qquad (4\text{--}38)$$

We call s_{Ln} a *lower sum* and s_{Un} an *upper sum*. Since $y_{*k}h \le y_k^*h$ for all k, $s_{Ln} \le s_{Un}$. In Figure 4–10, s_{Ln} is simply the area of the shaded region while s_{Un} is the area of the shaded region plus the area of the crosshatched region.

Let us now denote by s the area of the set of points in Figure 4–8. It is the value s that we are trying to determine. Note that each lower rectangle is either on or below the graph of $f(x)$, but never above it. Thus it must be true that $s_{Ln} \le s$. Similarly, each upper rectangle is either on or above the graph of $f(x)$, but never below it. Hence it must be true that $s \leq s_{Un}$. It therefore follows that

$$s_{Ln} \leq s \leq s_{Un} . \tag{4-39}$$

We have, then, not only developed a procedure for approximating s but in addition have obtained two estimates which bracket the true value.

Observe that we can go through the above procedure for every natural number n and in so doing determine numbers s_{Un} and s_{Ln}. Furthermore (4–39) will hold for each n. As n increases, $h = (b - a)/n$ becomes smaller and smaller and we expect that both s_{Ln} and s_{Un} will give better and better approximations to s. From (4–36) we see that

$$s_{Un} - s_{Ln} = \frac{b - a}{n} \sum_{k=1}^{n} w_k , \tag{4-40}$$

which is simply the area of the crosshatched region in Figure 4–10. As n becomes larger and larger, this area and $s_{Un} - s_{Ln}$ becomes smaller and smaller. Figure 4–11 shows the crosshatched region for $n = 16$ instead of the value $n = 8$ used in Figure 4–10. The area of the crosshatched region in Figure 4–11 is considerably smaller than that of the corresponding region in Figure 4–10.

For each natural number n we can then compute two numbers s_{Ln} and s_{Un} in the manner described above. In this way two sequences $\{s_{Ln}\}$ and $\{s_{Un}\}$ are generated, and it now appears that we may have a method for determining the area of the shaded region in Figure 4–9 exactly. Consider the two sequences $\{s_{Ln}\}$ and $\{s_{Un}\}$. If both of these sequences converge and if, in addition, they have the same limit, then because of (4–39) this limit must be s, the area we are trying to compute. From our above discussion it is intuitively clear that $\{s_{Ln}\}$ and $\{s_{Un}\}$ should approach a common limit which is s, that is,

$$s = \lim_{n \to \infty} s_{Ln} = \lim_{n \to \infty} s_{Un} . \tag{4-41}$$

Here then, it would appear, we have a method for computing exactly areas bounded by curves.

In specific cases, it is actually possible to evaluate the limits in (4–41) directly and hence to compute areas in this way. We shall show how this can be done by giving two simple examples. Consider first the case where $f(x) = x$, $a = 0$ and $b = 2$. The situation is illustrated in Figure 4–12. The area we wish to compute is the area of a right triangle, that is, the area of the interior of the right triangle. We already know from elementary geometry that the area of a right triangle is equal to one-half the product of the length of the base times the altitude, which yields $\frac{1}{2}(2)(2) = 2$ in this case. Let us now go through the limiting procedure described above and show that we do indeed obtain this result.

The minimum value of $f(x) = x$ for x in the interval $x_{k-1} \leq x \leq x_k$ is

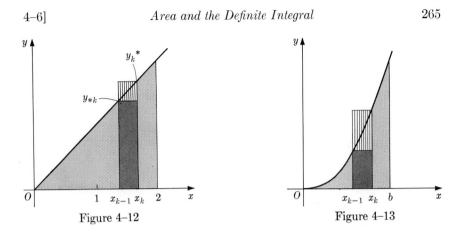

Figure 4–12   Figure 4–13

simply $f(x_{k-1}) = x_{k-1}$, so that $y_{*k} = x_{k-1}$. Similarly, the maximum value of $f(x)$ over this interval is $f(x_k) = x_k$ so that $y_k^* = x_k$. Since $a = 0$ and $b = 2$, we see from (4–35) that $x_k = 2k/n$. Then $y_{*k} = 2(k-1)/n$ and $y_k^* = 2k/n$. Thus for each n, we see from (4–37) that on using (4–30), (4–33) and $\Sigma_{k=1}^n 1 = n$, s_{Ln} becomes

$$s_{Ln} = \frac{2}{n} \sum_{k=1}^n 2\left(\frac{k-1}{n}\right) = \frac{4}{n^2}\left[\sum_{k=1}^n k - n\right]. \qquad (4\text{--}42)$$

To proceed we must evaluate explicitly

$$\sigma = \sum_{k=1}^n k = 1 + 2 + \cdots + n.$$

This can easily be done by using a trick and writing

$$\sigma = 1 + 2 + \cdots + n$$
$$\sigma = n + n - 1 + \cdots + 1,$$

or on adding

$$2\sigma = \underbrace{(n+1) + (n+1) + \cdots + (n+1)}_{n \text{ times}} = n(n+1).$$

Therefore

$$\sum_{k=1}^n k = \frac{n(n+1)}{2}, \qquad (4\text{--}43)$$

and

$$s_{Ln} = \frac{4}{n^2}\left[\frac{n(n+1)}{2} - n\right] = 2 - \frac{2}{n}. \qquad (4\text{--}44)$$

We see at once that the sequence $\{s_{Ln}\}$ does indeed converge and that its limit is 2, since

$$\lim_{n \to \infty} s_{Ln} = \lim_{n \to \infty} 2 - 2 \lim_{n \to \infty} \frac{1}{n} = 2 .$$

Next we can observe that by (4–38)

$$s_{Un} = \frac{2}{n} \sum_{k=1}^{n} \frac{2k}{n} = \frac{4}{n^2} \frac{n(n+1)}{2} = 2 + \frac{2}{n} . \tag{4-45}$$

The sequence $\{s_{Un}\}$ also converges and has 2 as a limit. Thus $\{s_{Ln}\}$ and $\{s_{Un}\}$ both converge to the same limit, which is the area of the triangle.

Let us now study a somewhat more complicated case where we do not know the answer ahead of time. Suppose that $f(x) = x^2$, $a = 0$ and that we simply use b for the other end point of the interval rather than a specific number. The situation is illustrated in Figure 4–13. The minimum value of $f(x) = x^2$ for x satisfying $x_{k-1} \le x \le x_k$ is $f(x_{k-1}) = x_{k-1}^2$, and maximum value is $f(x_k) = x_k^2$. Thus $y_{*k} = x_{k-1}^2$ and $y_k^* = x_k^2$. Now $x_k = bk/n$, since $a = 0$. Thus $y_{*k} = b^2(k-1)^2/n^2$ and $y_k^* = b^2k^2/n^2$. Hence from (4–37)

$$s_{Ln} = \frac{b}{n} \sum_{k=1}^{n} \frac{b^2(k-1)^2}{n^2} = \frac{b^3}{n^3} \sum_{k=1}^{n} (k-1)^2 . \tag{4-46}$$

To proceed we must evaluate $\sum_{k=1}^{n} (k-1)^2$. Now

$$\sum_{k=1}^{n} (k-1)^2 = 0^2 + 1^2 + \cdots + (n-1)^2 = \sum_{k=1}^{n-1} k^2 . \tag{4-47}$$

We shall next evaluate explicitly $\sum_{k=1}^{n-1} k^2$. To do this, observe that

$$(k+1)^3 - k^3 = k^3 + 3k^2 + 3k + 1 - k^3 = 3k^2 + 3k + 1 .$$

Thus

$$\sum_{k=1}^{n-1} [(k+1)^3 - k^3] = 3 \sum_{k=1}^{n-1} k^2 + 3 \sum_{k=1}^{n-1} k + \sum_{k=1}^{n-1} 1 . \tag{4-48}$$

However,

$$\sum_{k=1}^{n-1} [(k+1)^3 - k^3] = (2^3 - 1^3) + (3^3 - 2^3) + \cdots + [n^3 - (n-1)^3]$$

$$= n^3 - 1 ,$$

and

$$\sum_{k=1}^{n-1} k = \frac{n(n-1)}{2} ; \qquad \sum_{k=1}^{n-1} 1 = n - 1 .$$

Thus from (4–48)

$$\sum_{k=1}^{n-1} k^2 = \frac{1}{3} \left[n^3 - 1 - \frac{3}{2} n(n-1) - (n-1) \right] \tag{4-49}$$

$$= \frac{1}{3} \left[n^3 - \frac{3}{2} n^2 + \frac{1}{2} n \right] ,$$

which is the expression desired.

We then see from (4–46) and (4–47) that

$$s_{Ln} = \frac{b^3}{3n^3}\left[n^3 - \frac{3}{2}n^2 + \frac{1}{2}n\right] = \frac{b^3}{3}\left[1 - \frac{3}{2}\frac{1}{n} + \frac{1}{2}\frac{1}{n^2}\right]. \qquad (4\text{–}50)$$

Since the sequences $\{1/n\}$ and $\{1/n^2\}$ converge to 0, we see immediately that the sequence $\{s_{Ln}\}$ does indeed converge and has the limit $b^3/3$.

We showed above that $y_k^* = b^2k^2/n^2$. Thus s_{Un} is given by

$$s_{Un} = \frac{b^3}{n^3}\sum_{k=1}^{n} k^2 . \qquad (4\text{–}51)$$

Now to evaluate $\Sigma_{k=1}^n k^2$, it is only necessary to replace n by $n + 1$ in (4–50) (why?). Thus

$$\sum_{k=1}^{n} k^2 = \frac{1}{3}\left[(n + 1)^3 - \frac{3}{2}(n + 1)^2 + \frac{1}{2}(n + 1)\right]$$

$$= \frac{1}{3}\left[n^3 + 3n^2 + 3n + 1 - \frac{3}{2}n^2 - 3n - \frac{3}{2} + \frac{n}{2} + \frac{1}{2}\right] \qquad (4\text{–}52)$$

$$= \frac{1}{3}\left[n^3 + \frac{3}{2}n^2 + \frac{n}{2}\right],$$

so

$$s_{Un} = \frac{b^3}{3}\left[1 + \frac{3}{2}\frac{1}{n} + \frac{1}{2}\frac{1}{n^2}\right]. \qquad (4\text{–}53)$$

The same analysis as we applied to $\{s_{Ln}\}$ shows that $\{s_{Un}\}$ also converges and its limit is $b^3/3$. Therefore both $\{s_{Ln}\}$ and $\{s_{Un}\}$ converge to the same limit $b^3/3$ and hence the area of the shaded region in Figure 4–13 is $b^3/3$.

4–7 THE DEFINITE INTEGRAL

In the previous section we showed how to construct two sequences, $\{s_{Ln}\}$ and $\{s_{Un}\}$, which we concluded both converged to the same limit, this limit being the area of the shaded region in Figure 4–8. Let us now note that there are many other sequences we can generate by approximating the area with rectangles which should also converge to s. For example, instead of using y_k^* or y_{*k} as the altitudes of the rectangles, suppose that we select in any way desired a number ξ_k in the kth subinterval, and use $f(\xi_k)$ as the altitude of the kth rectangle; this is done for each k. Then

$$s_{Rn} = \sum_{k=1}^{n} f(\xi_k)h = \frac{b - a}{n}\sum_{k=1}^{n} f(\xi_k) \qquad (4\text{–}54)$$

is an approximation to the area of the region which should get better and better as n increases. In fact, $y_{*k} \le f(\xi_k) \le y_k^*$, since y_{*k} and y_k^* are respectively the smallest and largest values of $f(x)$ in the kth subinterval. Hence $y_{*k}h \le f(\xi_k)h \le y_k^*h$, or on summing over k we conclude that

$$s_{Ln} \le s_{Rn} \le s_{Un} \qquad (4\text{–}55)$$

for every n. Thus if $\{s_{Ln}\}$ and $\{s_{Un}\}$ converge to s, so must $\{s_{Rn}\}$. We shall call any sequence $\{s_{Rn}\}$ whose nth term is given by (4–54) a Riemann sequence. The name of the German mathematician Riemann is associated with these sequences because of the fundamental work he did in the theory we are studying. The sequences $\{s_{Ln}\}$ and $\{s_{Un}\}$ are, of course, special cases of (4–54) and are Riemann sequences also. We have now seen that each Riemann sequence defined by (4–54) should have a limit s which is the area of the shaded region in Figure 4–8.

There are still other sequences which we can construct to approximate the area of the shaded region of Figure 4–8 and which should converge to s. In (4–54) it is assumed that there are n subintervals, that is, n rectangles, and that each subinterval has the same length $(b - a)/n$. There is no reason, however, that we must partition I_{ab}^c up into subintervals in such a way that each subinterval has the same length. Indeed, this was not done in Figure 4–9. Neither is it necessary that the nth term in the sequence have n subintervals, that is, n rectangles are used to approximate the area. There could, for example, be $2n$ or $3n$ or $2n + 1$. We expect that any such sequence will converge to s provided that the length of the longest subinterval approaches 0. Any of these sequences can also be referred to as Riemann sequences. With one exception, we shall not need to consider sequences where the subintervals are not all of the same length or where the number of subintervals associated with the nth term is not n. However, such sequences exist and could be used if desired.

Our intuitive discussion above has suggested that we expect any Riemann sequence $\{s_{Rn}\}$ with s_{Rn} given by (4–54) to converge to the area of the shaded region in Figure 4–8. We did not prove that this will always be the case, although we did show it was true when $f(x) = x$ and $f(x) = x^2$. Let us now ask under what conditions *every* Riemann sequence $\{s_{Rn}\}$ will converge and will have the same limit. *It can be proved that, if $f(x)$ is continuous over I_{ab}^c, then this will indeed be true.* This is a very important result. We shall not give the proof since, although it is not difficult, it is rather long and involves some material we have not developed in detail.

We can now note that the process of forming a Riemann sequence can be completely divorced from the geometric idea of finding areas. Given any function $f(x)$ which is continuous over the interval I_{ab}^c we can form the Riemann sequence $\{s_{Rn}\}$ with s_{Rn} given by (4–54), and from the theorem quoted above we know that this sequence will converge to a limit, call it s. Many different Riemann sequences can be formed corresponding to all ways of selecting the ξ_k. The above theorem tells us that each of these will have the same limit s. We can think of the original geometric problem of finding areas merely as suggesting that the study of Riemann sequences may be of considerable practical interest. Riemann sequences can be constructed and studied for a given function $f(x)$ over a specified interval I^c_{ab} without attempting to provide any geometric interpretation of them. The situation here is similar to that for differentiation. We originally motivated the derivative concept by studying the limiting behavior of secants to a curve, but once the fundamental limit involved in defining a derivative was introduced, then the original geometric interpretation was no longer needed. Just as differentiation has much wider usefulness than merely finding the slope of a curve, so will the problem of finding the limit of a Riemann sequence have much greater applicability than merely to the determination of areas.

Recall that, given any function $f(x)$ and a closed interval I^c_{ab}, we can generate a Riemann sequence $\{s_{Rn}\}$ for $f(x)$ over this interval as follows. To determine s_{Rn}, the nth term in the sequence, we subdivide I^c_{ab} into n subintervals, each of which has the length $(b - a)/n$. In the kth subinterval a number ξ_k is specified. This is done for each of the n subintervals. Then s_{Rn} is given by (4–54) for every $n = 1, 2, 3, \ldots$. Different Riemann sequences can be generated by using different rules for selecting the ξ_k. For example, one rule is to use $\xi_k = y_{*k}$ while another is to use $\xi_k = y_k^*$. Still another would be to use $\xi_k = (x_k + x_{k-1})/2$, that is, the midpoint of the kth interval. There are, of course, an infinite number of different sequences which can be generated in this way.

From the basic result stated above, but not proved, we know that is $f(x)$ is continuous over I^c_{ab} then each and every Riemann sequence (including those in which the subintervals are not of the same length) will converge, and all will have the same limit. The function $f(x)$ does not have to be continuous in order for this to occur, but we are sure that it will occur when $f(x)$ is continuous. *When all Riemann sequences for $f(x)$ over I^c_{ab} converge and all have the same limit s, we give a special name to this limit s and call it the definite integral of $f(x)$ from a to b.* The definite integral as defined here is often called the Riemann integral, after the German mathematician of the same name. Other more general theories of integration have been developed by mathematicians such as Stieltjes and Lebesgue, and thus references to Stieltjes integrals or Lebesgue integrals are also found. We shall be dealing only with Riemann integrals, and hence shall merely refer to them as integrals rather than Riemann integrals.

It is convenient to use a notation for the definite integral which indicates the function involved and the interval, rather than merely using a symbol such as s. The notation used for the definite integral of $f(x)$ from a to b is

$$\int_a^b f(x) \, dx \, . \tag{4–56}$$

The symbol $\int$ is called an *integral sign*. After the integral sign we write $f(x)$ to indicate the function involved; $f(x)$ is referred to as the *integrand*. At the bottom of the integral sign we write a, the smaller end point of I_{ab}^c, and at the top of the integral sign we write b; a and b are referred to as the *limits of integration*, a being called the *lower limit* and b the *upper limit*.

The symbol dx following $f(x)$ is more or less of an historical accident and has no particular significance. Some authors omit it and write (4–56) as

$$\int_a^b f(x) \, .$$

However, (4–56) is the standard notation, and as we shall see, the dx does serve one useful purpose. The variable x in $f(x)$ is called the *variable of integration*. The value of the definite integral is cleanly independent of what symbol is used for the variable of integration. Thus, for example,

$$\int_a^b f(x) \, dx = \int_a^b f(y) \, dy = \int_a^b f(\tau) \, d\tau = \int_a^b f(\zeta) \, d\zeta \, .$$

The usefulness of dx is in telling us which symbol is the one referring to the variable of integration. This can be important when the symbol $f(x)$ is replaced by a specific expression that contains in it several symbols which are parameters. Without some means of identification, there would be no way to tell which of the symbols is the one that refers to the variable of integration.

By definition

$$\lim_{n \to \infty} s_{Rn} = \int_a^b f(x) \, dx \, , \qquad (4\text{–}57)$$

where $\{s_{Rn}\}$ is any Riemann sequence for $f(x)$ over I_{ab}^c. The definite integral of $f(x)$ from a to b is defined only when all these Riemann sequences converge and have the same limit; $\int_a^b f(x) \, dx$ is the common limit of all these sequences. There exist functions for which $\int_a^b f(x) \, dx$ does not exist. However, $\int_a^b f(x) \, dx$ *always* exists when $f(x)$ is continuous at each point in I_{ab}^c, and this is the only case that will be of interest to us.

The process of finding a definite integral is referred to as integration. If we desired to find $\int_a^b f(x) \, dx$ for some continuous function $f(x)$ we could do this by constructing any one of the Riemann sequences $f(x)$ over I_{ab}^c and then determining its limit. The same answer would be obtained regardless of which Riemann sequence was used. The evaluation of $\int_a^b f(x) \, dx$ by constructing a Riemann sequence and then determining its limit is normally a very inefficient way to carry out the integration, just as the use of the definition of a derivative is not an efficient way to differentiate a complicated function. In the next chapter we shall develop some rules which make it much easier to evaluate many definite integrals. First, however, some additional material must be developed.

4–8 **PROPERTIES OF DEFINITE INTEGRALS**

We have seen that the area of the shaded region in Figure 4–8 is $\int_a^b f(x)\,dx$. Thus the definite integral in this case can be interpreted as the area of the set of points $y - f(x) \leq 0$, $y \geq 0$, $x \geq a$, $x \leq b$. A definite integral can always be given such an interpretation when $f(x) \geq 0$ for $x \in I_{ab}^c$. However, $f(x)$ does not have to be non-negative at every point in I_{ab}^c in order that $\int_a^b f(x)\,dx$ exists. The integral will exist if $f(x)$ is continuous, regardless of what the sign of $f(x)$ is or how many times it changes sign. Consider now a function $f(x)$ which is negative everywhere, such as that shown in Figure 4–14, and let us try to give a geometric interpretation to $\int_a^b f(x)\,dx$. We

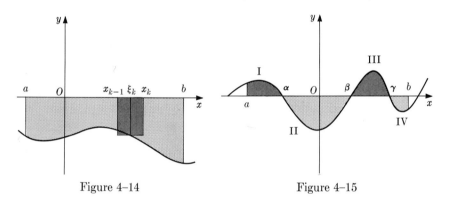

Figure 4–14   Figure 4–15

shall study the shaded region, which is the set of points defined by the inequalities $y - f(x) \geq 0$, $y \leq 0$, $x \geq a$, $x \leq b$. Suppose that we consider a Riemann sequence $\{s_{Rn}\}$, where

$$s_{Rn} = \frac{b-a}{n} \sum_{k=1}^{n} f(\xi_k) = h \sum_{k=1}^{n} f(\xi_k)\,, \tag{4–58}$$

and to be specific suppose ξ_k is the midpoint of the kth interval. Now $s_{Rn} < 0$, since $h > 0$ and $f(\xi_k) < 0$, so $\int_a^b f(x)\,dx$, which is the limit of this sequence, will be negative. By the definition of absolute values, $f(\xi_k) = -|f(\xi_k)|$ when $f(\xi_k) < 0$. Thus

$$s_{Rn} = -\sum_{k=1}^{n} |f(\xi_k)| h\,.$$

But $|f(\zeta_k)|h$ is precisely the area of the darkly shaded rectangle in Figure 4–14 and hence $\Sigma_{k=1}^n |f(\xi_k)|h$ is an approximation to the area of the shaded set of points which gets better and better as n increases. Thus the Riemann sequence $\{s_{Rn}\}$ must converge to a number which is exactly the negative of the area of the shaded set of points.

If we next consider a situation where the function looks like that shown in Figure 4–15, then $\int_a^b f(x)\, dx$ is a number which is equal to the area of the darkly shaded regions minus the area of the lightly shaded ones. One way to see this is to break up the sum (4–58) into four parts, the first referring to subintervals lying in $I_{a\alpha}^c$, the next containing intervals in $I_{\alpha\beta}^c$, the next containing subintervals in $I_{\beta\gamma}^c$, and the final one containing the subintervals in $I_{\gamma b}^c$. Now that part of the sum containing subintervals in $I_{a\alpha}^c$ approximates the area of region I, while that part of the sum containing intervals in $I_{\alpha\beta}^c$ is negative and approximates the negative of the area of region II, and so on. Thus we see that $\int_a^b f(x)\, dx$ cannot necessarily be interpreted as the area of some region. If desired, however, it can always be interpreted as the area of a set of points, the negative of the area of some set of points or the difference of the areas of two sets of points.

Let us now obtain some very simple properties of definite integrals. It is convenient to introduce the following two definitions.

$$\int_a^a f(x)\, dx = 0 \; ; \tag{4–59}$$

$$\int_a^b f(x)\, dx = -\int_b^a f(x)\, dx \; . \tag{4–60}$$

The intuitive justification for (4–59) is as follows. If $f(x) > 0$, the set of points $y - f(x) \le 0$, $y \ge 0$, $x \ge a$, $x \le a$ is simply a vertical line segment drawn from $(a, 0)$ to $(a, f(a))$. The area of this line segment is 0, and hence if $\int_a^a f(x)\, dx$ is to be interpreted as an area, then (4–59) must hold. This is not a proof of (4–59), however; (4–59) must be taken as a definition, and we ask the reader to explain why in the problems. A convenient intuitive way to think of (4–60) is to imagine that changing the limits on the integral changes the sign of h in (4–54). If $b > a$ then $h > 0$ and if $b < a$ then $h < 0$. In other words, we originally assumed that $a < b$ and we numbered the points x_k in (4–35) from left to right so that $x_k > x_{k-1}$. We can now think of the lower limit on the integral as telling us where we start in numbering the x_k. If $b < a$, we then start numbering from right to left so that $x_k < x_{k-1}$. In this case $h = x_k - x_{k-1} < 0$. Given (4–60) we no longer need to have the lower limit on a definite integral be less than the upper limit. By (4–60) we can, of course, convert an integral with the lower limit greater than the upper limit to one with the limits reversed. Thus

$$\int_5^{-2} x^2\, dx = -\int_{-2}^5 x^2\, dx$$

Let us now show that *the definite integral of* $\lambda f(x)$ *over any interval is* λ *times the definite integral of* $f(x)$ *over the interval,* that is,

$$\int_a^b \lambda f(x)\, dx = \lambda \int_a^b f(x)\, dx . \qquad (4\text{–}61)$$

We shall suppose that $f(x)$ is continuous over I_{ab}^c. Then $g(x) = \lambda f(x)$ is also continuous over I_{ab}^c and $\int_a^b g(x)\, dx$ exists as well as $\int_a^b f(x)\, dx$. Consider now any Riemann sequence $\{s_{Rn}\}$ for $g(x)$, with

$$s_{Rn} = \frac{b-a}{n} \sum_{k=1}^n g(\xi_k) = \frac{b-a}{n} \sum_{k=1}^n \lambda f(\xi_k) = \lambda s_{Rn}' ,$$

where

$$s_{Rn}' = \frac{b-a}{n} \sum_{k=1}^n f(\xi_k) .$$

But $\{s_{Rn}'\}$ is a Riemann sequence for $f(x)$ over I_{ab}^c which converges to $\int_a^b f(x)\, dx$. Then by (4–6), $\{s_{Rn}\}$ converges to $\lambda \int_a^b f(x)\, dx$. However, $\{s_{Rn}\}$ is a Riemann sequence for $g(x)$ and hence converges to $\int_a^b g(x)\, dx$. Thus $\int_a^b g(x)\, dx = \lambda \int_a^b f(x)\, dx$, which is what we wished to show. Thus, for example,

$$\int_3^8 2x^2\, dx = 2 \int_3^8 x^2\, dx .$$

We shall next show that *the definite integral of the sum of two functions over any interval is the sum of the definite integrals of each of the functions over the interval.* More precisely, suppose that $f_1(x)$ and $f_2(x)$ are continuous over I_{ab}^c. Consider the function $g(x) = f_1(x) + f_2(x)$. Then the definite integral of $g(x)$ over I_{ab}^c exists and

$$\begin{aligned}
\int_a^b g(x)\, dx &= \int_a^b [f_1(x) + f_2(x)]\, dx \\
&= \int_a^b f_1(x)\, dx + \int_a^b f_2(x)\, dx .
\end{aligned} \qquad (4\text{–}62)$$

The proof of this is also very simple. Since $f_1(x)$ and $f_2(x)$ are continuous, so is $f_1(x) + f_2(x) = g(x)$. Hence $\int_a^b g(x)\, dx$ exists. Let $\{s_{Rn}\}$ be a Riemann sequence for $g(x)$ with

$$\begin{aligned}
s_{Rn} &= \frac{b-a}{n} \sum_{k=1}^n g(\xi_k) = \frac{b-a}{n} \sum_{k=1}^n [f_1(\xi_k) + f_2(\xi_k)] \\
&= \frac{b-a}{n} \sum_{k=1}^n f_1(\xi_k) + \frac{b-a}{n} \sum_{k=1}^n f_2(\xi_k) = s_{Rn}' + s_{Rn}'' .
\end{aligned}$$

Now $\{s_{Rn}'\}$ is a Riemann sequence for $f_1(x)$ over I_{ab}^c which converges to $\int_a^b f_1(x)\, dx$, while $\{s_{Rn}''\}$ is a Riemann sequence for $f_2(x)$ and converges to $\int_a^b f_2(x)\, dx$. Thus $\{s_{Rn}\}$ converges to $\int_a^b f_1(x)\, dx + \int_a^b f_2(x)\, dx$. However,

$\{s_{Rn}\}$ is a Riemann sequence for $g(x)$ and converges to $\int_a^b g(x)\,dx$. Thus (4–62) holds, which is what we wished to prove.

It will be noted that (4–61) and (4–62) are similar to (4–6) and (4–7). However, it is definitely not true that the definite integral of the product of two functions is the product of the definite integrals of the individual functions, nor is the definite integral of the quotient of the definite integrals of the individual functions. The situation here is similar to that encountered with derivatives. We shall see later how to obtain a useful formula for the definite integral of the product of two functions similar to that for the derivative of the product of two functions.

There is one final property of definite integrals that we shall consider here. Suppose that $f(x)$ is continuous at each point in I_{ab}^c so that $\int_a^c f(x)\,dx$ exists. Now let γ be any point in the interior of I_{ab}^c. Then we shall prove that

$$\int_a^b f(x)\,dx = \int_a^\gamma f(x)\,dx + \int_\gamma^b f(x)\,dx\ . \qquad (4\text{--}63)$$

Equation (4–63) is obvious when thought of in terms of areas. In Figure 4–16, the area of the entire shaded region (lightly and darkly shaded) is

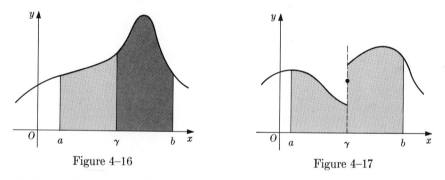

Figure 4–16 Figure 4–17

$\int_a^b f(x)\,dx$. The area of the lightly shaded region is $\int_a^\gamma f(x)\,dx$, and the area of the darkly shaded region is $\int_\gamma^b f(x)\,dx$. The area of the entire shaded region is the area of the lightly shaded region plus the area of the darkly shaded region, which is (4–63). This geometric reasoning does not prove (4–63) but certainly suggests that it is true.

To prove (4–63) note that $\int_a^\gamma f(x)\,dx$ and $\int_\gamma^b f(x)\,dx$ exist, since $f(x)$ is continuous over $I_{a\gamma}^c$ and $I_{\gamma b}^c$. Let $\{s_{Rn}'\}$ with

$$s_{Rn}' = \frac{\gamma - a}{n} \sum_{k=1}^n f(\xi_k) \qquad (4\text{--}64)$$

and $\{s_{Rn}''\}$ with

$$s_{Rn}'' = \frac{b - \gamma}{n} \sum_{k=1}^n f(\xi_k) \qquad (4\text{--}65)$$

be Riemann sequences for $f(x)$ over the intervals $I_{a\gamma}^c$ and $I_{\gamma b}^c$, respectively. Then $\{s_{Rn}'\}$ converges to $\int_a^\gamma f(x)\,dx$ and $\{s_{Rn}''\}$ converges to $\int_\gamma^b f(x)\,dx$. We can now construct a Riemann sequence $\{s_{Rn}\}$ for $f(x)$ over I_{ab}^c with the property that for every n

$$s_{Rn} = s_{Rn}' + s_{Rn}'' . \tag{4–66}$$

All we need do to obtain s_{Rn} is to use over $I_{a\gamma}^c$ the same subintervals used in s_{Rn}' and over $I_{\gamma b}^c$ the same subintervals used in s_{Rn}''. Furthermore, the same ξ_k are chosen in each subinterval as in s_{Rn}' and s_{Rn}''. Thus $\{s_{Rn}\}$ with s_{Rn} defined by (4–66) will form a Riemann sequence for $f(x)$ over I_{ab}^c. However, it is not a Riemann sequence in which all subintervals have the same length. The subintervals in $I_{a\gamma}^c$ have length $(\gamma - a)/n$ while those in $I_{\gamma b}^c$ have length $(b - \gamma)/n$. Furthermore, $2n$, not n, subintervals are used in forming s_{Rn}. Nonetheless, the length of the longest subinterval approaches 0 as n increases and $\{s_{Rn}\}$ is a Riemann sequence. Since $\int_a^b f(x)\,dx$ exists, the limit of $\{s_{Rn}\}$ is $\int_a^b f(x)\,dx$. However,

$$\lim_{n \to \infty} s_{Rn} = \lim_{n \to \infty} s_{Rn}' + \lim_{n \to \infty} s_{Rn}'' = \int_a^\gamma f(x)\,dx + \int_\gamma^b f(x)\,dx .$$

Thus (4–63) follows, which is what we wished to show.

We can use (4–63) to see that $f(x)$ does not have to be continuous in order for $\int_a^b f(x)\,dx$ to exist. Suppose that $f(x)$ is continuous over I_{ab}^c except at the point γ where it has a jump discontinuity, as shown in Figure 4–17. The $\int_a^b f(x)\,dx$ should be simply the area of the shaded region. However, from (4–63), this shaded area is $\int_a^\gamma f(x)\,dx + \int_\gamma^b f(x)\,dx$ and the latter integrals should exist. Thus we see that $\int_a^b f(x)\,dx$ should exist and should be given by (4–63). This is indeed correct. We shall, however, omit the details of the rigorous proof.

4–9 THE FUNDAMENTAL THEOREM OF THE CALCULUS

We are now ready to study what is perhaps the most important result in the calculus, and for this reason it is referred to as *the fundamental theorem of the calculus*. This theorem provides the connection between differentiation and integration. At the moment, the reader will probably see no connection whatever between derivatives and definite integrals. We shall see, however, that there is a very intimate and important connection which, among other things, provides a means for conveniently evaluating many definite integrals.

There are two forms in which the fundamental theorem can be stated and we shall consider one in this section and the other in the next. Let us begin with what is called the first form of the fundamental theorem. *Sup-*

pose that $F(x)$ is a function which possesses a derivative at each point in the closed interval I_{ab}^c. Let $F'(x) = f(x)$ so that $f(x)$ is the derivative function for $F(x)$. Assume that $f(x)$ is continuous at each point in I_{ab}^c. Then

$$\int_a^b f(x)\, dx = F(b) - F(a) . \tag{4-67}$$

This theorem says that, if we are trying to evaluate $\int_a^b f(x)\, dx$ for some continuous function, this can be done very easily if, by one means or another, we can find *any* function $F(x)$ such that $F'(x) = f(x)$ for each $x \in I_{ab}^c$, since $\int_a^b f(x)\, dx$ is simply $F(b) - F(a)$. *Any function $F(x)$ such that $F'(x) = f(x)$ for all x in some interval is called a primitive function or antiderivative for $f(x)$ over the interval.* The first form of the fundamental theorem then says that it is easy to evaluate $\int_a^b f(x)\, dx$ if a primitive function for $f(x)$ is known; we simply use (4-67). The problem of evaluating definite integrals is then reduced to that of finding primitive functions. Let us now prove this form of the fundamental theorem.

First of all, since $f(x)$ is assumed to be continuous over I_{ab}^c, it follows that $\int_a^b f(x)\, dx$ exists and can be determined by finding the limit of one of the Riemann sequences for $f(x)$ over I_{ab}^c. Let us then proceed to divide the interval I_{ab}^c into n subintervals by the points

$$x_k = a + \frac{b-a}{n} k, \quad k = 1, \ldots, n-1, \quad x_0 = a, \quad x_n = b ,$$

so that, as usual, the subintervals are of equal length. Now note that for every n

$$\begin{aligned} F(b) - F(a) &= F(x_n) - F(x_0) \\ &= [F(x_n) - F(x_{n-1})] + [F(x_{n-1}) - F(x_{n-2})] \\ &\quad + \cdots + [F(x_2) - F(x_1)] + [F(x_1) - F(x_0)] \\ &= \sum_{k=1}^n [F(x_k) - F(x_{k-1})] . \end{aligned} \tag{4-68}$$

To proceed, we make use of the mean value theorem which was quoted but not proved in Section 3–16. The mean value theorem states that, if $F(x)$ is differentiable at each point in $I_{\alpha,\alpha+h}^c$, then there exists an ξ in the interior of this interval for which $F(\alpha + h) - F(\alpha) = F'(\xi)h$. The function $F(x)$ we are studying possesses a derivative in each point in each subinterval. Furthermore, $x_k = x_{k-1} + h$.

Therefore, we can apply the mean value theorem to conclude that for each k there exists an ξ_k, $x_{k-1} < \xi_k < x_k$ such that

$$F(x_k) - F(x_{k-1}) = F'(\xi_k)h = f(\xi_k)h . \tag{4-69}$$

Then

$$\sum_{k=1}^{n} [F(x_k) - F(x_{k-1})] = h \sum_{k=1}^{n} f(\xi_k) = \frac{b-a}{n} \sum_{k=1}^{n} f(\xi_k) . \qquad (4\text{–}70)$$

If we now write

$$s_{Rn} = \frac{b-a}{n} \sum_{k=1}^{n} f(\xi_k) , \qquad (4\text{–}71)$$

then $\{s_{Rn}\}$ is a Riemann sequence for $f(x)$ over I_{ab}^c. We have assumed that $F'(x) = f(x)$ is continuous over I_{ab}^c, and therefore $\{s_{Rn}\}$ converges to $\int_a^b f(x)\, dx$. However, from (4–68), (4–70) and (4–71) we conclude that for each n

$$s_{Rn} = F(b) - F(a) = \lambda .$$

Hence each term in the sequence $\{s_{Rn}\}$ is a constant λ and from (4–10) we know that the limit of this sequence is λ. Thus

$$\lim_{n \to \infty} s_{Rn} = F(b) - F(a) = \int_a^b f(x)\, dx ,$$

which is what we wished to prove. The key to proving this form of the fundamental theorem of the calculus is the mean value theorem, which makes it possible to express $F(x_k) - F(x_{k-1})$ in terms of $F'(x)$.

A notation which is frequently used is

$$F(b) - F(a) = F(x) \Big|_a^b . \qquad (4\text{–}72)$$

With this notation, we can write

$$\int_a^b f(x)\, dx = F(x) \Big|_a^b \qquad (4\text{–}73)$$

Let us now illustrate the usefulness of the first form of the fundamental theorem by giving several simple examples.

EXAMPLES. 1. Note that $d\, \lambda x/dx = \lambda$. Since $f(x) = \lambda$ is continuous over any interval I_{ab}^c, the definite integral of λ over this interval exists, and by (4–67)

$$\int_a^b \lambda\, dx = \lambda x \Big|_a^b = \lambda(b - a) . \qquad (4\text{–}74)$$

When $\lambda > 0$, $\int_a^b \lambda\, dx$ is simply the area of the set of points $y \geq 0$, $y \leq \lambda$, $x \geq a$, $x \leq b$, which is a rectangle, and its interior, the rectangle having a base of length $b - a$ and an altitude of length λ. The result (4–74), then, is nothing but the formula for the area of a rectangle. We started out by

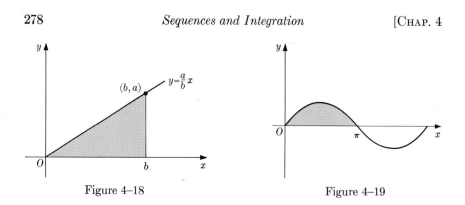

Figure 4–18   Figure 4–19

assuming that the formula for the area of a rectangle was known, so (4–74) cannot be looked upon as a proof of the formula for computing the area of a rectangle.

2. Consider the right triangle shown in Figure 4–18. The area of this triangle is the area of the set of points $y \geq 0$, $y \leq ax/b$, $x \geq 0$, $x \leq b$, and this is

$$\int_0^b \frac{ax}{b}\, dx \,.$$

Now

$$\frac{d}{dx}\left(\frac{ax^2}{2b}\right) = \frac{ax}{b}\,.$$

Therefore, since $f(x) = ax/b$ is continuous over I^c_{ab}, $\int_a^b f(x)\, dx$ exists and

$$\int_0^b \frac{ax}{b}\, dx = \frac{ax^2}{2b}\,\Big|_0^b = \frac{ab}{2}\,,$$

which is the familiar formula for the area of a right triangle.

3. Let us compute $\int_0^3 x^3\, dx$. Clearly x^3 is continuous and thus the integral exists. Furthermore, if $F(x) = x^4/4$, then $F'(x) = x^3$. Thus by (4–67)

$$\int_0^3 x^3\, dx = F(3) - F(0) = \frac{3^4}{4}\,.$$

The reader should interpret this result in terms of areas.

4. Let us compute

$$\int_0^\pi \sin x\, dx \,.$$

The definite integral exists since $\sin x$ is continuous for all x. Furthermore, if $F(x) = -\cos x$, then $F'(x) = \sin x$. Thus

$$\int_0^\pi \sin x\, dx = -\cos \pi + \cos 0 = 2\,,$$

since $\cos \pi = -1$. Here we have shown that the area of the shaded region in Figure 4–19 is 2. Note that

$$\int_0^{2\pi} \sin x \, dx = -\cos 2\pi + \cos 0 = 0 \, .$$

The reader should interpret this result geometrically using Figure 4–19.

5. The first form of the fundamental theorem can be restated in a form which is very important for many practical applications. Recall that if $y = F(x)$, the rate of change of y with respect to x is $F'(x) = f(x)$. Then (4–67) says that the definite integral of the rate of change of y with respect to x from a to b is the value of y at $x = b$ minus the value of y at $x = a$. Thus, for example, if we were given the speed of a car as a function of time, the distance traveled from time 0 to t is the integral of the speed from 0 to t. Practical problems where the change in some variable is found by integrating its rate of change arise frequently.

4-10 SECOND FORM OF THE FUNDAMENTAL THEOREM

Suppose that $f(x)$ is continuous at each point in I_{ab}^c. If we select a specific value of x in I_{ab}^c, say t, then the definite integral

$$\int_a^t f(x) \, dx \qquad\qquad (4\text{–}75)$$

exists for each $t \in I_{ab}^c$. This is true even when $t = a$ because of (4–59). For each $t \in I_{ab}^c$ there is determined a real number (4–75). This rule of associating a number with each $t \in I_{ab}^c$ serves to define a function $F(t)$ whose domain is I_{ab}^c, and we can write

$$F(t) = \int_a^t f(x) \, dx \, . \qquad\qquad (4\text{–}76)$$

Thus the concept of a definite integral can be used to define functions.

We would now like to study the relationship between $F(t)$ and $f(x)$ when $F(t)$ is defined by (4–76). Let t and $t + h$ be in I_{ab}^c. Then $F(t + h)$ and $F(t)$ are defined, and by (4–63)

$$F(t + h) - F(t) = \int_a^{t+h} f(x) \, dx - \int_a^t f(x) \, dx = \int_t^{t+h} f(x) \, dx \, .$$

For h very small $\int_t^{t+h} f(x) \, dx \doteq f(t)h$, as we can see intuitively from Figure 4–20, and

$$\frac{F(t + h) - F(t)}{h} \doteq \frac{f(t)h}{h} = f(t) \, . \qquad\qquad (4\text{–}77)$$

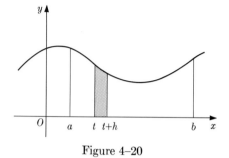

Figure 4–20

This approximation should get better and better as h gets smaller and smaller. Thus it should be true that

$$\lim_{h \to 0} \frac{F(t + h) - F(t)}{h} = f(t) \ . \tag{4–78}$$

In other words, it appears that the function (4–76) is differentiable and its derivative function is $f(t)$. We have not provided a rigorous proof because (4–77) does not hold exactly, and hence we have not rigorously demonstrated that (4–78) holds. This does happen to be correct and it can be proved rigorously, although we shall not give the detailed proof. The second form of the fundamental theorem is essentially a statement that $F(t)$ is differentiable and that $f(t)$ is its derivative. The precise statement of the second form of the fundamental theorem is as follows. *If $f(x)$ is continuous at each point in the closed interval I_{ab}^c and if $F(t)$ is defined by (4–76), then $F(t)$ is differentiable for every t in the open interval I_{ab}^0 and $F'(t) = f(t)$.* Another way of stating this result is that the function $F(t)$ defined by (4–76) is a primitive function for $f(t)$. This proves, then, that if $f(x)$ is continuous over some interval it will have a primitive function.

   There is still another useful way of interpreting the second form of the fundamental theorem. We can think of t in (4–76) as being a variable upper limit on the definite integral. Then the second form of the fundamental theorem simply tells us how to differentiate an integral with respect to its upper limit, that is,

$$\frac{d}{dt} \int_a^t f(x) \ dx = f(t) \ . \tag{4–79}$$

   Instead of having a variable upper limit we could, in the above development, have made the lower limit a variable and considered an integral of the form

$$G(t) = \int_t^b f(x) \ dx \ . \tag{4–80}$$

This defines a function as indicated. However, by (4–60) and (4–61),

$$\int_t^b f(x)\,dx = -\int_b^t f(x)\,dx = \int_b^t -f(x)\,dx\ .$$

Then by (4–79) we conclude that

$$\frac{d}{dt}G(t) = \frac{d}{dt}\int_t^b f(x)\,dx = -f(t)\ , \tag{4–81}$$

and (4–81) tells how to differentiate an integral with respect to a variable lower limit.

4–11 INDEFINITE INTEGRALS

In Section 4–9 any function $F(x)$ having the property that $F'(x) = f(x)$ over some interval was called a primitive function for $f(x)$. Once we know a primitive function for $f(x)$, then from the fundamental theorem we can easily evaluate $\int_a^b f(x)\,dx$. Its value is simply $F(b) - F(a)$. The basic problem of the integral calculus, then, is to find a primitive function $F(x)$ for any given function $f(x)$, or more simply, to find a function whose derivative is $f(x)$.

In our above discussion we have said nothing about whether the primitive function is unique or whether there can be many different primitive functions. Note that specifying $f(x)$ specifies the slope of the primitive function $F(x)$ at each x, but it does not specify the value of $F(x)$ for any x. Intuitively, it would appear that if we specify the value of $F(x)$ at just one value of x, then the slopes will determine $F(x)$ for all other x. Thus it would appear that specifying $f(x)$ determines the shape of $F(x)$, but does not determine its precise location. This intuitive idea is correct and we shall now make it more precise. Suppose that $F_1(x)$ is a primitive function for $f(x)$ so that $F_1'(x) = f(x)$. Then

$$F(x) = F_1(x) + \lambda, \quad \lambda \text{ any constant}\ , \tag{4–82}$$

is also a primitive function for $f(x)$, since $F'(x) = F_1'(x) = f(x)$. This shows that, if there is one primitive function, there are an infinite number of primitive functions which can be generated by adding a constant to the given primitive function. We shall now prove that *if $F_1(x)$ and $F_2(x)$ are any two primitive functions for $f(x)$, then $F_1(x) - F_2(x) = \lambda$, a constant, for all x, so that any two primitive functions differ only by a constant. In other words, if $F_1(x)$ is any primitive function for $f(x)$, then every other primitive function for $f(x)$ over the same interval can be written in the form (4–82)*.

The proof of this result depends on the mean value theorem, just as did the proof of the first form of the fundamental theorem. Suppose that we have two functions $F_1(x)$ and $F_2(x)$ which are differentiable over I_{ab}^0, and suppose that $F_1'(x) = F_2'(x)$ for each $x \in I_{ab}^0$. Consider now the function

$G(x) = F_1(x) - F_2(x)$. Then $G(x)$ is differentiable for each $x \in I_{ab}^0$. Thus $G'(x)$ is differentiable at each point in the closed interval whose end points are α and ζ when $a < \alpha < \zeta < b$. The mean value theorem can then be applied to $G(x)$ over this closed interval to conclude that

$$G(\zeta) - G(\alpha) = G'(\xi)(\zeta - \alpha) , \qquad (4\text{–}83)$$

where ξ is in the interior of the closed interval with end points α and ζ. But $G'(\xi) = 0$, so

$$G(\zeta) = G(\alpha)$$

for every $\zeta \in I_{ab}^0$, or since $G(x) = F_1(x) - F_2(x)$,

$$F_1(\zeta) - F_2(\zeta) = G(\alpha) = \lambda = F_1(\alpha) - F_2(\alpha) . \qquad (4\text{–}84)$$

In other words, for all $x \in I_{ab}^0$, the function $F_1(x) - F_2(x)$ is a constant λ whose value is $F_1(\alpha) - F_2(\alpha)$. This is precisely what we wished to prove.

EXAMPLE. If $f(x) = x$, then $F_1(x) = x^2/2$ is a primitive function for $f(x)$ for all x. Every other primitive function can be written

$$F(x) = F_1(x) + \lambda = \frac{x^2}{2} + \lambda .$$

The set of all primitive functions is obtained by allowing λ to take on all real values, and is the one-parameter family of parabolas shown in Figure 4–21. Each parabola has the property that its derivative function is $f(x) = x$.

We have now completely characterized the primitive functions for a given function $f(x)$ over any interval. The primitive functions are unique

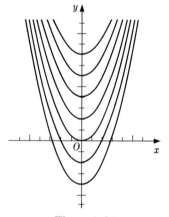

Figure 4–21

up to an additive constant, so that if $F_1(x)$ is any primitive function, every other primitive function can be written $F_1(x) + \lambda$ for some value of λ. A special symbolism is used to denote the entire one-parameter family of primitive functions. Instead of the usual set notation, the set of all primitive functions for $f(x)$ is denoted by

$$\int f(x)\, dx \, , \tag{4–85}$$

and this set is called *the indefinite integral* of $f(x)$. The symbolism for the indefinite integral looks precisely like that for the definite integral except that no limits are placed on the integral. It is important to note that, while the symbolism for definite and indefinite integrals is similar, they have quite different meanings. A definite integral is a number, while an indefinite integral is a set of functions. There is a connection between definite and indefinite integrals in the sense that, if we select any function $F(x)$ from the set $\int f(x)\, dx$, then $\int_a^b f(x)\, dx = F(b) - F(a)$. Using set notation, we can write

$$\int f(x)\, dx = \{F(x)|F(x) = F_1(x) + \lambda, \quad \text{all real } \lambda\} \, , \tag{4–86}$$

where $F_1(x)$ is any one particular primitive function.

There are two simple properties of indefinite integrals which are frequently useful and which we shall now obtain. Suppose that $F_1(x)$ is a primitive function for $f(x)$. Then $\alpha F_1(x)$ is a primitive function for $\alpha f(x)$, and consequently

$$\int \alpha f(x)\, dx = \{F(x)|F(x) = \alpha F_1(x) + \lambda, \quad \text{all } \lambda\} \, . \tag{4–87}$$

Also, if $F_1(x)$ and $F_2(x)$ are primitive functions for $f_1(x)$ and $f_2(x)$ respectively, then $F_1(x) + F_2(x)$ is a primitive function for $f_1(x) + f_2(x)$. Consequently

$$\int [f_1(x) + f_2(x)]\, dx = \{F(x)|F(x) = F_1(x) + F_2(x) + \lambda, \quad \text{all } \lambda\} \, . \tag{4–88}$$

In general, then, if $F_j(x)$ is a primitive function for $f_j(x)$

$$\int \left[\sum_{j=1}^n \alpha_j f_j(x) \right] dx = \left\{ F(x)|F(x) = \sum_{j=1}^n \alpha_j F_j(x) + \lambda, \quad \text{all } \lambda \right\} . \tag{4–89}$$

When writing indefinite integrals such as (4–89), the set symbolism is often omitted and we simply write the abbreviated form

$$\int \left[\sum_{j=1}^n \alpha_j f_j(x) \right] dx = \sum_{j=1}^n \alpha_j F_j(x) + \lambda \, , \tag{4–90}$$

where it is understood that λ takes on all real values. Thus by (4–90) we mean (4–89).

Examples. 1. Recall that $dx^n/dx = nx^{n-1}$. Thus $x^{n+1}/(n+1)$ is a primitive function for x^n, $n = 1, 2, \ldots$. This also is true for $n = 0$ when x^0 is defined to be 1. Using the notation of (4–90),

$$\int x^n \, dx = \frac{x^{n+1}}{n+1} + \lambda \, . \tag{4-91}$$

Thus if $f(x)$ is the nth degree polynomial

$$f(x) = \sum_{j=0}^{n} a_j x^j \, ,$$

we see from (4–90) that

$$\int f(x) \, dx = \sum_{j=0}^{n} \frac{a_j}{j+1} x^{j+1} + \lambda = \frac{a_n}{n+1} x^{n+1} + \cdots + a_0 x + \lambda \, . \tag{4-92}$$

Thus each primitive function for a polynomial of degree n is a polynomial of degree $n + 1$.

2. Recall that $dx^\alpha/dx = \alpha x^{\alpha-1}$, $x > 0$ and α a rational number. Thus $x^{\alpha+1}/(\alpha + 1)$ is a primitive function for x^α, $x > 0$ when $\alpha \neq -1$, so

$$\int x^\alpha \, dx = \frac{x^{\alpha+1}}{\alpha + 1} + \lambda, \quad x > 0, \quad \alpha \neq -1 \, . \tag{4-93}$$

The reader will note that $\alpha = -1$ is not included in the above because division by 0 would be involved. Note there is no α such that $d\beta x^\alpha/dx = 1/x$. It would have to be x^0. But $x^0 = 1$ and $d1/dx = 0$. Thus we can find a primitive function for x^α for every α except $\alpha = -1$ using what we have obtained previously. Since $1/x$ is continuous for $x > 0$, we know that it has a primitive function. The primitive function, however, is not one that we have studied as yet. It will be introduced in the next chapter.

3. Recall that

$$\frac{d}{dx} \sin x = \cos x; \quad \frac{d}{dx} \cos x = -\sin x \, .$$

Thus $\sin x$ is a primitive function for $\cos x$ and $-\cos x$ is a primitive function for $\sin x$. Hence

$$\int \sin x \, dx = -\cos x + \lambda, \quad \text{all } x \, ; \tag{4-94}$$

$$\int \cos x \, dx = \sin x + \lambda, \quad \text{all } x \, . \tag{4-95}$$

REFERENCES

The references given at the end of Chapter 3 are also appropriate for this chapter.

PROBLEMS

Section 4–1

In Problems 1 through 9 compute the first ten terms of the sequence $\{a_n\}$ and plot these on diagrams of the type shown in Figures 4–1 and 4–2. Try to estimate the limit of the sequence in each case. Do not attempt to prove that your estimate is indeed the limit.

1. $a_n = 2 - \dfrac{3}{n}$;

2. $a_n = 1 + \dfrac{1}{n^2}$;

3. $a_n = \dfrac{1}{n+1}$;

4. $a_n = \dfrac{n-1}{n+1}$;

5. $a_n = \dfrac{3n-2}{n+1}$;

6. $a_n = \dfrac{n+2}{n^2+1}$;

7. $a_n = \dfrac{n^2+3}{n^2+2}$;

8. $a_n = \dfrac{n-1}{3+n}$;

9. $a_n = \dfrac{3 + (-1)^n \dfrac{1}{n}}{2 + (-1)^{n+1} \dfrac{1}{n}}$.

10. Is $\{a_n\}$ a sequence if $a_n = [(-1)^n/n]^{1/2}$?

11. For the sequence of Problem 1, determine a value of n, call it n_0, such that if $n > n_0$, $|a_n - \alpha| < 10^{-6}$, where α is the limit of the sequence. What is an n_0 if 10^{-6} is replaced by 10^{-12}?

12. For the sequence of Problem 2, determine a value of n, call it n_0, such that if $n > n_0$, $|a_n - \alpha| < 10^{-6}$, where α is the limit of the sequence. What is an n_0 if 10^{-6} is replaced by 10^{-12}?

13. Show that the function $g(\epsilon)$ used in the definition of a limit is not unique. In particular, show that $g_1(\epsilon) = g(\epsilon) + \gamma, \gamma > 0$, could be used as well, as could $g_2(\epsilon) = \beta g(\epsilon), \beta > 1$.

14. Note that the limiting behavior of a sequence $\{a_n\}$ depends only on the nature of the terms for very large n. Thus one can arbitrarily redefine the first n_0 terms of a sequence, where n_0 is any natural number, and the limiting behavior will be unchanged. In particular, prove that if $\{a_n\}$ converges to α, and if $\{b_n\}$ is a sequence with $b_n = a_n, n > n_0$, then $\{b_n\}$ converges to α regardless of how the first n_0 terms of b_n are defined.

15. Given the result of Problem 14, what was the basis for our estimating the limit of a sequence by looking at the behavior of the first few terms?

Section 4–2

In Problems 1 through 12 plot a number of terms of the sequence $\{a_n\}$ on a diagram of the type shown in Figure 4–2. From the graphical results so obtained try to decide whether or not the sequence approaches a limit and what the limit is if there is one. If the sequence appears to diverge, try to decide how many points of accumulation there are, if any. Do not attempt to determine rigorously the behavior of the sequence. Simply use the results obtained graphically.

1. $a_n = \dfrac{3n + 1}{2 + 4n}$;

2. $a_n = 3 + \dfrac{2 - \dfrac{1}{n}}{n}$;

3. $a_n = \dfrac{4 + n}{n^2 + 2}$;

4. $a_n = 1 + (-1)^n \left(3 - \dfrac{1}{n} \right)$;

5. $a_n = 2 + (-1)^{n+1} \left(4 + \dfrac{2}{n} \right)$;

6. $a_n = \begin{cases} 2, & n \text{ even} \\ 2 + \dfrac{1}{n}, & n \text{ odd}; \end{cases}$

7. $a_n = \begin{cases} 3 - \dfrac{1}{n^2} & n \text{ even} \\ 3 + \dfrac{1}{n}, & n \text{ odd}; \end{cases}$

8. $a_n = \begin{cases} 3 + (-1)^{n/2} \dfrac{1}{n + 1}, & n \text{ even} \\ 2 - \dfrac{4}{n}, & n \text{ odd}; \end{cases}$

9. $a_n = \begin{cases} 4 + \dfrac{n - 1}{n + 1}, & n \text{ even} \\ 5 - \dfrac{3}{n}, & n \text{ odd}; \end{cases}$

10. $a_n = \begin{cases} -1 + \dfrac{3n}{n + 1}, & n \text{ even} \\ n^{1/2}, & n \text{ odd}; \end{cases}$

11. $a_n = \begin{cases} -1 + (-1)^{n/2} \dfrac{2n - 1}{n + 1}, & n \text{ even} \\ (-1)^n, & n \text{ odd}; \end{cases}$

12. $a_n = \begin{cases} 2 + (-1)^{n/2} \left[3 + (-1)^{n/2} \dfrac{1}{n} \right], & n \text{ even} \\ 4 + (-1)^{(n+1)/2} \left[3 + \dfrac{2}{n^2} \right], & n \text{ odd} . \end{cases}$

Section 4–3

In Problems 1 through 12 determine the limit of the sequence $\{a_n\}$ using the rules discussed in this section. Give in detail the reasoning involved in applying the various rules.

1. $a_n = \dfrac{1}{n} + 3$;

2. $a_n = \dfrac{2}{n} - \dfrac{3}{n^2}$;

3. $a_n = \left(3 - \dfrac{2}{n} \right) + \left(4 + \dfrac{1}{n^2} \right)$;

4. $a_n = n \left[2 + \dfrac{(-1)^n}{n^3} \right] \dfrac{1}{n} + \dfrac{2}{n^2}$;

5. $a_n = \left(5 + \dfrac{2}{3 + \dfrac{1}{n}} \right) \left(3 - \dfrac{2}{n} \right)$;

6. $a_n = \dfrac{2 + \dfrac{1}{n}}{3 - \dfrac{5}{n^2}}$;

7. $a_n = \dfrac{6n - 1}{7n + 2}$;

8. $a_n = \dfrac{3n^2 - n}{2n^3 - n}$;

9. $a_n = \dfrac{2n - \dfrac{1}{n}}{n^2 + 3 - \dfrac{2}{n}}$;

10. $a_n = \dfrac{2n^2 - 3n + 1}{4n^2 + 2}$;

11. $a_n = \dfrac{\left(2 - \dfrac{1}{n}\right)\left(3 + \dfrac{6}{n^2}\right) - \dfrac{8}{n}}{\left(3 + \dfrac{2}{n^2}\right)\left(1 + \dfrac{1}{n}\right)\left(3 + \dfrac{2}{n}\right)}$;

12. $a_n = \dfrac{2n^2 + \left(\dfrac{n - 1}{n + 3}\right)}{n^3 + 3\left(\dfrac{n^4 + 1}{2n}\right)}$.

13. Actually prove (4–7). Hint: $|c_n - \alpha - \beta| \le |a_n - \alpha| + |b_n - \beta|$.

14. For the sequence of Problem 1 actually determine a function $g(\epsilon)$ such that $|a_n - \alpha| < \epsilon$ when $n > g(\epsilon)$.

15. Construct an example illustrating a situation where $\{c_n\}$ converges while $\{a_n\}$ and $\{b_n\}$ diverge, but where $c_n = a_n + b_n$ for all n.

16. Construct an example illustrating a situation where $\{c_n\}$ converges while $\{a_n\}$ and $\{b_n\}$ diverge, but where $c_n = a_n b_n$ for all n.

17. Construct an example illustrating a situation where $\{c_n\}$ converges while $\{a_n\}$ and $\{b_n\}$ diverge, but where $c_n = a_n/b_n$ for all n.

18. Construct an example where $\{b_n\}$ converges to 0 and $\{c_n\}$, $c_n = a_n/b_n$ also converges.

Section 4–4

In Problems 1 through 5 determine the sum of the geometric series for the given value of r. Compare the result so obtained with the sum of the first five terms of the series.

1. $r = 0.2$;   **2.** $r = -0.2$;   **3.** $r = 0.6$;   **4.** $r = 0.9$;   **5.** $r = -0.95$.

In Problems 6 through 10 find the sum of the given infinite series when it converges. Also determine when the infinite series does converge.

6. $1 + \dfrac{\alpha}{1 + \alpha} + \left(\dfrac{\alpha}{1 + \alpha}\right)^2 + \left(\dfrac{\alpha}{1 + \alpha}\right)^3 + \cdots$;

7. $(1 - r)^{-1} + (1 - r)^{-2} + (1 - r)^{-3} + \cdots$;

8. $(1 + \alpha)^{-n} + (1 + \alpha)^{-2n} + (1 + \alpha)^{-3n} + \cdots$;

9. $1 + \left(\dfrac{r}{2 + r}\right)^3 + \left(\dfrac{r}{2 + r}\right)^6 + \left(\dfrac{r}{2 + r}\right)^9 + \cdots$;

10. $\alpha(1 - \alpha)^2 + \alpha(1 - \alpha)^3 + \alpha(1 - \alpha)^4 + \cdots$.

11. Prove that the infinite series generated by the sequence $\{a_n\}$ with $a_n = 1/n(n + 1)$ converges to 1. Hint: For all natural numbers n

$$\frac{1}{n(n + 1)} = \frac{1}{n} - \frac{1}{n + 1}.$$

12. Consider a geometric series with $r = -1$. Determine the sequence $\{s_n\}$ and characterize its behavior.

In Problems 13 through 18 determine the rational number represented by the non-terminating periodic decimal. The underlined digits are repeated unendingly.

13. $0.76\underline{143125}$;   **14.** $0.891\underline{246135}$;   **15.** 0.555111;

16. 6.999<u>3331</u>; **17.** 0.162421<u>7070123</u>; **18.** 0.1<u>010333762</u>.

19. Show that $0.24999 \cdots$ is the rational number $\frac{1}{4}$, just as is 0.25.

20. Prove that, if $\{a_n\}$ generates an infinite series which converges to s, $\{b_n\}$ with $b_n = \lambda a_n$ generates an infinite series which converges to λs. How can this result be interpreted intuitively?

21. Prove that, if $\{a_n\}$ generates an infinite series which converges to s_1 and $\{b_n\}$ generates an infinite series which converges to s_2, then $\{c_n\}$ with $c_n = a_n + b_n$ generates an infinite series which converges to $s_1 + s_2$. How can this result be interpreted intuitively?

Section 4–5

In Problems 1 through 10 simplify the summation given using summation notation.

1. $a_1 + 2a_2 + 3a_3 + \cdots + na_n$;   **2.** $2 + 2^2 + 2^3 + \cdots + 2^n$;

3. $b_1 a_2 + b_2 a_3 + \cdots + b_n a_{n+1}$;   **4.** $a_1^2 - b_1 + a_2^2 - b_2 + \cdots + a_n^2 - b_n$;

5. $a_1 b_{1k} + a_2 b_{2k} + \cdots + a_{20} b_{20.k}$;   **6.** $a_{1ij} + a_{2ij} + \cdots + a_{mij}$;

7. $a_{i1} b_{1j} + a_{i2} b_{2j} + \cdots + a_{in} b_{nj}$;   **8.** $1 + x + x^2 + x^3 + \cdots + x^n$;

9. $a_1 f_1(x) + a_2 f_2(x) + \cdots + a_n f_n(x)$;

10. $a_m b_{m+2}^2 + a_{m+1} b_{m+3}^3 + \cdots + a_{m+q} b_{m+q+2}^{2+q}$.

In Problems 11 through 20 write out explicitly the sums implied by the expression given.

11. $\displaystyle\sum_{j=1}^{5} (2 + j^2)$;   **12.** $\displaystyle\sum_{j=4}^{10} \frac{1}{j}$;   **13.** $\displaystyle\sum_{j=1}^{11} 3^j$;

14. $\displaystyle\sum_{j=1}^{b} \left[2j - \frac{3}{j^2} \right]$;   **15.** $\displaystyle\sum_{j=1}^{6} a_{ij} b$;   **16.** $\displaystyle\sum_{i=1}^{6} a_{ij} b_j$;

17. $\displaystyle\sum_{j=1}^{10} (a_i + 3b_j)$;   **18.** $\displaystyle\sum_{j=1}^{5} j^i$;   **19.** $\displaystyle\sum_{j=1}^{n} [a_j f_i(x) + b_i g_i(x)]$;

20. $\displaystyle\sum_{j=m}^{n} [a_{ij} b_{jk} f_k(x) + d_{ij}^2 g_j(x)]$.

In Problems 21 through 25 determine whether or not the indicated equation is correct. If it is correct, explain in detail why it is, and if not, explain why not.

21. $\displaystyle\sum_{j=1}^{n} (j^2 + 1) = 1 + \sum_{j=1}^{n} j^2$;   **22.** $\displaystyle\sum_{j=1}^{n} x_i y_i^2 = x_i \sum_{j=1}^{n} y_i^2$;

23. $\displaystyle\sum_{j=1}^{n} (j^2 + 1) = n(n + 1) + \sum_{j=1}^{n-1} j^2$;   **24.** $\displaystyle\sum_{j=1}^{n} x_j y_j = \left(\sum_{j=1}^{n} x_j \right) \left(\sum_{j=1}^{n} y_i \right)$;

25. $\displaystyle\sum_{j=1}^{n} (j + 6)^3 = \sum_{j=7}^{n+6} j^3$.

Section 4–6

1. Consider the sequences $\{s_{Ln}\}$ and $\{s_{Un}\}$ with s_{Ln} and s_{Un} given by (4–44) and (4–45), respectively. Evaluate s_{Ln} and s_{Un} for $n = 10$, 100 and 1000 and compare the results so obtained with the actual area of the triangle. Is there any n for which $s_{Ln} = s_{Un}$?

2. Consider again the sequences defined by (4–44) and (4–45). Construct carefully a graph of $y = x$, and for $n = 10$ draw on this figure the rectangles the sum of whose areas is s_{Ln} and the rectangles the sum of whose areas is s_{Un}.

3. Consider the sequences $\{s_{Ln}\}$ and $\{s_{Un}\}$ with s_{Ln} and s_{Un} given by (4–50) and (4–53) respectively. Evaluate s_{Ln} and s_{Un} for $n = 10$, 100 and 1000, with $b = 3$, and compare the results with the actual area of the region. Is there any n for which $s_{Ln} = s_{Un}$?

4. Consider again the sequences defined by (4–50) and (4–53). Construct carefully a graph of $y = x^2$ and for $n = 10$ and $b = 2$ draw on this figure the rectangles the sum of whose areas is s_{Ln} and the rectangles the sum of whose areas is s_{Un}.

5. Illustrate geometrically the set of points which are solutions to the inequalities $y - x \le 0$, $y \ge 0$, $x \ge 1$, $x \le 3$. Determine the area of this region using the methods introduced in this section. Also compute the area using results known from plane geometry and show that the same value is obtained.

6. Illustrate geometrically the set of points which are solutions to the inequalities $y - x^2 \le 0$, $y \ge 0$, $x \ge 1$, $x \le 3$. Determine the area of this region using the methods introduced in this section. Can the area also be computed from a result obtained in the text?

7. Illustrate geometrically the set of points which are solutions to the inequalities $y + (x - 2)^2 \le 4$, $y \ge 0$. Determine the area of this region using the methods introduced in this section.

8. Illustrate geometrically the set of points which are solutions to the inequalities $y + x \le 6$, $y \ge 0.5x$, $x \ge 0$, $x \le 2$. Determine the area of this region using the methods introduced in this section.

9. Illustrate geometrically the set of points which are solutions to the inequalities $y - x \le 3$, $y - x^2 \ge 0$, $x \ge 0$, $x \le 2$. Determine the area of this region using the methods developed in this section.

10. Illustrate the set of points which are solutions to the set of inequalities $y - x^3 \le 0$, $y \ge 0$, $x \ge 0$, $x \le 3$. Determine the area of this region using the methods introduced in this section.

11. Use the method described in this section to determine approximately the area of the region characterized by $y \ge 0$, $y \le (1 - x^2)^{1/2}$, that is, the area of half of the unit circle. Compute s_{Ln} and s_{Un} for $n = 10$. From this obtain approximately the area of the unit circle. Note that this procedure provides a method for computing π as accurately as desired. Can you carry out the limiting process to find the area exactly? What are the difficulties involved?

12. Use the method described in this section to determine approximately the area of the set of points $y \geq 0$, $y \leq \sin x$, $0 \leq x \leq \pi$. Illustrate this set geometrically. Compute s_{Ln} and s_{Un} for $n = 10$. Can you carry out the limiting process to find the area exactly? What are the difficulties involved?

Section 4–7

1. Determine the area of the region in Figure 4–12 using a Riemann sequence with ξ_k being the midpoint of the kth subinterval.

2. Determine the area of the region in Figure 4–13 using a Riemann sequence with ξ_k being the midpoint of the kth subinterval.

3. Re-solve Problem 1 with ξ_k being one-third of the distance from x_{k-1} to x_k.

4. Re-solve Problem 2 with ξ_k being one-third of the distance from x_{k-1} to x_k.

5. Construct a Riemann sequence for finding the area of the region in Figure 4–12 where the subintervals are not of equal length, and determine the limit of this sequence. Hint: One way to do this is to divide the interval $0 \leq x \leq 0.5$ into n parts and the interval $0.5 \leq x \leq 2$ into n parts. Then in computing s_{Rn}, $2n$ subintervals are used. Are these of equal length?

6. Repeat Problem 5 for the region of Figure 4–13.

In Problems 7 through 18 evaluate the definite integral by constructing an appropriate Riemann sequence and determining its limit.

7. $\displaystyle\int_0^2 0.5x \, dx;$ **8.** $\displaystyle\int_0^4 3x^2 \, dx;$ **9.** $\displaystyle\int_{-1}^2 x \, dx;$

10. $\displaystyle\int_{-1}^1 x^2 \, dx;$ **11.** $\displaystyle\int_0^4 (3 + x) \, dx;$ **12.** $\displaystyle\int_0^3 (2 + 3x) \, dx;$

13. $\displaystyle\int_{-2}^3 (1 + x) \, dx;$ **14.** $\displaystyle\int_0^3 (x^2 + x) \, dx;$ **15.** $\displaystyle\int_{-2}^4 (x - x^2) \, dx;$

16. $\displaystyle\int_0^6 (3 - x) \, dx;$ **17.** $\displaystyle\int_0^6 (3 - 2x) \, dx;$ **18.** $\displaystyle\int_0^3 (2 - x + 3x^2) \, dx.$

19. Show that, if the function $f(x)$ has an infinite discontinuity at some point in I_{ab}^c, then $\int_a^b f(x) \, dx$ does not exist. Thus show that $\int_0^1 dx/x$ does not exist. Hint: Will s_{Un} exist for any n?

20. Show that $\int_0^1 f(x) \, dx$ does not exist when

$$f(x) = \begin{cases} 1, & x \text{ irrational} \\ 0, & x \text{ rational}. \end{cases}$$

Hint: Determine $\{s_{Ln}\}$ and $\{s_{Un}\}$.

Section 4–8

1. Evaluate $\int_{-1}^1 x \, dx$ by constructing a Riemann sequence and determining its limit. Interpret the result geometrically.

2. Evaluate $\int_{-3}^{2} (x^2 - 2) \, dx$ by constructing a Riemann sequence and determining its limit. Interpret this result geometrically.

3. Explain why the intuitive justification for (4–59) is not a proof.

4. Why cannot (4–60) be proved?

5. Show by constructing the appropriate Riemann sequences and finding their limits that

$$\int_0^3 2x \, dx = 2 \int_0^3 x \, dx .$$

6. Show by constructing the appropriate Riemann sequences and finding their limits that

$$\int_0^2 (x + x^2) \, dx = \int_0^2 x \, dx + \int_0^2 x^2 \, dx .$$

7. Explain why the argument based on the use of Figure 4–16 did not prove (4–63).

8. Construct an appropriate Riemann sequence and determine its limit to evaluate each of the following integrals:

$$\int_{-1}^{1} x \, dx; \qquad \int_{-1}^{-0.2} x \, dx; \qquad \int_{-0.2}^{1} x \, dx .$$

Thus, verify in this case that

$$\int_{-1}^{1} x \, dx = \int_{-1}^{-0.2} x \, dx + \int_{-0.2}^{1} x \, dx .$$

9. Prove that (4–63) holds even if γ does not lie between a and b. Assume that $f(x)$ is continuous over all the intervals concerned.

10. Prove that

$$\int_a^b f(x) \, dx \leq \int_a^b |f(x)| \, dx .$$

Section 4–9

1. It is interesting to note that the proof of the fundamental theorem proves another surprising fact. This is the fact that, by properly choosing the ξ_k in each interval, it is possible to have s_{Rn} equal exactly to $\int_a^b f(x) \, dx$ for each n. Give a geometric discussion which suggests intuitively that this should be the case. Note that this holds even if $n = 1$. When $n = 1$, $s_{Rn} = f(\xi)(b - a)$. Hence from the proof of the fundamental theorem we can conclude that there exists an ξ, $a \leq \xi \leq b$, such that

$$\int_a^b f(x) \, dx = f(\xi)(b - a) .$$

This is a useful result which is called the mean value theorem for integrals. Find the ξ such that

$$\int_0^2 x^2 \, dx = 2\xi^2 .$$

2. Find the area of the set of points which form the set of solutions to the set of inequalities $y \leq x^{1/2}$, $y \geq 0$, $x \geq 0$, $x \leq 4$. Illustrate this region geometrically.

3. Find the area of the set of points which form the set of solutions to the set of inequalities $y \leq \cos x$, $y \geq 0$, $x \geq 0$, $x \leq \pi/2$. Illustrate the region geometrically.

In Problems 4 through 14 evaluate the given definite integral by finding a suitable primitive function.

4. $\displaystyle\int_{-3}^{4} 5x^2 \, dx$;

5. $\displaystyle\int_{1}^{6} (2 + x) \, dx$;

6. $\displaystyle\int_{0}^{4} (x^{1/2} + x) \, dx$;

7. $\displaystyle\int_{-2}^{2} x^3 \, dx$;

8. $\displaystyle\int_{-1}^{3} (x + \sin x) \, dx$;

9. $\displaystyle\int_{0}^{4} x^{5.431} \, dx$;

10. $\displaystyle\int_{2}^{5} (x^{4.16} + x^{-3.15}) \, dx$;

11. $\displaystyle\int_{-1}^{7} (x^2 + 2x + 3) \, dx$;

12. $\displaystyle\int_{4}^{6} \frac{1}{x^2} \, dx$;

13. $\displaystyle\int_{1}^{3.5} (x - 3)^2 \, dx$;

14. $\displaystyle\int_{2}^{6} (2x^{1/2} + x^{-1/2}) \, dx$.

Section 4–10

1. Determine $F'(t)$ in each of the following cases.

    (a) $F(t) = \displaystyle\int_{0}^{t} x^{1/2} \, dx$;

    (b) $F(t) = \displaystyle\int_{-5}^{t} (x^2 - 3x + 1) \, dx$;

    (c) $F(t) = \displaystyle\int_{-\pi}^{t} \sin x \, dx$;

    (d) $F(t) = \displaystyle\int_{t}^{3} (3 + x) \, dx$;

    (e) $F(t) = \displaystyle\int_{t}^{6} (x^2 + 4x) \, dx$.

2. Determine explicitly $F(t)$ when

    (a) $F(t) = \displaystyle\int_{-3}^{t} x^2 \, dx$;

    (b) $F(t) = \displaystyle\int_{10}^{t} (4 + x) \, dx$;

    (c) $F(t) = \displaystyle\int_{0}^{t} x^{4.732} \, dx$;

    (d) $F(t) = \displaystyle\int_{-4}^{t} (x + \sin x) \, dx$.

3. The second form of the fundamental theorem can be proved rigorously using the mean value theorem for integrals developed in Problem 1 for Section 4–9. Give the rigorous proof. Hint: Show that $|f(\xi) - f(t)|$ can be made less than ϵ when $|h| < g(\epsilon)$.

4. Suppose that $h(t)$ is differentiable for all t in some open interval I^0_{ab} and that $f(x)$ is continuous for all x. Let

$$F(t) = \int_{c}^{h(t)} f(x) \, dx \, , \, c \in I^0_{ab} \, .$$

Show that $F(t)$ is differentiable for each $t \in I^0_{ab}$ and

$$F'(t) = f[h(t)]h'(t) .$$

Hint: Recall the notion of compound functions and the chain rule.

5. Compute $F'(t)$ using the result of Problem 4 and also by evaluating $F(t)$ explicitly when

$$F(t) = \int_0^{t^2+3} x^3 \, dx .$$

6. Use the results of Problem 4 to determine $F'(t)$ when

(a) $F(t) = \int_0^{t^2+2} (x^2 + 2) \, dx;$ (b) $F(t) = \int_a^{\sin t} (x - 3) \, dx .$

Section 4–11

1. Sketch the one-parameter family of curves which are graphs of the functions in the set $\int x^2 \, dx$.

2. Determine

(a) $\int (3x^3 - 2x + 1) \, dx;$ (b) $\int (x^5 + 6x - 5) \, dx .$

In Problems 3 through 10 find the set of all functions $y = f(x)$ whose derivative is that given. Sketch the graphs of the one-parameter family so obtained.

3. $\dfrac{dy}{dx} = 6x^2 + 1;$ **4.** $\dfrac{dy}{dx} = 2x^{1/2} + 6x^{-1/2};$ **5.** $\dfrac{dy}{dx} = x^{5.162};$

6. $\dfrac{dy}{dx} = \sin(x + 3);$ **7.** $\dfrac{dy}{dx} = 5x^{5/3};$ **8.** $\dfrac{dy}{dx} = x + 3;$

9. $\dfrac{dy}{dx} = (2 + x)^2;$ **10.** $\dfrac{dy}{dx} = x(3 + x^3) .$

11. Find that primitive function for Problem 3 which passes through the point $(1, 3)$.

12. Suppose that we have two functions $F_1(x)$ and $F_2(x)$ such that for each x in some open interval I^0_{ab}, $F_1''(x) = F_2''(x)$. Prove that there then exist numbers λ_1 and λ_2 such that $F_2(x) = F_1(x) + \lambda_1 x + \lambda_2$ for all $x \in I^0_{ab}$. Thus show that the set of all functions whose second derivative function is $f(x)$ is the set of functions $F_1(x) + \lambda_1 x + \lambda_2$, where $F_1(x)$ is any function such that $F_1''(x) = f(x)$ and λ_1 and λ_2 are any real numbers. Hint: Apply the mean value theorem twice, once to relate $F_1'(x)$ and $F_2'(x)$ an then to relate $F_1(x)$ and $F_2(x)$.

In Problems 13 through 20 use the results of Problem 12 to find the set of all functions whose second derivative is that given. Hint: Compute $dy/dx = \int d^2y/dx^2 \, dx$ first.

13. $\dfrac{d^2y}{dx^2} = 6;$ **14.** $\dfrac{d^2y}{dx^2} = 2x;$ **15.** $\dfrac{d^2y}{dx^2} = \sin x;$

16. $\dfrac{d^2y}{dx^2} = 6 + 2x;$ **17.** $\dfrac{d^2y}{dx^2} = x - 3x^2;$ **18.** $\dfrac{d^2y}{dx^2} = x^{1/2};$

19. $\dfrac{d^2y}{dx^2} = x^{1/3} + \cos x;$ **20.** $\dfrac{d^2y}{dx^2} = x + x^{1/2} .$

21. Find the function $y = f(x)$ for Problem 13 which passes through the point (1, 1) and has a slope of -1 at (1, 1). Is the function uniquely determined? Sketch the graph of the function or functions so obtained.

22. The speed s of a car (in miles per hour) as it travels along is the following function of time t (in hours)

$$s = 35 - 35 \cos t.$$

Determine the distance d that the car traveled from time 0 to time τ. Sketch the graphs of s and d.

CHAPTER 5

Additional Developments of Differentiation and Integration

5–1 THE NATURAL LOGARITHM FUNCTION

We did not study in any detail in the previous chapter how a primitive function for some given function could be determined, and one of the things we shall do now is to study this problem in a little more detail. First, however, we shall introduce two new functions which play a very important role in almost all applications and which we shall want to consider in developing techniques for integration. These functions are the natural logarithm and exponential functions.

Recall that we have previously shown how to find a primitive function for x^α for every rational number α except $\alpha = -1$. None of the functions we have studied thus far has $1/x$ as a derivative function. However, $1/x$ is continuous for all $x > 0$, that is, over the interval $I_{0\,\infty}^0$, and hence we know by the second form of the fundamental theorem that there is a function $F(x)$ such that $F'(x) = 1/x$ for all $x > 0$. Indeed, the second form of the fundamental theorem tells us that

$$F(x) = \int_\alpha^x \frac{1}{t}\, dt, \quad \alpha > 0, \quad x > 0 \tag{5-1}$$

is such a function. Since we customarily think of x as the independent variable in our functions, it is convenient to use t as the variable of integration in (5–1) and x as the upper limit. Although we could write (5–1) as $\int_1^x dx/x$, it is confusing to use the same symbol for both the variable of integration and one of the limits. We shall now proceed to use (5–1) to define a primitive function for $1/x$, $x > 0$. It is convenient to take $\alpha = 1$ in making the definition. The function defined by (5–1) for $\alpha = 1$ is called the *natural logarithm of* x and is symbolized by log x. The natural logarithm function is defined only for $x > 0$, and by definition

$$\log x = \int_1^x \frac{1}{t}\, dt, \quad x > 0. \tag{5-2}$$

Note that log x is simply a symbol for the function, just as sin x is, and it tells us nothing about the nature of the function.

We now want to study the nature of the function defined by (5–2). It is easy to give a geometric interpretation to log x. Consider Figure 5–1. Let us

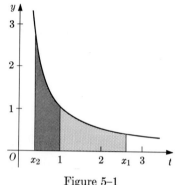

Figure 5–1

select a specific value of x, say x_1, such that $x_1 > 1$. Then log x_1 is the area of the lightly shaded region in Figure 5–1, that is, the area of the set of points $t \geq 1$, $t \leq x_1$, $y \geq 0$, $y \leq 1/t$. Consider next a specific x, say x_2, such that $0 < x_2 < 1$. Then

$$\log x_2 = \int_1^{x_2} \frac{1}{t}\, dt = -\int_{x_2}^1 \frac{1}{t}\, dt. \tag{5-3}$$

However, $\int_{x_2}^1 dt/t$ is simply the area of the darkly shaded region in Figure 5–1, and log x_2 is then the negative of this area. We have thus shown that log x is positive when $x > 1$ and is negative when $x < 1$. When $x = 1$

$$\log 1 = \int_1^1 \frac{1}{t}\, dt = 0 \tag{5-4}$$

by the definition (4–59).

The natural logarithm has a number of remarkable properties. We shall now derive them by using the fact, proved in the previous chapter, that if two functions have the same derivative function then they can differ only by a constant. The function log x was defined in such a way that

$$\frac{d}{dx} \log x = \frac{1}{x}, \quad \text{all } x > 0. \tag{5-5}$$

Since log x *is differentiable, it is a continuous function for all* $x > 0$.

Consider now the function $\log ax$, $a > 0$, $x > 0$. By the chain rule for differentiation, we have on writing $w = ax$

$$\frac{d}{dx} \log ax = \left(\frac{d}{dw} \log w \right) \frac{dw}{dx} = \frac{1}{w} a = \frac{a}{ax} = \frac{1}{x}. \tag{5–6}$$

Surprisingly enough, the derivative of $\log ax$ is precisely the same as the derivative of $\log x$. Hence $\log ax$ and $\log x$ can differ only by a constant, so that

$$\log ax = \log x + \lambda. \tag{5–7}$$

Equation (5–7) holds for all $x > 0$ and in particular for $x = 1$. However, $\log 1 = 0$. Hence $\lambda = \log a$. Consequently, we have proved that for all $x > 0$ and $a > 0$

$$\log ax = \log x + \log a. \tag{5–8}$$

Another convenient way of writing (5–8) is

$$\log x_1 x_2 = \log x_1 + \log x_2, \quad x_1 > 0, \quad x_2 > 0. \tag{5–9}$$

Thus *the natural logarithm of the product of two positive numbers is the sum of the natural logarithms of each of the numbers.* This is an extremely useful property of natural logarithms.

Consider next the function $\log (x/a)$, $x > 0$, $a > 0$. By the chain rule

$$\frac{d}{dx} \log \frac{x}{a} = \frac{1/a}{x/a} = \frac{1}{x}. \tag{5–10}$$

Hence the derivative of $\log (x/a)$ is the same as that of $\log x$ and therefore there exists a λ such that

$$\log \frac{x}{a} = \log x + \lambda. \tag{5–11}$$

Equation (5–11) holds for all $x > 0$ and, in particular, for $x = a$. On setting $x = a$ and using (5–4), we see that $\lambda = -\log a$, so that

$$\log \frac{x}{a} = \log x - \log a \tag{5–12}$$

or

$$\log \frac{x_2}{x_1} = \log x_2 - \log x_1, \quad x_2 > 0, \quad x_1 > 0. \tag{5–13}$$

Thus *the natural logarithm of the quotient of two positive numbers is equal to the natural logarithm of the numerator minus the natural logarithm of the denominator.* In particular, if we take $x_2 = 1$ in (5–13) we obtain

$$\log \frac{1}{x_1} = -\log x_1, \quad x_1 > 0, \tag{5–14}$$

so that *the natural logarithm of the reciprocal of x_1 is simply the negative of the logarithm of x_1.* Equation (5–14) shows us that, if we know the natural logarithms of all numbers $x > 1$, we can also compute the natural logarithms of all numbers in the interval $0 < x < 1$. To compute the natural logarithm of a number x in this interval, we determine $w = 1/x$ and $w > 1$. Then $\log x = -\log w$.

We shall obtain one final property of logarithms by applying the chain rule to differentiate the function $\log x^\alpha$, α any rational number. We obtain

$$\frac{d}{dx} \log x^\alpha = \frac{\alpha \, x^{\alpha-1}}{x^\alpha} = \frac{\alpha}{x}, \quad x > 0. \qquad (5\text{--}15)$$

However,

$$\frac{d}{dx} (\alpha \log x) = \frac{\alpha}{x}. \qquad (5\text{--}16)$$

Thus the functions $\log x^\alpha$ and $\alpha \log x$ have the same derivative and can differ only by a constant, so that

$$\log x^\alpha = \alpha \log x + \lambda, \quad \text{all } x > 0. \qquad (5\text{--}17)$$

When $x = 1$, $x^\alpha = 1$ and $\log x^\alpha = 0$. Also $\alpha \log x = 0$ when $x = 1$. Hence $\lambda = 0$ and

$$\log x^\alpha = \alpha \log x, \quad x > 0, \quad \alpha \text{ any rational number}. \qquad (5\text{--}18)$$

In words, *the natural logarithm of a power of x is merely the power times the natural logarithm of x.*

We have not as yet provided any numerical procedure for evaluating $\log x$ for a given x. One way to do this would be to approximate the integral (5–2) by the sum of areas of rectangles. This can indeed be done, and we shall consider the numerical computation of $\log x$ in more detail in the next chapter. It is not a simple task to evaluate accurately $\log x$ by hand, and for this reason extensive tables of the natural logarithm function have been computed. A brief table is given in Table B at the end of the text. By use of this table we can easily sketch the graph of $\log x$, which is shown in Figure 5–2. Note that it crosses the x-axis at $x = 1$ and $\log x > 0$ if $x > 1$ and $\log x < 0$ if $x < 0$, as we have shown previously should be the case. We can easily prove that $\log x_2 > \log x_1$ when $x_2 > x_1$, since

$$\log x_2 - \log x_1 = \int_1^{x_2} \frac{1}{t} \, dt - \int_1^{x_1} \frac{1}{t} \, dt = \int_{x_1}^{x_2} \frac{1}{t} \, dt. \qquad (5\text{--}19)$$

Now the integral on the right in (5–19) is the area of the set of points satisfying the inequalities $t \geq x_1$, $t \leq x_2$, $y \geq 0$, $y \leq 1/t$, and is a positive number. A function $f(x)$ with the characteristic that $f(x_2) > f(x_1)$ when $x_2 > x_1$ is said to be *monotonic increasing*. Thus $\log x$ is monotonic increasing.

We can now easily see that $\log x$ becomes arbitrarily large as x becomes larger and larger. To see this note that $\log 2^n = n \log 2$, and from Table B at the end of the text $\log 2 = 0.6931$. Hence $\log 2^n = 0.6931n$ and by taking n

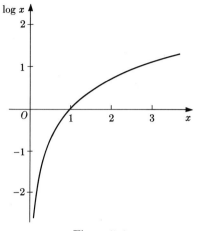

Figure 5–2

large enough we can make log 2^n as large as is desired. Thus we have shown that there is no largest value of log x. From this result and (5–14) we can see that log x becomes more and more negative as x gets closer and closer to 0, since log $2^{-n} = -0.6931n$. We can make log 2^{-n} as large a negative number as we please by taking n to be large enough. Therefore, $\lim_{x \to 0+} \log x$ does not exist, since log x becomes more and more negative. The function log x then has a vertical asymptote at $x = 0$. The domain for log x is the set of all positive real numbers and the range for log x is the set of all real numbers.

We have defined log x so that log x is a primitive function for $1/x$ when $x > 0$. Now $1/x$ is also continuous for $x < 0$. Hence there exists a primitive function for $1/x$ for $x < 0$. Log x is not a primitive function when $x < 0$ because log x is defined only when $x > 0$. Indeed $\int_1^x dt/t$ does not exist when $x < 0$. The reason for this is that $1/t$ has an infinite discontinuity at $t = 0$. However, we do feel intuitively that somehow we should be able to modify the natural logarithm function to yield the desired primitive function. This can indeed be done. Consider the function log $|x|$. By the chain rule

$$\frac{d}{dx} \log |x| = \frac{1}{|x|} \frac{d|x|}{dx}.$$

Now go back to page 196 and Figure 3–11. Observe that $d|x|/dx = -1$ when $x < 0$. Thus for $x < 0$

$$\frac{d}{dx} \log |x| = -\frac{1}{|x|} = \frac{1}{x}. \tag{5–20}$$

Therefore, log $|x|$ is a primitive function for $x < 0$. When $x > 0$, $|x| = x$ and log $|x|$ is also a primitive function for $1/x$ when $x > 0$. Hence log $|x|$ is a primitive function for $1/x$ for all $x \neq 0$. Consequently, we can write

$$\int \frac{1}{x}\, dx = \log |x| + \lambda, \quad x \neq 0 . \tag{5-21}$$

The reader should be careful not to interpret (5–21) as meaning that the logarithm of a negative number is log $|x|$. We have not defined the natural logarithm of a negative number, and we shall not do so. We could define the natural logarithm of a negative number to be log $|x|$ but this is not what is normally done. We shall always take as the domain of log x the set of all positive real numbers, and no other numbers will be in the domain.

5–2 THE EXPONENTIAL FUNCTION

In the previous section we showed that log x is monotonic increasing. Thus there cannot be two different values of x, say x_1 and x_2, which have the same natural logarithm, since one would have to be smaller than the other, say $x_1 < x_2$, which would imply that log $x_1 <$ log x_2. Therefore, given any y, there can be only one x such that $y = \log x$. Furthermore, for every real number y there is a positive real number x such that $y = \log x$. We shall not attempt to prove this rigorously, but it is intuitively clear on examining the graph of log x shown in Figure 5–2. We see, therefore, that the inverse representation of log x will consist of a single function whose domain consists of all real numbers y and whose range is the set of all positive real numbers. The graph of the inverse representation will be precisely the same as the graph of log x. The inverse representation of log x is given a special name; it is called the *exponential function* and is written $x = \exp y$. Once again exp y is merely the symbolism for the function and tells us nothing about the nature of this function.

The exponential function is even more important in mathematics than is the natural logarithm function. Normally, x is used as the independent variable in the exponential function and thus we shall usually write this function as

$$y = \exp x . \tag{5-22}$$

The domain of exp x is all real x and exp $x > 0$ for each x. Furthermore, since log $1 = 0$, exp $0 = 1$. The graph of (5–22) would be that shown in Figure 5–2 if the x-axis was taken to be vertical. When we use the horizontal axis for the x-axis, we then obtain the graph shown in Figure 5–3. The exponential function is monotonic increasing, just as is log x. To see this, suppose that $x_2 > x_1$, and write $y_2 = \exp x_2$, $y_1 = \exp x_1$. Then $x_1 = \log y_1$ and $x_2 = \log y_2$. But then log $y_2 >$ log y_1, which implies that $y_2 > y_1$, that is, exp $x_2 >$ exp x_1. The exponential function is continuous just as is log x.

The exponential function possesses a number of remarkable properties which we shall now study. The results will be obtained using the properties of log x. Suppose that x_1 and x_2 are any two values of x and that $y_1 = \exp x_1$

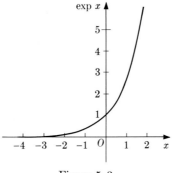

Figure 5–3

and $y_2 = \exp x_2$. Then $x_1 = \log y_1$ and $x_2 = \log y_2$, since the exponential function gives the inverse representation of the natural logarithm function. Now

$$\log y_1 y_2 = \log y_1 + \log y_2 = x_1 + x_2 .$$

Hence $\exp (x_1 + x_2) = y_1 y_2$, or from the definition of y_1 and y_2

$$\exp (x_1 + x_2) = (\exp x_1)(\exp x_2) . \tag{5–23}$$

In words, *the exponential function evaluated at $x_1 + x_2$ is equal to the product of $\exp x_1$ and $\exp x_2$.*

Next observe that since $y = \exp x$ implies that $x = \log y$, and since $\log 1/y = -\log y = -x$, it follows that $\exp (-x) = 1/y$, that is,

$$\exp (-x) = \frac{1}{\exp x} \tag{5–24}$$

for every x. Then on replacing x_2 by $-x_2$ in (5–23), we see from (5–24) that

$$\exp (x_1 - x_2) = \frac{\exp x_1}{\exp x_2} . \tag{5–25}$$

To continue, observe that, since $x = \log y$ when $y = \exp x$, and since $\log y^\alpha = \alpha \log y = \alpha x$ for any rational number x, it follows that $\exp \alpha x = y^\alpha$, that is,

$$\exp \alpha x = (\exp x)^\alpha , \quad \alpha \text{ rational} . \tag{5–26}$$

In particular, if we take $x = 1$ in (5–26) we obtain

$$\exp \alpha = (\exp 1)^\alpha \tag{5–27}$$

for any rational number α. Let us denote by e the number whose natural logarithm is 1, that is, $\log e = 1$. From Table B at the end of the text we see that $e \doteq 2.7$. Then it follows from (5–27) that

$$\exp \alpha = e^\alpha , \quad \alpha \text{ any rational number} . \tag{5–28}$$

Recall that in Chapter 1 we defined a^α when $a > 0$ and α is any rational number. Thus e^α has a meaning to us. Since $e > 1$, we see from (5–28) that there are numbers α for which exp α is arbitrarily large. Hence there is no largest value of exp α. Also, from (5–24), exp $(-\alpha) = e^{-\alpha} = 1/e^\alpha$, and thus there exist negative numbers for which exp x is arbitrarily close to 0. In fact, the x-axis is a horizontal asymptote for exp x.

It will be recalled that we have never given a meaning to a number raised to a power which is irrational, that is, to a^α where α is an irrational number. We are now in a position to define what is meant by one such expression. Note that (5–28) holds for all rational numbers. Recall also that exp x is defined for every real number. *We shall now simply define e^x to be* exp x *even when x is irrational.* Thus for all real x

$$e^x = \exp x . \tag{5–29}$$

We proved this holds when x is rational, and we define e^x to be exp x when x is irrational. Given (5–29), we shall see in the next section how to define a^α, $a > 0$ and α irrational. In the future we shall find it convenient to use e^x to represent the exponential function. Note that in terms of this notation (5–23) and (5–24) become

$$e^{x_1 + x_2} = e^{x_1} e^{x_2}; \qquad e^{-x} = \frac{1}{e^x} , \tag{5–30}$$

and in this form the properties of the exponential function look like the familiar properties of exponents.

We can easily obtain the derivative of e^x using the result for differentiating the inverse representation obtained in Section 3–11. If we write $x = \log y$, then $dx/dy = 1/y$ and hence by (3–86)

$$\frac{dy}{dx} = y = e^x ,$$

so

$$\frac{d}{dx} e^x = e^x, \quad \text{all } x . \tag{5–31}$$

The exponential function thus has the remarkable property that its derivative function is the exponential function itself. Given (5–31) we see that the exponential function is a primitive function for the exponential function, so that

$$\int e^x \, dx = e^x + \lambda . \tag{5–32}$$

We shall discuss in the next chapter how e^x can be evaluated numerically. It is arduous to compute e^x by hand and for this reason extensive tables have been computed. Brief tables of e^x and e^{-x} are given in Table C at the end of the text.

EXAMPLES. 1. If $f(x)$ is differentiable for all x, then $h(x) = e^{f(x)}$ is defined, continuous and differentiable for all x. Hence by the chain rule and (5–31)

$$\frac{d}{dx} e^{f(x)} = f'(x) e^{f(x)} . \tag{5–33}$$

Thus .

$$\frac{d}{dx} e^{\sin x} = (\cos x) e^{\sin x} ;$$

$$\frac{d}{dx} e^{\exp x} = e^x e^{\exp x} ;$$

$$\frac{d}{dx} e^{-x^2} = -2x e^{-x^2} .$$

2. Note that since e^x is defined and positive for all real x then $e^{-x} = 1/e^x$ is also defined and positive for all real x. Using the data of Table C at the end of the text we can easily obtain the graph of e^{-x}. It is shown in Figure 5–4.

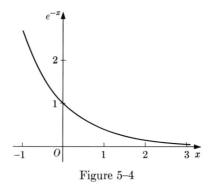

Figure 5–4

3. Since e^x is continuous everywhere, if $\lim_{x \to a} f(x)$ exists and is equal to β, we know from (3–45) that

$$\lim_{x \to a} e^{f(x)} = e^\beta . \tag{5–34}$$

Thus, for example,

$$\lim_{x \to 2} \exp \frac{x - 3}{x + 4} = e^{-1/6} ,$$

since

$$\lim_{x \to 2} \frac{x - 3}{x + 4} = -\frac{1}{6} .$$

4. Since if $y = \log x$ then $x = e^y$, it follows from (3–85) that

$$e^{\log x} = x \quad \text{and} \quad \log e^y = y . \tag{5–35}$$

5-3 GENERALIZED POWER AND LOGARITHM FUNCTIONS

At last we are ready to define a^α, $a > 0$, when α is an irrational number. In the previous section this was done for the special case where $a = e$. Consider first a^α, where α is rational. By (5–35)

$$a^\alpha = e^{\log a^\alpha}, \quad a > 0, \quad \alpha \text{ rational} . \tag{5–36}$$

But $\log a^\alpha = \alpha \log a$. Hence

$$a^\alpha = e^{\alpha \log a}, \quad a > 0, \quad \alpha \text{ rational} . \tag{5–37}$$

Let us now note that for any real α, rational or irrational, $\alpha \log a$ is simply a real number. Since e^x is defined for every real x, then

$$e^{\alpha \log a} \tag{5–38}$$

is defined for every real α and is a positive real number. Consequently, we now have a procedure for defining a^α, $a > 0$, when α is irrational. We define a^α for α irrational to be (5–38). Thus for all real α

$$a^\alpha = e^{\alpha \log a}, \quad a > 0, \quad \text{any real } \alpha . \tag{5–39}$$

It might be worthwhile for the reader to go back and trace through the evolution of our concept of a number raised to a power. We began with a very simple idea: a^n means $a \cdots a$, a appearing n times. The notion gradually grew more complex as we introduced a^{-n} and a^α, α a rational number and $a > 0$. Now we have defined a^α for α irrational. The notion of a number raised to an irrational power is a rather complicated concept, as the definition (5–39) shows.

Whenever the notion of a power was generalized, it always turned out that the familiar rules for exponents were still valid. Let us now show that this remains true even when α in a^α is irrational. Consider $a^{\alpha_1} a^{\alpha_2}$. By (5–39) and (5–23)

$$a^{\alpha_1} a^{\alpha_2} = \exp(\alpha_1 \log a) \exp(\alpha_2 \log a) = \exp(\alpha_1 \log a + \alpha_2 \log a)$$
$$= \exp[(\alpha_1 + \alpha_2) \log a] = a^{\alpha_1 + \alpha_2} .$$

Thus

$$a^{\alpha_1} a^{\alpha_2} = a^{\alpha_1 + \alpha_2}, \quad a > 0, \quad \text{any real } \alpha_1 \text{ and } \alpha_2 . \tag{5–40}$$

Similarly,

$$(a^{\alpha_1})^{\alpha_2} = [\exp(\alpha_1 \log a)]^{\alpha_2} = \exp[\alpha_2 \log(e^{\alpha_1 \log a})]$$
$$= \exp(\alpha_1 \alpha_2 \log a) = a^{\alpha_1 \alpha_2} ,$$

since

$$\log e^{\alpha_1 \log a} = \alpha_1 \log a$$

by (5–35). Therefore

$$(a^{\alpha_1})^{\alpha_2} = a^{\alpha_1 \alpha_2}, \quad a > 0, \quad \text{any real } \alpha_1 \text{ and } \alpha_2 . \tag{5–41}$$

In particular, note that (5–41) implies that

$$e^{x_1 x_2} = (e^{x_1})^{x_2} = (e^{x_2})^{x_1} .\qquad(5\text{–}42)$$

Finally

$$a^{-\alpha} = e^{-\alpha \, \log a} = \frac{1}{e^{\alpha \, \log a}} = \frac{1}{a^\alpha}$$

so that

$$a^{-\alpha} = \frac{1}{a^\alpha}, \quad a > 0, \quad \text{all real } \alpha .\qquad(5\text{–}43)$$

Equations (5–40), (5–41) and (5–43) show that the familiar laws of exponents hold in general.

We have shown previously that (5–18) holds. We can now easily see that (5–18) holds even if α is irrational, since by (5–35)

$$\log x^\alpha = \log e^{\alpha \, \log x} = \alpha \log x, \quad a > 0, \quad \text{any real } \alpha .\qquad(5\text{–}44)$$

For any real number α we can now define a function $f(x) = x^\alpha$ whose domain consists of all positive real numbers x. The function $f(x) = x^\alpha$ is continuous for all $x > 0$. This follows from the continuity of e^u, the continuity of $u = \alpha \log x$ and the result proved in Chapter 3 that the composition of continuous functions is continuous. It is also true that x^α is differentiable for all $x > 0$, and by the chain rule

$$\frac{d}{dx} x^\alpha = \frac{d}{dx} e^{\alpha \, \log x} = \frac{\alpha}{x} e^{\alpha \, \log x} = \alpha \, x^{\alpha-1} ,$$

so

$$\frac{d}{dx} x^\alpha = \alpha \, x^{\alpha-1}, \quad x > 0, \quad \text{any real } \alpha .\qquad(5\text{–}45)$$

This generalizes the corresponding result which we obtained in Chapter 3 for rational α. Given (5–45), we can immediately generalize the indefinite integral (4–93) to yield

$$\int x^\alpha \, dx = \frac{x^{\alpha+1}}{\alpha + 1} + \lambda, \quad x > 0, \quad \alpha \text{ any real number not } -1 .\qquad(5\text{–}46)$$

EXAMPLES. 1. $3^{\sqrt{2}}$ represents a number raised to an irrational power. By (5–39) and the tables at the end of the text

$$3^{\sqrt{2}} = e^{\sqrt{2} \, \log 3} \doteq e^{1.54} \doteq 4.66 .$$

2. $\dfrac{d}{dx} x^{\sqrt{2}} = \sqrt{2} \, x^{\sqrt{2}-1} \doteq 1.414 x^{0.414} .$

We can now introduce functions of the form $f(x) = a^x$, $a > 0$, which are called generalized exponential functions. It is easy to obtain the graph of

$y = a^x$ when we can compute values of the natural logarithm and exponential functions, since $a^x = e^{x \log a}$. The graphs of $y = a^x$ for various values of a are shown in Figure 5–5. The domain of a^x is the set of all real x and its

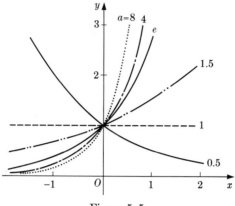

Figure 5–5

range is the set of all positive real numbers. The same reasoning as used for x^α shows that a^x is continuous and differentiable for all x. The derivative is given by

$$\frac{d}{dx} a^x = \frac{d}{dx} e^{x \log a} = (\log a) e^{x \log a} = a^x \log a ,$$

so that

$$\frac{d}{dx} a^x = a^x \log a, \quad \text{all } x, \quad a > 0 . \tag{5–47}$$

Consequently

$$\int a^x \, dx = \frac{a^x}{\log a} + \lambda, \quad \text{all } x, \quad a > 0 . \tag{5–48}$$

The reader should be careful not to confuse the functions x^α and a^x. In the first case the variable is raised to a fixed power; in the second, the variable is the exponent.

As can be seen from Figure 5–5, the inverse representation of a^x will consist of just a single function. The inverse representation of $y = e^x$ is $x = \log y$. In general, the inverse representation of $y = a^x$ will be called *the logarithm function to the base a*, and we write this function as

$$x = \log_a y . \tag{5–49}$$

Equation (5–49) is read the logarithm to the base a of y is x. Note that when $a = e$, the inverse representation is $\log y$. Thus the natural logarithm is what we are now calling the logarithm to the base e. Note that, in general, $\log_a y$ is simply the number such that

$$y = a^{\log_a y} . \tag{5–50}$$

For natural logarithms e is the base. However, any $a > 0$ can be used as the base for a logarithm function. If we can compute natural logarithms we can compute logarithms to any base, because there is a simple relation between $\log_a y$ and $\log y$. To obtain this relation note that if $y = a^x = e^{x \log a}$, then since $\log e^w = w$,

$$\log y = x \log a . \tag{5–51}$$

But on substituting the value of x from (5–49) into (5–51) we obtain

$$\log_a y = \frac{\log y}{\log a} . \tag{5–52}$$

To compute $\log_a y$ we merely divide the natural logarithm of y by the natural logarithm of a. From (5–52) it is clear that the rules (5–9), (5–13), (5–14) and (5–44) also apply for logarithms to any base. Thus, for example,

$$\log_a x_1 x_2 = \log_a x_1 + \log_a x_2 ; \tag{5–53}$$

$$\log_a \frac{1}{x_1} = - \log_a x_1 . \tag{5–54}$$

From (5–52)

$$\frac{d}{dx} \log_a x = \frac{1}{x \log a} . \tag{5–55}$$

There are only two systems of logarithms that the reader is ever likely to encounter. One is the natural logarithm function with base e, and the other is the system of logarithms with base 10, which are sometimes referred to as Naperian logarithms. The latter system is the one studied in high school. The natural logarithm function is the basic one which appears naturally in mathematics. Naperian logarithms were used extensively in the past for making numerical computations by hand. The advent of high-speed computers has essentially eliminated the usefulness of logarithms in making numerical computations, and thus only the natural logarithm function remains as a function of great interest.

The material that we have developed in this chapter can now be applied to determine several interesting limits which cannot be determined by the methods developed in Chapter 3. By the definition of a derivative and from (5–47) we see that

$$\lim_{v \to 0} \frac{a^{x+v} - a^x}{v} = a^x \lim_{v \to 0} \frac{a^v - 1}{v} = \frac{d}{dx} a^x = a^x \log a . \tag{5–56}$$

Therefore,

$$\lim_{v \to 0} \frac{a^v - 1}{v} = a^{-x} \lim_{v \to 0} \frac{a^{x+v} - a^x}{v} = \log a \,. \qquad (5\text{--}57)$$

This is an interesting result, and the need to know this limit arises in practice.

Consider next $d(\log_a x)/dx$. By definition of the derivative, this is

$$\lim_{v \to 0} \frac{\log_a(x + v) - \log_a x}{v} = \lim_{v \to 0} \frac{1}{v} \log_a \left(\frac{x + v}{x} \right)$$

$$= \frac{1}{x} \lim_{v \to 0} \frac{x}{v} \log_a \left(1 + \frac{v}{x} \right)$$

$$= \frac{1}{x} \lim_{v \to 0} \log_a \left(1 + \frac{v}{x} \right)^{x/v} \qquad (5\text{--}58)$$

$$= \frac{d}{dx} \log_a x = \frac{1}{x \log a} \,.$$

Consequently

$$\lim_{v \to 0} \log_a \left(1 + \frac{v}{x} \right)^{x/v} = \frac{1}{\log a} \,, \quad x > 0 \,. \qquad (5\text{--}59)$$

In particular, for $a = e$ and $x = 1$, (5–59) becomes

$$\lim_{v \to 0} \log (1 + v)^{1/v} = 1 \,. \qquad (5\text{--}60)$$

Now recall that if $\lim_{x \to \alpha} f(x) = \beta$, then

$$\lim_{x \to \alpha} e^{f(x)} = e^{\beta} \,.$$

Hence

$$\lim_{x \to 0} \exp [\log (1 + x)^{1/x}] = \lim_{x \to 0} (1 + x)^{1/x} = e^1 = e \,,$$

that is,

$$\lim_{x \to 0} (1 + x)^{1/x} = e \,. \qquad (5\text{--}61)$$

This is a very interesting result, and the need to evaluate this limit often arises in practice.

5–4 TECHNIQUES OF INTEGRATION

We have pointed out in the previous chapter that the basic problem in integral calculus is to find a function which is a primitive function for some given function, or equivalently to find the indefinite integral of a given function. In Chapters 3 and 4 we introduced techniques which made it possible to differentiate essentially any function. The situation is much more complicated when integration is studied. We shall not be able to provide techniques by which the indefinite integral of any continuous function can be obtained. Generally speaking, integration is much more difficult to carry out than differentiation. One reason for this is that integration, unlike differentiation, often introduces new types of functions. (Recall that in differentiation, the derivative of a function always yielded a function of essentially the same type as that being differentiated or at least did not introduce any new types of functions.) Consequently, when we are given a function, we are often not sure whether the primitive function is a new type of function which is not one of those studied previously or whether the primitive function can be expressed in terms of familiar functions. Even when the primitive function can be expressed in terms of familiar functions, however, it may be extremely difficult to do so.

There are several general procedures which are useful in determining indefinite integrals. We shall discuss two of these in the next two sections. Once we get away from simple cases, the determination of indefinite integrals becomes more of an art than a science. We shall not attempt to cover the many tricks that are used in integration, since the need for them does not arise with great frequency in most areas of application. Because integration is so difficult, extensive tables of definite integrals have been compiled. One such useful compilation is Dwight's Tables [1].

5-5 INTEGRATION OF COMPOUND FUNCTIONS

The reader will recall that the chain rule was very useful for computation of derivatives. The application of the chain rule in reverse provides an equally useful method for evaluating indefinite integrals. Recall that if $H(u)$ and $g(x)$ are differentiable, then so is $H[g(x)]$, and the derivative of $H[g(x)]$ is $H'[g(x)]g'(x)$. Suppose that $h(u)$ is the derivative function for $H(u)$. Then

$$\frac{d}{dx} H[g(x)] = h[g(x)]g'(x) . \qquad (5\text{-}62)$$

Assume that $g'(x)$ is continuous over some interval I_{ab}^0 and also that $h(u)$ is continuous for each $u = g(x)$, $x \in I_{ab}^0$. Then $f(x) = h[g(x)]g'(x)$ is continuous over I_{ab}^0 and possesses a primitive function. By (5-62) the indefinite integral of $f(x)$ is

$$\int h[g(x)]g'(x) \, dx = H[g(x)] + \lambda, \quad x \in I_{ab}^0 . \qquad (5\text{-}63)$$

Let us now explain how (5-63) may be useful in evaluating the indefinite integral of some given function $f(x)$.

To use (5-63) in finding the indefinite integral of $f(x)$, we try to determine functions $h(u)$ and $g(x)$ so that $f(x) = h[g(x)]g'(x)$. When this is done the problem of integrating $f(x)$ reduces to what is hopefully the simpler problem of finding a primitive function for $h(u)$, since once such a primitive function is known, the indefinite integral of $f(x)$ is given by (5–63). The best way to illustrate the procedure, which we shall refer to as the compound function rule, is through the use of examples.

EXAMPLES. 1. Suppose that we wish to determine

$$\int \frac{2x}{1 + x^2} \, dx \ .$$

Now note that $2x$ is the derivative of $1 + x^2$. If we write $g(x) = 1 + x^2$, then $f(x) = g'(x)/g(x)$, which will have the form $h[g(x)]g'(x)$ if we take $h(u) = 1/u$. By (5–21), $\log |u|$ is a primitive function for $h(u)$. Hence $H(u) = \log |u|$, and by (5–63)

$$\int \frac{2x}{1 + x^2} \, dx = \log |1 + x^2| + \lambda, \quad \text{all } x \ . \tag{5–64}$$

The absolute value signs are not needed in (5–64), because $1 + x^2$ is always positive.

2. Consider

$$\int x \, e^{ax^2} \, dx \ .$$

Suppose we write $g(x) = ax^2$. Then $g'(x) = 2ax$. Hence

$$f(x) = \frac{g'(x)}{2a} \, e^{g(x)} \ ,$$

and this has the form $h[g(x)]g'(x)$ if $h(u) = e^u/2a$. Now by (5–31), $H(u) = e^u/2a$ is a primitive function for $h(u)$ and hence by (5–63)

$$\int x \, e^{ax^2} \, dx = \frac{1}{2a} \, e^{ax^2} + \lambda, \quad \text{all } x \ . \tag{5–65}$$

3. Let us determine

$$\int \frac{3x}{(x^2 + 2)^{1/2}} \, dx \ .$$

If $g(x) = x^2 + 2$, then $g'(x) = 2x$ and

$$f(x) = \frac{3}{2} \frac{g'(x)}{[g(x)]^{1/2}} \ .$$

This has the form $h[g(x)]g'(x)$ if $h(u) = 3/(2u^{1/2})$. Now $H(u) = 3u^{1/2}$ is a primitive function for $h(u)$, and thus by (5–63)

$$\int \frac{3x}{(x^2 + 2)^{1/2}} \, dx = 3(x^2 + 2)^{1/2} + \lambda, \quad \text{all } x \, . \qquad (5\text{–}66)$$

4. Consider

$$\int x \sin x^2 \, dx \, .$$

If we take $g(x) = x^2$, then, $g'(x) = 2x$ and

$$f(x) = \frac{1}{2} g'(x) \sin g(x) \, .$$

Thus $f(x)$ has the form $h[g(x)]g'(x)$ if $h(u) = \frac{1}{2} \sin u$. A primitive function for $h(u)$ is $H(u) = -\frac{1}{2} \cos u$. Hence by (5–63)

$$\int x \sin x^2 \, dx = -\frac{1}{2} \cos x^2 + \lambda, \quad \text{all } x \, . \qquad (5\text{–}67)$$

After going through the above examples the reader may wonder how we decided what to use for $g(x)$. In simple examples like those given, it is fairly obvious to anyone with a little experience. What we attempt to do is select $g(x)$ in a way that it will be easy to find a primitive function for the $h(u)$ so determined. In general, this is a trial-and-error process and several different $g(x)$ functions may be tried before an $h(u)$ is found whose primitive function can be determined. It is possible, of course, that no $g(x)$ exists for which the primitive function for $h(u)$ can be expressed in terms of known functions. One reason for this is that any primitive function for $f(x)$ may simply be a new type of function. However, even if $\int f(x) \, dx$ can be expressed in terms of known functions, there is no guarantee that the above procedure will allow us to effect the integration.

Consider, for example,

$$\int x^3 \, e^{-ax^2} \, dx \, . \qquad (5\text{–}68)$$

If we take $g(x) = -ax^2$, then $g'(x) = -2ax$ and

$$f(x) = \frac{1}{2a^2} g(x) \, g'(x) \, e^{g(x)} \, .$$

This is of the form $h[g(x)]g'(x)$ if $h(u) = ue^u/2a^2$. However, we cannot currently determine a primitive function for $h(u)$. The $g(x)$ we used is about the only logical one to try, and hence the procedure has not worked here. In the next section, however, we shall show how to determine a primitive function for ue^u. Given this information we can then evaluate (5–68) using the above procedure. The methods of this section will not work to evaluate $\int e^{-ax^2} \, dx$ either. In this case, the reason is that a primitive function for e^{-ax^2} is a new type of function which we have not studied previously.

It is important to note that it is always straightforward to check whether or not $\int f(x)\, dx$ has been evaluated correctly. If we obtain $\int f(x)\, dx = F(x) + \lambda$, it is only necessary to differentiate $F(x)$ to see if $f(x)$ is obtained. For example, consider (5–66). Note that

$$\frac{d}{dx} 3(x^2 + 2)^{1/2} = \frac{3}{2}(x^2 + 2)^{-1/2}(2x) = \frac{3x}{(x^2 + 2)^{1/2}} = f(x)\,,$$

and thus the indefinite integral is indeed correct.

Equation (5–63) can be converted to a form which is convenient to use in evaluating definite integrals. Given (5–63), we know from the fundamental theorem of the calculus that if $g(x)$ and $g'(x)$ are continuous over $I_{\alpha\beta}^c$ and $h(u)$ is continuous for each $u = g(x)$, then

$$\int_\alpha^\beta f(x)\, dx = \int_\alpha^\beta h[g(x)]g'(x)\, dx = H[g(\beta)] - H[g(\alpha)]\,. \qquad (5\text{–}69)$$

Now since $H(u)$ is a primitive function for $h(u)$,

$$\int_\gamma^\delta h(u)\, du = H(\delta) - H(\gamma)\,. \qquad (5\text{–}70)$$

Thus from (5–69), it follows that

$$\int_\alpha^\beta f(x)\, dx = \int_{g(\alpha)}^{g(\beta)} h(u)\, du\,. \qquad (5\text{–}71)$$

For example,

$$\int_0^{\pi/2} (\cos x)\cos[\sin x]\, dx = \int_{\sin 0}^{\sin \pi/2} \cos u\, du = \int_0^1 \cos u\, du$$

$$= \sin 1 - \sin 0 = 0.841\,.$$

Here we used $g(x) = \sin x$ so that $g'(x) = \cos x$.

5–6 INTEGRATION BY PARTS

In this section we shall develop a technique for integration which corresponds to the rule for differentiating the product of two functions. Recall that, if $f_1(x)$ and $f_2(x)$ are differentiable, then

$$\frac{d}{dx}[f_1(x)f_2(x)] = f_2(x)f_1'(x) + f_1(x)f_2'(x)\,. \qquad (5\text{–}72)$$

We can write (5–72) as

$$f_1(x)f_2'(x) = \frac{d}{dx}[f_1(x)f_2(x)] - f_2(x)f_1'(x)\,. \qquad (5\text{–}73)$$

Now suppose that $R(x)$ is a primitive function for $f_2(x)f_1'(x)$. Clearly $f_1(x)f_2(x)$ is a primitive function for $d\,f_1(x)f_2(x)/dx$. Therefore, $f_1(x)f_2(x) - R(x)$ is a primitive function for $f_1(x)f_2'(x)$, since

$$\frac{d}{dx}[f_1(x)f_2(x) - R(x)] = f_1(x)f_2'(x) + f_2(x)f_1'(x) - f_2(x)f_1'(x)$$

$$= f_1(x)f_2'(x)\,.$$

Consequently, if $f_1(x)$, $f_2(x)$, $f_1'(x)$ and $f_2'(x)$ are continuous over some interval I_{ab}^c, then $f_1(x)f_2'(x)$ and $f_2(x)f_1'(x)$ are continuous and have primitive functions, and by what we have just shown

$$\int f_1(x)f_2'(x)\,dx = f_1(x)f_2(x) - R(x) + \lambda\,. \qquad (5\text{–}74)$$

Equation (5–74) is sometimes referred to as the *integration by parts* formula. Let us now explain how it can be used.

Suppose that we wish to integrate $f(x)$ and suppose that we can imagine that $f(x) = f_1(x)f_2'(x)$, where we know a primitive function $f_2(x)$ for $f_2'(x)$. Then, according to (5–74), we can integrate $f(x)$ if we can find a primitive function for $f_2(x)f_1'(x)$. In other words, we have converted the problem of finding a primitive function for $f_1(x)f_2'(x)$ to one of finding a primitive function for $f_2(x)f_1'(x)$. Interestingly enough, this procedure is a very useful one for determining indefinite integrals. Let us illustrate its use with some examples.

EXAMPLES. 1. Consider

$$\int x\,e^{ax}\,dx, \quad a \neq 0\,.$$

We can think of $f(x) = x\,e^{ax}$ as a product $f_1(x)f_2'(x)$ if $f_1(x) = x$ and $f_2'(x) = e^{ax}$. Now $f_2(x) = e^{ax}/a$ is a primitive function for $f_2'(x)$. Thus by (5–74)

$$\int x\,e^{ax}\,dx = \frac{x}{a}\,e^{ax} - R(x) + \lambda\,,$$

where $R(x)$ is a primitive function for $f_2(x)f_1'(x) = e^{ax}/a$. Clearly a primitive function for e^{ax}/a is e^{ax}/a^2. Thus

$$\int x\,e^{ax}\,dx = \frac{x}{a}\,e^{ax} - \frac{1}{a^2}\,e^{ax} + \lambda = \frac{e^{ax}}{a^2}\,(ax - 1) + \lambda\,. \qquad (5\text{–}75)$$

The trick in obtaining (5–75) is to remove the x multiplying e^{ax} in the integrand by using the integration by parts formula. In applying the technique there were two obvious choices for $f_1(x)$. One was x, the other e^{ax}. If we try $f_1(x) = e^{ax}$, then $f_2'(x) = x$ and $f_2(x) = x^2$. Now $f_2(x)f_1'(x) = ax^2\,e^{ax}$, and it appears more difficult to determine a primitive function for this than for the original integrand. This shows that, in order for the integration by parts scheme to be useful, $f_1(x)$ and $f_2'(x)$ must be carefully selected.

Given (5–75) we can now evaluate the integral studied on p. 311. To do so we must find a primitive function for $ue^u/2a^2$. From (5–75), a primitive function for ue^u is $e^u(u - 1)$, so that a primitive function for $ue^u/2a^2$ is $e^u(u - 1)/2a^2$. Hence

$$\int x^3 e^{-ax^2} dx = -\frac{e^{-ax^2}}{2a^2}(1 + ax^2), \quad \text{all } x.\tag{5–76}$$

This example points out that, to evaluate any given definite integral, a combination of the compound function rule and integration by parts may be needed.

2. Consider now

$$\int x^2 e^{-ax^2} dx.$$

We have noted previously that a primitive function for e^{-ax^2} cannot be expressed in terms of functions we have studied. The same happens to be true of primitive functions for $x^2 e^{-ax^2}$. However, if we denote by $\Omega(x)$ a primitive function for e^{-ax^2}, then the primitive functions for $x^2 e^{-ax^2}$ can be expressed in terms of $\Omega(x)$ and other familiar functions. Let us now see how this can be done, using integration by parts. To do so we must split up the integrand properly. Let us write $f_1(x) = x$ so that $f_2'(x) = x e^{-ax^2}$. A primitive function for $f_2'(x)$ is then $-e^{-ax^2}/2a$, and

$$\int x^2 e^{-ax^2} dx = -\frac{x}{2a} e^{-ax^2} - K(x) + \lambda,$$

where $K(x)$ is a primitive function for

$$f_2(x)f_1'(x) = -\frac{1}{2a} e^{-ax^2}.$$

A primitive function for $f_2(x)f_1'(x)$ is $-\Omega(x)/2a$. Thus

$$\int x^2 e^{-ax^2} dx = -\frac{1}{2a}[x e^{-ax^2} - \Omega(x)].\tag{5–77}$$

In general, all integrals of the form $\int x^n e^{-ax^2} dx$ with n odd can be evaluated in terms of familiar functions (the previous example illustrated this for $n = 3$), while those with n even can be expressed in terms of familiar functions and $\Omega(x)$.

3. Consider

$$\int \log x \, dx, \quad x > 0.$$

Since $\log x$ is continuous for $x > 0$, it has a primitive function. It is not immediately obvious, however, how integration by parts could be useful in finding a primitive function for $\log x$. The trick is to take $f_1(x) = \log x$ and $f_2'(x) = 1$. Then $f_2(x) = x$ is a primitive function for $f_2'(x) = 1$. Thus

$$\int \log x \, dx = x \log x - K(x) + \lambda ,$$

where $K(x)$ is a primitive function for

$$f_2(x)f_1'(x) = x\left(\frac{1}{x}\right) = 1 ,$$

since $d(\log x)/dx = 1/x$. A primitive function for 1 is x. Thus we can take $K(x) = x$ and

$$\int \log x \, dx = x \log x - x + \lambda . \tag{5-78}$$

4. As a final example we shall illustrate yet another way in which the integration by parts technique can sometimes be employed to evaluate an integral. Consider

$$\int e^{ax} \cos bx \, dx, \quad b \neq 0 .$$

Let us write $f_1(x) = e^{ax}$ and $f_2'(x) = \cos bx$. Then $f_2(x) = (\sin bx)/b$ is a primitive function for $f_2'(x)$, and hence a primitive function $F(x)$ for $e^{ax} \cos bx$ is

$$F(x) = \frac{1}{b} e^{ax} \sin bx - K(x) , \tag{5-79}$$

where $K(x)$ is a primitive function for

$$f_2(x)f_1'(x) = \frac{a}{b} e^{ax} \sin bx . \tag{5-80}$$

This would appear to have gotten us nowhere because we do not know a primitive function for (5–80). Let us apply the same procedure all over again to (5–80) to try to obtain $K(x)$. Given the function $(a/b)e^{ax} \sin bx$, let us write $\hat{f}_1(x) = (a/b) e^{ax}$ and $\hat{f}_2'(x) = \sin bx$. Then $-(\cos bx)/b$ is a primitive function for $\hat{f}_2'(x)$. Hence

$$K(x) = -\frac{a}{b^2} e^{ax} \cos bx - K_1(x) , \tag{5-81}$$

where $K_1(x)$ is a primitive function for

$$\hat{f}_2(x)\hat{f}_1'(x) = -\frac{a^2}{b^2} e^{ax} \cos bx .$$

Now we have said that $F(x)$ is a primitive function for $e^{ax} \cos bx$. Hence as $K_1(x)$ we can use

$$K_1(x) = -\frac{a^2}{b^2} F(x) . \qquad (5\text{-}82)$$

Substituting this in (5–81) and then using (5–81) in (5–79) we obtain

$$F(x) = \frac{1}{b} e^{ax} \sin bx + \frac{a}{b^2} e^{ax} \cos bx - \frac{a^2}{b^2} F(x) . \qquad (5\text{-}83)$$

We can then solve for $F(x)$ to obtain

$$F(x) = \frac{e^{ax}}{a^2 + b^2} [b \sin bx + a \cos bx] . \qquad (5\text{-}84)$$

Therefore

$$\int e^{ax} \cos bx \, dx = \frac{e^{ax}}{a^2 + b^2} [b \sin bx + a \cos bx] + \lambda, \quad \text{all } x . \qquad (5\text{-}85)$$

This procedure was remarkable in that we applied the integration by parts twice and ended up with an equation which involved only the unknown primitive function of interest.

This will conclude our discussion of techniques for evaluating indefinite integrals. The two techniques discussed in this section and the previous one are adequate in many areas of application. For those areas in which the problem of evaluating complicated integrals analytically often arises, it is necessary to study in some detail the many tricks that can be employed.

5–7 IMPROPER INTEGRALS

Recall that, if $f(x)$ is continuous over I_{ab}^c, then we can define a new function $F(t)$ whose domain is I_{ab}^c by

$$F(t) = \int_a^t f(x) \, dx . \qquad (5\text{-}86)$$

If $f(x)$ is continuous for all $x \geq a$, then the domain of $F(t)$ defined by (5–86) includes every $t \geq a$. We shall now study the behavior of $F(t)$ as t gets larger and larger. We shall be particularly interested in cases where $F(t)$ approaches some number β. Figures 5–6 and 5–7 illustrate cases where this sort of phenomenon occurs. Let us now try to make precise what we have in mind when we say that $F(t)$ approaches β as t becomes arbitrarily large. The idea is essentially the same as that for a limit of a sequence. Recall that $\{a_n\}$ converges to the limit α if there exists a function $g(\epsilon)$ whose domain is the set of all positive numbers, such that when $n > g(\epsilon)$ then $|a_n - \alpha| < \epsilon$. Similarly, *we say that $F(t)$ has the limit β as t becomes arbitrarily large if there exists a function $g(\epsilon)$, whose domain consists of all positive numbers, having the property that when $t > g(\epsilon)$, then $|F(t) - \beta| < \epsilon$.* This is indicated sym-

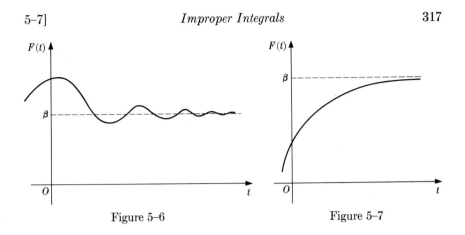

Figure 5–6   Figure 5–7

bolically by writing

$$\lim_{t \to \infty} F(t) = \beta , \qquad (5\text{-}87)$$

which is read the limit of $F(t)$ as t approaches infinity is β. Intuitively what (5–87) means is that, for all very large values of t, $F(t)$ is close to β and $F(t)$ can be made arbitrarily close to β by making t sufficiently large. It need not be true, of course, that $F(t)$ has a limit as t approaches infinity. For example, $F(t) = t$ has no limit because $F(t)$ becomes arbitrarily large as t increases. Also $F(t) = \sin t$ does not because $\sin t$ continually oscillates between -1 and 1.

When the function $F(t)$ defined by (5–86) approaches a limit as t approaches infinity, that is, (5–87) holds, a special notation $\int_a^\infty f(x)\,dx$ is used to represent the number β which is the limit. Thus by definition

$$\lim_{t \to \infty} F(t) = \int_a^\infty f(x)\,dx . \qquad (5\text{-}88)$$

We assign a meaning to $\int_a^\infty f(x)\,dx$ only when $\lim_{t \to \infty} F(t)$ exists. When this limit does exist it is called, that is, $\int_a^\infty f(x)\,dx$ is called, *the improper integral of $f(x)$ from a to ∞.* If $\int_a^\infty f(x)\,dx$ exists, we say that $\int_a^t f(x)\,dx$ *converges* as t approaches infinity. If $\int_a^\infty f(x)\,dx$ does not exist, we say that $\int_a^t f(x)\,dx$ *diverges* as t approaches infinity.

EXAMPLES. 1. Consider

$$F(t) = \int_1^t \frac{1}{x^4}\,dx = \frac{1}{3}\left(-\frac{1}{t^3} + 1\right) = \frac{1}{3}\left(1 - \frac{1}{t^3}\right). \qquad (5\text{-}89)$$

Now it is clear intuitively that, as t becomes larger and larger, $F(t)$ approaches $\frac{1}{3}$. To prove this rigorously, note that $|F(t) - \frac{1}{3}| = |-\frac{1}{3}t^{-3}| = \frac{1}{3}t^{-3}$. This is less than ϵ if $t^3 > 1/\epsilon$ or if $t > (1/\epsilon)^{1/3}$. Thus the function $g(\epsilon) = (1/\epsilon)^{1/3}$ serves to prove that $\lim_{t \to \infty} F(t) = \frac{1}{3}$, and we can write

$$\int_1^\infty \frac{1}{x^4}\,dx = \frac{1}{3}\,.\tag{5-90}$$

Intuitively, (5-90) can be interpreted as saying that the area of the set of points $y \leq 1/x$, $y \geq 0$, $x \geq 1$ is $\frac{1}{3}$, or in other words, the area of the shaded region in Figure 5-8 is $\frac{1}{3}$.

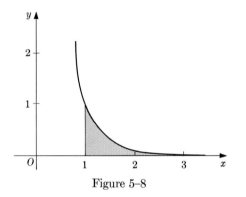

Figure 5-8

2. Consider next

$$F(t) = \int_1^t \frac{1}{x^\alpha}\,dx = \begin{cases} \dfrac{1}{\alpha - 1}\,(1 - t^{1-\alpha}), & \alpha \neq 1 \\[2mm] \log t, & \alpha = 1\,. \end{cases}\tag{5-91}$$

Since $\log t$ becomes arbitrarily large as t increases, it is clear that $\int_1^t dx/x$ diverges as t approaches infinity. If $1 - \alpha > 0$ or $\alpha < 1$, then $t^{1-\alpha}$ gets larger and larger as t increases and $\int_1^t dx/x^\alpha$ diverges. When $\alpha > 1$, then $1 - \alpha < 0$ and $t^{1-\alpha}$ gets smaller and smaller as t increases. In this case $\int_1^t dx/x^\alpha$ converges and

$$\int_1^\infty \frac{1}{x^\alpha}\,dx = \frac{1}{\alpha - 1}\,, \quad \alpha > 1\,.\tag{5-92}$$

For the rigorous proof of (5-92) we can use $g(\epsilon) = [(\alpha-1)\epsilon]^{-1/(\alpha-1)}$, the reasoning being the same as in the first example.

3. The integral

$$\int_a^t e^{-x}\,dx = e^{-a} - e^{-t} = F(t)$$

converges to e^{-a} as t approaches infinity for every a, that is,

$$\int_a^\infty e^{-x}\,dx = e^{-a}\,.\tag{5-93}$$

To prove this, note that $|F(t) - e^{-a}| = e^{-t} = 1/e^t$, which is less than ϵ if

$e^t > 1/\epsilon$. However, $e^t > 1/\epsilon$ if $t > \log 1/\epsilon$, since $e^a > e^b$ when $a > b$ and $e^{\log 1/\epsilon} = 1/\epsilon$. Hence the function $g(\epsilon) = \log 1/\epsilon = -\log \epsilon$ serves to prove that $F(t)$ converges to e^{-a}.

When $f(x) \geq 0$ for $x \geq a$ and $\int_a^\infty f(x)\,dx$ exists, it seems reasonable, as we have noted in the first example above, to think of this improper integral as being the area of the set of points which are solutions to the inequalities $y - f(x) \leq 0$, $y \geq 0$, $x \geq a$. In many areas of application it is convenient to think of things in this way. From a rigorous point of view, we simply define what we mean by the area in this case to be $\int_a^\infty f(x)\,dx$.

Suppose now that $f(x)$ is continuous for $x \leq a$. Consider the function $F(t)$ defined by

$$F(t) = \int_t^a f(x)\,dx \tag{5–94}$$

whose domain includes all $t \leq a$. Let us study the behavior of this function as t becomes an arbitrarily large negative number. If $F(t)$ approaches a number β, we write

$$\lim_{t \to -\infty} F(t) = \beta, \tag{5–95}$$

which is read the limit of $F(t)$ as t approaches minus infinity is β. The precise definition of what (5–95) means is as follows. *If there exists a function $g(\epsilon)$ whose domain consists of all positive numbers such that if $t < g(\epsilon)$, then $|F(t) - \beta| < \epsilon$, we say that β is the limit of $F(t)$ as t approaches minus infinity.* When $F(t)$ defined by (5–94) has a limit as t approaches minus infinity, this limit is denoted by $\int_{-\infty}^a f(x)\,dx$ and is called *the improper integral of $f(x)$ from $-\infty$ to a.* If $\int_{-\infty}^a f(x)\,dx$ exists, we say that $\int_t^a f(x)\,dx$ converges as t approaches minus infinity; if $F(t)$ has no limit, we say that $\int_t^a f(x)\,dx$ diverges as t approaches minus infinity. When

$$\int_0^\infty f(x)\,dx \quad \text{and} \quad \int_{-\infty}^0 f(x)\,dx$$

both exist, we denote the sum of these two numbers by $\int_{-\infty}^\infty f(x)\,dx$. Thus by definition

$$\int_{-\infty}^\infty f(x)\,dx = \int_{-\infty}^0 f(x)\,dx + \int_0^\infty f(x)\,dx. \tag{5–96}$$

It is easy to show that, if $\int_a^\infty f(x)\,dx$ and $\int_a^\infty g(x)\,dx$ exist, then

$$\int_a^\infty \lambda f(x)\,dx \quad \text{and} \quad \int_a^\infty [f(x) + g(x)]\,dx$$

exist, and furthermore

$$\int_a^\infty \lambda\, f(x)\, dx = \lambda \int_a^\infty f(x)\, dx \qquad (5\text{–}97)$$

and

$$\int_a^\infty [f(x) + g(x)]\, dx = \int_a^\infty f(x)\, dx + \int_a^\infty g(x)\, dx . \qquad (5\text{–}98)$$

We ask the reader to provide the proofs of these results in the problems.

5–8 AREAS, VOLUMES AND LENGTHS OF CURVES

We originally motivated the concept of the definite integral by attempting to find the area of a set of points bounded on one side by an arbitrary continuous curve. It was assumed that we understood what was meant by area. The notion of area which we used, however, was a completely intuitive one. How do we proceed to define rigorously what we mean by the area of a set of points whose boundaries are curves? One way to do this now is to reverse our direction and define what we mean by areas using the concept of a definite integral. In other words, for example, if $f(x)$ is continuous and positive over I_{ab}^c, then the area of the set of points $y - f(x) \leq 0$, $y \geq 0$, $x \geq a$, $x \leq b$ is simply defined to be the number $\int_a^b f(x)\, dx$. To be convinced that this definition agrees with our intuitive concepts, we would have to show that the definition possesses certain properties. One of these would be the requirement that the area would not change if we traced the region on a piece of paper and then moved it around with respect to the coordinate system. We could indeed verify that this and all the other desired properties are satisfied, but we shall not attempt to do so. Rather, we shall continue to use the intuitive concepts of area, using definite integrals to determine the areas of various regions.

In Chapter 4 we only studied the problem of evaluating the area of a region one of whose sides was the x-axis. Precisely the same techniques can be used to determine the area of more complicated regions. We shall illustrate with two simple examples.

EXAMPLES. 1. Let us determine the area of the set of points $y + 0.5(x - 1)^2 \leq 4$, $y - x \geq 0$, $0 \leq x \leq 2$. This set of points is the darkly shaded region shown in Figure 5–9. Now the area of the darkly shaded region is the area of both shaded regions minus the area of the lightly shaded region. The area of the shaded regions combined is

$$\int_0^2 [4 - 0.5(x - 1)^2]\, dx ,$$

and the area of the lightly shaded region is

$$\int_0^2 x \, dx \, .$$

Thus the area of the darkly shaded region is

$$\int_0^2 [4 - 0.5(x - 1)^2 - x] \, dx = \int_0^2 4 \, dx - 0.5 \int_0^2 (x - 1)^2 \, dx - \int_0^2 x \, dx$$

$$= 4x \Big|_0^2 - \frac{0.5}{3} (x - 1)^3 \Big|_0^2 - \frac{x^2}{2} \Big|_0^2$$

$$= 8 - \frac{1}{3} - 2$$

$$= 5\frac{2}{3} \, .$$

2. Let us determine the area of the set of points $y \le x^{1/2}$, $y \ge x^2$. The set of points satisfying these inequalities is the shaded region in Figure 5–10. The two graphs intersect at $x = 0$ and $x = 1$. The same reasoning used in the previous example then shows that the area is

$$\int_0^1 (x^{1/2} - x^2) \, dx = \int_0^1 x^{1/2} \, dx - \int_0^1 x^2 \, dx$$

$$= \frac{2}{3} x^{3/2} \Big|_0^1 - \frac{x^3}{3} \Big|_0^1$$

$$= \frac{2}{3} - \frac{1}{3}$$

$$= \frac{1}{3} \, .$$

It is straightforward to evaluate areas provided we can evaluate the resulting integrals. It is not always easy to evaluate these integrals analytically, although we shall see how to do so numerically in the next chapter. The reader may wonder why we never gave as an example the determina-

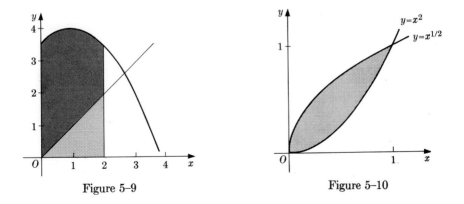

Figure 5–9   Figure 5–10

tion of the area of a circle. Interestingly enough, the integral involved here is relatively complicated to evaluate and requires the introduction of some functions we have not studied. It is possible, of course, to show using integration that the area of a circle of radius r is πr^2.

We can determine not only areas of sets of points by integration, but we can also determine volumes, surface areas and lengths of curves, to mention just a few problems of interest in geometry. We shall now show how to find volumes of surfaces of revolution and how to find the lengths of curves. First consider the determination of volumes.

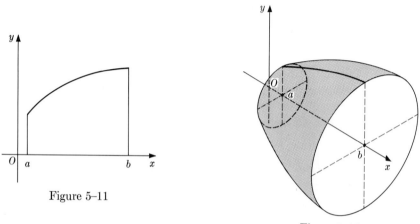

Figure 5–11

Figure 5–12

Many everyday containers, such as ordinary cylindrical tin cans, ice-cream cones, spherical tanks at an oil refinery, bowls used in the kitchen and vases, can be thought of as surfaces of revolution. We can define a surface of revolution as follows. Suppose that $f(x)$ is a function which is continuous and positive for each $x \in I_{ab}^c$. The graph of $f(x)$ for $x \in I_{ab}^c$ might then look like that shown in Figure 5–11. Let us now rotate the xy-plane using the x-axis as an axis of rotation. The graph of $f(x)$ as it moves around generates a surface of revolution. This is shown in Figure 5–12. The intersection of this surface with a plane perpendicular to the x-axis is a circle. For example, if $f(x) = 0.5x$ and we use the interval $0 \leq x \leq 5$, the surface of revolution generated by revolving the graph of $0.5x$ about the x-axis is what we would call a cone. We would like to find the volume of the space contained in a surface of revolution. This is often referred to as the volume of the surface, that is, the volume of the cone, for example, just as the area of the inside of a circle is referred to as the area of the circle. If we took the surface and placed a bottom on it if needed (as with a tin can) and then filled it with water, the volume of water it would hold is the volume we shall compute.

To determine the volume we shall proceed in exactly the same way as in determining areas by first dividing I_{ab}^c into n subintervals of equal length. Let y_{*k} and y_k^* be the minimum and maximum values of $f(x)$ over the kth subinterval. Consider now the two cylindrical surfaces generated by rotating $f_1(x) = y_{*k}$ and $f_2(x) = y_k^*$, $x_{k-1} \leq x \leq x_k$, about the x-axis. These are shown in Figure 5–13. We shall call the one generated by $f_1(x)$ an inner cylinder and that generated by $f_2(x)$ an outer cylinder. Just as we assumed that we knew how to compute the area of a rectangle when developing the theory of areas, we shall here assume that we know how to find the volume

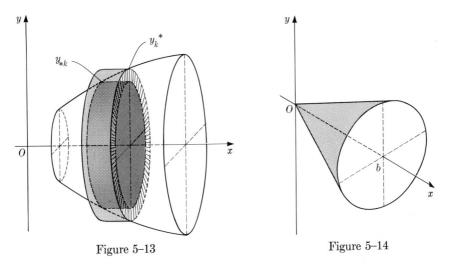

Figure 5–13   Figure 5–14

of a cylinder. The volume of a cylinder is equal to the area of its base times its altitude. The volume of the kth outer cylinder is then $\pi(y_k^*)^2 h$ and the volume of the kth inner cylinder is $\pi(y_{*k})^2 h$, where $h = (b - a)/n$.

We can now determine approximately the volume of the surface by adding up the volumes of the inner cylinders or the outer cylinders. This yields two numbers

$$s_{Ln} = \pi \frac{b-a}{n} \sum_{k=1}^{n} (y_{*k})^2; \qquad s_{Un} = \pi \frac{b-a}{n} \sum_{k=1}^{n} (y_k^*)^2 . \qquad (5\text{–}99)$$

Furthermore, since the surface of interest is always inside the outer cylinders and outside the inner cylinders, then the volume v of the surface must satisfy

$$s_{Ln} \leq v \leq s_{Un} . \qquad (5\text{–}100)$$

Now for each natural number n we can determine an s_{Ln} and s_{Un}, that is, we can generate the sequences $\{s_{Ln}\}$ and $\{s_{Un}\}$. However, these sequences are nothing but Riemann sequences for the function $\pi[f(x)]^2$ over I_{ab}^c. The function $\pi[f(x)]^2$ is continuous over I_{ab}^c since we assumed that $f(x)$ is continuous. Therefore, both Riemann sequences converge and have the same limit, which is $\pi \int_a^b [f(x)]^2 \, dx$. Thus from (5–100) we conclude that the volume we are trying to compute must be

$$v = \pi \int_a^b [f(x)]^2 \, dx . \tag{5–101}$$

EXAMPLES. 1. Suppose that we revolve the line $y = ax$, $a > 0$, about the x-axis and find the volume of the surface so generated for x in the interval $0 \le x \le b$. The surface is what we call a cone and looks like that shown in Figure 5–14. By (5–101) the volume is

$$v = \pi \int_0^b a^2 x^2 \, dx = \frac{\pi a^2 b^3}{3} . \tag{5–102}$$

2. Consider the surface obtained by revolving the graph of $y = x^{1/2}$ about the x-axis. The surface is called a paraboloid of revolution since $y = x^{1/2}$ is part of a parabola. The volume of the paraboloid for x in the interval $0 \le x \le b$ is

$$v = \pi \int_0^b x \, dx = \frac{\pi b^2}{2} . \tag{5–103}$$

3. Let us compute the volume of a sphere having radius r. A sphere of radius r is generated by revolving the graph of $y = (r^2 - x^2)^{1/2}$ about the x-axis. The appropriate interval is $-r \le x \le r$. Then according to (5–101), the volume v of the sphere is

$$
\begin{aligned}
v &= \pi \int_{-r}^r (r^2 - x^2) \, dx \\
&= \pi \left(r^2 x - \frac{x^3}{3} \right) \Big|_{-r}^r \\
&= \pi \left[r^3 - \frac{r^3}{3} + r^3 - \frac{r^3}{3} \right] \\
&= \frac{4}{3} \pi r^3 ,
\end{aligned}
$$

which is the well-known expression for the volume of a sphere. It is interesting to note that, whereas it is relatively difficult to evaluate the integral for the area of a circle, it is quite easy to determine the volume of a sphere. However, it must be kept in mind that we had to know the expression for the area of a circle in order to compute the volume of a sphere, because the expressions for the volumes of the inner and outer cylinders assume that we know how to determine the area of a circle.

As a final example of how integration can be employed in the solution of geometric type problems, let us study the problem of finding the length of some given curve. Suppose that we wish to find the length of the graph for $f(x)$, $x \in I_{ab}^c$, that is, we wish to find the length of the curve represented by the graph of $f(x)$ which joins the points $(a, f(a))$ and $(b, f(b))$. The curve might then look like that shown in Figure 5–15. We shall, as usual, assume that $f(x)$ is continuous at each point in I_{ab}^c. For the current problem, however, we shall also need to assume that $f'(x)$ exists and is continuous for each $x \in I_{ab}^c$. We feel intuitively that we understand what the length of the curve in Figure 5–15 means. If we etched a scale on a thin straight piece of wire, bent the wire into the shape of the curve in Figure 5–15 and placed the zero point of the scale at $(a, f(a))$, the reading on the scale at $(b, f(b))$ would then be the length of the curve.

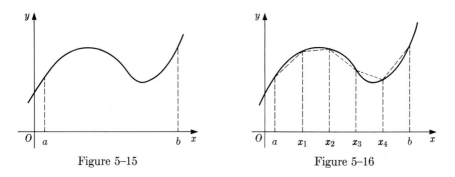

Figure 5–15   Figure 5–16

We can determine approximately the length of the curve as follows. Let us subdivide the interval I_{ab}^c into n subintervals of equal length $(b - a)/n$ by the $n - 1$ points

$$x_k = a + \frac{b - a}{n} k, \quad k = 1, \ldots, n - 1. \tag{5–104}$$

Also write $x_0 = a$ and $x_n = b$. Consider now the curve formed over the kth subinterval by joining the points $(x_{k-1}, f(x_{k-1}))$ and $(x_k, f(x_k))$ on the graph of $f(x)$ by a straight line segment. Imagine that this is done for each subinterval. There results a curve K, defined over I_{ab}^c, which consists of a series of straight line segments. This is the dashed curve shown in Figure 5–16. Now the length of K is approximately equal to the length of the curve of interest. Furthermore, the approximation should get better and better as n is increased.

From the results of Section 2–13 we can compute the length of K, since the length of the straight line segment joining $(x_{k-1}, f(x_{k-1}))$ to $(x_k, f(x_k))$ is simply the distance between these two points, that is,

$$\{(x_k - x_{k-1})^2 + [f(x_k) - f(x_{k-1})]^2\}^{1/2}.$$

Thus the length of K is

$$\sum_{k=1}^{n} \{(x_k - x_{k-1})^2 + [f(x_k) - f(x_{k-1})]^2\}^{1/2} . \tag{5-105}$$

We now employ the same technique used in proving the fundamental theorem of the calculus and apply the mean value theorem. Note that $x_k - x_{k-1} = h$. Thus by the mean value theorem

$$f(x_k) - f(x_{k-1}) = f'(\xi_k)h , \tag{5-106}$$

where ξ_k is in the kth subinterval. In order to apply the mean value theorem we must assume that $f(x)$ is differentiable, which is the reason that we assumed $f(x)$ to be differentiable initially. Thus the length of K becomes

$$s_{Rn} = \sum_{k=1}^{n} \{h^2 + [f'(\xi_k)]^2 h^2\}^{1/2} = \frac{b - a}{n} \sum_{k=1}^{n} \{1 + [f'(\xi_k)]^2\}^{1/2} . \tag{5-107}$$

For each natural number n we can determine a curve K whose length is given by (5–107). We can now observe that the sequence $\{s_{Rn}\}$ is a Riemann sequence for the function $g(x) = [1 + \{f'(x)\}^2]^{1/2}$ over the interval I_{ab}^c. Now we assumed initially that $f'(x)$ is continuous over the interval and thus $g(x)$ is also. Hence, we know that $\{s_{Rn}\}$ converges and its limit is

$$L = \int_a^b \{1 + [f'(x)]^2\}^{1/2} \, dx . \tag{5-108}$$

From the behavior of $\{s_{Rn}\}$ it would appear that the length of the curve of interest is (5–108). The situation is a little more subtle here than for our discussion of areas and volumes. In the latter two cases we obtained two sequences with the property that for each n the value of the area or volume lay between the values of the nth terms of these two sequences. We cannot obtain directly two such sequences for the length of a curve, and thus it is not quite so clear that L is the length of the curve. From a rigorous point of view, we simply define (5–108) to be the length of the curve. Frequently the integral (5–108) turns out to be difficult to evaluate analytically. We shall, however, give one example where this can be done.

EXAMPLE. Let us compute the length of $f(x) = x^{3/2}$ over the interval $0 \le x \le 1$. Then $f'(x) = \frac{3}{2}x^{1/2}$, which is continuous over the interval. Thus by (5–108) the length is

$$L = \int_0^1 \left(1 + \frac{9}{4} x\right)^{1/2} dx .$$

We shall evaluate this using the compound function rule for integration. If we take $g(x) = 1 + \frac{9}{4}x$, then $g'(x) = \frac{9}{4}$ and

$$\left(1 + \frac{9}{4} x\right)^{1/2} = \frac{4}{9} [g(x)]^{1/2} g'(x) ,$$

which is of the form $h[g(x)]g'(x)$ if $h(u) = \frac{4}{9}u^{1/2}$. Now $g(0) = 1$ and $g(1) = 13\frac{3}{4}$. Thus by (5–71)

$$L = \frac{4}{9} \int_{1}^{13/4} u^{1/2}\, du = \frac{8}{27}\left[\left(\frac{13}{4}\right)^{3/2} - 1\right] \doteq 1.43\,.$$

5–9 .DIFFERENTIAL EQUATIONS

We have in the past considered a number of different ways of characterizing a function. In this section we shall briefly study a new way of characterizing a function which is very important in practice. Suppose that we are given some continuous function $g(x)$. We have in this chapter considered in some detail the problem of finding all functions $f(x)$ whose derivative function is $g(x)$. If $y = f(x)$ is a function whose derivative is $g(x)$, then $f(x)$ must satisfy the equation

$$f'(x) = g(x) \quad \text{or} \quad \frac{dy}{dx} = g(x)\,. \tag{5–109}$$

Note that in (5–109), $g(x)$ is specified while $f(x)$ is not. Equation (5–109) is the simplest example of what is called a *differential equation*. Any function $f(x)$ whose derivative function is $g(x)$ is called *a solution* of the differential equation. If we know a primitive function $G(x)$ for $g(x)$, then we can write down easily the set of all solutions to the differential equation (5–109). Every function $f(x) = G(x) + \lambda$, λ any real number, is a solution. The problem of finding the set of all functions which are solutions to (5–109) is simply equivalent to the problem of finding the indefinite integral of $g(x)$. There are an infinite number of solutions to (5–109) and thus the differential equation (5–109) alone does not determine a unique function. However, a unique solution will be determined if one point in the graph of the solution is specified. In other words, if it is specified that the value of the function at the value x_1 in its domain is to be y_1, there is only one solution to (5–109) with this property, since $y_1 = f(x_1) = G(x_1) + \lambda$. Hence $\lambda = y_1 - G(x_1)$ and $f(x) = G(x) - G(x_1) + y_1$ is the unique solution to (5–109). Thus by specifying the differential equation (5–109) and the requirement that the graph of the solution must contain the point (x_1, y_1), a unique function is determined which is that solution to (5–109) having $f(x_1) = y_1$.

Let us now generalize somewhat our notion of a differential equation. Imagine that $g(y)$ and $h(x)$ are continuous functions, and suppose that we would like to find the set of all functions $y = f(x)$ such that

$$g[f(x)]\,f'(x) = h(x)\,. \tag{5–110}$$

In other words, we wish to find all functions with the property that, for each x in the domain, if we compute $g[f(x)]$ and multiply this number by

$f'(x)$, we obtain the number $h(x)$. We can write (5–110) in a simple form by replacing $f(x)$ by y and writing $dy/dx = f'(x)$. Then (5–110) becomes

$$g(y)\frac{dy}{dx} = h(x) \, . \tag{5–111}$$

Equation (5–111) or (5–110) is also called a differential equation. More generally, an equation containing symbols representing a function, its derivative function and possibly the independent variable for the function is called a differential equation. Thus

$$\frac{dy}{dx} + y^2 = 0; \qquad \frac{dy}{dx} - xy = e^x;$$

$$\frac{dy}{dx} + ay = xe^x; \qquad \left(\frac{dy}{dx}\right)^2 - y = x^2$$

are examples of differential equations with y being the symbol for the function, dy/dx the symbol for the derivative function, and x the symbol for the independent variable. Any function $f(x)$ is called a solution to the differential equation if the differential equation holds when, for each value ξ in the domain of the function, we replace in the differential equation the symbol for the independent variable by ξ, the symbol for the function by $f(\xi)$ and the symbol for the derivative of the function by $f'(\xi)$. The only differential equations we shall study here will be of the form (5–111).

We shall now see how to determine all solutions to (5–111). Let $G(y)$ and $H(x)$ be any primitive functions for $g(y)$ and $h(x)$ respectively over the set of values y and x for which primitive functions exist. By the chain rule, we note that $G[f(x)]$ is a primitive function for $g[f(x)]f'(x)$. Recall that, if two functions have the same derivative for all x, then the functions can differ only by a constant. Thus if $f(x)$ is a solution to (5–111), $G[f(x)]$ and $H(x)$ can differ only by a constant, so that there exists a λ such that

$$G[f(x)] = H(x) + \lambda \, . \tag{5–112}$$

Consider now the relation

$$G(y) = H(x) + \lambda \tag{5–113}$$

for any specified value of λ. We know from Chapter 2 that there may be no points or there may be only one point in the graph of (5–113). Let us suppose, however, that for the given λ, the graph of (5–113) is a curve. Then the graph of (5–113) will, as we know from Chapter 2, be the union of the graphs of one or more functions, say $y = f_1(x), \ldots; y = f_k(x)$. Then for each x in the domain of $f_i(x)$, it must be true that

$$G[f_i(x)] = H(x) + \lambda \, , \tag{5–114}$$

or when $f_i(x)$ is differentiable we have, by the chain rule,

$$g[f_i(x)]f_i'(x) = H'(x) = h(x) \,, \qquad (5\text{–}115)$$

since two functions which are equal must have the same derivative function. Therefore each $f_i(x)$ is a solution to the differential equation (5–111) over the domain for which $f_i(x)$ is differentiable.

Consider then the set S of all functions which are implicitly defined by the relation (5–114) as we allow λ to take on all real values. From what we have just shown, every function in S is a solution to the differential equation provided the function is differentiable. However, by (5–112), every solution to (5–111) must be one of these functions for some value of λ. Thus the set of solutions to (5–111) must be S. There will generally be an infinite number of functions in S, and in order to determine uniquely one of these, additional information must be given. This normally takes the form of specifying one point on the graph of the function.

The task of finding a solution or all solutions to a differential equation is referred to as *integrating* or *solving the differential equation*. We can solve (5–111) if we can integrate $g(y)$ and $h(x)$. Let us now illustrate with some examples how differential equations of the form (5–111) can be solved.

EXAMPLES. 1. Let us determine all solutions for the differential equation

$$\frac{dy}{dx} = \alpha y \,, \qquad (5\text{–}116)$$

where α is a specified constant. If a solution $y = f(x)$ has $y \neq 0$ for all x, then (5–116) can be written

$$\frac{1}{y}\frac{dy}{dx} = \alpha \,, \qquad (5\text{–}117)$$

which is of the form (5–111) with $g(y) = 1/y$ and $h(x) = \alpha$. Now $\log |y|$ is a primitive function for $g(y)$ and αx is a primitive function for $h(x)$. Thus every function which is a solution to (5–117) must satisfy the relation

$$\log |y| = \alpha x + \lambda \qquad (5\text{–}118)$$

for some λ, and conversely every differentiable function defined by (5–118) is a solution. Now the graph of (5–118) is precisely the same as the graph of

$$|y| = e^{\alpha x + \lambda} = e^{\lambda} e^{\alpha x} \,, \qquad (5\text{–}119)$$

since the graph of $x = \log y$ and $y = \exp x$ are the same by the way $\exp x$ was defined. Now for every real number λ, the graph of (5–119) is the union of the graphs of two everywhere differentiable functions which are

$$y = e^{\lambda} e^{\alpha x}; \qquad y = -e^{\lambda} e^{\alpha x} \,. \qquad (5\text{–}120)$$

Note that $e^{\lambda} > 0$ and $-e^{\lambda} < 0$ for each real number λ, and given any positive number β there is a λ such that $\beta = e^{\lambda}$. Thus the set of all solutions to (5–117) is the set of all functions

$$y = \beta\, e^{\alpha x}, \quad \text{all real } \beta, \quad \beta \neq 0 . \qquad (5\text{-}121)$$

Each of these solutions has the property that there is no x for which $y = 0$. Furthermore, if we specify that our solution must pass through a given point (x_1, y_1), $y_1 \neq 0$, then a unique solution $y = y_1\, e^{\alpha(x-x_1)}$ is determined. Through any point in the xy-plane which does not lie on the x-axis there passes precisely one solution to (5–117). No solution to (5–117) touches or crosses the x-axis.

Now every solution to (5–117) is also a solution to (5–116). Furthermore, any solution to (5–116) which is different from 0 over a given interval will be a solution to (5–117) and will be different from 0 for all x. There is, however, one solution to (5–116) which is not a solution to (5–117). This is the function $y = 0$ for all x. Note that this is a solution to (5–116). Thus the set of all solutions to (5–116) is the set of functions $y = \beta\, e^{\alpha x}$, β any real number (including 0), and through any point in the xy-plane there passes one and only one solution to (5–116). The reader should sketch these solutions for the case where $\alpha > 0$, $\alpha = 0$ and $\alpha < 0$.

The simple differential equation (5–116) is an important one which arises frequently in the real world. We shall illustrate in the next section some practical problems which lead to such a differential equation.

2. Let us find all solutions for the differential equation

$$y \frac{dy}{dx} = -x . \qquad (5\text{-}122)$$

This has the form (5–111) with $g(y) = y$ and $h(x) = -x$. Primitive functions for $g(y)$ and $h(x)$ are respectively $y^2/2$ and $-x^2/2$. Every solution to (5–122) must then satisfy the relation

$$y^2 + x^2 = 2\lambda \qquad (5\text{-}123)$$

for some λ, and every differentiable function defined by (5–123) is a solution. For each $\lambda > 0$ the graph of the relation (5–123) is the union of the graphs of the two functions

$$y = (2\lambda - x^2)^{1/2}; \quad y = -(2\lambda - x^2)^{1/2} , \quad -(2\lambda)^{1/2} \leq x \leq (2\lambda)^{1/2} , \quad (5\text{-}124)$$

which are differentiable in the interior of their domain of definition. When $\lambda < 0$ there are no points satisfying (5–123) and when $\lambda = 0$ there is just the single point $(0, 0)$. Thus the set of all solutions to (5–122) is the set of functions (5–124) for all $\lambda > 0$, where the domain of each function is the open interval $-(2\lambda)^{1/2} < x < (2\lambda)^{1/2}$. Through any point in the plane not on the x-axis there passes a unique curve which is the graph of a solution to (5–122). The functions (5–124) are, of course, either the upper or lower half of a circle with center at the origin and radius $(2\lambda)^{1/2}$.

3. As a final example we shall find all solutions to the differential equation

$$e^y \frac{dy}{dx} = 2x \, . \tag{5–125}$$

Here $g(y) = e^y$ and $h(x) = 2x$. Thus primitive functions for $g(y)$ and $h(x)$ are respectively e^y and x^2. Hence every solution to (5–125) must satisfy

$$e^y = x^2 + \lambda \tag{5–126}$$

for some λ. However, the graph of (5–126) is the same as the graph of

$$y = \log(x^2 + \lambda) \, . \tag{5–127}$$

The domain of the function (5–127) includes all x when $\lambda > 0$ and includes all x for which $x^2 > |\lambda|$ when $\lambda \leq 0$. The graphs of the functions (5–127) are shown in Figure 5–17. Note the interesting behavior of these functions.

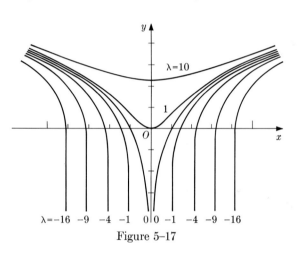

Figure 5–17

Given any point (x_1, y_1), a unique function (5–127) can be determined such that the graph of the function passes through (x_1, y_1).

5–10 APPLICATIONS—MATHEMATICAL MODELS

The process by which mathematics is employed to solve real-world problems can usually be thought of as a two-step process. First a *mathematical model* of the relevant portions of the real world is constructed, and then the mathematical model is analyzed or solved. The solution to the model is then used as the "solution" to the real world problem. Mathematics does not deal directly with practical everyday objects such as atoms, people, planets or dollars. It deals only with symbols and relations between these symbols. In one way or another, then, the relevant portions of the actual situation must be described in mathematical terms. This process of describing the real world in mathematical terms we refer to as the construction of a mathematical model.

A mathematical model consists of nothing but a set of symbols, a set of statements describing any relevant characteristics of the symbols and a set of mathematical expressions of one sort or another which relate the symbols. In constructing mathematical models, several points must be kept in mind. First of all, a model need not, and indeed cannot, provide a complete description of the system under consideration. Only those features of the system which are relevant for the problem of interest need be represented. For example, in a particular problem the only characteristic of a given object which may be of interest to us is its production cost. Its shape, color and size may be entirely irrelevant and hence do not need to be represented in the mathematical model. One task then, which can be a difficult one, is to determine precisely what characteristics of the real word should be represented in the model. Another important thing to recognize is that the nature of the real world can never be described with complete accuracy in a mathematical model. Some approximations are always needed. One of the most difficult tasks in constructing models is deciding what are realistic and allowable approximations to make. The notion that mathematical models always represent only an approximation to reality is an extremely important one and the reader should think about it to convince himself of its correctness.

Let us now discuss one type of approximation which must always be made in constructing a mathematical model if the methods of calculus are to be applied to the model. Everything of interest in the real world is, in essence, made up of discrete units. These units may be people, molecules, quanta of light, the smallest monetary unit or the smallest natural unit, such as one automobile, in which something is produced or sold. Suppose now that one variable x in a mathematical model refers to the amount of some physical quantity which is made up of discrete units. Thus x might be the number of people in the United States or the sales of a department store in some given period. For any value of x that will be of interest in the model there may be millions or billions of the discrete units involved in yielding this value of x, for example, there are more than 190 million people in the United States. In the model, we are not only interested in values of x but are also concerned with changes in x when some other variable is changed. Let us suppose that the changes in x which will be of interest also involve a large number of the discrete units. For example, if we are interested in the population change in the United States from one year to another, this change will be at least 100,000 people, which is a large number of the discrete units. In such situations, if is often convenient to assume in the mathematical model that x is a continuous variable and can take on all real values, not merely some finite number of discrete values, in a particular interval.

Let us now investigate what is gained and lost by representing x by a continuous variable in the model. The great advantage gained is that the methods of the calculus can be introduced, including the notion of the instantaneous rates of change of x with respect to time or other variables —in other words, derivatives. It is instructive to look in a little more detail at what is involved in replacing a discrete variable by a continuous one. Suppose that we wish to consider the change in the population of the United States with time. If we plotted the actual population of the U.S. as a function of time, it would look something like that shown in Figure 5–18. The

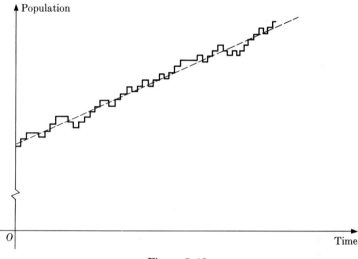

Figure 5–18

graph consists of many very small steps which are shown greatly exaggerated in size. The population remains constant until someone is born or dies (or enters or leaves the country), then the population either increases or decreases by one. When we treat the population as a continuous variable we are, in effect, replacing the graph with many small steps in it by a smooth curve, which is also shown in Figure 5–18. The actual step-type curve is barely distinguishable from the smooth curve, and if drawn to scale it would not be distinguishable on a figure of the size shown.

Consider now the slope of the smooth curve, that is, dx/dt, at some give t. What is this slope? For the idealized situation where we treat the population as continuous, it is the instantaneous rate of change of the population at t (in the units of people per year perhaps). There are now two important things to note about dx/dt. First of all, even though the smooth curve approximates very closely the step-like graph, dx/dt does not approximate closely the actual instantaneous rate of change of the population. The reason for this is that the rate of change of the population is 0 except at those points in time where the population increases or decreases by one, and at such points the step-like curve does not have a derivative.

In other words, the notion of an instantaneous rate of change of population has little meaning for the actual situation. Even though dx/dt does not approximate the actual instantaneous rate of change of the population, it is nonetheless true that dx/dt can be used to approximate the population change over a short interval. The population change over a short interval of length τ which starts at time t is $x(t + \tau) - x(t)$, and we can use $x(t + \tau)$ and $x(t)$ as the values on the smooth curve since they approximate closely the actual values. But from Chapter 3 we know that for small τ, $x(t + \tau) - x(t) \doteq \tau \, dx/dt$. Consequently, the slope of the smooth curve can be used to approximate changes in the population over small intervals, and this is what we are really interested in doing. For large time intervals, note that

$$x(t + \tau) - x(t) = \int_t^{t+\tau} \frac{dx}{dt} \, dt \,,$$

so that by integrating the derivative function for the smooth curve we can accurately determine population changes over long time intervals. Thus we see that the derivative function of the smooth curve is very useful, even though the instantaneous rate of change for the smooth curve does not accurately approximate the actual rate of change. The actual rate of change is really of no interest; it is the slope of the smooth curve which is of interest.

What has been lost by using a continuous variable x instead of a discrete one? The ability to account for the discreteness has been lost. Thus, in using a continuous variable x, we might determine the change in population over some interval to be 101,270.56. This cannot be the population change, since the population must always change by a natural number. However, we really don't care whether the change was, for example, 101,269 or 101,271. When a large number of the discrete units is involved, the fact that the answer may not be a natural number does not bother us. We can merely round off to the nearest natural number.

Whenever we wish to use the methods of the calculus in treating some problem we must generally introduce the approximation that the variables will be treated as continuous. Frequently this is an extremely good approximation and the errors introduced by it are negligible. Nonetheless, there are many important problems where discreteness cannot be ignored and where it is not legitimate to replace discrete situations by continuous approximations. Thus it is necessary to consider carefully whether or not such an approximation is valid.

Remarkably, many problems in such diverse areas as physics, engineering and economics can all lead to basically the same mathematical model.

It is this fact which makes it feasible to gain through a study of a relatively limited number of mathematical topics tools which can be usefully employed in many different areas. If each and every real-world problem required a completely different type of mathematics for its solution, the possibilities for using mathematics would be severely limited. The task of formulating mathematical models is outside of mathematics proper, since frequently a very detailed knowledge of the real world situation is required. For this reason it is not possible to discuss in a text like this detailed practical applications of the material developed in areas such as physics or economics. We shall, however, close this section by giving one simple example.

We have used as an example in our above discussion the population of the United States. Suppose now that we would like to construct a model from which we can predict the population of the U.S. at different future points in time. If we denote by x the population at time t, then we wish to determine a function $x = g(t)$. As discussed above, it is convenient to treat x as being a continuous variable. Many models could be constructed which would vary widely in their complexity. The simplest model is based on the empirical observation that the rate of increase of the population is proportional to the population. In other words, the larger the population, the faster it increases, and the rate of increase is directly proportional to the population. (Why should it be proportional to the population rather than the square of population for example?) Since the rate of change of the population is dx/dt, the above statement translated into mathematical terms becomes

$$\frac{dx}{dt} = \lambda x . \tag{5–128}$$

The constant $\lambda = (dx/dt)/x$ is the fractional increase in the population per unit of time. This constant cannot be obtained from the model. It must be obtained from historical data, and it varies from one country to another. Equation (5–128) tells how the population will change with time in the model. If we now specify the population to be x_0 at some time t_0, then we should be able to predict the population for all future times. The mathematical model in this case consists of nothing more than (5–128) with λ specified and the statement that the value of x at t_0 is x_0.

Now (5–128) is a differential equation of the type studied in the previous section. We saw there that its solution is $x = x_0 e^{\lambda(t-t_0)}$ when we require that $x = x_0$ at $t = t_0$. Here, then, we have the solution to the model, which says that the population will increase exponentially with time (assuming that $\lambda > 0$). Simple as this model is, it is correct in its gross predictions. The populations of countries do tend to increase exponentially with time. Some increase at a faster rate than others because they have a higher λ value.

Interestingly enough, there are many practical problems which can lead to precisely the same mathematical model. Let us consider very briefly just one of these. Certain chemical elements, such as uranium, are radioactive, and the nuclei of the atoms of such elements can spontaneously emit one of several types of particles, thus causing the element to change into a different element. Consider a radioactive element A which by emission of a particle changes into the element B; B is not radioactive. Consequently, if we start out with a given amount of pure A, as time goes on the mass of A will decrease and the mass of B will increase, because atoms of A are changing into atoms of B. It is found experimentally that the rate of change of the number of atoms of A at any time is proportional to the number of atoms of A present at that time. Thus if we denote by x the amount of A (number of atoms or weight) present at time t, then (5–128) holds if we treat x as continuous. If we denote by x_0 the quantity of A present at time t_0 ($t_0 = 0$ normally), we see that the model of radioactive decay is precisely the same as the model for population growth. There is typically a difference in the nature of the solutions, however, and this is due to the fact that λ is generally positive for population problems and is always negative for radioactive decay. Thus the quantity of A present decreases exponentially with time, that is, $x = x_0\,e^{-\beta t}$, $\beta = -\lambda$, $t_0 = 0$. Many other problems lead to this same model, including the variation of atmospheric pressure with altitude, discharge of capacitors and simple growth models of the economy, to mention just a few.

REFERENCES

The references given at the end of Chapter 3 are also appropriate for this chapter.

1. Dwight, H. B., *Tables of Integrals and Other Mathematical Data.* Macmillan: New York, 1961.

PROBLEMS

Section 5–1

1. Use Table B at the end of the text to draw carefully the graph of $\log x$.

In Problems 2 through 15 compute the derivative of the given function and indicate the set of x for which the derivative exists.

2. $\log x^2$;

3. $x \log x$;

4. $x \log |x|$;

5. $\log (\sin^2 x)$;

6. $\log(1 + x^2)$;

7. $x^2 \log(x^2 - 2x + 1)$;

8. $(\log x)^5$;

9. $\log(\log x)$;

10. $\dfrac{\log x^2}{3x - 2}$;

11. $\log(\sin x/\cos x)$;   **12.** $\sin(\log x)$;   **13.** $x^2 \sin(\log x^2)$;

14. $\dfrac{x}{\log x}$;   **15.** $\log\left(\dfrac{x^3 + 2x + 1}{x + 6}\right)$.

16. Use the data in Table B at the end of the text to determine the graphs of $\log x$, $\log 3x$ and $\log 5x$. From these results show that (5–6) appears to be reasonable intuitively.

17. Use the data in Table B at the end of the text to verify numerically that (5–9) is satisfied in the following cases.

     (a) $x_1 = 3$; $x_2 = 6$;   (b) $x_1 = 4$; $x_2 = 8$;   (c) $x_1 = 0.2$, $x_2 = 5$;
     (d) $x_1 = 0.5$; $x_2 = 18$.

18. Use the data in Table B at the end of the text to verify numerically that (5–14) is satisfied in the following cases.

     (a) $x = 2$;   (b) $x = 5$;   (c) $x = 10$;   (d) $x = 4$.

19. Provide, with the aid of Figure 5–1, an intuitive explanation of why we would expect that $\log 1/x = -\log x$. Hint: $1/(1/x) = x$.

In Problems 20 through 24 determine the derivative of the given function and specify the set of x for which the derivative exists. In determining the derivative use the properties of logarithms to simplify as much as possible the task of computing the derivative.

20. $\log [(x^2 + 1)(x + 2)(x + 3)]$;   **21.** $\log [x^{1/2}(x + 3)^{3/2}]$;

22. $\log [(x + 1)(x + 5)]^{1/2}$;   **23.** $\log \left[\dfrac{(x + 2x + 1)^{1/2}}{x + 3} \right]$;

24. $\log \left[\dfrac{(x + 2)\sqrt{x + 6}}{(x^2 + 1)\sqrt{x^2 + 3x}} \right]$.

25. Prove that if $f(x) > 0$, then if $f'(x)$ exists,

$$f'(x) = f(x) \frac{d}{dx} \log f(x) .$$

This result is sometimes called the logarithmic differentiation formula. Occasionally it can be used to simplify the task of computing $f'(x)$. Illustrate how the method can be usefully applied to compute $f'(x)$ when

$$f(x) = \frac{(x^2 + 2)^{1/2}(x^4 + 2)}{|x + 6|(x^2 + 6)} .$$

26. Sketch the graph of $y = \log |x|$. On the same figure sketch the graph of the derivative function.

27. Sketch the graph of

$$y = \frac{1}{2} \log \left| \frac{1 + x}{1 - x} \right| .$$

On the same figure sketch the graph of the derivative function.

Section 5–2

1. Use Table C at the end of the text to draw the graph of e^x.

In Problems 2 through 20 determine the derivative of the given function and indicate the values of x for which the derivative exists.

2. e^{-ax};   3. e^{x^2};   4. xe^x;

5. $x^2 e^{x^2}$;   6. $e^x \log x$;   7. $\log (x + e^x)$;

8. $e^{x^2 + 2x}$;   9. $\exp \left(\dfrac{x^2 + 1}{x - 2} \right)$;   10. $\exp (\sin x^2)$;

11. $\exp (x \sin x)$;   12. $\log \left(\dfrac{x^2 + 1}{1 + e^x} \right)$;   13. $\sin (e^x \log x)$;

14. $\dfrac{1 + e^x}{1 + e^{-x}}$;   15. $e^{\sqrt{x} + 2}$;   16. $\exp \left(\dfrac{e^x + e^{-x}}{2x} \right)$;

17. $\dfrac{x^n e^x}{n!}$;   18. $\exp (e^{\cos x})$;   19. $(\cos e^{2x}) \sin (\log x)$.

20. $\log \left[\log \left(\dfrac{2 + e^x}{\log x} \right) \right]$

21. Use the data in Table C at the end of the text to verify (5–23) numerically in the following cases.
   (a) $x_1 = 0.20, \ x_2 = 6$;   (b) $x_1 = 0.15, \ x_2 = 4$;   (c) $x_1 = 2; \ x_2 = 1.8$.

22. Use the data in Table C at the end of the text to verify (5–24) numerically in the following cases.
   (a) $x = 0.1$;   (b) $x = 2$;   (c) $x = 4.2$.

23. Use the data in Table C at the end of the text to verify (5–26) numerically in the following cases.
   (a) $\alpha = 2, \ x = 0.2$;   (b) $\alpha = 2, \ x = 2$;   (c) $\alpha = 2, \ x = 1.8$.

24. Use the data in Table C at the end of the text to draw the graph of e^{-x}.

25. Use the data in Table C at the end of the text to sketch the graphs of $e^{0.1x}$, e^x, and e^{2x}.

26. Sketch the graph of $y = \exp (-1/x)$. On the same figure, sketch the graph of the derivative function.

27. Sketch the graph of $y = \exp (-1/x^2)$. On the same figure, sketch the graph of the derivative function.

In Problems 28 through 34 determine whether or not the given equation is an identity. If it is, prove that it is. If not, explain why not.

28. $e^{2x} = (e^x)^2$;   29. $e^{x^3} = (e^x)^3$;   30. $e^{1/x} = 1/e^x$;   31. $e^{2x - 3y} = e^{2x}/e^{3y}$;

32. $e^x + e^y = e^{x+y}$;   33. $\log ae^x = x + \log a$;   34. $e^{\log x_1 x_2} = x_1 x_2$.

35. In certain areas of application the functions $\frac{1}{2}(e^x - e^{-x})$ and $\frac{1}{2}(e^x + e^{-x})$ occur frequently enough that it is desirable to give them special names. The first is denoted by sinh x, that is,

$$\sinh x = \frac{1}{2}\left(e^x - e^{-x}\right),$$

and is called the hyperbolic sine of x. This is a peculiar name and we shall not try to justify it. The other is denoted by $\cosh x$, that is,

$$\cosh x = \frac{1}{2}\left(e^x + e^{-x}\right),$$

and is called the hyperbolic cosine of x. Sketch the graphs of $\sinh x$ and $\cosh x$.

36. For the functions defined in Problem 35 show that

$$\frac{d}{dx}\sinh = \cosh x; \qquad \frac{d}{dx}\cosh x = \sinh x.$$

Section 5–3

In Problems 1 through 15 evaluate the derivative of the given function and indicate the set of x for which the derivative exists.

1. x^x;

2. x^{x^x};

3. $\left(x + \dfrac{2}{x}\right)^{e^x}$;

4. $(\sin x)^{\log x}$;

5. $(\log x)^x$;

6. $(\log x)^{e^x}$;

7. $(e^x \log x)^x$;

8. $(e^x \sin x)^{\log x}$;

9. $(\log x)^{\sin x}$;

10. $(x e^x)^{x \log x}$;

11. $x^{\sqrt{x}}$;

12. $\left(\dfrac{x+2}{x^2+1}\right)^{e^x}$;

13. $(x^2 \log x)^{(\log x)/x}$;

14. $(\exp e^x)^{1/\log x}$;

15. $2^{(x^2 \log x)^x}$

In Problems 16 through 20 evaluate approximately the indicated number.

16. $(\sqrt{2})^{\sqrt{2}}$; **17.** $\log_{5.14} 6.72$; **18.** $e^{(\sqrt{2})^3}$; **19.** $\log_{17}\sqrt{3}$; **20.** $2^{\sqrt{2}\log\sqrt{2}}$

In Problems 21 through 30 determine whether or not the expression given is an identity. If it is, prove that it is. If not, explain why not.

21. $e^{\sqrt{x_1 x_2}} = e^{\sqrt{x_1}} e^{\sqrt{x_2}}$;

22. $3^{x_1 x_2} = (3^{x_2})^{x_1}$;

23. $x^{\sqrt{2}+2} = (x^{\sqrt{2}})^2$;

24. $x^{x^x} = x^{\exp(x \log x)}$;

25. $(2.314)^x (x)^{2.314} = (2.314x)^{2.314x}$;

26. $2^{x-y} = \dfrac{2^x}{2^y}$;

27. $2^{x/2} = (2^x)^{1/2}$;

28. $a^{x_1 x_2} = [\exp(x_2 \log a)]^{x_1}$;

29. $\log_a a = 1$;

30. $a^{\log a} = 1$.

31. Evaluate $(1 + x)^{1/x}$ for $x = 1$, 0.1 and $.01$, and compare these values with e.

32. Use the tables at the end of the text to sketch the graph of a^x for $a = 0.1$, 1 and 1.5.

33. Use the tables at the end of the text to sketch the graph of a^{-x} for $a = 0.1$, 1.2 and 3.

34. Use the tables at the end of the text to sketch the graph of x^α for $\alpha = 0.25$ and 1.5.

Section 5–5

In Problems 1 through 30 evaluate the indefinite integral given and determine the domain for the primitive function. Check the correctness of the answer by differentiation.

1. $\displaystyle \int (2x - 4)^2\, dx;$ **2.** $\displaystyle \int x(3x^2 + 1)\, dx;$ **3.** $\displaystyle \int \frac{1}{(x + 2)^3}\, dx;$

4. $\displaystyle \int \frac{2x}{x^2 + 17}\, dx;$ **5.** $\displaystyle \int \frac{1}{(3x + 1)^{1/2}}\, dx;$ **6.** $\displaystyle \int \frac{x}{(2x^2 + 1)^{1/2}}\, dx;$

7. $\displaystyle \int 2x^2(x^3 + 3)\, dx;$ **8.** $\displaystyle \int \frac{(3x^2 + 2x)}{x^3 + x^2 + 1}\, dx;$ **9.** $\displaystyle \int (\sin x)(\cos x)\, dx;$

10. $\displaystyle \int \frac{1}{x(1 + \log x)}\, dx;$ **11.** $\displaystyle \int \frac{1}{x^2(1 + 1/x)}\, dx;$ **12.** $\displaystyle \int \frac{1}{y(\log y)^2}\, dy;$

13. $\displaystyle \int \frac{13 \log x}{x}\, dx;$ **14.** $\displaystyle \int \frac{1}{3 + 4x}\, dx;$ **15.** $\displaystyle \int \frac{x^3}{1 + x^4}\, dx;$

16. $\displaystyle \int \frac{1}{u^{1/2}(1 + u^{1/2})}\, du;$ **17.** $\displaystyle \int \frac{\cos \theta}{2 + 3 \sin \theta}\, d\theta;$ **18.** $\displaystyle \int \frac{\sin x}{\cos x}\, dx;$

19. $\displaystyle \int \frac{\sin \theta}{1 + \cos \theta}\, d\theta;$ **20.** $\displaystyle \int e^{3x}\, dx;$

21. $\displaystyle \int e^{\sin x} \cos x\, dx;$ **22.** $\displaystyle \int (2x + 1)\, e^{x^2 + x + 2}\, dx;$

23. $\displaystyle \int \frac{e^x}{1 + e^x}\, dx;$ **24.** $\displaystyle \int \frac{e^x}{(3 + 4e^x)^2}\, dx;$

25. $\displaystyle \int (\sin x)(\cos x) \exp(\sin^2 x)\, dx;$ **26.** $\displaystyle \int \frac{e^t - e^{-t}}{e^t + e^{-t}}\, dt;$

27. $\displaystyle \int (\sin \theta)(\cos^2 \theta)\, d\theta;$ **28.** $\displaystyle \int 2^x\, dx;$

29. $\displaystyle \int 4^{3x}\, dx;$ **30.** $\displaystyle \int x(2^{x^2 + x})\, dx.$

31. Provide an alternative derivation of (5–9) by noting that

$$\log x_1 x_2 = \log x_1 + \int_{x_1}^{x_1 x_2} \frac{1}{x}\, dx\ .$$

Hint: Multiply the integrand by x_1/x_1.

32. Provide another derivation of (5–14) by noting that

$$\log \frac{1}{x} = \int_1^{1/x} \frac{1}{t}\, dt\ .$$

Hint: Multiply the integrand by x/x.

Section 5–6

In Problems 1 through 12 evaluate the indefinite integral given and indicate the set of x for which a primitive function exists.

1. $\int (x - 3)\, e^x\, dx$;   **2.** $\int x^2 e^x\, dx$;   **3.** $\int x\, e^{2x}\, dx$;

4. $\int x^3 e^x\, dx$;   **5.** $\int x \log x\, dx$;   **6.** $\int x^2 \log x\, dx$;

7. $\int (x - a)\, e^{-bx^2}\, dx$;   **8.** $\int (x - a)^2 e^{-bx^2}\, dx$;   **9.** $\int x \cos x\, dx$;

10. $\int x \sin x\, dx$;   **11.** $\int x^2 \cos x\, dx$;   **12.** $\int x^3 \sin x\, dx$.

13. Could you determine $\int x^2\, dx$ if a primitive function for x were known? Show how $\int x^n\, dx$ could be determined if only a primitive function for $f(x) = 1$ were known.

Section 5–7

1. Show that, if (5–87) holds, then there must exist a t_0 such that $F(t)$ is defined for all $t > t_0$. In other words, (5–87) cannot hold if it is possible to find arbitrarily large values of t for which $F(t)$ is not defined.

2. Sketch the graph of $\sin t$ and use a graphical argument to explain why $\sin t$ does not have a limit as t approaches infinity.

3. Show that $\lim_{x \to \infty} e^{-x} = 0$. Illustrate geometrically.

4. Prove rigorously (5–92).

5. Prove that $\lim_{x \to \infty} 1/x = 0$. Illustrate geometrically.

6. Prove that $\lim_{x \to \infty} (\sin x)/x = 0$. Illustrate geometrically.

7. Prove that $\lim_{x \to \infty} e^{-x} \sin bx = 0$. Illustrate geometrically.

8. Prove that, if $\lim_{x \to \infty} F(x) = \beta$, then $\lim_{x \to \infty} \lambda\, F(x) = \lambda\beta$. Use this result to prove (5–97).

9. Prove that, if $\lim_{x \to \infty} F_1(x) = \beta_1$ and $\lim_{x \to \infty} F_2(x) = \beta_2$, then

$$\lim_{x \to \infty} [F_1(x) + F_2(x)] = \beta_1 + \beta_2.$$

Use this to prove (5–98).

10. Show that, if $\int_a^\infty f_2(x)f_1'(x)\, dx$ exists and $\lim_{x \to \infty} f_1(x)f_2(x) = \beta$, $\int_a^\infty f_1(x)f_2'(x)\, dx$ exists and

$$\int_a^\infty f_1(x)f_2'(x)\, dx = \beta - f_1(a)f_2(a) - \int_a^\infty f_2(x)f_1'(x)\, dx.$$

11. Evaluate $\int_3^\infty dx/x^2$ and $\int_3^\infty dx/x^3$.

12. Show that, if $\int_a^\infty f(x)\, dx$ exists, then so does $\int_b^\infty f(x)\, dx$ when $b > a$ and

$$\int_b^\infty f(x)\, dx = \int_a^\infty f(x)\, dx - \int_a^b f(x)\, dx.$$

13. Show that

$$\int_0^\infty e^{-ax} \sin bx \, dx, \quad a > 0$$

exists, and actually evaluate the improper integral. Give a geometric interpretation of this integral.

Section 5–8

In Problems 1 through 10 find the area of the set of points representing the solutions to the given set of inequalities. Illustrate geometrically the set of points whose area is to be determined.

1. $y \le x, \quad y \ge x^2$;

2. $y \le x, \quad y \ge 0.5(x - 2)^2$;

3. $y \le x, \quad y \ge -3, \quad x \ge 0, \quad x \le 4$;

4. $y \le x^2, \quad y \ge -x, \quad x \ge 0, \quad x \le 10$;

5. $y \ge x^3, \quad y \le x, \quad x \ge 0$;

6. $y \le \log x, \quad y \ge 0, \quad x \ge 1, \quad x \le 5$;

7. $y \le \cos x, \quad y \ge \sin x, \quad x \ge 0, \quad x \le \pi/2$;

8. $y \le x^a, \quad y \ge 0, \quad x \ge 0, \quad x \le 1, \quad \alpha > 0$;

9. $y \ge x^3, \quad y \le x^{1/2}$;

10. $y \ge 0.5x^2, \quad y \le x + 2$.

11. Find the area of the set of points satisfying $x \ge y^2$, $x \le 6$ in two different ways. Hint: For one of the ways, use y as the independent variable.

In Problems 12 through 19 compute the interior volume to the surface of revolution formed by rotating $y = f(x)$ about the x-axis for x in the interval $a \le x \le b$. Make a perspective sketch of the surface under consideration.

12. $y = x^2, a = 0, b = 5$;

13. $y = 1/x, a = 1, b = 4$;

14. $y = 2 + x, a = 1, b = 10$;

15. $y = x^{1/3}, a = 0, b = 3$;

16. $y = e^{-x}, a = 0, b = 1$;

17. $y = xe^{-x}, a = 0, b = 3$;

18. $y = 0.5(x - 2)^2 + 2, a = 0, b = 6$;

19. $y = x^{1/2}, a = 1, b = 5$.

In Problems 20 through 25 set up the integral which gives the lengths of the curve which is the graph of the given function over the indicated interval. Evaluate the integral if you can. If you cannot evaluate it discuss the difficulties involved.

20. $y = x^2, a = 0, b = 1$;

21. $y = 1/x, a = 1, b = 3$;

22. $y = x^{1/3}, a = 0, b = 4$;

23. $y = e^{-x}, a = 0, b = 3$;

24. $y = \log x, a = 1, b = 5$;

25. $y = \sin x, a = 0, b = \pi/2$.

Section 5–9

In Problems 1 through 20 find the set of all solutions to the given differential equation. Illustrate geometrically the nature of the solutions. Determine whether or not there exist any points in the plane through which there does not pass a unique solution to the differential equation.

1. $y \dfrac{dy}{dx} = x^2;$ **2.** $y^2 \dfrac{dy}{dx} = x;$ **3.** $y \dfrac{dy}{dx} = \dfrac{1}{x};$

4. $y \dfrac{dy}{dx} = \dfrac{1}{x^2};$ **5.** $\dfrac{1}{y} \dfrac{dy}{dx} = x;$ **6.** $\dfrac{1}{y^2} \dfrac{dy}{dx} = x;$

7. $y \dfrac{dy}{dx} = \sin x;$ **8.** $y^2 \dfrac{dy}{dx} = \sin x;$ **9.** $\dfrac{1}{y} \dfrac{dy}{dx} = \dfrac{1}{x};$

10. $\dfrac{1}{y} \dfrac{dy}{dx} = x^2;$ **11.** $y \dfrac{dy}{dx} = e^x;$ **12.** $e^y \dfrac{dy}{dx} = e^x;$

13. $e^y \dfrac{dy}{dx} = \dfrac{1}{x};$ **14.** $(1 + y) \dfrac{dy}{dx} = x;$ **15.** $(1 + y) \dfrac{dy}{dx} = 1 - x;$

16. $(\sin y) \dfrac{dy}{dx} = x;$ **17.** $\dfrac{1}{y^2} \dfrac{dy}{dx} = e^x$ **18.** $\dfrac{1}{y^2} \dfrac{dy}{dx} = \dfrac{1}{x};$

19. $y^2 \dfrac{dy}{dx} = \dfrac{1}{x};$ **20.** $y^2 \dfrac{dy}{dx} = e^x.$

Section 5–10

1. If the population of the U.S. was 175 million in 1965 and if the percentage increase per year is 2%, what should the population be in 1970 and in 1975?

2. Re-solve Problem 1 if the percentage increase per year was 3%.

3. Given the solution obtained in the text for radioactive decay, how long will it take for precisely half the original mass of A to have changed into B? This is called the half life of the element. A particular element has a half life of two years. If there are originally 10^9 atoms of A, how many will have decayed in six months?

4. Consider a reservoir of some type such that a material, call it A, is continually flowing into the reservoir at one end and out of the reservoir at the other end. Let x be the amount of A in the reservoir at time t and x_0 the amount in the reservoir at time 0. If $G(t)$ is the quantity of A which has flowed into the reservoir from time 0 to t and $H(t)$ is the quantity of A which has flowed out in this time period, then show that $x = x_0 + G(t) - H(t)$. Assume that $G(t)$ and $H(t)$ are differentiable and that $g(t)$ and $h(t)$ are the derivative functions for $G(t)$ and $H(t)$ respectively. Then show that

$$\frac{dx}{dt} = g(t) - h(t) .$$

This equation is very useful in practice. It says that the rate of change of the quantity in the reservoir is equal to the rate of inflow minus the rate of outflow. The reservoir could be a dam where water is flowing in and out or a large corporation's bank account where money flows in as customers pay for goods received and money flows out as the corporation pays its bills. Many other interpretations could be given. Suppose that the rate of outflow from the reservoir is proportional to the amount of A in the reservoir. What does the above equation become in this case? Suppose, in addition, that $g(t) = 0$, so there is no inflow. Determine the amount of A in the reservoir as a function of time.

5.   For the situation described in Problem 4, suppose that the reservoir is a dam and that the rate of outflow is a constant α gallons per day. Suppose that the rate of inflow is $\beta \sin \pi t/365$ when t is measured in days. Determine the quantity in the reservoir at each future point in time if x_0 gallons were present at $t = 0$. What value must β have if the inflow over the period of a year is precisely equal to the outflow? Sketch the graph of x, the quantity of water in the reservoir as a function of time.

CHAPTER 6

Numerical Computation

6-1 DIGITAL COMPUTERS

In this chapter we shall consider the methods which can be used to determine a numerical answer to some given problem. We shall be mainly interested in showing how high-speed digital computers can be used in assisting us to solve problems numerically. Until ten years ago the task of making numerical computations was usually an exceedingly arduous one which often required spending days or even months using a mechanical desk calculator and extensive sets of tables. A large number of interesting problems could not be solved because hundreds of man-years of effort would be required. In the mid 1950's a dramatic change took place as a result of the introduction of high-speed electronic digital computers. These computers could perform in seconds what a man at a desk calculator would require a year to carry out. In the decade or so since their introduction digital computers have undergone revolutionary advances in their reliability, speed of operation and general usefulness. Today, a computer can perform something like 100,000 multiplications or divisions in a single second. Electronic computers are now so generally available that it is unnecessary even to consider making a complicated computation by hand. A computer would unquestionably be used.

A digital computer is basically a machine for performing very rapidly the four basic arithmetic operations of addition, subtraction, multiplication and division. These are the only mathematical operations the computer can perform, and every problem to be solved on a computer must be reduced to a form which requires nothing more than performing a sequence of these four operations. Thus a computer cannot evaluate $\sqrt{2}$ unless we can reduce the problem of computing $\sqrt{2}$ to one involving a sequence of the four basic arithmetic operations (we shall see how to do this later). Similarly, a computer cannot evaluate $\int_1^8 \log x \, dx$ unless we can reduce this to a form which requires only a finite number of additions, subtractions, multiplications and divisions.

The characteristics which make modern computers so useful are that, although they can only perform the four basic arithmetic operations, they also have the capability to make certain simple logical decisions and they have a memory. The memory of a computer is a place where numbers can be stored for use by the computer and, in addition, where numbers generated by the computer can be stored for use later in the computations. The memory of the computer has one other very important use. In order for the computer to solve a problem it is necessary to make up a set of instructions, called a code or program, which tells the computer in complete detail how to solve the problem. These instructions are fed into the computer's memory, and the computer then follows the instructions, performing one after another until the problem is solved.

This ability to give the computer a set of instructions means that we do not have to communicate with the computer while it is solving the problem. If we had to stay at the computer and tell it what to do next after each operation was performed, all of the computer's advantage of speed would be lost. It is the ability to use stored programs which makes it possible to use a computer's speed efficiently, since it can follow the instructions in its memory much faster than anyone could communicate with the computer from the outside. In order to use stored programs, the computer must be able to make simple logical decisions, such as to do one thing if a computed number is positive or zero and do something else if it is negative. The circuitry of a computer does allow it to do such things. The precise logical operations which a computer can perform vary somewhat from one make or model to another.

Let us next consider how numbers are represented inside the computer. Numbers are represented as numbers in a form which is referred to as the floating point format. In actuality, numbers are represented in the computer using the binary number system, not the decimal system. We need not be concerned with this technicality since numbers are always given to the computer in decimal form and the computer always prints out numbers in decimal form. The conversion to binary form is made automatically by the computer. We shall discuss things, then, as if the computer actually used numbers in decimal form. Consider any number y. If $y \neq 0$, then we showed in Chapter 1 that y can be written

$$y = \pm a_0.b_1b_2b_3 \cdots \times 10^k, \tag{6-1}$$

where a_0 is a natural number satisfying $1 \leq a_0 \leq 9$ and k is an integer (positive, negative, or 0). If $y > 0$ the $+$ sign is used, and if $y < 0$ the $-$

sign is used. The right-hand side of (6–1) is called the *floating point representation of y*. The floating point representation of y then, except for sign, represents y as the product of a number v satisfying $1 \le v < 10$ multiplied by some power of 10. For example, the floating point representation of 1013.2 is 1.0132×10^3 and of -0.0000265 is -2.65×10^{-5}.

Recall that the decimal representation of a number may be nonterminating. Only terminating decimals can be represented in a computer. Generally, a computer will represent each number using a fixed number of digits in the floating point representation. Typically, eight digits are used, so that each number represented in the computer will be represented in the form

$$y = \pm a_0.b_1 b_2 \cdots b_7 \times 10^k . \tag{6–2}$$

Numbers whose floating point representation involves more than eight digits will be represented only approximately in the computer. Thus 28713.456921 would be represented as 2.8713457×10^4, $\sqrt{2}$ would be represented as 1.4142136×10^0 and 3 would be represented as 3.0000000×10^0. Note that any number (6–2) can be completely characterized by writing $\alpha a_0 b_1 b_2 \cdots b_7 k$, where $\alpha = 0$ if a plus sign is intended and $\alpha = 1$ for a minus sign. This is the way the number would be represented in the computer. No decimal point would appear nor would 10^k. The location of the decimal point is known for the floating point form, and the 10 in 10^k is superfluous. It is possible, if desired, to obtain sixteen digits in the floating point representation of a number in a computer which normally uses eight digits. This doubling of the number of the digits is referred to as the use of *double precision*. The ordinary mode of operation with eight digits is referred to as *single precision*. The only representations of numbers in the computer will be with eight or sixteen digits. It is not normally possible, then, to use three or nine or eighteen digits, for example. Computers have been built which allow some freedom as to the number of digits used, but these are not in widespread use.

6–2 ERRORS

Many of the problems in numerical analysis involve evaluating a function $y = f(x)$ for one or more values of its argument. It is normally the case that $f(x)$ for a given x can be determined only approximately. One reason may be that x cannot be represented exactly. Another is that $f(x)$ cannot be computed exactly for any given value of x. We shall see as we go along why $f(x)$ cannot be computed exactly. Now we shall study ways to characterize the errors made in computing $f(x)$.

If y is the exact value of $f(x)$ and y_c is the approximate value of $f(x)$ which we have computed, then $e = y_c - y$ is called *the error* in the computation. Thus $y = y_c - e$. The *relative error* e_r is defined as

$$e_r = \frac{y_c - y}{y} = \frac{y_c}{y} - 1 = \frac{e}{y}, \tag{6-3}$$

and the *percentage error* e_p is defined to be $100 \, e_r$. Generally, only the magnitude of the error or relative error is of interest, and for this reason we shall deal only with $|e|$ and $|e_r|$.

Another way that is frequently employed to describe the accuracy of a computation is to refer to the number of *significant figures* obtained. Suppose now that $y_c = \pm a_0.b_1 b_2 \cdots b_u \times 10^k$ is the approximate value of y which we have computed. Roughly speaking, we say that y has been computed correct to v significant figures if, when rounding the floating point form of y to v digits ($v - 1$ after the decimal place), we obtain $\pm a_0.b_1 b_2 \cdots b_{v-2} b_{v-1}^c$, where $b_{v-1}^c = b_{v-1}$ or $b_{v-1} + 1$ or $b_{v-1} - 1$. We assume that the rounding is done so as to minimize the error in rounding. This means that the first $v - 1$ digits of y_c are same as those of y and the vth digit does not differ by more than one from the vth digit of y. More precisely, the computation is made correct to v significant figures if $|e| = |y_c - y| < 5 \times 10^{k-v}$. Thus

$$y = (a_0.b_1 b_2 \cdots b_u \pm \eta) \times 10^k, \tag{6-4}$$

where $\eta < 5 \times 10^{-v}$.

Another way of characterizing accuracy to v significant figures is to say that b_v in y_c cannot differ by more than 5 from the correct corresponding vth digit after the decimal point in y. Note that the notion of significant figures involves only the number of correct digits in the *floating point* form and not on the power of 10, that is, on k. Thus if $y_c = 0.000325$, we say that y has been computed correct to three (not six) significant figures if $|e| < 5 \times 10^{-7}$, so that y may be as large as 0.0003255 or as small as 0.0003245. Similarly, 32500 is expressed correct to three significant figures if the magnitude of the error is as large as 50, but no larger, and is expressed correct to five significant figures if the magnitude of the error is not greater than 0.5.

There is a very close connection between the relative error and the notion of significant figures. Suppose that the magnitude of the relative error $|e_r|$ for the computed value y_c of y satisfies $|e_r| < 5 \times 10^{-v}$. This means that $|e|/|y| < 5 \times 10^{-v}$ or $|e| < 5 \times 10^{-v}|y|$. Now if $|y| = w \times 10^k$, $1 \le w < 10$, then $|e| < 5w \times 10^{k-v}$, where $5 \le 5w < 50$. Hence, if w is close to 1, then y_c is correct essentially to v significant figures. If w is close to 10, y_c may not contain v significant figures but will certainly have $v - 1$. Thus, if we arrange our computations so that $|e_r| < 5 \times 10^{-v}$, then we shall definitely compute y correct to $v - 1$ significant figures and possibly to an accuracy of essentially v significant figures. We shall find this result a convenient one to use in the future.

Generally speaking, we are interested in the relative error or the number of significant figures obtained in making the computations rather than in the error itself. The reason for this is the following. Suppose that the magnitude of the error made in computing some number is 5×10^{-2}. If the number was 3125.496, then we would feel that the computation has been made fairly accurately, since it is correct to five significant figures. However, if the number was 0.3125496, we feel that the computation has not been made accurately, since it is correct to only one significant figure. Thus $|e|$ tells us nothing about the accuracy of the computation unless we happen to know the magnitude of y. The use of $|e_r|$ or significant figures eliminates this problem because the error is measured relative to the magnitude of y.

We have been discussing the fact that, in general, we cannot evaluate $f(x)$ exactly. The important thing to realize is that, to solve real-world problems, we don't need to know $f(x)$ exactly. The final answers desired for most engineering and scientific problems rarely require more than four significant figure accuracy, while computations in the social sciences often require even less. It is a complete waste of time and money to make some computation correct to twenty-five significant figures if four is quite adequate. In solving a problem, the required accuracy should be kept clearly in mind, and the computations should be set up to obtain this accuracy without doing any more work than necessary.

At this point the reader may wonder why computer designers provided for eight digits if no more than four significant figures are required. Let us see why it is generally necessary for the computer to be able to represent numbers to many more digits than are needed in the final answer. There are two very important reasons for this.

The first reason lies in what are called round-off errors. Each time the computer performs an addition, subtraction, multiplication or division, it will usually need to perform a rounding operation. For example, the product of two eight-digit numbers yields a sixteen-digit number. The computer actually obtains all sixteen digits, but to express the result as an eight-digit floating point number, it must round the sixteen-digit number to eight digits. We ask the reader to show that the same sort of rounding operation will, in general, be needed when performing each of the other arithmetic operations. Now the computer actually rounds the binary form of the number. If it were rounding the decimal form, then each rounding operation could introduce an error of as much as one-half in the last digit, so that after only about ten such operations the resulting number might, if all errors added and if all were as large as possible, be correct to only seven significant figures rather than eight. After 100 operations it might correct only to six significant figures.

Essentially the same conclusions apply even though rounding is done in binary. In actuality, of course, the errors do not always add. There will be some cancellation due to the fact that some numbers are rounded up and other ones are rounded down. Furthermore, the errors do not always have their largest possible values. Thus round-off errors tend to accumulate much more slowly than the above analysis suggests they could. Nonetheless, it is clear that, if millions of operations are required in solving a problem, the resulting numbers may quite possibly be correct to four or even less significant figures. Unfortunately, there is no way of determining precisely what the round-off error will be in any particular case, although the maximum round-off error can be estimated. Equally well, there is no way to prevent round-off errors. The only way to increase the accuracy is to represent the numbers in the computer with more digits. This is one reason why it is often desirable to use double precision in the computer.

The other reason that it is necessary to use more digits in the computations than are required in the final answer arises through phenomena like the following. Suppose in some problem $x_1 = 1.2314256$ and $x_2 = 1.2314121$, and it is necessary to compute $x_1 - x_2 = 1.35 \times 10^{-5}$. Now we have no more than three significant figures of accuracy in $x_1 - x_2$ (the computer would fill in the remaining five digits with zeros to yield the standard eight-digit floating point format). This is no problem provided $x_1 - x_2$ is only added or subtracted to other numbers which are much larger. However, if we multiply or divide any numbers by $x_1 - x_2$, or if, say, at the next step we multiply $x_1 - x_2$ by 10^6 to yield 1.35×10^1, we can be in trouble if the other numbers are of the order of 1 to 10, since we have been reduced to three significant figure accuracy. The problem of losing significance by subtracting numbers which are almost equal is a serious one which we try to avoid insofar as possible. It is not always possible, however, and for this reason it is desirable to represent the numbers in the computer using as many digits as possible.

6–3 TAYLOR'S FORMULA

In our previous discussions we have introduced a number of functions without providing any way of evaluating these functions numerically. Thus we have no convenient way to evaluate the functions $\sin x$, $\cos x$, $\log x$, e^x or a^α. Indeed, we have no efficient method to compute $x^{1/2}$. If the reader checks back, he will see that the only functions we can evaluate with relative ease are polynomials and rational functions, and even these can be tedious to evaluate if the polynomials involved are of high degree. However, to evaluate a polynomial or rational function at a given value of the argument only the four arithmetic operations of addition, subtraction, multiplication and division need to be performed. Thus these functions can easily be evaluated on a computer. Let us explain an efficient procedure for evaluating a polynomial such as

$$a_4 x^4 + a_3 x^3 + a_2 x^2 + a_1 x + a_0 \tag{6–5}$$

for a given x. We could merely compute x^2, x^3 and x^4 and then a_4x^4, a_3x^3, a_2x^2 and a_1x, and next, by addition, obtain (6–5). However, this involves seven multiplications and four additions. A method which requires less computational effort is to write the polynomial as

$$\{[(a_4x + a_3)x + a_2]x + a_1\}x + a_0 . \tag{6–6}$$

We first compute a_4x, add a_3 to this, then multiply $a_4x + a_3$ by x and add a_2 to this, then multiply by x, and so forth. This requires only four multiplications and four additions, and is the way a polynomial is normally evaluated on a computer.

Let us now turn our attention to methods for evaluating the other functions which we have introduced but cannot currently evaluate. Interestingly enough, this will be done for a number of these functions by approximating the functions by a polynomial. The key to doing this is known as Taylor's formula. Recall that, if $f(t)$ and $f'(t)$ are continuous over an open interval which contains the points 0 and x, then the fundamental theorem of the calculus states that

$$f(x) = f(0) + \int_0^x f'(t)\, dt . \tag{6–7}$$

Suppose now that $f''(t)$ exists and is also continuous over the same interval. Then so is the function $(x - t)f''(t)$, and if we integrate this function by parts, writing $f_1(t) = x - t$ and $f_2'(t) = f''(t)$, we obtain

$$\int_0^x (x - t)f''(t)\, dt = (x - t)f'(t)\Big|_0^x + \int_0^x f'(t)\, dt , \tag{6–8}$$

which when combined with (6–7) yields

$$f(x) = f(0) + f'(0)x + \int_0^x (x - t)f''(t)\, dt . \tag{6–9}$$

We shall now prove by induction that, if all derivatives of $f(t)$ through $f^{(n+1)}(t)$ exist and this latter function is continuous, then

$$f(x) = f(0) + f'(0)x + \frac{f''(0)}{2}x^2 + \cdots + \frac{f^{(n)}(0)}{n!}x^n$$

$$+ \int_0^x \frac{(x - t)^n}{n!}f^{(n+1)}(t)\, dt . \tag{6–10}$$

This is referred to as Taylor's theorem. We could easily prove (6–10) by repeated integration by parts. A proof by induction, however, is still easier. We have already shown that (6–10) holds for $n = 1$. Using a single integration by parts, we can show that if it holds for $k = n - 1$ it must also hold for $k = n$. On taking $f_1(t) = (x - t)^n/n!$ and $f_2'(t) = f^{(n+1)}(t)$, we see that

$$\int_0^x \frac{(x - t)^n}{n!} f^{(n+1)}(t) \, dt = \frac{(x - t)^n}{n!} f^{(n)}(t) \Big|_0^x + \int_0^x \frac{n(x - t)^{n-1}}{n!} f^{(n)}(t) \, dt$$

$$= -\frac{f^{(n)}(0)}{n!} x^n + \int_0^x \frac{(x - t)^{n-1}}{(n - 1)!} f^{(n)}(t) \, dt . \qquad (6\text{--}11)$$

Hence, if the result holds for $k = n - 1$, then

$$f(x) = \sum_{j=0}^{n-1} \frac{f^{(j)}(0)}{j!} x^j + \int_0^x \frac{(x - t)^{n-1}}{(n - 1)!} f^{(n)}(t) \, dt . \qquad (6\text{--}12)$$

On substituting for the value of the integral on the right in (6–11) its value from (6–12), we obtain (6–10). Thus, if the result holds for $k = n - 1$, it also holds for $k = n$. Hence by the induction principle it holds for all natural numbers n (and $n = 0$ as well). The reader should note that, when our assumptions are satisfied, all of the integrals involved exist since the integrands are continuous.

The interesting thing about (6–10) is that we have written $f(x)$ as the sum of a polynomial plus an additional term. If we write

$$s_n(x) = f(0) + f'(0)x + \frac{f''(0)}{2} x^2 + \cdots + \frac{f^{(n)}(0)}{n!} x^n , \qquad (6\text{--}13)$$

this is a polynomial of degree n or less (it is of degree n if $f^{(n)}(0) \neq 0$). Also write

$$r_n(x) = \int_0^x \frac{(x - t)^n}{n!} f^{(n+1)}(t) \, dt . \qquad (6\text{--}14)$$

Thus when $f^{(n+1)}(t)$ is continuous over an interval including 0 and x,

$$f(x) = s_n(x) + r_n(x) . \qquad (6\text{--}15)$$

If $f(t)$ possesses continuous derivatives of all orders then we can obtain an expression (6–15) for each natural number n. Now the interesting thing about Taylor's formula is the behavior of $r_n(x)$ for a specified x as n increases; $r_n(x)$ is called *the remainder* term in Taylor's formula. Note that

$$|r_n(x)| = |f(x) - s_n(x)| . \qquad (6\text{--}16)$$

Hence if $|r_n(x)|$ is very close to 0, $s_n(x)$ will yield a good approximation to $f(x)$. Many of the functions of interest to us have the characteristic that $|r_n(x)|$ can be made arbitrarily small by taking n to be sufficiently large. More precisely, if we consider the sequence $\{a_n\}$ with $a_n = |r_n(x)|$ then $\{a_n\}$ converges to 0. This suggests that we might hope to reduce the problem of evaluating $f(x)$ to one of evaluating a polynomial $s_n(x)$ and that the result obtained in this way will have whatever accuracy is desired. This is precisely what we shall do.

Note that the magnitude of the relative error if $s_n(x)$ is used for $f(x)$ is

$$|e_{rt}| = \frac{|r_n(x)|}{|f(x)|}, \tag{6-17}$$

since $|e| = |r_n(x)|$; $|e_{rt}|$ is called the relative *truncation* error, for it is the error resulting from omitting the remainder term in Taylor's formula. The subscript t is used to indicate truncation error. Now $|e_{rt}|$ is not the magnitude of the relative error that will result if we evaluate $s_n(x)$ on a computer and use the computed number instead of $f(x)$. The reason for this is that, on account of round-off errors, we shall not really obtain $s_n(x)$. Instead, we shall obtain some other number, call it $s_n^c(x)$, which is the number the computer generates as a result of attempting to evaluate $s_n(x)$. The relative error in determining $f(x)$ will then be

$$e_r = \frac{s_n^c(x) - f(x)}{f(x)} = \frac{s_n^c(x) - s_n(x) + s_n(x) - f(x)}{f(x)}$$
$$\doteq \frac{s_n^c(x) - s_n(x)}{s_n(x)} + \frac{s_n(x) - f(x)}{f(x)} = e_{r0} + e_{rt}, \tag{6-18}$$

where e_{r0} is the relative error caused by round off in evaluating $s_n(x)$. Thus the relative error in $f(x)$ is approximately the sum of the relative round-off and truncation errors.

What we would like to do is determine a value of n (the smallest one we can find) such that, for each x in some interval I_{ab}^c, we can use $s_n(x)$ given by (6–13) to evaluate $f(x)$, and simultaneously have $|e_{rt}| < \alpha$, where α is specified. The important thing to note is that we want $|e_{rt}| < \alpha$ for every $x \in I_{ab}^c$. We want to avoid using different values of n for different values of x if possible. All we can do is require that the magnitude of the relative truncation error be less than α. There is nothing that can be done about round-off errors. We shall be interested, however, in determining the maximum value of $|e_{r0}|$.

In order to work with $|e_{rt}|$, it will be convenient to convert $r_n(x)$ to a different form. It can be proved, using a slight generalization of the mean value theorem for integrals (introduced in Problem 1 for Section 4–9), that

$$r_n(x) = f^{(n+1)}(\xi) \int_0^x \frac{(x-t)^n}{n!} \, dt = \frac{f^{(n+1)}(\xi)}{(n+1)!} x^{n+1}, \tag{6-19}$$

where ξ lies between 0 and x. We shall not prove this, but we shall make use of it. Then

$$|e_{rt}| = \frac{1}{(n+1)!} \left| \frac{f^{(n+1)}(\xi)}{f(x)} \right| |x|^{n+1}. \tag{6-20}$$

It is (6–20) that we shall use to find an n such that $|e_{rt}| < \alpha$ for each $x \in I_{ab}^c$. We shall choose $\alpha = 5 \times 10^{-9}$ so that $f(x)$ will always be computed correct to eight significant figures in the absence of round-off errors. This is the maximum number of significant figures that can be represented in the computer using single precision. For many functions, such as e^x or $\sin x$, we wish to be able to evaluate these functions for any real number x. However, it is not possible to find an n such that $|e_{rt}| < \alpha$ for every real x. Fortunately, we need only be able to evaluate the functions over relatively small intervals using the above method to evaluate the function for every real x. We shall see how to do this in the individual cases as they are studied.

6–4 EVALUATION OF e^x

Recall that if $f(x) = e^x$ then $f'(x) = e^x$. Hence $f^{(n)}(x) = e^x$ for every n and the exponential function possesses derivative functions of all orders, each of which is the exponential function. Thus $f^{(n)}(0) = e^0 = 1$ and $s_n(x)$ of (6–13) becomes

$$s_n(x) = 1 + x + \frac{x^2}{2} + \frac{x^3}{3!} + \cdots + \frac{x^n}{n!} \tag{6–21}$$

and

$$r_n(x) = \frac{e^\xi x^{n+1}}{(n+1)!} \tag{6–22}$$

Then from (6–20)

$$|e_{rt}| = \frac{1}{(n+1)!} \left| \frac{e^\xi}{e^x} \right| |x|^{n+1} \tag{6–23}$$

Consider now the problem of evaluating e^x for any $x > 0$. Note that x can be written as $k + 0.b_1 b_2 b_3 \cdots$, that is, as the sum of a non-negative integer k plus a fraction $0.b_1 b_2 b_3 \cdots$. Furthermore,

$$e^x = e^k e^{0.b_1 b_2 b_3 \cdots} \tag{6–24}$$

If e is computed accurately and stored in the computer's memory, then e^k can be determined merely by repeatedly multiplying e by itself. All that remains is to evaluate e^y, $0 \le y < 1$, where $y = 0.b_1 b_2 b_3 \cdots$. Thus we see that we can evaluate e^x for any $x > 0$ if we can evaluate e^y, $0 \le y \le 1$. Suppose now that $x < 0$, say $x = -w$. Then $e^x = e^{-w} = 1/e^w$. We can thus evaluate e^x for $x < 0$ if we can evaluate e^w, $w = -x$. This can be done in the manner just described. Consequently, we can evaluate e^x for all real x if we can evaluate e^x for $0 \le x \le 1$.

Let us now see how to evaluate e^x, $0 \le x \le 1$, correct to eight significant figures in the absence of round-off errors. This will be accomplished if we have $|e_{rt}| < 5 \times 10^{-9}$ for each x in the interval of interest; $|e_{rt}|$ is given by

(6–23). When $0 \leq x \leq 1$, $|x|^{n+1} \leq 1$. Also since ξ in (6–23) satisfies $0 \leq \xi \leq x$, and since e^x is monotonic increasing, $|e^\xi/e^x| < 1$. Thus for each x, $0 \leq x \leq 1$,

$$|e_{rt}| \leq \frac{1}{(n+1)!} . \tag{6–25}$$

Now $\frac{1}{11!} \doteq 2.5 \times 10^{-8}$ and $\frac{1}{12!} \doteq 2 \times 10^{-9}$. Therefore, if we take $n + 1 = 12$ or $n = 11$, $s_n(x)$ given by (6–21) will yield e^x correct to eight significant figures for $0 \leq x \leq 1$. Thus when $0 \leq x \leq 1$, to eight significant figures

$$e^x \doteq s_{11}(x) = 1 + x + \frac{x^2}{2} + \frac{x^3}{6} + \cdots + \frac{x^{11}}{11!}, \tag{6–26}$$

and e^x is being approximated by a polynomial of degree 11. Once the coefficients $1/j!$ have been determined, only ten multiplications and eleven additions are needed to evaluate e^x, $0 \leq x \leq 1$. Hence the maximum round-off error could not amount to more than 1 in the seventh digit, and would normally not be more than 2 or so in the eighth digit.

We have now developed one method for evaluating e^x for any x. To do this, all we really need to be able to do is evaluate e^x for $0 \leq x \leq 1$.

EXAMPLES. 1. Although it is very easy for the computer to evaluate (6–26) using eight digits, it is quite tedious to do this by hand. Instead, we shall give a more modest example and check the value of e^x given in Table C at the end of the text for $x = 2.1$. The number in Table C is given to five significant figures and hence we shall make the computation to this accuracy. Now $e^{2.1} = e^2 e^{0.1}$ and to six significant figures $e = 2.71828$ (we shall use six figures in the computations to avoid round-off problems) so $e^2 = 7.38906$. It remains to evaluate $e^{0.1}$.

For $x = 0.1$,

$$|e_{rt}| \leq \frac{(0.1)^{n+1}}{(n+1)!} .$$

For $n = 3$, $(0.1)^4/4! \doteq 0.5 \times 10^{-5}$, and for $n = 4$, $(0.1)^5/5! \doteq 10^{-7}$. Thus if we take $n = 4$, $e^{0.1}$ will be obtained to five significant figures. Therefore we shall use

$$e^x \doteq s_4(x) = 1 + x + \frac{x^2}{2} + \frac{x^3}{6} + \frac{x^4}{24} = \left\{ \left[\left(\frac{x}{24} + \frac{1}{6} \right) x + \frac{1}{2} \right] x + 1 \right\} x + 1 .$$

Now $\frac{1}{24} = 0.0416667$ and $\frac{1}{6} = 0.166667$. Hence

$$e^{0.1} \doteq s_4(0.1) = \{[(0.00416667 + 0.166667)(0.1) + 0.5](0.1) + 1\}(0.1) + 1$$
$$= [(0.5170834)(0.1) + 1](0.1) + 1 = 1.10517 .$$

Finally

$$e^{2.1} = e^2 e^{0.1} = 7.38906(1.10517) = 8.16617 .$$

When this is rounded to five digits the result given in Table C is obtained. The value of $e^{2.1}$ given happens to be correct to six significant figures rather than just five.

2. Let us compute $e = e^1$ correct to four significant figures. Here $|e_{rt}| \leq 1/(n + 1)!$. Now $1/7! \doteq 2 \times 10^{-4}$ and $1/8! \doteq 2.5 \times 10^{-5}$. Thus, if we take $n + 1 = 8$ or $n = 7$, we shall obtain the desired accuracy. We shall use five figures in the computations to avoid round-off errors. Hence we wish to compute

$$s_8(1) = 1 + 1 + \frac{1}{2} + \frac{1}{6} + \frac{1}{24} + \frac{1}{120} + \frac{1}{720} + \frac{1}{5040} .$$

It is clear that we have been conservative here and the last term is not needed, since it makes no contribution to the third decimal place. Now

$$\frac{1}{6} = 0.16667; \quad \frac{1}{24} = 0.041667; \quad \frac{1}{120} = 0.0083333; \quad \frac{1}{720} = 0.0013889 .$$

Thus

$$e \doteq s_8(1) = 2.66667 + 0.04167 + 0.00833 + 0.00139 = 2.7181 ,$$

which is correct to four (but not five) significant figures.

6–5 COMPUTATION OF sin x

Let us next consider the evaluation of $\sin x$. Note that

$$\frac{d}{dx} \sin = \cos x; \qquad \frac{d^2}{dx^2} \sin x = -\sin x;$$

$$\frac{d^3}{dx^3} \sin x = -\cos x; \qquad \frac{d^4}{dx^4} \sin x = \sin x . \tag{6-27}$$

To compute $d^5 \sin x/dx^5$ we differentiate $\sin x$. Thus we are back to where we started and the above sequence of functions continually repeat themselves. In general then, $\sin x$ possesses derivatives of all orders, and it can be proved by induction that

$$\frac{d^j}{dx^j} \sin x = \begin{cases} (-1)^{(j-1)/2} \cos x, & j \text{ odd} \\ (-1)^{j/2} \sin x, & j \text{ even} . \end{cases} \tag{6-28}$$

Note that $f^{(j)}(0) = 0$ for j even, since $\sin 0 = 0$, and $f^{(j)}(0) = (-1)^{(j-1)/2}$ for j odd, since $\cos 0 = 1$. Consequently, each polynomial $s_n(x)$ involves only odd powers of x. The coefficients of the even powers are zero. Suppose that we write $n = 2k + 1$ when n is odd and $n = 2k$ when n is even. Then

$$s_{2k+1}(x) = \sum_{j=0}^{2k+1} \frac{f^{(j)}(0)}{j!} x^j$$

$$= x - \frac{x^3}{3!} + \frac{x^5}{5!} - \cdots + (-1)^k \frac{x^{2k+1}}{(2k+1)!} \tag{6-29}$$

$$= \sum_{j=0}^{k} (-1)^j \frac{x^{2j+1}}{(2j+1)!}.$$

Note that $s_{2k+2}(x) = s_{2k+1}(x)$, since $f^{(2k+2)}(0) = 0$. Thus the polynomial for n even is precisely the same as the polynomial for $n - 1$ ($n - 1$ being odd). Consequently, we need only to restrict our attention to polynomials $s_{2k+1}(x)$, that is, polynomials with n odd.

We shall first show how to evaluate $\sin x$ to eight significant figures, in the absence of round-off errors, for x in the interval $0 \le x \le \pi/2$. We shall then show this is all we need to evaluate $\sin x$ for any x. When n is odd, that is, $n = 2k + 1$, then

$$|e_{rt}| = \frac{|x|^{2k+2}}{(2k+2)!} \left| \frac{\sin \xi}{\sin x} \right|, \tag{6-30}$$

since $r_n(x) = (-1)^{(n+1)/2} x^{n+1} \sin \xi/(n+1)!$; $\sin \xi$ appears because $n + 1$ is even. Now when x lies in the interval $0 \le x \le \pi/2$, $|\sin \xi/\sin x| \le 1$, since $\sin x$ is monotonic increasing over this interval. Also, inasmuch as $\pi/2 \doteq 1.562 \cdots < 2$, $x^{2k+2} < 2^{2k+2}$. Hence

$$|e_{rt}| < \frac{2^{2k+2}}{(2k+2)!} \tag{6-31}$$

From Table 6–1 we see that $|e_{rt}| < 5 \times 10^{-9}$ when $k = 7$, or $2k + 1 = 15$. . Thus $\sin x$ can be evaluated to eight significant figures, in the absence of round-off errors, for x in the interval $0 \le x \le \pi/2$ using

$$\sin x = s_{15}(x) = \sum_{j=0}^{7} (-1)^j \frac{x^{2j+1}}{(2j+1)!}$$

$$= x - \frac{x^3}{3!} + \frac{x^5}{5!} - \frac{x^7}{7!} + \frac{x^9}{9!} - \frac{x^{11}}{11!} + \frac{x^{13}}{13!} - \frac{x^{15}}{15!} \tag{6-32}$$

which is a polynomial of degree 15. Only eight multiplications and seven additions or subtractions are needed to evaluate this polynomial, and hence no more than 15 rounding operations are involved, so that the value of $\sin x$ computed could not be off by more than 8 in the eighth digit. Normally, it will not be off by more than 2 or so in the eighth digit.

Table 6–1

Determination of k

k	2^{2k+2}	$(2k+2)!$	$\dfrac{2^{2k+2}}{(2k+2)!}$
4	1.024×10^3	3.6×10^6	0.3×10^{-3}
5	4.04×10^3	4.8×10^8	1×10^{-5}
6	1.6×10^4	8.7×10^{10}	2.5×10^{-7}
7	6.4×10^4	2×10^{13}	3×10^{-9}

Let us now see how the evaluation of $\sin x$ for any x can be reduced to the problem of evaluating $\sin y$ for $0 \leq y \leq \pi/2$. Recall that $\sin x$ is periodic with period 2π so that $\sin(y + 2\pi n) = \sin y$ for any natural number n. Recall also that $\sin(-x) = -\sin x$. From this latter relation we see immediately that we can evaluate $\sin x$ for $x < 0$ if we can evaluate $\sin y$, $y = -x$, since $\sin x = -\sin y$. Thus we can evaluate $\sin x$ for any x if we can evaluate $\sin x$ for any $x \geq 0$. Consider then an $x > 0$. Divide x by 2π to yield k, a natural number or zero, plus a remainder x_1, $0 \leq x_1 < 2\pi$. Then $\sin x = \sin x_1$, since $x = 2\pi k + x_1$. If $0 \leq x_1 \leq \pi/2$, we can evaluate $\sin x_1$ from (6–32) and hence $\sin x$. If $\pi/2 < x_1 \leq \pi$, $\sin x_1 = \sin(\pi - x_1)$ and $0 \leq \pi - x_1 < \pi/2$. Thus we can evaluate $\sin(\pi - x_1)$ using (6–32) and hence we can evaluate $\sin x$. If $\pi < x_1 \leq 3\pi/2$, $\sin x_1 = -\sin(x_1 - \pi)$, and $0 \leq x_1 - \pi \leq \pi/2$. Thus we can evaluate $\sin(x_1 - \pi)$ from (6–32) and hence $-\sin x$. Finally, if $3\pi/2 < x_1 < 2\pi$, $\sin x_1 = -\sin(2\pi - x_1)$ and $0 < 2\pi - x_1 < \pi/2$, so we can evaluate $\sin(2\pi - x_1)$ from (6–32) and hence $\sin x$. We have thus shown that we can evaluate $\sin x$ for every real number x if we can evaluate $\sin x$, $0 \leq x \leq \pi/2$.

EXAMPLES. 1. Let us determine $\sin 0.541$ to three significant figures. This will be accomplished if $|e_{rt}| < 5 \times 10^{-4}$. From (6–30), since $x = 0.541 < 0.6$,

$$|e_{rt}| < \frac{(0.6)^{2k+2}}{(2k+2)!}. \tag{6–33}$$

For $k = 1$, $0.6^4/4! = 5 \times 10^{-3}$, and for $k = 2$, $(0.6)^6/6! = 6.5 \times 10^{-5}$. Thus we can use $k = 2$, that is, $s_5(x)$ for the computation. Now

$$s_5(x) = x - \frac{x^3}{6} + \frac{x^5}{120} = \left[\left(\frac{x^2}{120} - \frac{1}{6} \right) x^2 + 1 \right] x .$$

To avoid round-off problems, four significant figures will be used. Note that $1/120 = 0.008333$, $1/6 = 0.1667$, and $x^2 = (0.541)^2 = 0.2927$. Hence

$$\sin 0.541 = [(0.008333(0.2927) - 0.1667)(0.2927) + 1](0.541)$$
$$= [(0.002439 - 0.1667)(0.2927) + 1](0.541)$$
$$= [-0.04808 + 1](0.541) = 0.5149779 \, ,$$

and at the last step we have shown all digits obtained in multiplying together the last two numbers. On rounding to three places we obtain $\sin 0.541 = 0.515$, which is correct to three significant figures. To six significant figures, $\sin 0.541 = 0.514993$, so that the answer we obtained is accurate to more than four significant figures.

2. It is interesting to illustrate geometrically the way in which the polynomials $s_n(x)$ approximate $\sin x$. In Figure 6–1 we have plotted $s_1(x)$, $s_3(x)$,

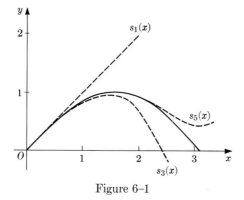

Figure 6–1

$s_5(x)$ and $\sin x$. Note that the approximation quickly becomes very poor as x increases above $\pi/2$. The larger the value of x, the larger that n must be for the same relative truncation error. This explains why we did not attempt to find an n such that $s_n(x)$ can be used to compute $\sin x$ to eight significant figures for any x. No such n exists. To keep n as small as possible we used the smallest interval possible.

In the problems we ask the reader to obtain a polynomial which can be used to compute $\cos x$, $0 \le x \le \pi/2$, to eight significant figures in the absence of round-off errors, and from this to show how to compute $\cos x$ for any x. Once $\sin x$ and $\cos x$ can be computed, $\tan x = \sin x/\cos x$ can be determined for all x in the domain of this function. Thus we now see how any of the trigonometric functions can be determined.

6–6 NUMERICAL INTEGRATION

We shall interrupt our discussion of the numerical evaluation of functions introduced previously to consider how definite integrals can be evaluated numerically on a computer. This material will be needed in our study of the numerical evaluation of $\log x$.

If $F(x)$ is a primitive function for the continuous function $f(x)$, then the fundamental theorem of the calculus states that

$$\int_a^b f(x)\, dx = F(b) - F(a)\,, \tag{6–34}$$

and the problem of evaluating $\int_a^b f(x)\, dx$ is reduced to evaluating $F(b)$ and $F(a)$. Thus if $F(x)$ is known, $\int_a^b f(x)\, dx$ would normally be evaluated on a computer by evaluating $F(b) - F(a)$. We have seen, however, that in many cases it may be very difficult or impossible to express $F(x)$ in terms of known functions, and in such cases we need some other procedure for evaluating $\int_a^b f(x)\, dx$. The key to developing a suitable numerical procedure is to go back to the definition of the definite integral. Recall that

$$\int_a^b f(x)\, dx = \lim_{n \to \infty} s_{Rn}\,, \tag{6–35}$$

where $\{s_{Rn}\}$ is any Riemann sequence for $f(x)$ over I_{ab}^c. Thus, choosing n large enough, the magnitude of the difference between $\int_a^b f(x)\, dx$ and s_{Rn} can be made arbitrarily small. Suppose that we choose a Riemann sequence of the type we have normally used in the past, where equally spaced points are used to subdivide the interval and the length of each subinterval is $h = (b - a)/n$. Suppose also that we take $\xi_k = x_k$. Then

$$\int_a^b f(x)\, dx \doteq \frac{b - a}{n} \sum_{j=1}^n f(x_j)\,. \tag{6–36}$$

We could very well evaluate the right-hand side of (6–36) on the computer and use it as our approximation to $\int_a^b f(x)\, dx$. This approximation is one where, if $f(x) > 0$, the definite integral is being approximated by the sum of areas of rectangles as shown in Figure 6–2. We can now note that we can increase the accuracy of the approximation for a given n if, instead of

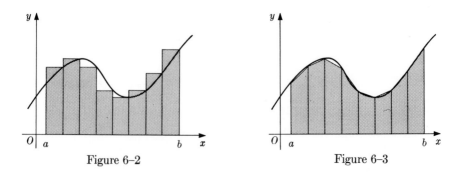

Figure 6–2   Figure 6–3

rectangles, we use trapezoids as shown in Figure 6–3. The trapezoids are formed by joining the points $(x_{k-1}, f(x_{k-1}))$ and $(x_k, f(x_k))$ by a straight line. The area of the kth trapezoid is

$$\frac{h}{2}[f(x_{k-1}) + f(x_k)] = h\left[\frac{f(x_{k-1})}{2} + \frac{f(x_k)}{2}\right]. \tag{6-37}$$

The proof of this is very easy and we ask the reader to give it in the problems. The sum of the areas of the trapezoids is then

$$h\sum_{k=1}^{n}\left[\frac{f(x_{k-1})}{2} + \frac{f(x_k)}{2}\right]$$

$$= h\left[\frac{f(x_0)}{2} + \frac{f(x_1)}{2} + \frac{f(x_1)}{2} + \frac{f(x_2)}{2} + \frac{f(x_2)}{2}\right.$$

$$\left. + \frac{f(x_3)}{2} + \cdots + \frac{f(x_{n-1})}{2} + \frac{f(x_n)}{2}\right] \tag{6-38}$$

$$= h\left[\frac{f(x_0)}{2} + f(x_1) + f(x_2) + \cdots + f(x_{n-1}) + \frac{f(x_n)}{2}\right].$$

Thus we can write

$$\int_a^b f(x)\,dx \doteq \frac{b-a}{n}\left\{\left[\frac{f(x_0)}{2} + \frac{f(x_n)}{2}\right] + \sum_{k=1}^{n-1} f(x_k)\right\} = s_{Tn}, \tag{6-39}$$

and (6–39) is referred to as the *trapezoidal rule* for determining approximately the definite integral. Clearly (6–39) can be used even if $f(x)$ is not positive for all $x \in I_{ab}^c$.

It is possible to determine an estimate of the error involved in using s_{Tn} for $\int_a^b f(x)\,dx$. However, it is not so easy to estimate the relative error and, consequently, it is often not easy to determine in advance how large n should be to compute the integral to, say, eight significant figures in the absence of round-off errors. To avoid trying to decide ahead of time what n should be, we shall introduce a new procedure called an *iterative technique* which allows the computer to decide what n should be. In this way we avoid the necessity of making any decision on the matter ourselves. The procedure is as follows. We select arbitrarily a value of n, call it n_0. The value of n_0 might be something like 100 or 1000. The computer then determines s_{Tn_0}. The computer next uses a new $n > n_0$, call it n_1; it is often convenient to have $n_1 = 2n_0$. It then computes s_{Tn_1}. If the difference between s_{Tn_1} and s_{Tn_0} is small enough, the computer stops and s_{Tn_1} is used as $\int_a^b f(x)\,dx$. If the difference is not small enough, the computer uses a new $n > n_1$, call it n_2, and computes s_{Tn_2}. This is then compared with s_{Tn_1} and, if the difference is small enough, s_{Tn_2} is used for $\int_a^b f(x)\,dx$, and so on.

How does the computer decide whether it is necessary to increase n or to use the value currently calculated? A convenient way for the computer to do this is to use a ratio which, in form, looks like the relative error. Thus it would compute $\alpha = |s_{Tn_1} - s_{Tn_0}|/|s_{Tn_1}|$ and if this is less than some pre-specified number, say 5×10^{-9}, it would stop and s_{Tn_1} would be used. Otherwise, the value of n would be increased and the procedure repeated. The computational procedure thus consists of a series of steps, or *iterations* as they are called. At the jth iteration s_{Tn_j} is computed as well as $|s_{Tn_j} - s_{Tn_{j-1}}|/|s_{Tn_j}|$, and if this latter quantity is small enough, the iterative procedure is terminated and s_{Tn_j} is used for $\int_a^b f(x)\, dx$. Otherwise an $n_{j+1} > n_j$ is selected (typically we use $n_{j+1} = 2n_j$) and iteration $j + 1$ is performed. This is continued until

$$\frac{|s_{Tn_j} - s_{Tn_{j-1}}|}{|s_{Tn_j}|} < \epsilon , \qquad (6\text{--}40)$$

where $\epsilon = 5 \times 10^{-9}$, for example.

The criterion (6–40) which the computer uses for deciding if n is large enough is called the *convergence criterion*. The iterative criterion just described could have been used for evaluating e^x and $\sin x$. However, the iterative procedure requires more computation than if n can be selected in advance. This could be done easily for the computation of e^x and $\sin x$. There are many problems, however, where it cannot be decided in advance how much computation is needed. Iterative techniques similar to those just described, which allow the computer to make the decisions, provide powerful methods for solving such problems accurately. If $\epsilon = 5 \times 10^{-9}$ in (6–40) we will be essentially determining $\int_a^b f(x)\, dx$ correct to eight significant figures in the absence of round-off errors, although we cannot guarantee that it will be precisely eight. In general, it is not easy to determine exactly what the magnitude of the relative error is, in the absence of round-off errors, at the point where the computer stops. It is not of great value to do so because it is not possible to determine the round-off error. In general, thousands of operations will be performed by the computer in evaluating $\int_a^b f(x)\, dx$ and thus, even if this definite integral were correct to eight significant figures in the absence of round-off errors, it may be correct only to six or even fewer significant figures when round-off errors are taken into account.

EXAMPLE. Consider the integral

$$\int_0^1 \frac{4}{1 + x^2}\, dx . \qquad (6\text{--}41)$$

The material we have discussed previously does not allow us to evaluate this integral analytically, since we are unable to find a primitive function for $4/(1 + x^2)$. We can evaluate it numerically, however. Interestingly enough, it can be proved that the integral (6–41) has the value π. We shall not attempt to prove this, but knowing it is true we then can use numerical integration of (6–41) as a means for determining π numerically; π is an irrational number, but in principle π can be determined as accurately as desired from (6–41).

Let us illustrate the use of the trapezoidal rule by determining approximately the numerical value of π. We shall subdivide the interval of integration into ten subintervals of length $h = 0.1$, that is, $n = 10$. Then according to (6–39)

$$\int_0^1 \frac{4}{1 + x^2}\, dx = \pi$$

$$\doteq 0.4\left[\frac{1}{2} + \frac{1}{1 + (0.1)^2} + \frac{1}{1 + (0.2)^2} + \frac{1}{1 + (0.3)^2} + \frac{1}{1 + (0.4)^2}\right.$$

$$+ \frac{1}{1 + (0.5)^2} + \frac{1}{1 + (0.6)^2} + \frac{1}{1 + (0.7)^2} + \frac{1}{1 + (0.8)^2}$$

$$\left. + \frac{1}{1 + (0.9)^2} + \frac{1}{4}\right]$$

$$= 0.4[0.50000 + 0.99010 + 0.96154 + .091743 + 0.86207$$
$$+ 0.80000 + 0.73529 + 0.67114 + 0.60976$$
$$+ 0.55249 + 0.25000]$$

$$= 0.4(7.84982)$$
$$= 3.139928\,.$$

The correct value of π to six significant figures is 3.14159, so the magnitude of the relative error is $1.76/3141.59$ or about 2 parts in 3000, which is quite good considering that such a small value of n was used.

6–7 COMPUTATION OF LOGARITHMNS AND a^α

The function $\log x$ is different from functions such as e^x and $\sin x$ in that its domain consists of positive numbers only and it has a vertical asymptote at $x = 0$. The natural logarithm is not continuous over any interval which contains 0, and thus we cannot apply Taylor's formula as developed in Section 6–3 to determine polynomials to approximate $\log x$. Although polynomial-type expressions to use in computing $\log x$ can be found by other means, these are really not needed since $\log x$ can readily be evaluated by numerical integration. Recall that

$$\log x = \int_1^x \frac{1}{t}\, dt\,. \tag{6–42}$$

Let us now explain how to compute $\log x$ for any x. Recall that $\log 1/x = -\log x$. Thus if $0 < x < 1$, $\log x = -\log w$, where $w = 1/x$. Consequently, we can compute $\log x$ for all $x > 0$ if we can compute $\log x$ for $x > 1$. Consider now the computation of $\log x$ for $x > 1$. In floating point format, $x = y(10)^k$, $1 \leq y < 10$,

$$\log x = \log y + k \log 10 , \qquad (6\text{–}43)$$

and if $\log 10$ is stored in the computer, $\log x$ can be determined for any $x > \hat{0}$ if we can compute $\log y$, $1 \leq y < 10$. This procedure can be made even more efficient if we recall that in the computer x is represented as $x = y(2)^u$, $1 \leq y < 2$, so

$$\log x = \log y + u \log 2 . \qquad (6\text{–}44)$$

Now u is available in the computer (k of (6–43) is not) so that, if $\log 2$ is stored in the computer's memory, we can evaluate $\log x$ for any $x > 0$ if we can evaluate $\log x$ for $1 \leq x < 2$. $\text{Log } x$ for $1 \leq x \leq 2$ can be very conveniently determined from (6–42) using numerical integration, as described in the previous section. The use of numerical integration to compute $\log x$, $1 \leq x \leq 2$, is not the most efficient procedure, since many more operations are required by the computer than if the polynomial-type approximation is used. It is, nonetheless, a perfectly satisfactory way to evaluate $\log x$. It can be shown, although we shall not do so, that in the absence of round-off errors, $\log(1 + w)$, $0 \leq w < 1$, is given correct to eight significant figures by the expression

$$\log(1 + w) = 2 \sum_{k=1}^{9} \frac{1}{2k - 1} \left(\frac{w}{2 + w} \right)^{2k-1}. \qquad (6\text{–}45)$$

This expression is not a polynomial in w, but is a polynomial in the variable $u = w/(2 + w)$. It is (6–45) that would normally be used to evaluate $\log x$ for $1 \leq x < 2$.

Now that we know how to evaluate e^x and $\log x$ for any x, we can easily see how to evaluate a^α for any $a > 0$ and any α. Recall that

$$a^\alpha = e^{\alpha \log a} . \qquad (6\text{–}46)$$

Thus to evaluate a^α, the computer first evaluates $\log a$ in the manner described above and then $\beta = \alpha \log a$, and finally computes e^β in the manner described in Section 6–4. This would be a very arduous computation to carry out by hand, but it can be done on the computer in 0.01 seconds or less. Thus, for example, if we wished to evaluate $(3.84)^{7.163}$ on the computer, $\log 3.84$ would be determined first, then $\beta = 7.163 \log 3.84$ and finally e^β. The procedure just described provides a way to compute $a^{1/2}$ or $a^{1/3}$. It is an inefficient way, however, to compute square or cube roots, and in the next section we shall introduce an efficient procedure for determining $a^{1/2}$ or $a^{1/3}$.

6–8 NEWTON'S METHOD

Problems are often encountered where it is of interest to find the roots of $f(x)$, that is, those values of x for which $f(x) = 0$. This can be a difficult problem even when a computer is available, and we shall not attempt to study it in any detail. Instead we wish to introduce one simple technique, called Newton's method, which is frequently used, especially in cases where it is known that $f(x)$ has only one root in some interval of interest.

Suppose that we know or suspect that $f(x)$ has just one root λ in some given interval and we would like to determine λ numerically. Assume that x_0 is a value of x such that $f(x)$ is close to 0. Now if the graph of $y = f(x)$ does not move far away from the line tangent to $f(x)$ at x_0 in the interval between x_0 and λ, then the point where the tangent line crosses the x-axis

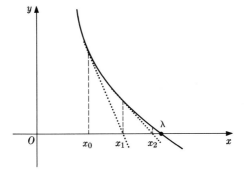

Figure 6–4

should give a much better approximation to λ than x_0. This is illustrated in Figure 6–4. The equation of the line tangent to $f(x)$ at x_0 is

$$y = f(x_0) + f'(x_0)(x - x_0) . \tag{6–47}$$

This crosses the x-axis at a value of x, call it x_1, which is

$$x_1 = x_0 - \frac{f(x_0)}{f'(x_0)}, \quad f'(x_0) \neq 0 . \tag{6–48}$$

If we write $h_1 = x_1 - x_0$, then $h_1 = -f(x_0)/f'(x_0)$ and we expect $x_1 = x_0 + h_1$ to be closer to λ than x_0.

We can now repeat the procedure and find the line tangent to $f(x)$ at x_1. This has the form (6–47) with x_0 replaced by x_1. The point x_2 where it crosses the x-axis should then be closer to λ than x_1. Now $x_2 = x_1 + h_2$, where $h_2 = -f(x_1)/f'(x_1)$. This procedure can be continued indefinitely, and we can thus generate a sequence $\{x_n\}$ where $x_n = x_{n-1} + h_n$ and

$$h_n = - \frac{f(x_{n-1})}{f'(x_{n-1})} . \tag{6–49}$$

From Figure 6–4 it would appear that the sequence $\{x_n\}$ should converge to λ, and hence we have a numerical procedure which could be used in principle to determine λ as accurately as desired. The procedure described, which is called Newton's method, is another example of an iterative procedure. At the nth iteration h_n is computed from (6–49) and $x_n = x_{n-1} + h_n$. If $\{x_n\}$ *converges to* λ, *the iterative procedure is said to converge.* Otherwise it is said to diverge. Unfortunately, it is not always true that the iterative procedure will converge. We shall not attempt to determine the conditions under which it is certain to converge. The mere fact that it does converge and that $\{x_n\}$ has the limit λ is not enough to make the technique computationally useful. If millions of iterations were required, the method would be of little value. It must converge sufficiently rapidly that a relatively few iterations will be needed, say no more than 100, or 500 at the very most. Fortunately, in many cases of interest, the convergence is very rapid and no more than 10 or so iterations are needed.

No attempt need be made to decide ahead of time whether Newton's method will converge for any given x_0. The computer can decide this for itself by examining the sequence $\{f(x_n)\}$ to see if it is converging to 0. The manner in which the computer can make all the relevant decisions is as follows. The computer initially performs m iterations, m might be 10, for example. If $|f(x_m)| \geq |f(x_0)|$, Newton's method is diverging and the computer stops, printing out an indication of this. If $|f(x_m)| < |f(x_0)|$, it is tentatively decided that the method is converging. Then $\alpha_1 = |x_m - x_{m-1}|/|x_m|$ is determined. If $\alpha_1 < \epsilon$, ϵ may be 5×10^{-9}, for example, the computer next checks to see if $|f(x_m)|$ is sufficiently close to 0, say $< \eta$. When this is true, the computer prints out x_m as the root λ. If either $\alpha_1 \geq \epsilon$ or $|f(x_m)| \geq \eta$, another m iterations are performed. Then the above testing procedure is repeated all over again. First $|f(x_{2m})|$ is compared to $|f(x_m)|$. If $|f(x_{2m})| \geq |f(x_m)|$, an indication of divergence is given. Otherwise $\alpha_2 = |x_{2m} - x_{2m-1}|/|x_{2m}|$ is determined. If $\alpha_2 < \epsilon$, and $|f(x_{2m})| < \eta$, x_{2m} is printed out as λ. Otherwise another m iterations are performed. This is continued until either the computer stops by one of the above means or $m > M$, $M = 100$, for example. If m becomes greater than M, the computer stops with an indication that either the process is not converging or convergence is too slow. The reader will note that the above convergence test is fairly complicated. He should go through it again to get clearly in mind the logic involved. No provision was made in the above for the possibility that some $x_n = 0$ and that the computer might attempt to divide by this x_n in computing an α. If this could be a problem due to the root being close to 0, then one could build into the code the alternative of using perhaps $\alpha = |x_n - x_{n-1}|$ if $x_n = 0$.

Newton's method can be used to derive an efficient way to compute $a^{1/2}$. Note that $a^{1/2}$ is a root of $x^2 - a = 0$. Thus we can determine $a^{1/2}$ by finding the $x > 0$ which is the root of $f(x) = x^2 - a = 0$. Here $f'(x) = 2x$, and from (6–49) Newton's method becomes for this case

$$x_n = x_{n-1} - \frac{x_{n-1}^2 - a}{2x_{n-1}} = x_{n-1} - \frac{x_{n-1}}{2} + \frac{a}{2x_{n-1}},$$

so

$$x_n = \frac{1}{2}\left(x_{n-1} + \frac{a}{x_{n-1}}\right). \qquad (6\text{--}50)$$

This yields a sequence $\{x_n\}$ which converges to $a^{1/2}$ for any initial $x_0 > 0$. The convergence is very rapid. As an example, let us compute $7^{1/2}$ using $x_0 = 7$. The details are given in Table 6–2. Now $7^{1/2} = 2.645751$, and in

TABLE 6–2
COMPUTATION OF $7^{1/2}$

x_n	$\dfrac{7}{x_n}$	$x_n + \dfrac{7}{x_n}$	x_{n+1}
7	1	8	4
4	1.728	5.728	2.864
2.864	2.444	5.308	2.654
2.65400	2.63752	5.29152	2.64576

just four iterations of Newton's method, starting with a poor initial guess, we have obtained a result which is off by only 1 in the sixth significant figure. In the problems we ask the reader to show how Newton's method can be used to evaluate $a^{1/3}$.

6–9 COMPUTATION OF MAXIMA AND MINIMA

The procedure introduced in Section 3–13 to determine the absolute maximum of the differentiable function $f(x)$ over I_{ab}^c is to determine the roots $x_1, \ldots, x_k$ of $f'(x)$ in I_{ab}^c and then to evaluate $f(a), f(x_1), \ldots, f(x_k)$ and $f(b)$. The absolute maximum of $f(x)$ over I_{ab}^c is then the largest of these numbers. The difficulty of determining all the roots of $f'(x)$ in the interval I_{ab}^c is sufficiently great that it is often convenient to use an alternative approach which can easily be described by the use of Figure 6–5. We shall not attempt to give every detail that would be necessary in developing a code for the computer, but instead we shall merely convey the basic idea of the procedure. We would first select a number of relatively widely spaced points, x_k, referred to as a *coarse grid*, and evaluate $f(x_k)$ for each of these. The maximum of these values $f(x_k)$ would be found, then a finer grid (dashed lines in Figure 6–5) would be used in the neighborhood of the maxi-

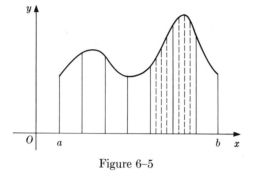

Figure 6–5

mum, and the maximum of $f(x)$ over these values of x would be determined. Finer and finer grids over progressively smaller intervals would be used until the value of x yielding the maximum value of $f(x)$ was determined with sufficient accuracy. During the coarse-grid search we would not only determine the value of x, call it x_m, which yielded the largest of the $f(x_k)$, but we would investigate the next largest $f(x_k)$ to see if it is $f(x_{m-1})$ or $f(x_{m+1})$. If it is not, then a fine-grid search would also be used in the neighborhood of the x yielding the second-largest value of the $f(x_k)$. The reason for this is that $f(x)$ may have two or even more relative maxima which yield nearly the same value of $f(x)$, and it is necessary to search each one carefully to determine correctly the value of x which yields the absolute maximum of $f(x)$. If it is known that $f(x)$ has only a single relative maximum, then more efficient procedures can be used to determine the maximum value of $f(x)$. We shall not discuss these. Clearly the procedure we have just discussed can be used equally well to determine the absolute minimum of $f(x)$ over I_{ab}^c.

6–10 DIFFERENTIAL EQUATIONS

If we desire to compute $f'(x)$ for a given x on a computer, we simply give the computer the function $f'(x)$ and have it evaluate this function. There would be no reason to give it instead $f(x)$ and attempt to have it approximate the derivative by some numerical procedure. Differentiation is so easy to carry out that there would never be any problem in obtaining $f'(x)$. Thus when $f(x)$ is known, no special numerical techniques similar to those introduced for integration are needed to compute derivatives. There exist cases, however, where numerical methods of computing derivatives from the function are needed. These arise in situations where $f(x)$ is not specifically known. This is the case, for example, in trying to solve a differential equation.

Let us now see how to solve numerically certain types of differential equations. It is easy to solve numerically much more complicated differential equations than can be solved analytically. We shall consider a general equation of the form

$$\frac{dy}{dx} = \theta(y)\varphi(x) , \qquad (6\text{–}51)$$

where $\theta(y)$ and $\varphi(x)$ are specified. A function $f(x)$ is a solution if for each x in its domain $f'(x) = \theta[f(x)]\varphi(x)$. Recall that, in order to determine a unique solution, one point on the graph of $f(x)$ must be specified. Suppose that it is required that $f(x_0) = y_0$. Instead of trying to determine $f(x)$ for all x in its domain, we shall try to evaluate $f(x)$ only at a finite number of points $x_k = x_0 + kh$, where h is specified and $k = 0, 1, 2, \ldots$. We can also take k to be negative. Let $y_k = f(x_k)$. Then it must be true that

$$\left(\frac{dy}{dx}\right)_k = \theta(y_k)\varphi(x_k) \qquad (6\text{–}52)$$

where $(dy/dx)_k$ is $f'(x_k)$. The trick which allows us to solve (6–51) numerically is to approximate $f'(x_k)$. We shall approximate $f'(x_k)$ by the slope of the secant passing through (x_k, y_k) and (x_{k+1}, y_{k+1}). This slope is $(y_{k+1} - y_k)/h$. With this approximation, (6–52) becomes

$$y_{k+1} = y_k + h\theta(y_k)\varphi(x_k) . \qquad (6\text{–}53)$$

Using (6–53) we can now determine the y_k successively, since

$$
\begin{aligned}
y_1 &= y_0 + h\theta(y_0)\varphi(x_0) \\
y_2 &= y_1 + h\theta(y_1)\varphi(x_1) \\
y_3 &= y_2 + h\theta(y_2)\varphi(x_2) ,
\end{aligned}
\qquad (6\text{–}54)
$$

.
.
.

and x_0 and y_0 have been specified. The value of h determines how widely spaced the x_k are. The way the computer would proceed to determine a solution of sufficient accuracy would be to compute a set of y_k for a given h. Then the computation would be made using a spacing of $h/2$. If the corresponding y_k for the two different solutions were close enough together then the second solution would be used. Otherwise a spacing of $h/4$ would be used and the procedure repeated. This could be continued until the convergence test is satisfied.

PROBLEMS

Section 6–1

1. Write the following numbers in floating point form.

   (a) 2007.6;   (b) −3;   (c) 16;   (d) 17 × 10⁻⁴;

   (e) 0.1;   (f) −18.765;   (g) − 18976;   (h) 2007060.

2.   What is the logical floating point representation of 0?

3.   Consider the numbers 6.213×10^2 and 7.144×10^2. Add these two numbers and write the result in floating point form. Explain what the computer must do to carry out the addition. Repeat this problem for the numbers 6.15×10^{-1} and 4.607×10^2. Explain how the operations could be conveniently carried out in the binary system.

4.   Re-solve Problem 3 when the numbers are to be multiplied rather than added.

5.   Show that the largest eight-digit number requires 28 binary bits for its representation. Computers typically use 28 binary bits to represent numbers, and this is essentially equivalent to eight digits.

Section 6–2

In Problems 1 through 6 we have given the computed value of some number and the error made in the computation. Determine the number of significant figures to which the computation has been made and the magnitude of the relative error.

1.   14.7621;
$e = -0.003$

2.   0.00215;
$e = 0.00007$

3.   5.721;
$e = 6 \times 10^{-6}$

4. 3×10^9;
$e = 4 \times 10^1$

5. 7.21×10^{-6};
$e = 7.3 \times 10^{-9}$

6.   3.0
$e = 0.$

7.   If we know that a number has been computed correct to v significant figures, but not to $v + 1$ significant figures, what does this tell us about $|e|$ and $|e_r|$?

8.   What differences exist between the "roughly speaking" definition of significant figures and the more precise definition?

9.   To add or subtract two numbers in floating point form, the computer first converts them to a form where both have the same power of 10 (power of 2 in the computer), then adds or subtracts the coefficients and converts the resulting number to floating point form. Illustrate this with several examples and show that in general a rounding operation will have to be performed to end up with eight digits in the floating point form of the number.

Sections 6–3 through 6–5

In Problems 1 through 20 check the value tabulated in the appropriate table at the end of the text for the function and argument indicated. To do this, first estimate the value of n needed in $s_n(x)$ to obtain the required number of significant figures, and then perform the computations in such a way that round-off causes no problems.

1. $e^{0.10}$;
2. $e^{0.44}$;
3. $e^{0.96}$;
4. $e^{1.7}$;

5. $e^{2.4}$;
6. $e^{3.6}$;
7. $e^{-0.1}$;
8. $e^{-0.8}$;

9. $e^{-1.3}$;
10. $e^{-2.5}$;
11. $\sin 0.02$;
12. $\sin 0.16$;

13. $\sin 0.24$;
14. $\sin 0.38$;
15. $\sin 0.68$;
16. $\sin 1.0$;

17. $\sin 1.24$;
18. $\sin 1.48$;
19. $\sin 1.52$;
20. $\sin \pi/2$.

21. Compute $\sin 18.23$ correct to three significant figures.

22. In the text we suggested that to compute e^x for $x < 0$ we first compute $e^{|x|}$ and then take its reciprocal. Show that it is unnecessary to do this, and that it is easy to compute e^x directly for $x < 0$. In this case the computation of e^x for any x can be reduced to the computation of e^x for $-1 < x < 1$. Prove that the polynomial used to compute e^x for $0 \le x < 1$ can be used to compute e^x for $-1 < x < 1$ to the same number of significant figures. Note that, in order to use this procedure, e^{-1} as well as e must be stored in the computer's memory.

23. In computing e^x in the text, we assumed that $x > 0$ was written as $n + 0.b_1 b_2 \cdots$. Now the computer does not actually have x available in this form but instead in the floating point format $u(2)^v$. Devise a way for computing e^x which allows the computer to use the floating point form of x directly, thus making it unnecessary to convert x to the form used in the text. Illustrate your procedure by checking the value of $e^{2.8}$ given in Table C at the end of the text.

24. Develop Taylor's formula for $\cos x$. Determine a value of n such that $s_n(x)$ can be used to compute $\cos x$ for $0 \le x \le \pi/2$ correct to eight significant figures, in the absence of round-off errors.

In Problems 25 through 30 use the Taylor's formula for $\cos x$ determined in Problem 24 to check the value of $\cos x$ tabulated in Table A at the end of the text for the indicated value of x.

25. $x = 0.22$; **26.** $x = 0.36$; **27.** $x = 0.48$; **28.** $x = 0.74$;

29. $x = 1.12$; **30.** $x = 1.42$.

31. Compute $\tan 0.44$ and check the value given in Table A at the end of the text.

32. What is the smallest value of n you can determine such that $s_n(x)$ can be used to evaluate e^x to eight significant figures, in the absence of round-off errors, for x in the interval $0 \le x \le 2$? What is your answer if the interval is $0 \le x \le 10$?

33. What is a value of n such that $s_n(x)$ can be used to evaluate e^x to sixteen significant figures, in the absence of round-off errors, for $0 \le x \le 1$?

34. What value should k have in order to use $s_{2k+1}(x)$ to compute $\sin x$ correct to sixteen significant figures, in the absence of round-off errors, for $0 \le x \le \pi/2$?

35. The discussion in the text may have given the reader the impression that it is not possible under any circumstances to compute a number to a greater accuracy than sixteen significant figures. This is not quite true. By using special techniques one can compute constants of great interest, such as π or e to almost any number of significant figures. For a discussion of how this is done, study the article on pp. 11–15 of the January, 1950, issue of *Mathematical Tables and Other Aids to Computation* which discusses the computation of π and e to more than 2000 significant figures. Prepare a brief report explaining the methods used.

Section 6–6

1. Prove that the area of the kth trapezoid is given by (6–37).

2. Compute approximately

$$\int_{-1}^{1} x \, dx$$

using (6–36) and the trapezoidal rule (6–39), subdividing the interval of integration into ten subintervals. Compare both results with the exact result. How much better is the trapezoidal rule?

3.   Carry out the computation of π in the manner illustrated in the text using $n = 20$. Compute $\alpha = |s_{T,20} - s_{T,10}|/|s_{T,20}|$, where $s_{T,20}$ and $s_{T,10}$ are the values determined for $n = 20$ and 10 respectively. How does α compare with the magnitude of the relative error on using $s_{T,20}$ for π?

4.   Why is it convenient to use $n_{j+1} = 2n_j$ in the iterative procedure described in the text? Hint: Can some previously computed values of $f(x)$ be used in the new computation?

5.   Evaluate approximately

$$\int_0^2 e^{-x^2}\, dx$$

using $n = 10$.

6.   Evaluate approximately

$$\int_2^4 \frac{1}{\log x}\, dx$$

using $n = 10$.

Section 6–7

In Problems 1 through 5 determine $\log x$ for the given value of x using numerical integration with $n = 10$. Compare the value so obtained with the correct value.

1. $x = 1.24$;   **2.** $x = 1.36$;   **3.** $x = 1.50$;   **4.** $x = 1.78$;

5. $x = 1.90$.

Section 6–8

1.   In the convergence test suggested in the text to be used with Newton's method, why is the test performed only after every m iterations rather than after every iteration?

2.   In the convergence test for Newton's method why is the computation not terminated when $\alpha < \epsilon$? Why is it desirable to also check the value of $|f(x)|$? Hint: What might happen if convergence were very slow?

3.   In the convergence test for Newton's method we could simplify the test and merely terminate the iterative procedure when $|f(x)|$ is small enough. Are there conditions under which this might not work? Hint: Suppose $|f(x)|$ is very small for all x over a fairly broad interval containing the root.

4.   Solve $e^x = 3$ to three significant figures using Newton's method. Illustrate the situation geometrically.

5.   Find the solution to the system

$$y = e^x; \qquad y = 6 - x$$

using Newton's method. Illustrate the situation geometrically.

6. Show by actually carrying out a sufficient number of iterations that, if $x_0 = 5$, Newton's method converges to the larger root of $f(x) = (x + 6)(x - 1)$, while if $x_0 = -10$, it converges to the smaller root.

In Problems 7 through 13 determine to five significant figures the positive square root of the given number.

7. 5.0; **8.** 365; **9.** 4221; **10.** 1.365; **11.** 0.872;

12. 0.0241; **13.** 0.007132.

14. Determine $2^{1/2}$ to ten significant figures.

15. Apply Newton's method to determine an iterative technique for computing $a^{1/3}$.

In Problems 16 through 22 compute the cube root of the given number to four significant figures using the results of Problem 15.

16. 14.21; **17.** −11.12; **18.** 0.892; **19.** 101.3; **20.** −0.0461;

21. 56.3; **22.** −2561.

In Problems 23 through 28 evaluate numerically, with $n = 10$, the integral obtained in the problem for Section 5–8 whose number is given. Determine the square roots using the methods developed in this section and use the tables at the end of the text for the other computations.

23. Problem 20; **24.** Problem 21; **25.** Problem 22;

26. Problem 23; **27.** Problem 24; **28.** Problem 25.

29. Try to sketch a curve having the characteristic that, for some x_0, Newton's method will not converge.

Section 6–10

1. Solve $dy/dx = 2y$ numerically for x in the interval $0 \leq x \leq 2$, using $h = 0.1$ and assuming that at $x = 0$, $y = 1$. On the same figure draw the graph of the exact solution, as well as the curve obtained by joining for each k (x_k, y_k) to (x_{k+1}, y_{k+1}) by a straight line.

2. Re-solve Problem 1 using $h = 0.05$ and compare the results obtained with the exact solution and with that obtained for $h = 0.1$.

3. Solve numerically $dy/dx = -x/y$ using $h = 0.1$ and assuming that at $x = 0$, $y = 2$. Determine the solution for $-2 < x < 2$. Compare the results with the exact analytical solution. Plot both on the same figure in the manner described in Problem 1.

CHAPTER 7

Functions of Several Variables

7–1 REAL VALUED FUNCTIONS OF TWO VARIABLES

Since the beginning of Chapter 2 we have been studying functions of one variable, that is, functions whose domain is some subset of the real numbers and whose range is also a subset of the real numbers. It was emphasized, however, in the original definition of a function that the elements of the domain could be anything at all and so could the elements of the range. In this chapter we shall study briefly more general types of functions. We shall begin by defining what is referred to as a function of two variables.

In our study of the graphs of relations in Chapter 2 we worked with expressions such as $x^2 + y^2$, xy, and $3(x - 2)^2 + 4(y - 3)^2$. These expressions have the characteristic that they involve two variables x and y. Furthermore, if we select any particular value of x, say 4, and any particular value of y, say 5, then we can determine a unique real number which is the value of any one of these expressions. Thus when $x = 4$ and $y = 5$, $x^2 + y^2 = 41$. In other words, given any ordered pair of numbers (x, y), there is determined a unique number which is the value of the expression under consideration. Expressions such as $x^2 + y^2$ and xy are examples of what we shall call functions of two variables.

In general, a function is called a function of two variables, or more precisely a real valued function of two real valued variables, if the domain of the function is a set of ordered pairs of real numbers and the range is a set of real numbers. We can give a formal definition as follows:

FUNCTION OF TWO VARIABLES. *Let A be a set whose elements are ordered pairs of real numbers of the form (x, y), and let B be a subset of the real numbers. Any rule which associates with each element (x, y) of A one and only one number z in B is called a function of two variables.*

The domain of a function of two variables may contain a finite or infinite number of ordered pairs (x, y). In most of the cases that will be of interest to us it will contain an infinite number of ordered pairs. To indicate that the number z is the image of the ordered pair (x, y), we shall frequently use a symbolism such as $z = f(x, y)$. This is an obvious generalization of the corresponding notation used for functions of one variable. Just as with functions of one variable, $z = f(x, y)$ is often given a double interpretation. Not only is it used to indicate that z is the image of (x, y), but it is also used as a symbolic representation for the entire function. We shall also frequently symbolize a function of two variables merely using $f(x, y)$.

Generally speaking, a function of two variables can be represented in all of the different ways that we can represent a function of one variable. If there are only a finite number of ordered pairs in the domain, then a table having three columns can be used. In each row we give in the first column the number x in the ordered pair (x, y) and in the second column we give y, and in the third column we give z, the image of (x, y). We shall be mainly interested in representing functions of two variables by use of mathematical expressions in the same manner as for functions of one variable. Thus the equations

$$z = 3x + 2y \quad \text{and} \quad z = x^2 + y^2 \qquad (7\text{–}1)$$

represent two different functions of two variables. We shall follow the convention in dealing with functions of two variables that was used when studying functions of one variable. When we write something like $z = xy$ we shall, unless otherwise specified, take the domain of the function to be the set of all ordered pairs (x, y) for which it is possible to compute a z. In the case under consideration, xy is defined for every pair of numbers (x, y), and thus the domain of $z = xy$ can be taken to be the set of all ordered pairs of numbers (x, y). Most of the functions of two variables we shall study will have the characteristic that their domains can be taken to be the set of all ordered pairs (x, y).

Now recall that we can geometrically interpret an ordered pair of numbers (x, y) as a point in a plane. This suggests a new and useful way to interpret the domain of a function of two variables. The domain is simply some set of points in a plane, and any element of the domain can then be thought of as a point. This is also true, of course, for a function of one variable. Any element x of the domain can be thought of as a point on a line, the line being the x-axis. Any element (x, y) of the domain of a function of two variables is a point in the xy-plane, that is, the plane containing the xy-coordinate system. When the domain of a function of two variables is the set of all ordered pairs (x, y), this is .equivalent to saying that the domain is the entire xy-plane. It is now convenient to introduce a terminology which will be especially useful when we later consider functions of n variables.

We have noted earlier that we can represent algebraically the geometric concept of a straight line by the set of all real numbers. Let us introduce the symbol E^1 to denote the set of all real numbers, so that $E^1 = \{x | \text{all real } x\}$. Similarly, we shall use E^2 to denote the set of all ordered pairs of real numbers, that is, $E^2 = \{(x, y) | \text{all real } x \text{ and } y\}$, and we have noted in Chapter 2 that E^2 can be used as the algebraic representation of a plane. Are we justified, then, in saying that E^1 is a straight line and E^2 is a plane? This depends on what we mean by a straight line and by a plane. If we think of lines and planes in terms of their usual geometric definitions, then clearly E^1 and E^2 are not lines and planes, respectively. Indeed, the geometric notion of straight lines and planes contains more than is implied in E^1 and E^2 since, for example, nothing in the definition of E^1 involves the notion of straightness. This concept is introduced algebraically by giving the rules for the distance between any two points in E^1. If the distance is defined to be $|x_1 - x_2|$, this introduces the notion of straightness into the algebraic representation. In all of our work we have really only been interested in the sets E^1 and E^2. These were not introduced to represent geometric concepts algebraically. Instead, we always moved in the reverse direction and gave a geometric interpretation to subsets of E^1 and E^2. We shall continue in this way. We shall be interested in certain sets whose elements are numbers, ordered pairs of numbers or, more generally, ordered n-tuples of numbers such as $(x_1, x_2, \ldots, x_n)$.

It will be convenient on occasion to interpret these sets geometrically. As in the past, we shall interpret E^1 as a straight line and E^2 as a plane. In mathematics, E^1, the set of all real numbers, is also referred to as a *one-dimensional Euclidean space*, while E^2 is referred to as a *two-dimensional Euclidean space*. The terms one- and two-dimensional are used because, geometrically, we think of a line as being one-dimensional and a plane as being two-dimensional. The Euclidean refers to the fact that we interpret E^1 and E^2 as lines or planes of the sort studied in Euclidean (that is, elementary) geometry. The elements of E^1 and E^2 are frequently referred to as *points*, the terminology again taken from the geometric interpretation. Using our new terminology we can then say that a function of one variable is one for which the elements of the domain and range are elements of E^1, while a function of two variables is one for which the domain is a subset of E^2 and the range is a subset of E^1.

In a function of two variables $z = f(x, y)$, the symbols x and y are referred to as the independent variables, while z is referred to as the dependent variable. Also, $f(x, y)$ is referred to as the value of the function at the point (x, y). Normally, the functions in which we shall be interested will be representable by a single equation such as $z = 3x - y^2$ over the entire domain. In general, however, different equations may be necessary to represent the function over different parts of the domain. For example, the following is an example of a function of two variables whose domain is all of E^2, but which is represented by one equation for points (x, y) lying inside and on the unit circle with center at the origin, and by a different equation for the points lying outside this circle.

$$z = \begin{cases} 2x - y, & x^2 + y^2 \leq 1 \\ xy, & x^2 + y^2 > 1 \, . \end{cases} \tag{7-2}$$

Functions of two variables arise very naturally in the real world. For example, if a firm produces two products, its profit will be a function of how much of each of the products is produced. Similarly, the yield in some chemical reaction is a function of the temperature and pressure in the reactor. Other examples will arise later.

7–2 GEOMETRIC REPRESENTATION

We showed in Chapter 2 that it was possible to give a geometric interpretation to $y = f(x)$ by considering the set of points $G = \{(x, y)|y = f(x)\}$ in the xy-plane. This set of points was called the graph of the function $y = f(x)$, and when x is a continuous variable, the graph will be represented geometrically as a curve. The graph of $y = f(x)$ is extremely useful for providing a vivid description of the function. We now wish to study the possibility of representing geometrically the function of two variables $z = f(x, y)$. We shall see that it is indeed possible to do this, and we shall consider two different ways of doing so. Unfortunately, however, the geometric representation is not nearly so vivid as for functions of one variable.

Let A be the domain of $z = f(x, y)$. Then for any point $(x, y) \in A$ there is determined a unique z which is the image of (x, y). Consider then the ordered triple of numbers (x, y, z), the first two numbers representing the element of the domain and the third the image of this element. We can now interpret (x, y, z) as a point in space, that is, in what we intuitively think of as the three-dimensional space in which we live. Indeed, we shall show that it is possible to establish a unique correspondence between the set of all ordered triples and the set of all points in space, so that there is one point corresponding to each triple and one triple corresponding to each point.

Consider Figure 7–1, where we have shown a perspective sketch of the xy-plane. Let us now show how it is possible to locate a unique point in space representing (x, y, z). We first locate (x, y) in the xy-plane in the manner discussed in Chapter 2. Consider now the line perpendicular to the xy-plane which passes through the point (x, y) in the xy-plane. This line is shown in Figure 7–1. There is only one such line. Let us now choose a unit of distance for making measurements along this line. Then if $z > 0$, we move along z units above the xy-plane and this locates a unique point (x, y, z) as shown in Figure 7–1. If $z < 0$, we move a distance $|z|$ below the xy-plane along the line and this again determines a unique point. If $z = 0$, we use the point (x, y) in the xy-plane (which is also a point in space) to represent (x, y, z). Thus we have shown how to determine a unique point in space corresponding to any triple (x, y, z).

To find a unique triple corresponding to any given point in space we simply reverse the procedure. We pass a line through the point which is perpendicular to the xy-plane. The distance h of the point from the xy-plane measured along the line is determined. If the point is above the plane take $z = h$, if below the plane take $z = -h$, and if $h = 0$, take $z = 0$. The point (x, y) in the xy-plane representing the intersection of the line with the xy-plane yields the values of x and y to use in (x, y, z).

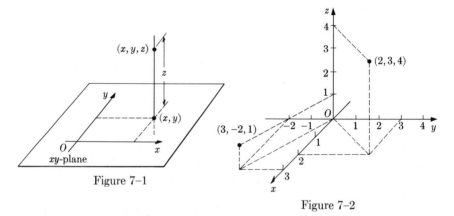

Figure 7–1

Figure 7–2

We can systematize the method for establishing a correspondence between the set of all ordered triples and all points in space. We shall introduce what is called a *coordinate system* for three-dimensional space. The usual coordinate system used consists of three mutually perpendicular lines which intersect in a single point. Such a set of lines is shown in the perspective drawing of Figure 7–2. The lines are called *coordinate axes*. There is an x-axis, a y-axis and a z-axis, and they are typically named as shown in Figure 7–2. The point of intersection of the three lines is called the origin of the coordinate system. It is usually denoted by 0 and represents the point $(0, 0, 0)$. We then imagine that the x- and y-axes serve to define the xy-plane, and the z-axis is used for making measurements perpendicular to the xy-plane. In Figure 7–2 we have plotted the points $(2, 3, 4)$ and $(3, -2, 1)$, the term plotting having the same connotation as in Chapter 2.

The reader will note that we encounter here the same sort of ambiguity in labeling points as we did in Chapter 2. A point in the xy-plane can be denoted by (x, y) or $(x, y, 0)$. Similarly, points on the x-, y- or z-axes can be denoted by x, y or z or by $(x, 0, 0)$, $(0, y, 0)$ or $(0, 0, z)$. The notation we use will again depend on what we have in mind. If we are thinking of a point lying in the xy-plane as a point in E^2 we shall label it (x, y). If we are thinking of it as a point in space which just happens to be in the xy-plane, we shall label it $(x, y, 0)$.

We shall denote the set of all possible triples (x, y, z) by E^3, so that

$$E^3 = \{(x, y, z) | \text{all real } x, y, z\} . \tag{7–3}$$

E^3 is called a *three-dimensional Euclidean space*. As we have just seen, we can interpret E^3 geometrically as the ordinary three-dimensional space in which we live. Conversely, we can use E^3 as our algebraic representation of three-dimensional space if there is a need to do this. Any element (x, y, z) of E^3 is often referred to as a *point*. Note that the xy-plane is a space of dimension two lying in E^3. The xy-plane is an example of a subspace of E^3, a space of lower dimension lying in E^3. The x-, y- and z-axes are also subspaces of E^3 having dimension one.

Consider now any function of two variables $z = f(x, y)$ with domain A. The set of points in E^3

$$G = \{(x, y, z) | z = f(x, y), \quad (x, y) \in A\} \tag{7–4}$$

will be called the graph of $z = f(x, y)$. The graph G of $z = f(x, y)$ is then a subset of E^3. Let us next proceed to study the problem of representing geometrically the graph of $z = f(x, y)$. The simplest case is that where the domain contains only a finite number of elements. Suppose, for example, $z = f(x, y)$ is described by the data in Table 7–1. We could represent this

TABLE 7–1
$z = f(x, y)$

x	y	z	x	y	z
-1	2	3	2	2	2
-1	5	0.5	2	5	1
0	2	1	3	2	0
0	5	0.5	3	5	4

function simply by placing a dot at each of the points (x, y, z) in the graph of the function. This is very confusing in a perspective sketch because we are unable to visualize precisely where the dot is. A clearer representation involves the use of a bar diagram. First we plot the points (x, y) in the domain of the function in the xy-plane. Then we draw a heavy bar from (x, y) to the point (x, y, z) as shown in Figure 7–3.

Let us next turn to the case which will be of major interest to us where

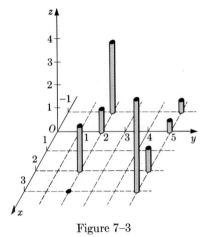

Figure 7–3

the domain of the function is all of E^2, or is some subset of E^2 which has a nonzero area. Once again corresponding to each point (x, y) in the domain, there is a point (x, y, z) in the graph of the function. The graph of $z = f(x, y)$ will in this case be what is referred to as a *surface*, just as the graph of $y = f(x)$ over some interval is referred to as a curve. It is possible to draw perspective diagrams to convey the general idea of what the graph of $z = f(x, y)$ looks like. For example, the graph might look like the surface shown in Figure 7–4. Note carefully that a surface such as that shown in Figure 7–4 is not "solid." There is only one point $(x, y, z) \in E^3$ corresponding to a particular point (x, y) in the domain. A surface, like a curve, has no "thickness."

It requires a considerable amount of artistic ability to represent clearly the nature of the graph of $z = f(x, y)$, which is three dimensional, in a two-dimensional perspective sketch. It is possible, with sufficient skill, to give a vivid portrayal of the graph of $z = f(x, y)$ in this way. However, even when this can be done, the resulting perspective diagram cannot be conveniently used to make quantitative measurements. It can only be used as a picture. We shall not spend any time in attempting to develop perspective drawings of the graphs of specific functions of two variables. Instead, we shall develop an alternative method of representation which requires less artistic ability and which, in addition, has the advantage that it is quantitative in the same sense that the graphs of $y = f(x)$ could be made as precise as desired.

To develop the alternative mode of representing the graph of $z = f(x, y)$, let us for the moment visualize it as a surface, the perspective representation of which might be that shown in Figure 7–4. Consider now a plane P_ζ parallel to the xy-plane which intersects the z-axis at $z = \zeta$. This is shown in Figure 7–5. Let us next study the K_ζ of points from G the graph of $z = f(x, y)$ which lie on this plane. All of these points are of the form (x, y, ζ),

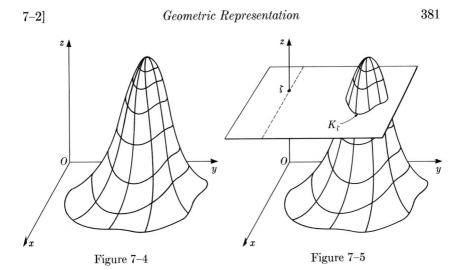

Figure 7–4   Figure 7–5

since the plane is parallel to the xy-plane and a distance ζ from it. It may be true that $k_\zeta = \varnothing$, that is, there are no points in G with $z = \zeta$, or K_ζ may contain only a single point. The interesting case is that where K_ζ contains more than a single point from G. When this occurs, K_ζ will normally contain an infinite number of points from G, and the set of points K_ζ will yield what we think of as a curve lying in the plane P_ζ. The curve K_ζ is shown in Figure 7–5. By definition K_ζ is the set

$$K_\zeta = \{(x, y, \zeta)|f(x, y) = \zeta\} . \qquad (7\text{–}5)$$

Imagine now that we move the plane P_ζ down the z-axis until it coincides with the xy-plane. Suppose that this is done in such a way that each point (x, y, ζ) originally on P_ζ becomes (x, y) when P_ζ is coincident with the xy-plane. The curve K_ζ is now a curve in the xy-plane and, of course, the shape of K_ζ has not been changed in any way by moving P_ζ. The curve K_ζ has thus become a curve $K_{xy\zeta}$ lying in the xy-plane, and $K_{xy\zeta}$ is simply the set of points

$$K_{xy\zeta} = \{(x, y)|f(x, y) = \zeta\} . \qquad (7\text{–}6)$$

$K_{xy\zeta}$ is, then, nothing but the graph of a relation, the relation being $f(x, y) = \zeta$, and for the case under consideration the graph might look like that shown in Figure 7–6.

The curve $K_{xy\zeta}$ is called a *level curve* for the graph of $z = f(x, y)$ and also a level curve for the function itself. The level curve $K_{xy\zeta}$ is the set of all points in the domain of $z = f(x, y)$ whose image is ζ. A level curve can be constructed for each value of z for which there are points in the domain whose image is z. There results a family of level curves, and if we draw a number of them on the same figure, something like Figure 7–7 is obtained. We can now make the very important observation that we can represent

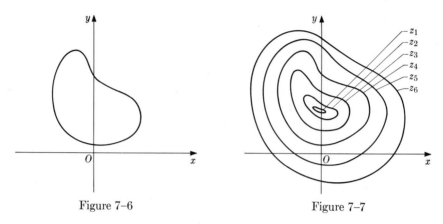

Figure 7–6   Figure 7–7

the graph of $z = f(x, y)$ geometrically by showing a set of level curves for this function such as those shown in Figure 7–7. The representation of a function of two variables by its level curves is the one that we shall use when a geometric interpretation is desired. The level curves are quantitative and can be drawn very accurately, if desired. Of course, each level curve must be labeled with the value of z it corresponds to in order for these curves to have any meaning.

Level curves are frequently used in everyday life to provide a graphical representation of functions of two variables. Anyone who looks at maps provided by the National Geographic Society, or many other maps as well, will find the concept employed in giving ocean depths—lines of constant depth are shown. Mathematically what is being done is representing geometrically a function of two variables. The ocean depth is a function of location, and the location can be described on a planar map using an xy-coordinate system. A similar procedure is often used to show the shapes of mountains on maps. Curves showing the shape of the mountain at various altitudes are given. Yet another illustration of the principle is found in the weather maps printed in newspapers. These maps will show curves representing curves of constant atmospheric pressure and curves of constant temperature.

Let us now illustrate by some specific examples how functions of two variables can be represented geometrically by use of level curves. Consider the function

$$z = 3x + 2y , \qquad (7\text{–}7)$$

whose domain is all of E^2. Suppose that we select a given value of z, say 6. Then the set of all points in E^2 which satisfy the relation $3x + 2y = 6$ is, as we know from Section 2–10, a straight line whose slope is $-\frac{3}{2}$. This line is shown in Figure 7–8. If a different value of z, say 12, is selected, we obtain another straight line whose slope is also $-\frac{3}{2}$. Indeed, every level curve will be a straight line with slope $-\frac{3}{2}$. Some of these are shown in Figure 7–8 along with the values of z they represent. Figure 7–8 then provides us with a geometric representation of the function. The graph in E^3 of a function of the form

$$z = ax + by \qquad (7\text{–}8)$$

is called a *plane*, since if we actually construct a three-dimensional coordinate system and plot the points, they will all be found to be on a plane. The function (7–8) is also referred to as a plane. Thus the function (7–7) is an example of a plane; the level curves for this plane are parallel lines. Consider next the function

$$z = x^2 + y^2 , \qquad (7\text{–}9)$$

whose domain is all of E^2. For any given value of $z > 0$, we see that the set of points in E^2 satisfying (7–9) is a circle with center at the origin having

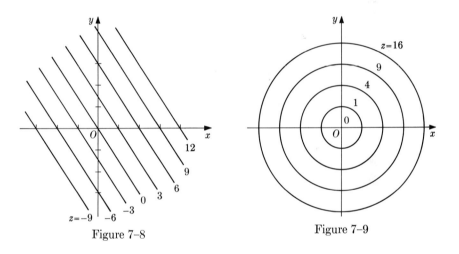

Figure 7–8

Figure 7–9

radius $z^{1/2}$. There are no points satisfying (7–9) for $z < 0$, and $(0, 0)$ is the only point satisfying (7–9) when $z = 0$. The level curves for the function (7–9) are then as shown in Figure 7–9. A perspective sketch of the graph of (7–9) would look like a bowl, as shown in Figure 7–10. The bowl has circular cross sections. The reader should note that Figure 7–9 provides the same information in a more precise form than Figure 7–10.

The labeling of the values of z on the level curves provides very important information. A variety of functions $z = f(x, y)$ can have level curves of the same shape, but the three dimensional surfaces are quite different, due to the fact that the values of z associated with the level curves are different. For example, the level curves for

$$z = (x^2 + y^2)^{1/2} \qquad (7\text{–}10)$$

are, for $z > 0$, circles with center at the origin, just as are the level curves for (7–9). However, a circle with radius r has $z = r$ for (7–10) and $z = r^2$ for (7–9). Thus the radius of a cross section of the surface for a given z will be larger for the function (7–10) than for (7–9) if $z > 1$ and smaller if $z < 1$. A perspective drawing of the graph of (7–10) is shown in Figure 7–11. This surface looks like a cone and is called a cone.

The level curves for the function

$$z = 2(x - 2)^2 + 6(y - 1)^2 , \tag{7–11}$$

whose domain is all of E^2, are ellipses for $z > 0$. For $z = 0$, $(2, 1)$ is the only point in E^2 satisfying (7–11), while for $z < 0$, there are no points satisfying (7–11). The three-dimensional surface representing (7–11) is again a bowl whose bottom touches the xy-plane at $(2, 1)$ and whose cross sections are ellipses. The level-curve representation of (7–11) is shown in Figure 7–12.

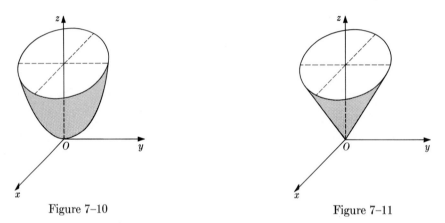

Figure 7–10   Figure 7–11

As a final example, let us consider the function

$$z = 0.5(x - 2)^2 - y , \tag{7–12}$$

whose domain is all of E^2. The level curves for (7–12) are the parabolas $y = 0.5(x - 2)^2 - z$, which open upward, have $x = 2$ as an axis of symmetry and cross the axis of symmetry at $y = -z$. These are shown in Figure 7–13. The three-dimensional surface which represents the graph of (7–12) may be a little hard for the reader to visualize at first. A perspective sketch is shown in Figure 7–14.

At this point we can make an interesting observation which provides a connection with what we did in Chapter 2. As the reader may have noted already, the graph of an equation such as $x^2 + y^2 = 6$, which represents a relation between two variables, is nothing but a level curve for the function of two variables $z = x^2 + y^2$ corresponding to $z = 6$. Indeed, using the notation for functions of two variables, we can represent symbolically an

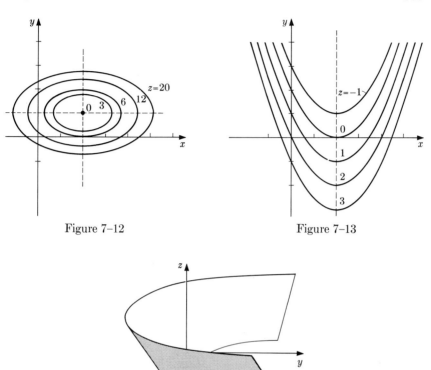

Figure 7–12   Figure 7–13

Figure 7–14

equation showing a relation between x and y as $f(x, y) = a$, where a is a specified constant. The set of solutions to this relation is the level curve for $z = f(x, y)$ at $z = a$, provided that a is the image of some points in the domain.

7-3 PARTIAL DERIVATIVES

Let us consider a function of two variables such as $z = 3x^2y + y^2$. The domain A of this function is all of E^2. Suppose now we consider all elements of the domain of the form $(x, 2)$, that is, elements for which $y = 2$. The image of any such point is $z = 6x^2 + 4$, as we see by setting $y = 2$ in $z = 3x^2y + y^2$. Denote by X the set of all numbers x such that $(x, 2) \in A$, that is, $(x, 2)$ is an element of the domain of the given function of two variables. For the case under consideration $X = E^1$. Now for each $x \in X$ we can determine a unique number z, this number being the image of $(x, 2)$ for the given function. We have in this way defined a function of one variable whose domain is X such that the image of each $x \in X$ is the image of $(x, 2)$ for the original function. An explicit representation of this function of one variable is $z = 6x^2 + 4$ and is obtained by setting $y = 2$ in $z = 3x^2y + y^2$.

In simple terms, what we have just shown is that, if we specify y to have a given value ξ in the function of two variables $z = f(x, y)$ with domain A, we then obtain a function of one variable $z = f(x, \xi)$ whose domain X_ξ is

$$X_\xi = \{x|(x, \xi) \in A\} . \tag{7–13}$$

This function of a single variable will be denoted by $z = g_\xi(x)$. Similarly, if it is specified that x have a specified value of η, we obtain another function of one variable $z = f(\eta, y)$ whose domain Y_η is

$$Y_\eta = \{y|(\eta, y) \in A\} . \tag{7–14}$$

We shall denote this function by $z = h_\eta(y)$. From a function of two variables we can then obtain two functions of one variable, one having x as the independent variable and one having y as the independent variable. This is done simply by fixing y or x, as the case may be, at a specific value.

EXAMPLES. 1. If $z = 2x^2 + 3y^2$, then $z = g_\xi(x) = 2x^2 + 3\xi^2$ and $X_\xi = E^1$. Also, $z = h_\eta(y) = 2\eta^2 + 3y^2$ and $Y_\eta = E^1$.

2. If $z = \log xy$, then $z = g_\xi(x) = \log \xi x$ and X_ξ is the set of all $x > 0$ if $\xi > 0$ and the set of all $x < 0$ if $\xi < 0$. Similarly, $z = h_\eta(y) = \log \eta y$, and Y_η is the set of all $y > 0$ if $\eta > 0$ and the set of all $y < 0$ if $\eta < 0$. The domain of $z = \log xy$ is the set of points in E^2 with $xy > 0$.

Now it may very well be true that the function $z = g_\xi(x)$ is differentiable at $x = \eta$. If $g'_\xi(\eta)$ exists, this number is called *the partial derivative of the function* $z = f(x, y)$ *with respect to* x *at the point* (η, ξ). It is denoted by $(\partial f/\partial x)_{(\eta, \xi)}$ or $\partial f(\eta, \xi)/\partial x$. Similarly, if $z = h_\eta(y)$ is differentiable at $y = \xi$, $h'_\eta(\xi)$ is called *the partial derivative of* $z = f(x, y)$ *with respect to* y *at the point* (η, ξ). This partial derivative is denoted by $(\partial f/\partial y)_{(\eta, \xi)}$ or $\partial f(\eta, \xi)/\partial y$. According to the above definitions,

$$\frac{\partial}{\partial x} f(\eta, \xi) = \lim_{v \to 0} \frac{f(\eta + v, \xi) - f(\eta, \xi)}{v} \tag{7–15}$$

and

$$\frac{\partial}{\partial y} f(\eta, \xi) = \lim_{v \to 0} \frac{f(\eta, \xi + v) - f(\eta, \xi)}{v} . \tag{7–16}$$

Intuitively, $\partial f(\eta, \xi)/\partial x$ gives the rate of change of z with respect to x when $y = \xi$, and $\partial f(\eta, \xi)/\partial y$ gives the rate of change of z with respect to y when

$x = \eta$. The reason for this is that $z = g_\xi(x)$ expresses z as a function of x when $y = \xi$, and $\partial f(\eta, \xi)/\partial x$ is the slope of $g_\xi(x)$ at $x = \eta$. Similarly, $z = h_\eta(y)$ expresses z as a function of y when $x = \eta$, and $\partial f(\eta, \xi)/\partial x$ is the slope of $h_\eta(y)$ at $y = \xi$.

Consider now the set D_x of all points in E^2 for which the partial derivative of $z = f(x, y)$ with respect to x exists. For each $(x, y) \in D_x$ we can associate a unique number $\partial f(x, y)/\partial x$. This rule defines a function which we call the partial derivative function with respect to x. We shall denote this function by $\partial f/\partial x$, $\partial f(x, y)/\partial x$ or $\partial z/\partial x$. Similarly, let D_y be the set of all points in E^2 for which the partial derivative of $z = f(x, y)$ with respect to y exists. For each $(x, y) \in D_y$ we can associate a unique number $\partial f(x, y)/\partial y$. This rule defines a function which we call the partial derivative function with respect to y. We shall denote this function by $\partial f/\partial y$, $\partial f(x, y)/\partial y$, or $\partial z/\partial x$.

It is normally very easy to determine the two partial derivative functions $\partial f/\partial x$ and $\partial f/\partial y$ for any given function of two variables $z = f(x, y)$. To obtain $\partial f/\partial x$ we merely imagine y to be fixed and differentiate $f(x, y)$ with respect to x, thus treating it as a function of a single variable x. All of the rules we developed for computing derivatives of a function of one variable can then be used to compute $\partial f/\partial x$. The function $\partial f/\partial y$ is determined in precisely the same way, differentiating $f(x, y)$ with respect to y and treating x as fixed.

In general, the domain D_x of $\partial f/\partial x$ does not need to be the same as the domain D_y of $\partial f/\partial y$, although for cases of interest to us it will be true that $D_x = D_y$ and, in addition, that $D_x = D_y = A$, where A is the domain of $f(x, y)$. Given any function $z = f(x, y)$ of two variables, then, we can normally generate two new functions of two variables which are $\partial f/\partial x$ and $\partial f/\partial y$. This process can be continued. From $\partial f/\partial x$ we can generate two functions which we shall write $\partial^2 f/\partial x^2$ and $\partial^2 f/\partial y \partial x$. These are the partial derivatives of $\partial f/\partial x$ with respect to x and y respectively. Similarly, we can generate two functions $\partial^2 f/\partial y^2$ and $\partial^2 f/\partial x \partial y$, which are the partial derivatives of $\partial f/\delta y$ with respect to y and x, respectively. The functions $\partial^2 f/\partial x^2$, $\partial^2 f/\partial y^2$, $\partial^2 f/\partial y \partial x$ and $\partial^2 f/\partial x \partial y$ are referred to as the second partial derivative functions for $f(x, y)$. We shall not have any need for second partial derivatives or for partial derivatives of higher order, which can be obtained by taking the partial derivatives of the second partial derivative functions.

EXAMPLES. 1. If $f(x, y) = 2x^2 + 3y^2$,   then

$$\frac{\partial f}{\partial x} = 4x; \qquad \frac{\partial f}{\partial y} = 6y;$$

$$\frac{\partial^2 f}{\partial x^2} = 4; \qquad \frac{\partial^2 f}{\partial y^2} = 6; \qquad \frac{\partial^2 f}{\partial x \, \partial y} = \frac{\partial^2 f}{\partial y \, \partial x} = 0 .$$

Note that y does not appear in $\partial f/\partial x$ and x does not appear in $\partial f/\partial y$. Are these functions of one variable or functions of two variables? They are functions of two variables, because the elements of the domain are points in E^2. It just so happens that for any point (x, y) the value of $\partial f/\partial x$ depends only on x and $\partial f/\partial y$ depends only on y. The present discussion also points up the interesting observation that we can think of any function $z = f(x)$ of one variable as also being a function of two variables in which the value of the function does not depend on y. It is important to keep clearly in mind, however, whether an expression such as $4x$ is being considered to be a function of one variable or a function of two variables. For example, if we considered $\partial f/\partial x$ above to be a function of one variable, the set of solutions to $\partial f/\partial x = 0$, that is, $4x = 0$ consists of the single number $x = 0$. However, if we think of $\partial f/\partial x$, as we should, as a function of two variables, the set of solutions to $\partial f/\partial x = 0$ is the set of all points $(0, y)$, that is, the y-axis in the xy-plane.

2. If $f(x, y) = x\, e^{xy}$ then

$$\frac{\partial f}{\partial x} = e^{xy} + xy\, e^{xy} = (1 + xy)\, e^{xy}$$

$$\frac{\partial f}{\partial y} = x^2\, e^{xy}.$$

The domain of $f(x, y)$, $\partial f/\partial x$ and $\partial f/\partial y$ is E^2.

7-4 MAXIMA AND MINIMA

In this section we shall study the problem of determining the largest or smallest value that some function $z = f(x, y)$ takes on over some specified set R which is a subset of E^2. Such a problem is often referred to as an *optimization problem* and is a type of problem which arises frequently in many fields of application. For example, a firm produces two different products and the total profit is a function of the quantities produced of each product. It is desired to determine how much of each item to produce so as to maximize the total profit. Let us begin by making precise what is meant by the absolute maximum of $z = f(x, y)$ over R.

Absolute Maximum. *The function $z = f(x, y)$ takes on its absolute maximum over R at $(x^*, y^*) \in R$ if $f(x, y) \le f(x^*, y^*)$ for each $(x, y) \in R$.*

The modifications needed to define an absolute minimum are obvious. There is no guarantee that there actually exists a point in R where $f(x, y)$ takes on an absolute maximum. However for most practical problems one knows there is at least one such point and the task is to find it. We shall concentrate our attention in the text on studying how this can be done. In the problems we shall illustrate a couple of the unusual cases where there is no such point.

Recall that, for a function of a single variable $f(x)$, we showed in Section 3–13 that if $f(x)$ is differentiable at each point in I_{ab}^e, the absolute maximum (or minimum) of $f(x)$ over I_{ab}^c occurs either at a root of $f'(x)$ or at one of the end points (boundaries) of the interval. We wish to develop a similar sort of technique for functions of two variables. This will involve the partial derivatives of $f(x, y)$. The situation, however, becomes much more complex for functions of two variables because of the fact that the end points of a one-dimensional interval become the boundaries of the set R in E^2, and the boundaries of R will consist of an infinite rather than a finite number of points. For example, if R is the set of points lying on or inside the circle of radius 1 with center at the origin, then every point on the circle $x^2 + y^2 = 1$ is a boundary point of R. We shall see why the boundaries can cause so many problems as we develop the theory.

Let us proceed in a manner completely analogous to the one-variable case by first defining what is meant by a relative maximum, and then obtaining some conditions which must be satisfied by any point where the function takes on a relative maximum. From this, we shall show how the absolute maximum and the points where it is taken on can be determined. Before defining a relative maximum we shall find it convenient to introduce what is called an ϵ neighborhood of a specified point $(\eta, \xi) \in E^2$. An ϵ neighborhood of (η, ξ), which we shall symbolize by $N_\epsilon(\eta, \xi)$, is the set of points in E^2 interior to the circle having its center at (η, ξ) and having radius $\epsilon > 0$, that is,

$$N_\epsilon(\eta, \xi) = \{(x, y) \mid (x - \eta)^2 + (y - \xi)^2 < \epsilon^2, \quad \epsilon > 0\}. \qquad (7\text{–}17)$$

An ϵ neighborhood of (η, ξ) is the shaded set of points shown in Figure 7–15, not including the circle.

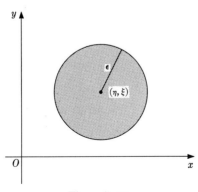

Figure 7–15

An alternative definition of an ϵ neighborhood is the set of all points in E^2 whose distance from (η, ξ) is less than ϵ. Notice that, if we consider two ϵ neighborhoods $N_{\epsilon_1}(\eta, \xi)$ and $N_{\epsilon_2}(\eta, \xi)$ with $\epsilon_1 < \epsilon_2$, then every point in the first one is also in the second, that is, $N_{\epsilon_1}(\eta, \xi) \subset N_{\epsilon_2}(\eta, \xi)$. When ϵ is small then all points in $N_\epsilon(\eta, \xi)$ are close to (η, ξ). We can now define what is meant by a relative maximum of $f(x, y)$.

RELATIVE MAXIMUM. *The function* $z = f(x, y)$ *takes on a relative maximum at the point* (η, ξ) *if there exists an* $\epsilon > 0$ *such that, for every point* (x, y) *in the* ϵ *neighborhood* $N_\epsilon(\eta, \xi)$ *of* (η, ξ), *it is true that* $f(x, y) \leq f(\eta, \xi)$.

In other words, for *all* points in E^2 sufficiently close to (η, ξ) it is true that $f(x, y)$ is not greater than $f(\eta, \xi)$. The above definition says nothing about how large ϵ is. It may be true that ϵ must be very small in order for the above condition to be satisfied. There is no limit to how small ϵ can be, provided $\epsilon > 0$. Note that if the above condition is satisfied, $f(x, y)$ must be defined for each $(x, y) \in N_\epsilon(\eta, \xi)$ since $f(x, y) \leq f(\eta, \xi)$ which implies $f(x, y)$ exists. Thus $N_\epsilon(\eta, \xi)$ is a subset of the domain of $f(x, y)$.

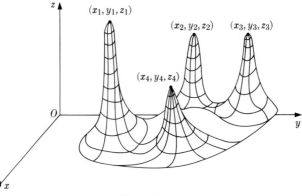

Figure 7–16

Intuitively, when we think of $z = f(x, y)$ as a surface in three dimensions, then the relative maxima correspond to hilltops. Thus the function shown in Figure 7–16 takes on a relative maximum at the points (x_1, y_1), (x_2, y_2), (x_3, y_3) and (x_4, y_4). The definition of a relative minimum is obtained simply by changing the direction of the inequality in the above definition. Relative minima correspond to the bottoms of valleys in the surface representing $f(x, y)$.

We shall now prove the important result that, *if* $f(x, y)$ *takes on a relative maximum (or a relative minimum) at* (η, ξ) *and if* $\partial f(\eta, \xi)/\partial x$ *and* $\partial f(\eta, \xi)/\partial y$ *exist, then*

$$\frac{\partial}{\partial x} f(\eta, \xi) = 0; \qquad \frac{\partial}{\partial y} f(\eta, \xi) = 0, \qquad (7\text{--}18)$$

that is, both partial derivatives must be equal to 0 at (η, ξ).

This is easy to prove. If $f(x, y)$ takes on a relative maximum at (η, ξ), then there exists an ϵ neighborhood $N_\epsilon(\eta, \xi)$ such that $f(x, y) \leq f(\eta, \xi)$,

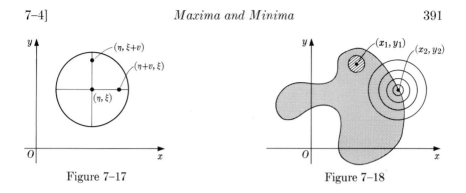

Figure 7–17   Figure 7–18

$(x, y) \in N_\epsilon(\eta, \xi)$. Suppose this ϵ neighborhood looks like that shown in Figure 7–17. Consider now the points on the horizontal and vertical line segments lying in $N_\epsilon(\eta, \xi)$ which pass through (η, ξ). These are also shown in Figure 7–17. Any point of the form $(\eta + v, \xi)$, $|v| < \epsilon$, lies on the horizontal line segment, and for any such point

$$f(\eta + v, \xi) - f(\eta, \xi) \leq 0, \quad |v| < \epsilon. \tag{7–19}$$

When $v > 0$, we can divide by v and (7–19) becomes

$$\frac{f(\eta + v, \xi) - f(\eta, \xi)}{v} \leq 0, \quad 0 < v < \epsilon. \tag{7–20}$$

Now since $\partial f(\eta, \xi)/\partial x$ exists,

$$\lim_{v \to 0+} \frac{f(\eta + v, \xi) - f(\eta, \xi)}{v} = \frac{\partial}{\partial x} f(\eta, \xi). \tag{7–21}$$

Hence from (7–20), $\partial f(\eta, \xi)/\partial x \leq 0$. If (7–19) is divided by $v < 0$, we obtain

$$\frac{f(\eta + v, \xi) - f(\eta, \xi)}{v} \geq 0, \quad -|\epsilon| < v < 0, \tag{7–22}$$

Taking the limit as v approaches 0 from the left we conclude that $\partial f(\eta, \xi)/\partial x \geq 0$, which when combined with $\partial f(\eta, \xi)/\partial x \leq 0$ yields $\partial f(\eta, \xi)/\partial x = 0$. Note the derivation here is the same as the one we used to show that, if $f(x)$ takes on a relative maximum at x_0 and $f'(x_0)$ exists, then $f'(x_0) = 0$. Precisely the same argument is used to show that $\partial f(\eta, \xi)/\partial y = 0$ when points $(\eta, \xi + v)$ lying on the vertical line segment are considered.

What we have proved is the following. If $f(x, y)$ possesses partial derivatives at every point in E^2, then every point in E^2 where $f(x, y)$ takes on a relative maximum (or minimum) must be a solution to the following system of two equations in two variables x and y:

$$\frac{\partial}{\partial x} f(x, y) = 0; \quad \frac{\partial}{\partial y} f(x, y) = 0. \tag{7–23}$$

In (7–23), $\partial f(x, y)/\partial x$ and $\partial f(x, y)/\partial y$ are the partial derivative functions for $f(x, y)$. If we knew the set S of all solutions to (7–23), then every point (η, ξ) where $f(x, y)$ takes on a relative maximum or minimum is an element of S. It is not necessarily true that $f(x, y)$ will take on a relative maximum or minimum at every point in S, but every point where $f(x, y)$ does take on a relative maximum or minimum will be in S. Any point in S is called a stationary point of $f(x, y)$. If there are points where $f(x, y)$ does not possess partial derivatives, then it is not necessarily true that every point where $f(x, y)$ takes on a relative maximum or minimum will be in S, since partial derivatives may not exist for some of these points. We shall not, however, be concerned with such cases.

EXAMPLE. Consider the function

$$z = 16 - 2(x - 3)^2 - (y - 7)^2 .$$

It is clear that $z \leq 16$ for every (x, y) and $z = 16$ at $(3, 7)$. Hence $f(x, y)$ takes on its absolute maximum at $(3, 7)$ and, of course, it also takes on a relative maximum at $(3, 7)$. Let us see now that (7–23) leads to this conclusion. The given function possesses partial derivatives at every point in E^2 and

$$\frac{\partial f}{\partial x} = -4(x - 3); \qquad \frac{\partial f}{\partial y} = -2(y - 7) .$$

The pair of equations (7–20) then becomes

$$-4(x - 3) = 0 \qquad x = 3$$
$$\text{or}$$
$$-2(y - 7) = 0 \qquad y = 7 .$$

There is only one solution $(3, 7)$ to these equations. We don't know just from this whether $f(x, y)$ takes on a relative maximum, a relative minimum or neither at $(3, 7)$. However, our above analysis has shown that $f(x, y)$ must take on a relative maximum. Thus we know that $f(x, y)$ has no other relative maxima and no relative minima.

Let us return to the problem of determining the absolute maximum of $z = f(x, y)$ over some given set R. The set R might possibly look like that shown in Figure 7–18, the shaded region representing R. We shall now define what is meant by an interior point of R.

INTERIOR POINT OF R. *The point* $(\eta, \xi) \in R$ *is said to be an interior point if there exists an* ϵ *neighborhood* $N_\epsilon(\eta, \xi)$ *of* (η, ξ) *with the characteristic that* $N_\epsilon(\eta, \xi) \subset R$, *that is, each point in* $N_\epsilon(\eta, \xi)$ *is in* R.

Any point in R which is not an interior point is called a *boundary point* of R. The characteristic of a boundary point (η, ξ) is that *every* ϵ neighborhood $N_\epsilon(\eta, \xi)$ contains points which are in R and points which are not in R. Thus in Figure 7–18, (x_1, y_1) is an interior point, since it is possible to find an ϵ

neighborhood, the cross-hatched region in Figure 7–18, which lies entirely in R. On the other hand (x_2, y_2) is a boundary point, for every ϵ neighborhood contains points which are in R and points which are not in R. We might note that a point (η, ξ) is called a boundary point of R even if (η, ξ) is not in R, provided that every ϵ neighborhood $N_\epsilon(\eta, \xi)$ contains points in R and points not in R. The set of all boundary points of R is what we call the boundary of R. In Figure 7–18, the boundary of R is simply the solid closed curve which bounds R. For problems of interest to us the boundary of R will be in R and we need not be concerned with boundary points which are not elements of R. Sets which contain their boundary are called *closed*, and we shall be dealing with closed sets R.

Let us now note that, if the absolute maximum of $f(x, y)$ over R is taken on at an interior point (x^*, y^*), then $f(x, y)$ takes on a relative maximum at (x^*, y^*). This follows, since $f(x, y) \leq f(x^*, y^*)$ for all $(x, y) \in R$ by the definition of an absolute maximum. However, since (x^*, y^*) is an interior point, there exists an ϵ neighborhood $N_\epsilon(x^*, y^*) \subset R$ and for each point in $N_\epsilon(x^*, y^*)$, $f(x, y) \leq f(x^*, y^*)$. Hence, by the definition of a relative maximum, $f(x, y)$ takes on a relative maximum at (x^*, y^*). Therefore, *the absolute maximum of $f(x, y)$ over R is either taken on at a relative maximum or on the boundary of R.*

Suppose now that $f(x, y)$ possesses partial derivatives at every point in R. Then any point where $f(x, y)$ takes on a relative maximum in R will be a solution to (7–23). Therefore, *if $z = f(x, y)$ has an absolute maximum over R, and $f(x, y)$ possesses partial derivatives at each point in R, then any point (x^*, y^*) where $f(x, y)$ takes on its absolute maximum will be a solution to (7–23) or will lie on the boundary of R.* This is the basic result which can be used in determining the absolute maximum of $f(x, y)$ over R. The same result applies, of course, for determining the absolute minimum of $f(x, y)$ over R. The difficult part of the problem involves determining if (x^*, y^*) lies on the boundary of R. For certain types of problems, we are quite sure that the absolute maximum of $f(x, y)$ exists and is taken on at an interior point. In this case, we determine the set S_R of all solutions to $\partial f/\partial x = \partial f/\partial y = 0$ lying in R, and evaluate $f(x, y)$ at each of these. The largest of these numbers z^* is the absolute maximum of $f(x, y)$. The point or points in S_R whose image is z^* are, then, the points where the absolute maximum is taken on. Before going on to study problems where it is necessary to examine the boundary of R, we shall provide some simple practical examples illustrating cases where the simpler procedure just described can be employed.

7–5 EXAMPLES

1. An electronics firm packages resistors in boxes, 1000 resistors per box. To hold 1000 resistors the box must have a volume of 500 cubic inches. The box

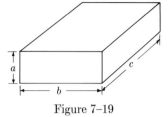

Figure 7–19

must have the shape of a parallelepiped as shown in Figure 7–19. However, the dimensions a, b, and c of the box can be chosen within rather wide limits, the only restriction being that the volume of the box is to be 500 cubic inches. It is desired to find the dimensions of the box which minimize the material needed to produce the box. We shall assume the material needed will be minimized if the surface area z of the box is minimized. Now the surface area is

$$z = 2(ab + bc + ac) . \qquad (7\text{–}24)$$

If v is the volume of the box, then v is the area of the base times the height, that is,

$$v = abc . \qquad (7\text{–}25)$$

Once a and b are selected then, by (7–25), $c = v/ab$. If this is substituted into (7–24), the surface area for a given volume v can be expressed as a function of a and b. Thus

$$z = 2\left(ab + \frac{v}{a} + \frac{v}{b}\right) . \qquad (7\text{–}26)$$

Equation (7–26) represents a function of two variables a and b. We wish to minimize this function. Let us suppose that each dimension cannot be less than one inch or greater than 100 inches. Thus we wish to minimize z over the set R of points which are solutions to

$$1 \le a \le 100; \qquad 1 \le b \le 100 ,$$

given that $v = 500$. From physical arguments it is clear that neither a nor b will be 1 or 100 so that the minimum will be taken on at an interior point of R where $\partial z/\partial a = \partial z/\partial b = 0$. Note that the equation $z = f(a, b)$ possesses partial derivatives at each point in R. Also

$$\frac{\partial z}{\partial a} = 2\left(b - \frac{v}{a^2}\right) ; \qquad \frac{\partial z}{\partial b} = 2\left(a - \frac{v}{b^2}\right) . \qquad (7\text{–}27)$$

Hence the equations $\partial z/\partial a = 0$ and $\partial z/\partial b = 0$ become

$$b - \frac{v}{a^2} = 0; \qquad a - \frac{v}{b^2} = 0 ,$$

or

$$ba^2 = v = ab^2 .$$

Hence $ba^2 = ab^2$ or $b = a$, and since $ba^2 = v$, it follows that $b^3 = 500$. Therefore $b = (500)^{1/3} = 7.92$ inches. Since $a = b$, $a = 7.92$ inches. Now

$$c = \frac{500}{ab} = \frac{500}{(500)^{2/3}} = (500)^{1/3} = 7.92 \text{ inches} .$$

Thus the box of minimum surface area is a cube, each of whose sides has length 7.92 inches. The point just obtained in the only stationary point of $z = f(a, b)$. It is clear intuitively that it does yield a relative minimum and the absolute minimum of z. If, for some reason, the cost of the top and bottom of the box were different from the cost of the sides then the minimum-cost box would not be a cube.

2. Suppose that we have a finite number n of points (x_j, y_j) which, when plotted, might look like what is shown in Figure 7–20. These points have the characteristic that, on the whole, they do not deviate too much from lying on a straight line. Consider then the problem of finding the equation $y = ax + b$ of the best straight line through these points. The question immediately arises as to what is meant by the "best" straight line through the points. A variety of interpretations is possible. Probably the most generally used criterion is referred to as the *least-squares criterion*. Let us now explain what it means. Suppose that we select any line $y = ax + b$. Consider the set of values x_j for which (x_j, y_j) is one of the given points. There is a point on the line having $x = x_j$. This is the point $(x_j, ax_j + b)$. Let $\epsilon_j = y_j - ax_j - b$; ϵ_j is the difference between the value of y for the point (x_j, y_j) and the value of y for the point on the line with the same value of x, that is, x_j. We can think of ϵ_j as the error that would be made if y_j were estimated using $ax_j + b$, in other words using the line $y = ax + b$. This is shown in Figure 7–20. The least-squares method determines that

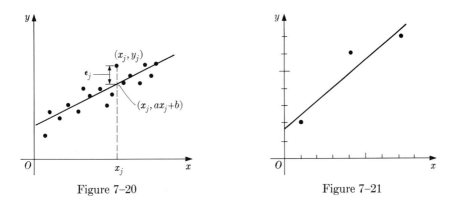

Figure 7–20   Figure 7–21

line which minimizes the sum of the squares of the errors. The line is determined once a and b are specified. Hence, it is desired to determine the values of a and b which minimize

$$f(a, b) = \sum_{j=1}^{n} \epsilon_j^2 = \sum_{j=1}^{n} (y_j - ax_j - b)^2 . \qquad (7\text{--}28)$$

Note carefully that a and b are the independent variables here, not x and y. There are no restrictions on a and b. Thus R is E^2 in this case.

To determine the a and b which minimize (7–25) we compute

$$\frac{\partial f}{\partial a} = -2 \sum_{j=1}^{n} x_j(y_j - ax_j - b);$$

$$\frac{\partial f}{\partial b} = -2 \sum_{j=1}^{n} (y_j - ax_j - b) . \qquad (7\text{--}29)$$

On setting $\partial f/\partial a = \partial f/\partial b = 0$, we obtain a system of two linear equations in a and b which are

$$\left(\sum_{j=1}^{n} x_j^2 \right) a + \left(\sum_{j=1}^{n} x_j \right) b = \sum_{j=1}^{n} x_j y_j$$

$$\left(\sum_{j=1}^{n} x_j \right) a + nb = \sum_{j=1}^{n} y_j . \qquad (7\text{--}30)$$

This system of equations has the unique solution (proof?)

$$a = \frac{n \sum_{j=1}^{n} x_j y_j - \left(\sum_{j=1}^{n} x_j \right)\left(\sum_{j=1}^{n} y_j \right)}{n \sum_{j=1}^{n} x_j^2 - \left(\sum_{j=1}^{n} x_j \right)^2} \qquad (7\text{--}31)$$

$$b = \frac{\left(\sum_{j=1}^{n} x_j^2 \right)\left(\sum_{j=1}^{n} y_j \right) - \left(\sum_{j=1}^{n} x_j \right)\left(\sum_{j=1}^{n} x_j y_j \right)}{n \sum_{j=1}^{n} x_j^2 - \left(\sum_{j=1}^{n} x_j \right)^2} , \qquad (7\text{--}32)$$

when the denominator in (7–31) and (7–32) is not 0. We have thus expressed a and b in terms of numbers obtainable from the given points through the rather fearsome looking equations (7–31) and (7–32). The function $f(a, b)$ has only one stationary point given by (7–31) and (7–32), and it does yield a relative minimum of $f(a, b)$ and also the absolute minimum of $f(a, b)$ over E^2. In any particular case this can be verified directly by drawing the level curves for $f(a, b)$. The line $y = ax + b$, with a and b given by (7–31) and (7–32), is then the least-squares line. If there are many given points (x_j, y_j) it is very tedious to determine a and b from (7–31) and (7–32) by hand. The computations can, of course, easily be carried out on a computer. Let us illustrate with a very simple example.

Suppose that we are given three points $(1, 2)$, $(4, 6)$ and $(7, 7)$. Let us determine the least-squares line through these points. The computations can be conveniently arranged in a tabular format such as that shown in Table 7–2. The last row gives the sums needed. Thus we see that

$$a = \frac{3(75) - 12(15)}{3(66) - (12)^2} = \frac{45}{54} = 0.834$$

$$b = \frac{66(15) - 12(75)}{54} = \frac{90}{54} = 1.668 .$$

The given points and the least-squares line are shown in Figure 7–21.

TABLE 7–2
COMPUTATIONS FOR EXAMPLE

	x_i	x_i^2	y_i	$x_i y_i$
	1	1	2	2
	4	16	6	24
	7	49	7	49
Sums	12	66	15	75

The problem of finding the least-squares line through a set of points arises in many areas dealing with experimental observations. For example, the length of a rod might be measured at different temperatures, thus yielding a set of points (x_i, y_i), where x refers to the temperature and y to the length of the rod. From theoretical considerations it might be thought that the length is related to the temperature by a linear equation. However, because of small errors introduced by the experimental technique, the points do not precisely lie on a line, and the best line through the points would normally be taken to be a least-squares line. As another example, a number of executives in a large corporation might be surveyed to determine their age and salary, thus yielding a set of points (x_i, y_i), x referring to the age of the executive and y to his salary. The best straight line through these data would be useful for estimating an executive's salary as a function of age.

7–6 CONSTRAINTS

We studied in the last section some simple examples of a type of problem where, from physical or economic reasoning, it is known that the optimal solution, that is, the point (or points) where $z = f(x, y)$ takes on its largest or smallest value over R, lies at an interior point of R. While some practical problems are of this form, the most interesting practical problems are such that an optimal solution may very well occur in the boundary of R. Indeed, for many classes of practical problems, we are certain that it occurs on the boundary, and the problem is to determine where on the boundary it occurs. We now shall study optimization problems where the boundary of R cannot *a priori* be ignored.

To begin it will be helpful to explain in more detail the way in which the set R is characterized in practical problems. Generally speaking, R will be the set of solutions for some specified system of inequalities or equations such as those studied in Section 2–12. The system of equations or inequalities can be characterized symbolically as

$$g_i(x, y)\{\leq\, =\, \geq\}b_i, \quad i = 1, \dots, m. \tag{7–33}$$

Each of the m equations or inequalities in (7–33) is called a *constraint*. In general, there is no limit to how large m may be. Each constraint will have one of the signs $\leq$, $=$ or $\geq$, and the sign can vary from one constraint to another. This is what is meant by $\{\leq\, =\, \geq\}$ in (7–33). Frequently, the variables x and y will represent physical quantities, such as quantities of products manufactured, which cannot be negative. Then it must be true that $x \geq 0$ and $y \geq 0$. These are referred to as *non-negativity restrictions* or *non-negativity constraints,* and if they are the only constraints on the prob-

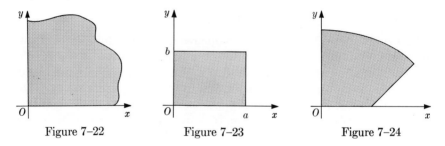

| Figure 7–22 | Figure 7–23 | Figure 7–24 |

lem, then R will be the set of points represented by the shaded region of Figure 7–22. It will also often be true that there will be limits on how large x and y can be. Thus there will be constraints of the form $x \leq a$, $y \leq b$. If the only constraints are $x \geq 0$, $y \geq 0$, $x \leq a$ and $y \leq b$, then R is the rectangle and its interior represented by the shaded region in Figure 7–23. A somewhat more complicated system of constraints is

$$0.2x^2 + 0.5y^2 \leq 25$$
$$x - y \leq 5$$
$$x \geq 0, \quad y \geq 0.$$

The set R in this case is shown in Figure 7–24.

Let us then examine the problem of determining the point or points where a function $z = f(x, y)$ takes on its absolute maximum (or minimum) over a set R which is the set of solutions to a system of constraints (7–33). The function $f(x, y)$ is referred to as the *objective function* for the problem. In attempting to solve such a problem in its very helpful to construct a figure on which the set R is shown and on which are also sketched the level curves for the objective function. When this is done, it is quite easy to locate where the maximum is taken on, and the precise point (or points) can then be determined in the manner to be described below. Let us now illustrate the solution procedure with some examples.

Consider a problem for which the set of constraints is represented by the system of linear inequalities

$$
\begin{aligned}
x + y &\leq 6 \\
x &\geq 1.5 \\
3x + y &\geq 6 \\
x - y &\leq 2 \\
-x + y &\leq 2.5 \, .
\end{aligned}
\tag{7-34}
$$

This set of inequalities is the same as (2–79) and the set R of solutions is the shaded region shown back in Figure 2–40. Suppose now that the objective function for the problem is

$$
z = 40 - 2(x - 2)^2 - 6(y - 3)^2 \, ,
\tag{7-35}
$$

and we wish to find the point or points in R which yield the largest value of z. In Figure 7–25 we have shown R as the shaded region. The level curves for the objective function have also been shown. It is clear that the maximum value of z is taken on at an interior point of R. This point must, then, be in the set of solutions to $\partial z / \partial x = \partial z / \partial y = 0$. As the reader can easily verify, $(2, 3)$ is the only solution to this system, and hence the absolute maximum of z over R is taken on at $(2, 3)$. When the absolute maximum is taken on at an interior point of R, then we say that the constraints are *inactive*.

Consider next a problem having the same set of constraints (7–34) as the one just studied, but for which the objective function is

$$
z = y - 0.5(x - 3)^2 \, .
\tag{7-36}
$$

Suppose that once again it is desired to maximize the objective function. The situation is illustrated in Figure 7–26. The level curves for the objective function are parabolas as shown in Figure 7–26. To find the point which yields the largest value of z we look for that parabola with the largest value

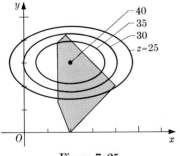

Figure 7–25

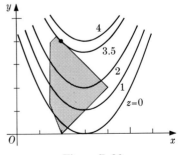

Figure 7–26

of z which has at least one point in common with R. This is the parabola with $z = 3.5$, and the point where z obtains its maximum corresponds to the black dot. In this case the optimum occurs on the boundary of R, and as we see from Figure 7–26, (x^*, y^*), the point yielding the largest value of z, lies on the line $x + y = 6$, which is the boundary of the constraint $x + y \leq 6$.

Let us now proceed to see how to determine (x^*, y^*) analytically. To be general in our discussion, suppose that we know that the maximum of $z = f(x, y)$ is taken on at a point (x^*, y^*) which lies on a boundary curve of R. Suppose that this boundary curve is the graph of the function $y = \varphi(x)$ ($y = 6 - x$ for the case under consideration) when $\alpha \leq x \leq \beta$. Assume also that it is known that x^* lies in the interior of $I^c_{\alpha\beta}$. Now, by definition of (x^*, y^*), $f(x, y) \leq f(x^*, y^*)$ for all $(x, y) \in R$. Hence, since every point on the boundary is in R for sets R that are of interest to us, $f(x, \varphi(x)) \leq f(x^*, y^*) = f(x^*, \varphi(x^*))$, $x \in I^c_{\alpha\beta}$. All this says is that each point $(x, \varphi(x))$ on the boundary curve cannot yield a value of $f(x, y)$ greater than $f(x^*, y^*)$. For each $x \in I^c_{\alpha\beta}$ we can then determine a real number $f(x, \varphi(x))$. This rule defines a function $h(x)$ of one variable whose domain is $I^c_{\alpha\beta}$, and

$$h(x) = f(x, \varphi(x)) . \tag{7–37}$$

From what we have just shown, $h(x) \leq h(x^*)$, $x \in I^c_{\alpha\beta}$. Since x^* is in the interior of $I^c_{\alpha\beta}$, it follows that $h(x)$ takes on a relative maximum at x^*. Hence if $h(x)$ is differentiable over $I^c_{\alpha\beta}$, x^* is a root of $h'(x)$ and to find x^* we can evaluate $h(x)$ at each root of $h'(x)$. The largest of these values is $f(x^*, y^*)$ and we simultaneously determine x^*; then $y^* = \varphi(x^*)$ and (x^*, y^*) is thus determined.

We can now use the method just developed to determine (x^*, y^*) for the example under consideration. As we noted above (x^*, y^*) lies on the line $y = 6 - x$. Then from (7–36)

$$h(x) = f(x, \varphi(x)) = 6 - x - 0.5(x - 3)^2 . \tag{7–38}$$

Now

$$h'(x) = -1 - 2(0.5)(x - 3) = -1 - x + 3 = 2 - x .$$

The only root of $h'(x)$ is $x = 2$. We can see from Figure 7–26 that $x = 2$ lies in the interval where $y = 6 - x$ is the boundary of R. Thus $x^* = 2$ and $y^* = 6 - 2 = 4$. Finally, z^*, the optimal value of the objective function is $z^* = 4 - 0.5 = 3.5$.

It will not always be possible to represent the graph of the boundary curve of interest in the form $y = \varphi(x)$. Sometimes it is necessary or more convenient to have y as the independent variable so that the curve is the graph of $x = \psi(y)$. In this case $q(y) = f(\psi(y), y)$ is introduced instead of $h(x)$ and it is noted that, when $q(y)$ is differentiable, y^* is a root of $q'(y)$.

Let us now give a final example which illustrates the one remaining type of behavior that may be encountered. Consider a problem in which the set of constraints is once again given by (7–34). Let us now suppose that the objective function we wish to maximize is

$$z = 0.5x + y . \tag{7–39}$$

An objective function whose level curves are straight lines is called a *linear objective function*. The objective function (7–39) is linear. The set R described by (7–34) is the set of solutions to a system of linear equations. Any problem that involves the maximization or minimization of a linear objective function over a set R, which is the set of solutions to a system linear inequalities, is called a *linear programming problem*. The current example, then, is a linear programming problem. The situation is illustrated geometrically in Figure 7–27. The maximum value of z over R is taken on at the point represented by the black dot in Figure 7–27. This point, which

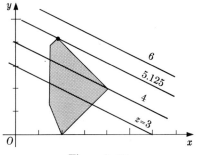

Figure 7–27

lies on the boundary, has the characteristic that it is a corner of the boundary, that is, the point of intersection of two of the boundary curves. It is the point of intersection of the lines $-x + y = 2.5$ and $x + y = 6$. The unique solution to this system of linear equations is $x = 1.75$ and $y = 4.25$. Therefore $(x^*, y^*) = (1.75, 4.25)$ and $z^* = 0.5(1.75) + 4.25 = 5.125$. It should be noted that, in this case, x^* cannot be determined by the method used for the previous example, because x^* is not a root of $h_1'(x)$, $h_1(x) = f(x, 2.5 + x)$ or $h_2'(x)$, $h_2(x) = f(x, 6 - x)$. This follows, since x^* occurs at the end point of the interval over which $y = 2.5 + x$ represents the boundary of R and also at the end point of the interval over which $y = 6 - x$ represents the boundary of R.

We can now combine the techniques introduced in each of the above examples to yield a method by which the maximum (or minimum) of $z = f(x, y)$ could be determined without constructing a figure to aid in locating the optimizing point. Even with this method, however, a figure showing R would still be helpful to locate clearly the boundaries of R. The procedure is as follows. First find all solutions to $\partial f/\partial x = \partial f/\partial y = 0$ lying in the interior of R and evaluate $f(x, y)$ at each of these points. Next, for each boundary curve, determine the functions $h(x)$ or $q(y)$ and the intervals over which they apply. Determine the stationary points of each $h(x)$ or $q(y)$ lying in the relevant interval and evaluate $f(x, y)$ for each of the points so obtained. Finally, evaluate $f(x, y)$ at the corners of the boundary where two boundary curves intersect. The largest of all these numbers z^* will be the absolute maximum of $f(x, y)$ over R (and the smallest will be the absolute minimum). The point or points yielding z^* will be (x^*, y^*), an optimal solution.

To illustrate how inequality constraints arise naturally in practical problems we shall, in the next section, give a very simple practical example. This will then explain why we characterized the set R in the manner we did.

7–7 LINEAR PROGRAMMING—A PRACTICAL EXAMPLE

Consider a plant that makes polyethylene plastics which are used for molded plastic parts and wire and cable coverings. The plant produces only the plastics in pellet form, not any final products, such as molded plastic bowls or dishes. An actual plant might produce between 10 and 100 different plastics; for our example, however, we shall suppose that only two different plastics are produced, call them 1 and 2. The production process is a rather simple one. It can be looked on as a two-step or two-stage process. First a chemical called ethylene is pumped through a long tube called a reactor at high temperature and pressure in the presence of a catalyst. The ethylene is polymerized and converted to polyethylene on passing through the reactor. The material coming out of the reactor is referred to as resin. Two resins are produced in the reactor; one is used in product 1 and the other in product 2.

There is just a single reactor in the plant under consideration, and both resins are produced in this reactor. The process of converting from the manufacture of one resin to the other is a simple one which does not require that the reactor be shut down. The operator merely changes the temperature and pressure and, in addition, changes the catalyst fed in with the ethylene. In the process of changing over from one resin to another, a small amount of material is produced which is substandard. It is, however, later mixed with the good resins and appears in quantities small enough not to cause any problems.

Although the resin is the major constituent in each of the final products 1 and 2, it is necessary to blend the resin with certain additives to give it color, the proper molding characteristics, and so forth. This blending of the resin with additives takes place in a mixing unit, called a compounder. The plant has only one compounding unit, and thus both products must be compounded in this unit. It is unnecessary to shut down the unit and clean it out when changing over from making one product to making the other. Once again a very small amount of substandard material is produced during changeover, but this is later recycled and blended into the products. The material coming out of the compounding unit is the final product and is ready for shipment to customers.

The management of the plant under consideration would like to determine how much of each product it should manufacture during the coming year so as to maximize total profit from sale of both products. Let us suppose that the profit per pound sold is \$0.14 for product 1 and \$0.09 for product 2. The mere fact that the profit per pound of 1 is higher than for product 2 does not imply that only 1 should be produced, as we shall see. It would not be possible to sell arbitrarily large quantities of 1 and 2 even if they could be produced. The marketing department has indicated that it cannot sell more than 9 million pounds of 1 and 12 million pounds of product 2. We can easily represent these marketing restrictions mathematically. Let x and y be the number of pounds manufactured of products 1 and 2 respectively. The amounts produced will not be greater than the amounts which can be sold. Thus it must be true that

$$x \leq 9 \times 10^6; \quad y \leq 12 \times 10^6 . \tag{7-40}$$

We did not write $x = 9 \times 10^6$ or $y = 12 \times 10^6$ because there is no reason to believe that it is optimal to produce the market potential for either one of these products.

In order to determine the optimal quantities of 1 and 2 to produce, it is necessary to take into account the technological constraints introduced by the nature of the production process. Let us suppose that the reactor can be operated for 8300 hours per year. Now the production rates on the reactor of the resins for products 1 and 2 are not the same. The reactor can produce 1000 pounds per hour of the resin for 1 and 2000 pounds per hour of the resin for 2. Assume that each pound of 1 requires 0.8 pounds of resin, and each pound of product 2 requires 0.7 pounds of resin. The remainder of 1 and 2 consists of what we referred to previously as additives. If we denote the resin used for 1 by α and the resin used for 2 by β, then if x pounds of 1 and y pounds of 2 are produced, $0.8x$ pounds of α and $0.7y$ pounds of β are needed. To produce $0.8x$ pounds of α requires $0.8x/1000$ hours of reactor time, since 1000 pounds per hour of α can be produced. Similarly, the reactor time needed to produce β is $0.7y/2000$. If we assume that the material produced on changeover from production of one resin to another is ultimately classified as either α or β, the total reactor time needed is

$$\frac{0.8}{1000} x + \frac{0.7}{2000} y = 8 \times 10^{-4}x + 3.5 \times 10^{-4}y . \tag{7-41}$$

This total time cannot be greater than the 8300 hours that the reactor can be operated. Thus x and y must satisfy the constraint

$$8 \times 10^{-4} x + 3.5 \times 10^{-4} y \leq 8300 . \tag{7-42}$$

We do not use an equality in (7–42) because there is no guarantee that it will be optimal or even possible to use the reactor to full capacity.

Consider next the compounding unit. The production rates for products 1 and 2 are not the same on the compounding unit. The production rate of 1 is 2080 pounds per hour and that of 2 is 1800 pounds per hour. The compounding unit can be operated for a total of 8000 hours per year. The time actually used is the sum of the times devoted to producing 1 and 2 and is

$$\frac{1}{2080} x + \frac{1}{1800} y = 4.81 \times 10^{-4} x + 5.55 \times 10^{-4} y .$$

This time must be less than or equal to the 8000 hours available. Hence x and y must satisfy the constraint

$$4.81 \times 10^{-4} x + 5.55 \times 10^{-4} y \leq 8000 . \qquad (7\text{–}43)$$

We have now developed all the constraints on the problem except the non-negativity restrictions $x \geq 0$ and $y \geq 0$, which guarantee that negative quantities cannot be produced.

The profit z as a function of x and y is

$$z = 0.14x + 0.09y . \qquad (7\text{–}44)$$

It is desired to find that point or points in R which is the set of solutions to the system of linear inequalities

$$x \leq 9 \times 10^6 \quad y \leq 12 \times 10^6$$
$$8 \times 10^{-4} x + 3.5 \times 10^{-4} y \leq 8300$$
$$4.81 \times 10^{-4} x + 5.55 \times 10^{-4} y \leq 8000$$
$$x \geq 0 \quad y \geq 0 \qquad (7\text{–}45)$$

that yields the largest value of z. This is a linear programming problem. The situation is illustrated geometrically in Figure 7–28. The optimal solu-

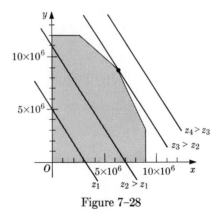

Figure 7–28

tion is represented by the black dot in the figure. The reader should check that the optimal quantities to produce are $x^* = 6.59 \times 10^6$ pounds and $y^* = 8.72 \times 10^6$ pounds. Note that for this solution both the reactor and the compounding unit in the plant are used to full capacity. However, neither product is produced in an amount equal to its market potential.

7–8 FUNCTIONS OF n VARIABLES

In the last section we noted that a polyethylene plant would normally produce many more than two products. If it can produce n products, and x_j is the number of pounds produced of product j while p_j is the profit per pound of product j, then the total profit z from all products is

$$z = p_1x_1 + p_2x_2 + \cdots + p_nx_n . \tag{7–46}$$

It seems natural in this case to write $z = f(x_1, x_2, \ldots, x_n)$ and to say that z is a function of the n variables $x_1, x_2, \ldots, x_n$. Here, then, we have arising in a natural way the notion of a function of n variables, where n can be any natural number whatever. Other illustrations of what we would automatically call functions of n variables are

$$z = (x_1 - a_1)^2 + (x_2 - a_2)^2 + \cdots + (x_n - a_n)^2;$$
$$z = x_1x_2 \cdots x_n; \qquad z = \exp(x_1 + x_2 + \cdots + x_n); \tag{7–47}$$
$$z = x_1x_2 + x_2x_3 + x_3x_4 + \cdots + x_{n-1}x_n .$$

Let us now give a precise definition of what we shall mean by a function of n variables. We shall call an ordered array of numbers $(x_1, x_2, \ldots, x_n)$ an *ordered n-tuple*. Then we can given the following definition.

FUNCTION OF n VARIABLES. *A function whose domain is a set of ordered n-tuples and whose range is a set of real numbers is referred to as a function of n variables.*

If $(x_1, \ldots, x_n)$ is any element in the domain of a function of n variables, the image z of this element will be denoted by the familiar type of notation such as $f(x_1, \ldots, x_n)$ so that $z = f(x_1, \ldots, x_n)$. Not only is $f(x_1, \ldots, x_n)$ used to represent the image of $(x_1, \ldots, x_n)$, but it is also used as a symbolic representation for the entire function. The symbols $x_1, \ldots, x_n$ in $z = f(x_1, \ldots, x_n)$ are referred to as the *independent variables*, and z is referred to as the dependent variable.

We shall denote the set of all ordered n-tuples $(x_1, x_2, \ldots, x_n)$ by E^n; E^n *is called an n-dimensional Euclidean space*, and any element of E^n is referred to as a *point* in this space. The reader should be careful not to try to give an interpretation to E^n which goes beyond the definition. E^n is the set of all ordered n-tuples. The use of the word space in naming E^n does not imply that E^n has any connection with physical space. Similarly, the use of the word point for $(x_1, x_2, \ldots, x_n)$ does not imply that it can be interpreted geometrically. It is convenient to use geometric language when discussing E^n only because for $n = 1$, 2 and 3 it is possible to give a geometric interpretation to E^n. This is not possible for $n > 3$.

We can define partial derivatives for a function of n variables $z = f(x_1, \ldots, x_n)$ in precisely the same way as for a function of 2 variables. The partial derivative with respect to x_j evaluated at the point $(\xi_1, \xi_2, \ldots, \xi_n)$ is defined as

$$\frac{\partial}{\partial x_j} f(\xi_1, \ldots, \xi_n)$$

$$= \lim_{v \to 0} \frac{f(\xi_1, \ldots, \xi_{j-1}, \xi_j + v, \xi_{j+1}, \ldots, \xi_n) - f(\xi_1, \ldots, \xi_n)}{v},$$

$$j = 1, \ldots, n. \quad (7\text{--}48)$$

There exist n partial derivatives for a function of n variables, one for each variable. From $z = f(x_1, \ldots, x_n)$ can be generated n new functions of n variables which are the partial derivative functions. The partial derivative function with respect to x_j will be denoted by $\partial f/\partial x_j$ or $\partial z/\partial x_j$. To obtain $\partial f/\partial x_j$ we merely differentiate $f(x_1, \ldots, x_n)$ with respect to x_j, treating all other variables as fixed. This can be accomplished, then, using the theory for differentiating functions of one variable. Thus, for example, if

$$z = \sum_{j=1}^{n-1} x_j e^{x_{j+1}} = x_1 e^{x_2} + x_2 e^{x_3} + \cdots + x_{n-1} e^{x_n}, \quad (7\text{--}49)$$

then

$$\frac{\partial z}{\partial x_j} = \begin{cases} e^{x_2}, & j = 1 \\ x_{j-1} e^{x_j} + e^{x_{j+1}}, & 1 < j < n \\ x_{n-1} e^{x_n}, & j = n. \end{cases} \quad (7\text{--}50)$$

The distance d between two points $(x_1, \ldots, x_n)$ and $(\xi_1, \ldots, \xi_n)$ in E^n is defined to be

$$d = \left[\sum_{j=1}^{n} (x_j - \xi_j)^2 \right]^{1/2} \quad (7\text{--}51)$$

Note that distance is merely a name given to the number (7–51). It is called distance because in E^1 and E^2 (and E^3 as we ask the reader to show in the problems), d can be interpreted geometrically as what is thought of as distance in the real world. An ϵ neighborhood of a point $(\xi_1, \ldots, \xi_n)$, which will be denoted by $N_\epsilon(\xi_1, \ldots, \xi_n)$, is the set of all points in E^n whose distance from $(\xi_1, \ldots, \xi_n)$ is less than ϵ. Thus

$$N_\epsilon(\xi_1, \ldots, \xi_n) = \left\{ (x_1, \ldots, x_n) \,\bigg|\, \sum_{j=1}^{n} (x_j - \xi_j)^2 < \epsilon^2, \quad \epsilon > 0 \right\}. \quad (7\text{--}52)$$

A very important class of problems encountered in practice involves finding the point or points in some subset R of E^n which yield the largest value of a function $z = f(x_1, \ldots, x_n)$. A point $(\xi_1, \ldots, \xi_n)$ is called an interior point of R if there exists an ϵ neighborhood of $(\xi_1, \ldots, \xi_n)$ which contains only points of R. The function $f(x_1, \ldots, x_n)$ is said to take on a relative maximum at the interior point $(\xi_1, \ldots, \xi_n)$ if there exists an ϵ neighborhood of $(\xi_1, \ldots, \xi_n)$ such that, for each point in $N_\epsilon(\xi_1, \ldots, \xi_n)$, $f(x_1, \ldots, x_n) \le f(\xi_1, \ldots, \xi_n)$. A relative minimum is defined in precisely the same way. If all n partial derivatives of $f(x_1, \ldots, x_n)$ exist at $(\xi_1, \ldots, \xi_n)$ and $f(x_1, \ldots, x_n)$ takes on a relative maximum or minimum at this point, then precisely the same arguments used for functions of two variables show that all n partial derivatives must be 0 at $(\xi_1, \ldots, \xi_n)$, that is,

$$\frac{\partial}{\partial x_j} (\xi_1, \ldots, \xi_n) = 0, \quad j = 1, \ldots, n. \tag{7–53}$$

Thus, the same reasoning used for functions of two variables shows that if it is known that the maximum or minimum of $f(x_1, \ldots, x_n)$ over R is taken on at an interior point of R, then the optimizing point $(x_1^*, \ldots, x_n^*)$ (each such point, if there is more than one) must be a solution to the system of n equations

$$\frac{\partial f}{\partial x_j} = 0, \quad j = 1, \ldots, n. \tag{7–54}$$

This result is frequently used, especially in economic analysis. The problems involved in locating the optimizing point when it may occur on the boundaries of R are quite complicated, and indeed such problems are areas of current research in mathematics. Two volumes devoted entirely to a study of such problems are references [1] and [2].

REFERENCES

Most of the calculus books referred to previously give at least a brief treatment of functions of several variables. None, however, considers optimization problems in detail. The following two works are concerned exclusively with the study of optimization problems.

1. Hadley, G., *Linear Programming.* Addison-Wesley: Reading, Mass., 1962.

2. Hadley, G., *Nonlinear and Dynamic Programming.* Addison-Wesley: Reading, Mass., 1964.

PROBLEMS

Sections 7–1 and 7–2

In Problems 1 through 20 sketch the level curves for the given function of two variables. Try also to give a perspective sketch of the surface which is the graph of the function. Indicate the domain of the function.

1. $z = 6x - y$;

2. $z = 2x + 5y$;

3. $z = x$;

4. $z = 2y$;

5. $z = (x - 2)^2 + (y - 3)^2$;

6. $z = 16 - x^2 - y^2$;

7. $z = 0.2(x - 4)^2 + 0.8(y - 7)^2 - 8$;

8. $z = y - x^2$;

9. $z = x - y^2$;

10. $z = 0.5(x + 4)^2 + y$;

11. $z = z^{1/3} - y$,

12. $z = xy$;

13. $z = x(y^2 - 1)$;

14. $z = y - \sin x$;

15. $z = y - e^{-x}$;

16. $z = ye^x$;

17. $z = y^2 e^x$;

18. $z = y - \log x$;

19. $z = y \log x$;

20. $z = e^y \log x$.

Section 7–3

As Problems 1 through 20 determine the two partial derivative functions for the function given in the corresponding problem for Sections 7–1 and 7–2. Determine the domain for these partial derivative functions.

In Problems 21 through 25 determine the two partial derivative functions for the given function and indicate the domain for each of these functions.

21. $z = e^{xy} + x^2$;

22. $z = xe^y + ye^x$;

23. $z = \log xy$;

24. $z = \exp(e^{xy})$;

25. $z = \sin xy^2$.

26. Consider the point (η, ξ) and suppose that $\partial f(\eta, \xi)/\partial x > 0$. Imagine now that a line parallel to the x-axis is passed through (η, ξ). Let z_0 be the value of z for the level curve passing through (η, ξ). How do the values of z for the level curves passing through points on the line which are close to (η, ξ) compare with z_0? Examine points on both sides of (η, ξ).

27. Consider the function $z = (x + 1)|y|$. Show that $\partial f(0, 0)/\partial x$ exists but $\partial f(0, 0)/\partial y$ does not. Try to sketch a perspective drawing of the surface which represents this function.

Sections 7–4 and 7–5

1. For the first example of Section 7–5 illustrate graphically the set R and the level curves for the objective function. In this way show that the absolute minimum is indeed taken on at the point obtained in the text.

2. For the first example of Section 7–5 suppose that the material needed to make the top and bottom of the box costs $0.01 per square foot while that used for the sides costs $0.008 per square foot. Determine the dimensions of the box which minimizes the cost of materials under the assumption that the total amount of material needed is equal to the total surface area.

3. Construct the level curves for $z = f(a, b)$ corresponding to the numerical illustration given in the second example of Section 7–5, and show that the absolute minimum does occur at the point obtained in the text.

4. Determine the least-squares line through the following points and illustrate geometrically. (1, 2), (1.5, 2.5), (3, 5), (4, 5), (5, 4), (5, 7), (7, 8) and (9, 9).

5. Given a set of points (x_i, y_i) we can determine a least-squares line $y = ax + b$. We can also determine a least-squares line $x = cy + d$ with y as the independent variable. Will the same line be obtained either way? Illustrate by determining $x = cy + d$ for the data used in the second example of this section.

6. Consider $z = xy$. Determine the unique solution to $\partial z/\partial x = \partial z/\partial y = 0$. Does z take on a relative maximum or minimum at this solution? Illustrate geometrically.

7. Let R be the set of points in E^2 satisfying $x \geq 0$ and $y \geq 0$. Is there a point in R where $z = 3x + 2y$ takes on its absolute maximum over R? Is there a point in R where z takes on its absolute minimum over R?

8. Let R be the set of points satisfying $0 \leq x \leq 1$ and $0 \leq y \leq 1$. Suppose $z = x/(y - 0.5)$. Is there a point in R where z takes on its absolute maximum over R?

9. Suppose that R is the set of points satisfying $x^2 + y^2 < 1$. Is there a point in R where $z = x + y$ takes on its absolute maximum over R?

Sections 7–6 and 7–7

In Problems 1 through 20 solve the optimization problem given and illustrate the situation geometrically. Determine whether $\partial f/\partial x = \partial f/\partial y = 0$ at (x^*, y^*). The "max" or "min" in front of z indicates whether it is desired to maximize or minimize the objective function.

1. $2x + 3y \leq 6$
$x + 4y \leq 4$
$x \geq 0, \quad y \geq 0,$
max $z = x + 1.5y;$

2. $5x + 10y \leq 50$
$x + y \geq 1$
$y \leq 4,$
$x \geq 0, \quad y \geq 0,$
max $z = x + y;$

3. $5x + 10y \leq 50$
$x + y \geq 1$
$y \leq 4$
$x \geq 0, \quad y \geq 0,$
min $z = 2x - y;$

4. $x - y \geq 0$
$0.5x - y \geq -1$
$x \geq 0, \quad y \geq 0,$
max $z = y - 0.75x;$

5. $x + 3y \geq 3$
$x + y \geq 2$
$x \geq 0, \quad y \geq 0$
min $z = 1.6x + 2.4y;$

6. $x + y \geq 1$
$x \leq 6, \quad y \leq 5$
$7x + 9y \leq 6$
$x \geq 0, y \geq 0$
max $z = 10x + 6.5y;$

7. $x + y \geq 1$
$-5x + y \leq 0$
$-x + 5y \geq 0$
$x - y \geq -1$
$x + y \leq 6$
$x \leq 3$
$x \geq 0, \quad y \geq 0$
max $z = 3x + 2y$;

8. $x + y \leq 12$
$x + y \geq 7$
$x \geq 5$
$y \geq 5$
$2x + 3y \leq 30$
$x \geq 0, \quad y \geq 0$
max $z = 2z + y$;

9. $y - 0.5(x - 4)^2 = 0$
min $z = x^2 + y^2$;

10. $xy = 4$
min $z = 0.2x^2 + 0.8y^2$;

11. $0.5x + y \leq 4$
$3x + y \leq 15$
$x + y \geq 1$
$x \geq 0, \quad y \geq 0$,
min $z = 4(x - 6)^2 + 6(y - 2)^2$;

12. $3x + 2y \leq 9$
$0.5x + y \leq 4$
$x \geq 0, \quad y \geq 0$,
max $z = xy$;

13. $0.5x + y \leq 4$
$3x + y \leq 15$
$x + y \geq 1$
$x \geq 0, \quad y \geq 0$
max $z = 3(x - 1.5)^2 + 6(y - 1.5)^2$;

14. $xy \geq 1$
$x^2 + y^2 \leq 9$
$x \leq 2$
$x \geq 0, \quad y \geq 0$
max $z = 8x^2 + 2y^2$;

15. $(x - 2)^2 + (y - 1)^2 \leq 9$
$x \geq 0, \quad y \geq 0$
max $z = 3x + 2y$;

16. $xy \geq 1$
$x^2 + y^2 \leq 9$
min $z = 7(x - 6)^2 + 3(y - 4)^2$;

17. $(x - 1)(y - 1) \leq 1$
$x + y \geq 3$
$x \geq 0, \quad y \geq 0$
min $z = 6(x - 5)^2 + (y - 4)^2$;

18. $x + y \leq 5$
$0.3x + y \leq 3$
$x \geq 0, \quad y \geq 0$,
max $z = 5x^2 + 3x - 4y$;

19. $(x - 3)(y - 3) \geq 1$
$x \geq 0, \quad y \geq 0$,
min $z = (x - 2.5)^2 + (y - 3.5)^2$;

20. $x^2 + (y - 3)^2 \leq 4$
$(x - 3)^2 + y^2 \leq 6$
$x \geq 0, \quad y \geq 0$
max $z = xy$;

21. What would be the optimal solution to the example of Section 7–7 if the profit per pound for 1 was \$0.11 and that for 2 was \$0.10? Illustrate this case geometrically.

22. What would be the optimal solution to the example of Section 7–7 if the number of hours available on the compounding unit was increased to 8400 hours?

23. A farmer has 1000 acres which he plans to use for wheat and corn. He wishes to determine how many acres should be devoted to wheat and how many to corn. The land will be imagined to be completely uniform, and one acre planted in corn yields 800 bushels while an acre planted in wheat yields 100 bushels. The profit per bushel of corn is \$0.20 and is \$2.30 per bushel of wheat. The farmer has available a total of 3000 hours for working and harvesting. One acre of corn requires 2 hours of labor while one acre of wheat requires 4 hours. How many acres should be planted in wheat and how many in corn? Illustrate the situation geometrically.

Section 7–8

1. Show that

$$d = [(x - \eta)^2 + (y - \xi)^2 + (z - \zeta)^2]^{1/2}$$

is the distance between (x, y, z) and (η, ξ, ζ) if these are considered to be points in ordinary three-dimensional space.

2. Prove (7–53) under the conditions stated in the text.

3. Let $f(x_1, \ldots, x_n)$ be the total cost of producing the quantities $x_1, \ldots, x_n$ of products $1, \ldots, n$ manufactured in some given plant. Assume that product j sells for p_j dollars per unit. Show that, provided positive amounts of each product should be produced, the optimal quantities to produce are solutions to

$$\frac{\partial f}{\partial x_j} = p_j, \qquad j = 1, \ldots, n .$$

The optimal quantities are assumed to be the quantities which maximize the total profit.

Tables

Tables

TABLE A. TRIGONOMETRIC FUNCTIONS

x	$\sin x$	$\cos x$	$\tan x$	x	$\sin x$	$\cos x$	$\tan x$
0	.000	1.000	.000	.80	.717	.697	1.030
.02	.020	1.000	.020	.82	.731	.682	1.072
.04	.040	.999	.040	.84	.745	.667	1.116
.06	.060	.998	.060	.86	.758	.652	1.162
.08	.080	.997	.080	.88	.771	.637	1.210
.10	.100	.995	.100	.90	.783	.622	1.260
.12	.120	.993	.121	.92	.796	.606	1.313
.14	.140	.990	.141	.94	.808	.590	1.369
.16	.159	.987	.161	.96	.819	.574	1.428
.18	.179	.984	.182	.98	.830	.557	1.491
.20	.199	.980	.203	1.00	.841	.540	1.557
.22	.218	.976	.224	1.02	.852	.523	1.628
.24	.238	.971	.245	1.04	.862	.506	1.704
.26	.257	.966	.266	1.06	.872	.489	1.784
.28	.276	.961	.288	1.08	.882	.471	1.871
.30	.296	.955	.309	1.10	.891	.454	1.965
.32	.315	.949	.331	1.12	.900	.436	2.066
.34	.333	.943	.354	1.14	.909	.418	2.176
.36	.352	.936	.376	1.16	.917	.399	2.296
.38	.371	.929	.399	1.18	.925	.381	2.427
.40	.389	.921	.423	1.20	.932	.362	2.572
.42	.408	.913	.447	1.22	.939	.344	2.733
.44	.426	.905	.471	1.24	.946	.325	2.912
.46	.444	.896	.495	1.26	.952	.306	3.113
.48	.462	.887	.521	1.28	.958	.287	3.341
.50	.479	.878	.546	1.30	.964	.267	3.602
.52	.497	.868	.573	1.32	.969	.248	3.903
.54	.514	.858	.599	1.34	.973	.229	4.256
.56	.531	.847	.627	1.36	.978	.209	4.673
.58	.548	.836	.655	1.38	.982	.190	5.177
.60	.565	.825	.684	1.40	.985	.170	5.798
.62	.581	.814	.714	1.42	.989	.150	6.581
.64	.597	.802	.745	1.44	.991	.130	7.602
.66	.613	.790	.776	1.46	.994	.111	8.989
.68	.629	.778	.809	1.48	.996	.091	10.983
.70	.644	.765	.842	1.50	.997	.071	14.101
.72	.659	.752	.877	1.52	.999	.051	19.670
.74	.674	.738	.913	1.54	1.000	.031	32.461
.76	.689	.725	.950	1.56	1.000	.011	92.621
.78	.703	.711	.989	1.57	1.000	.001	1255.8

TABLE B. NATURAL LOGARITHM FUNCTION

x	$\log x$	x	$\log x$	x	$\log x$
0	—	1.80	.5878	6.0	1.7918
.1	$\overline{7}$.6974*	1.82	.5988	6.1	1.8083
.2	$\overline{8}$.3906	1.84	.6098	6.2	1.8245
.3	$\overline{8}$.7960	1.86	.6206	6.3	1.8405
.4	$\overline{9}$.0837	1.88	.6313	6.4	1.8563
.5	$\overline{9}$.3069	1.90	.6418	6.5	1.8718
.6	$\overline{9}$.4892	1.92	.6523	6.6	1.8871
.7	$\overline{9}$.6433	1.94	.6627	6.7	1.9021
.8	$\overline{9}$.7769	1.96	.6729	6.8	1.9169
.9	$\overline{9}$.8946	1.98	.6831	6.9	1.9315
1.00	.0000	2.0	.6931	7.0	1.9459
1.02	.0198	2.1	.7419	7.1	1.9601
1.04	.0392	2.2	.7885	7.2	1.9741
1.06	.0583	2.3	.8329	7.3	1.9879
1.08	.0770	2.4	.8755	7.4	2.0015
1.10	.0953	2.5	.9163	7.5	2.0149
1.12	.1133	2.6	.9555	7.6	2.0281
1.14	.1310	2.7	.9933	7.7	2.0412
1.16	.1484	2.8	1.0296	7.8	2.0541
1.18	.1655	2.9	1.0647	7.9	2.0669
1.20	.1823	3.0	1.0986	8.0	2.0794
1.22	.1989	3.1	1.1314	8.1	2.0919
1.24	.2151	3.2	1.1632	8.2	2.1041
1.26	.2311	3.3	1.1939	8.3	2.1163
1.28	.2469	3.4	1.2238	8.4	2.1282
1.30	.2624	3.5	1.2528	8.5	2.1401
1.32	.2776	3.6	1.2809	8.6	2.1518
1.34	.2927	3.7	1.3083	8.7	2.1633
1.36	.3075	3.8	1.3350	8.8	2.1748
1.38	.3221	3.9	1.3610	8.9	2.1861
1.40	.3365	4.0	1.3863	9.0	2 1972
1.42	.3507	4.1	1.4110	9.1	2.2083
1.44	.3646	4.2	1.4351	9.2	2.2192
1.46	.3784	4.3	1.4586	9.3	2.2300
1.48	.3920	4.4	1.4816	9.4	2.2407
1.50	.4055	4.5	1.5041	9.5	2.2513
1.52	.4187	4.6	1.5261	9.6	2.2618
1.54	.4318	4.7	1.5476	9.7	2.2721
1.56	.4447	4.8	1.5686	9.8	2.2824
1.58	.4574	4.9	1.5892	9.9	2.2925
1.60	.4700	5.0	1.6094	10	2.3026
1.62	.4824	5.1	1.6292	12	2.4849
1.64	.4947	5.2	1.6487	14	2.6391
1.66	.5068	5.3	1.6677	16	2.7726
1.68	.5188	5.4	1.6864	18	2.8904
1.70	.5306	5.5	1.7047	20	2.9957
1.72	.5423	5.6	1.7228	30	3.4012
1.74	.5539	5.7	1.7405	40	3.6889
1.76	.5653	5.8	1.7579	50	3.9120
1.78	.5766	5.9	1.7750	100	4.6052

* A bar over the first digit indicates that $\log x$ is found by subtracting 10 from the given number.

TABLE C. EXPONENTIAL FUNCTIONS

x	e^x	e^{-x}	x	e^x	e^{-x}
0	1.0000	1.0000	1.0	2.7183	.3679
.02	1.0202	.9802	1.1	3.0042	.3329
.04	1.0408	.9608	1.2	3.3201	.3012
.06	1.0618	.9418	1.3	3.6693	.2725
.08	1.0833	.9231	1.4	4.0552	.2466
.10	1.1052	.9048	1.5	4.4817	.2231
.12	1.1275	.8869	1.6	4.9530	.2019
.14	1.1503	.8694	1.7	5.4739	.1827
.16	1.1735	.8521	1.8	6.0496	.1653
.18	1.1972	.8353	1.9	6.6859	.1496
.20	1.2214	.8187	2.0	7.3891	.1353
.22	1.2461	.8025	2.1	8.1662	.1225
.24	1.2712	.7866	2.2	9.0250	.1108
.26	1.2969	.7711	2.3	9.9742	.1003
.28	1.3231	.7558	2.4	11.023	.0907
.30	1.3499	.7408	2.5	12.182	.0821
.32	1.3771	.7261	2.6	13.464	.0743
.34	1.4050	.7118	2.7	14.880	.0672
.36	1.4333	.6977	2.8	16.445	.0608
.38	1.4623	.6839	2.9	18.174	.0550
.40	1.4918	.6703	3.0	20.086	.0498
.42	1.5220	.6570	3.1	22.198	.0450
.44	1.5527	.6440	3.2	24.533	.0408
.46	1.5841	.6313	3.3	27.113	.0369
.48	1.6161	.6188	3.4	29.964	.0334
.50	1.6487	.6065	3.5	33.115	.0302
.52	1.6820	.5945	3.6	36.598	.0273
.54	1.7160	.5827	3.7	40.447	.0247
.56	1.7507	.5712	3.8	44.701	.0224
.58	1.7860	.5599	3.9	49.402	.0202
.60	1.8221	.5488	4.0	54.598	.0183
.62	1.8589	.5379	4.1	60.340	.0166
.64	1.8965	.5273	4.2	66.686	.0150
.66	1.9348	.5169	4.3	73.700	.0136
.68	1.9739	.5066	4.4	81.451	.0123
.70	2.0138	.4966	4.5	90.017	.0111
.72	2.0544	.4868	4.6	99.484	.0101
.74	2.0959	.4771	4.7	109.95	.0091
.76	2.1383	.4677	4.8	121.51	.0082
.78	2.1815	.4584	4.9	134.29	.0074
.80	2.2255	.4493	5	148.41	.0067
.82	2.2705	.4404	6	403.43	.0025
.84	2.3164	.4317	7	1096.6	.0009
.86	2.3632	.4232	8	2981.0	.0003
.88	2.4109	.4148	9	8103.1	.0001
.90	2.4596	.4066	10	22,026	.00005
.92	2.5093	.3985	11	59,874	—
.94	2.5600	.3906	12	162,755	—
.96	2.6117	.3829	13	442,413	—
.98	2.6645	.3753	14	1,202,604	—

TABLE D. GREEK ALPHABET

Name	Cap.	l.c.	Name	Cap.	l.c.	Name	Cap.	l.c.
Alpha	A	α	Iota	I	ι	Sigma	Σ	σ
Beta	B	β	Kappa	K	κ	Tau	T	τ
Gamma	Γ	γ	Lambda	Λ	λ	Upsilon	Υ	υ
Delta	Δ	δ	Mu	M	μ	Phi	Φ	φ
		∂	Nu	N	ν	Chi	X	χ
Epsilon	E	ϵ	Xi	Ξ	ξ	Psi	Ψ	ψ
Zeta	Z	ζ	Omicron	O	o	Omega	Ω	ω
Eta	H	η	Pi	Π	π			
Theta	Θ	θ	Rho	P	ρ			

Index